SPACE-CHARGE FLOW

McGraw-Hill Physical and Quantum Electronics Series

Hubert Heffner and A. E. Siegman, Consulting Editors

Beam: Electronics of Solids

Collin: Foundations for Microwave Engineering

Elliott: Electromagnetics

Johnson: Field and Wave Electrodynamics

Kirstein, Kino, and Waters: Space-charge Flow

Louisell: Radiation and Noise in Quantum Electronics

Moll: Physics of Semiconductors

Papas: Theory of Electromagnetic Wave Propagation

Siegman: Microwave Solid-state Masers

Smith and Sorokin: The Laser

White: Basic Quantum Mechanics

RELATED BOOKS FROM McGRAW-HILL ELECTRICAL AND ELECTRONIC ENGINEERING SERIES

Frederick Emmons Terman, *Consulting Editor*
W. W. Harman and J. G. Truxal, *Associate Consulting Editors*

Atwater *Introduction to Microwave Theory*
Ghose *Microwave Circuit Theory and Analysis*
Greiner *Semiconductor Devices and Applications*
Harman *Fundamentals of Electronic Motion*
Harrington *Introduction to Electromagnetic Engineering*
Harrington *Time-harmonic Electromagnetic Fields*
Hayt *Engineering Electromagnetics*
Javid and Brown *Field Analysis and Electromagnetics*
Rogers *Introduction to Electric Fields*
Spangenberg *Fundamentals of Electron Devices*
Valdes *The Physical Theory of Transistors*
Van Bladel *Electromagnetic Fields*

OTHER RELATED McGRAW-HILL BOOKS

Chodorow and Susskind *Fundamentals of Microwave Electronics*
Collin *Field Theory of Guided Waves*
Plonsey and Collin *Principles and Applications of Electromagnetic Fields*
Uman *Introduction to Plasma Physics*

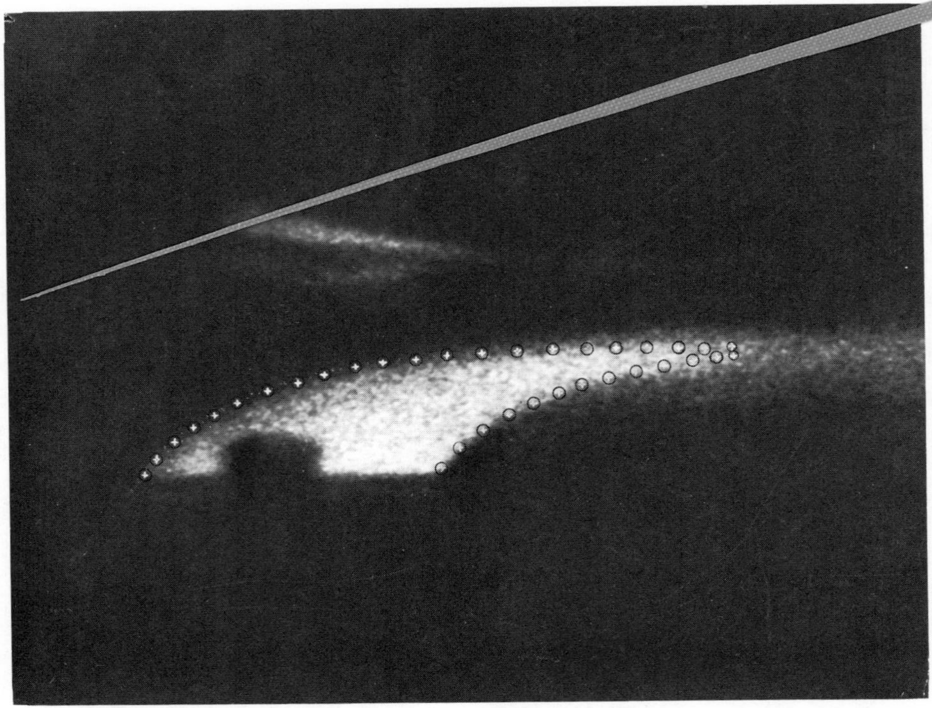

A photograph of the beam in a crossed-field gun taken by passing the beam into a gas. The circles and crosses on the photograph indicate the position of the beam edge given by zero-temperature theory.

SPACE-CHARGE FLOW

PETER T. KIRSTEIN, Ph.D.

Reader in Information Processing
Institute of Computer Science
London University, London, England

GORDON S. KINO, Ph.D.

Professor of Electrical Engineering
Stanford University, Stanford, California

WILLIAM E. WATERS, Ph.D.

Senior Engineer, Division Staff
Western Development Laboratory
Philco-Ford, Palo Alto, California

McGRAW-HILL BOOK COMPANY
New York San Francisco Toronto London Sydney

SPACE-CHARGE FLOW

 Library of Congress Catalog Card Number 66-17915

34867

1234567890MP72106987

Foreword

The theory of the electron optics of high-current beams in which space-charge effects are large is important for many applications. Subsequent to an early, fundamental paper by J. R. Pierce, there have been many contributions to the theory of beam formation and to methods of focusing; there now exists a relatively large body of sophisticated theory relating to the formation and control of high-density beams. However, no recent book treats this whole subject, particularly the developments of the last ten years or so, in a unified manner. It is very gratifying to have such a unified treatment of the entire theory presented in this book by a group of authors who, together and separately, have themselves contributed extensively to this theory over the last several years. Their own results have appeared in various separate papers, but this book represents the first collected and coherent account of this work to appear in one place with a suitable perspective of the whole set of problems.

The principal applications, of course, are to the electron flow in microwave tubes, in which one is always faced with the requirement of forming a small-diameter beam of large-current density and focusing it through a long, narrow path. Dimensions are determined by the conditions for interaction with some high-frequency circuit, and these conditions are usually quite severe, permitting little interception. This is not merely a matter of better performance, but in many cases is necessary to avoid destruction of the circuit or to reduce tube noisiness as much as possible. One has devices with extremely high-power densities, peak powers of the order of tens of megawatts per square centimeter in an electron beam, and/or average powers of the order of hundreds of kilowatts per square centimeter. Extreme numbers can be in the range of amperes through apertures measured in fractions of a millimeter.

One of the complicating factors is that cathode materials are capable of only limited emission density; in any electron-optical design, a given total current must be drawn from the cathode, often the beam must converge to a smaller cross section, and this cross section must be maintained over a relatively long distance. In general, then, one can divide the problem of electron optics into two parts, beam formation and beam focusing.

The problem of beam formation, i.e., how to control a beam leaving the cathode and how to converge it in a specified manner, was first attacked successfully in the fundamental paper by Pierce mentioned above, which described the method of designing what is now commonly known as a Pierce gun. Pierce's idea, basically, was to show how to solve Laplace's equation outside a finite beam to determine the form of the electrodes, using for the required boundary conditions the space-charge-flow solution for an infinite beam. A good deal of this book is concerned essentially with this problem, going far beyond the restrictions imposed by the original Pierce theory so as to provide greater flexibility in cathode design, new geometric configurations, and new analytic means for solving the electron-flow problem. The text also indicates how modern computers can be used successfully in the design of a variety of cathode geometries and space-charge-flow patterns. This generalized mathematical treatment of current flow between cathodes and anodes, and the various analytic and computer means for the design of such cathode-anode geometries represents, in good part, original work by the authors extending over a number of years. The principal value of this greatly enhanced capability in analyzing electron flow and new geometries is to provide the designer with many new possibilities and greater freedom in design. Many of the methods used represent interesting and unusual applications of computers and are not without mathematical interest in themselves, aside from the specific applications.

In addition to providing more flexible mathematical methods for the design of electron guns and a wider range of possibilities for cathode geometries, these methods have also been applied by the authors to another class of problems of great technical importance, but one which offers additional difficulties beyond the conventional convergent-flow gun. This is the problem of electron flow under conditions of tangential magnetic fields at the cathode surface. This condition changes the whole nature of the motion as compared to a field-free gun or one in which the magnetic flux is normal to the cathode surface. There are two important cases with tangential magnetic field at the cathode. One is the crossed-field gun which is used for injecting a beam into a crossed-field (perpendicular E and B) microwave device. The analytic design of such a cathode which will produce a well-defined beam in the presence of crossed-electric and magnetic fields represents an interesting and important application of some of the general techniques described in this book.

The second important application of electron flow with a tangential magnetic field at the cathode is to the so-called "magnetron injection gun"; a hollow beam is extracted from the open end of a coaxial cathode-anode geometry in which the center cylinder is the cathode and the magnetic field is approximately parallel to the axis of the cylinder. This is a method of getting high density hollow beams, and here again it is possible to do a considerable part, or all, of the design of such guns by the analytic techniques described in the text.

In addition to work on beam formation and electrode design over the past years there has been a great deal of invention of new methods of focusing a beam so that it can be transmitted over a long distance through a narrow channel. These innovations, due to many workers, have been treated in individual papers and, to some extent, in several books on microwave devices. The treatment in the current text, however, probably represents the most complete and systematic treatment of all these focusing methods, with some consideration as to the relations among, and relative merits of, these different methods of focusing.

Finally, the book also contains a detailed treatment of thermal effects and nonlaminar flow. This section concerns all of the factors which vitiate to some extent the straightforward hydrodynamic treatments of space-charge flow. The effect of thermal velocities has been treated in many places, but this text probably is the only one which treats all of these results in a unified manner.

The emphasis above on the applicability of these methods has been largely in terms of use for microwave tubes, and it is certainly true that this is probably the predominant application. However, there is at least one other important application, and that is the design of guns for ion propulsion. Here, also, space-charge effects are important and the methods described in this book should be exceedingly valuable for design. As a matter of fact, there are some electrode combinations treated in the text which are not common or desirable for microwave tubes but which would be useful for ion guns.

In general, this book will be of principal value to the designer of electron or ion guns, or for any focusing systems in which space charge is important. As such, it should be a definitive treatise on the subject for many years to come; it will no doubt be the standard reference. In addition, however, the applied mathematician, who is not a specialist in the design of guns or focusing systems, will find this text interesting as an example of application of some relatively sophisticated mathematical concepts and computer techniques for practical purposes.

Marvin Chodorow

Preface

In recent years, the problems of the design of electron guns, ion sources, and focusing systems have been the subject of intensive research. This work has centered around two main topics, the design of very fine spots, as in spectrometers and electron microscopes, and the design of dense beams for such typical applications as microwave tubes and ion-propulsion devices. In the first class of problems, the aberrations of the lenses are very important, but space-charge effects are usually negligible. In the second class, space-charge forces are very important.

Many of the basic ideas which have been used to deal with space-charge-flow problems have been described by Pierce in "Theory and Design of Electron Beams," D. Van Nostrand Company, Inc., 1954. Since this publication, however, there has been a very rapid development of the subject, and the analysis has reached a high level of sophistication. An important influence on the field has been the increased availability of large-scale computers. Because of the complexity and nonlinear nature of the equations of space-charge flow, only in recent years has it been reasonable to attempt to solve analytically any but the simplest types of space-charge-flow problems. Many of these newer analytical methods are described only in research papers; some are unpublished. In this book it is therefore our purpose to present a complete and systematic account of the mathematical techniques which can be used to analyze space-charge-flow problems and to show how these methods can be applied to the design and analysis of electron and ion guns and focusing systems. For lack of space, and because of their highly specialized nature, we have excluded certain methods which rely entirely on computer calculations and for which analytic results are not forthcoming. We do not present detailed sets of curves for the design of specific guns, but we trust that our methods are described in sufficient detail for application to practical problems.

Some of the methods developed here, e.g., the scaling laws of Chap. I, the paraxial methods of Chap. III, the treatment of thermal velocities in Chap. VI, and the electrode design methods in Chaps. VIII and IX, have relevance for the design of spectrometers and electron microscopes. The main purpose of this book, however, is to facilitate the design of beams where space-charge forces are strong.

The treatment of this book is restricted to time-independent electron and ion flows. Thus all effects of alternating electromagnetic fields, including noise in beams, are excluded. Although most of the methods of this book could be extended to relativistic beams, we ignore relativistic effects throughout. In physical beams, there are sometimes effects due to space-charge neutralization; such effects are ignored. Throughout the book it is assumed that, in any particular flow, particles are of only one type, usually electrons. Finally, all effects due to collisions between particles in the beam are ignored. It is assumed that the beam can be regarded as a fluid, though the particles in the fluid can cross each other; i.e., the flow can be nonlaminar.

The exact equations satisfied in a beam are complex, and solutions have been obtained only under idealized assumptions. In general, three problems must be solved: First, a flow must be found which satisfies all the equations of space-charge flow in a restricted region and yet has the properties which the user of the beam requires. Second, a set of electrodes must be found to produce this flow. Third, given a set of electrodes, the flow which they produce must be determined. The order of the book follows this pattern.

In Chap. I the general equations of space-charge flow are presented, and some definitions and classifications are made which are fundamental to the later chapters. In Chap. II, some exact solutions of the equations of space-charge flow are derived. Some of the most useful practical guns, e.g., the Pierce gun and magnetron injection gun, are designed by using the solutions given in this chapter.

In Chap. III, paraxial methods are discussed. In a paraxial beam particles are assumed to flow near some axis of the beam, and only a linear transverse variation of the electric and magnetic fields is considered. The formulation of this chapter is fundamental to the discussion of the focusing systems of Chaps. IV and V. In Chap. IV, uniform focusing systems are discussed, in which the electromagnetic fields have no longitudinal variations.

Chapter V is devoted to a description of periodic focusing; here the focusing system is composed of a number of identical sections, in each of which the electromagnetic fields vary.

Most of the analyses of Chaps. II to V ignore the effects of the spread in velocities which occurs in a real beam due to the spread of emission velocities of electrons from a thermionic cathode or ions from a gas discharge. These effects, called thermal effects, are discussed in Chap. VI. They often impose a limit on the attainable convergence of a beam, or to the percentage of the beam which can be transmitted through a long focusing system.

In Chaps. II to V, we discuss the properties of a beam of particles. There are two related problems: The first, how to design electrodes which will produce specific fields at the edge of the beam, is discussed in Chap. VII. The second, the kind of beam which arises from a specific electrode system, is treated in Chap. VIII. It is possible to solve the problems of both Chaps. VII and VIII experimentally; it is more convenient to solve them by representing the electromagnetic fields and particle motion in an analog fashion. The possible analogs that can be used are discussed in Chap. IX. One analog of particular importance is the digital computer.

Finally, there are several appendixes in which we have placed material which is important and relevant, but which would interrupt the main stream of the argument if placed in the body of the book. Examples of the contents of the appendixes are the vector relations in curvilinear coordinate systems and the properties of Mathieu's equations. Throughout the book rationalized mks units are used. A set of useful constants in mks units is given inside the front cover of the book.

For some purposes certain chapters can be omitted by the reader. For example, if approximate solutions and thermal effects in beams are of no interest to the reader, he can skip Chaps. III to VI. A certain amount of cross-referencing occurs throughout the book, but most chapters are fairly independent. If in one chapter material is required from another, this is specifically stated and the relevant equations are usually repeated.

A caution is appropriate at this point. The methods presented in this book include very complex analytic and numerical techniques. The reader should be careful not to use an unnecessarily complex method. For example, if the beam is long and thin, paraxial methods may be adequate, and there is no point in using exact methods in designing the beams. This point is well summarized in the closing paragraph of Pierce's book:

> A person studying beams to understand them and improving the art should of course be very careful and thorough. The person who wants to use an electron beam for some particular purpose may lose precious time by trying to do better than well enough.

Problem sets are included at the end of each chapter. Some of these problems have been used in a class at Stanford University, from notes on which this book was based. Others are designed to include material of importance, e.g., the strip-beam problems following Chap. VI, which is not included in the book, to avoid repetition.

The authors have drawn upon many sources for their material. Thanks are expressed particularly to Dr. Kenneth Harker and Professor Marvin Chodorow, whose comments and research ideas were especially stimulating to us while we were working at the Microwave Laboratory of the W. W. Hansen Laboratories of Physics at Stanford University. Without Professor Chodorow's continual encouragement, much of this work might never have been completed.

The preparation of the manuscript was greatly expedited by the facilities put at our disposal by the General Electric Company, and in particular by Miss Manuella Meier, who patiently typed the final manuscript. The authors would also like to thank Mrs. Marjorie Sowers for her help in preparing the final version of this book.

Finally, we should like to express our gratitude to our wives for remaining patient through the several years of manuscript preparation and revision. We are particularly indebted to Gwen Kirstein for comments contributing to the readability of the book.

Peter T. Kirstein
Gordon S. Kino
William E. Waters

Contents

List of Symbols

Note that many symbols are defined as they are used. This list covers only symbols used fairly consistently. Parentheses indicate where used.

A	vector potential
$\mathcal{A}$	value of A_z on a paraxial curve
B, B	magnetic field strength
$\mathcal{B}$	magnetic field variation on ray axis
C	curve label
c	velocity of light
dS	element of area
E	electric field
$\mathfrak{F}$, $\mathfrak{F}$	force
f	focal length of a lens (Chaps. III, VIII)
f	shape factor of periodic fields (Chap. V)
H	magnetic field
$\mathcal{H}$	total energy
h, H	grid mesh sizes (Chaps. VIII, IX)
h_1, h_2, h_3	scaling parameters in orthogonal curvilinear coordinate system; in orthogonal coordinates $d\ell^2 = \sum_{i=1}^{3} h_i^2\, dq_i^2$
I	total current in beam, positive in sign for electrons
$I_n(x)$	modified Bessel function of the first kind and nth order
$\mathcal{J}(x,y)$	special function of current [Eq. (5.31) of Chapt. VI]
i	$-nqv$ = current density, positive in sign for electrons
$J_n(x)$	Bessel function of the second kind and nth order
j	$(-1)^{1/2}$
$K_n(x)$	modified Bessel function of the third kind and nth order
$\mathcal{K}$	cathode shielding factor [Eq. (2.7) of Chap. V]
k	Boltzmann's constant
L	period in periodic system
$\mathcal{L}$	Langrangian

ℓ	width of strip beam in invariant direction
$d\ell$	element of length
M	magnification of beam
$\mathfrak{M}$	complex magnification; $\lvert\mathfrak{M}\rvert = M$
m	particle mass (usually electron)
N	magnitude of displacement of beam for unit transverse velocity
$\mathfrak{N}$	complex displacement of electron for unit transverse velocity; $\lvert\mathfrak{N}\rvert = N$
n(x)	number density of electrons
n(x;v)	phase-space density
P	perveance; perveance of 1 in text refers to 1 microperv.
p	perveance density
$P_n(x)$	Legendre polynomial of nth order
$\mathcal{P}$	space-charge factor [Eqs. (2.6) and (3.10) of Chap. V]
p	mv; momentum
Q	total charge in some volume
Q	$\partial W/\partial q_1$ (Chap. II)
q	electronic charge
q_1, q_2, q_3	orthogonal curvilinear coordinates
R	normalized r
R	resistance (Chap. IX)
$\mathcal{R}$	radius containing 95 percent of the beam (Chap. VI)
r	normal distance from ray axis in paraxial system
r, θ, z	cylindrical coordinates
r, θ, φ	spherical coordinates
S	normalized arc length (Chap. V)
$\mathcal{S}$	beam stiffness
s	arc length for paraxial beam
s, ψ	intrinsic coordinates
$\mathfrak{s}$	normalized arc length (Chap. III)
T	normalized time
T	temperature
$\mathfrak{T}$	kinetic energy
t	time
u	generalized velocity $= \mathbf{v} - \eta\mathbf{A}$
u	complex velocity in rotating system (Chap. III)
V	particle velocity on the ray axis
$\mathcal{V}$	normalized particle velocity βv (Chap. VI)
v	speed
v_w	complex transverse velocity, $v_w = v_x + iv_y$
v	velocity
W	action function, also called the velocity potential (Chap. II)
W	X + iY (Chaps. VII, VIII, IX, X)
w	$\nabla \times (\mathbf{v} - \eta\mathbf{A})$

X	normalized arc length (Chap. V)
x, y, z	cartesian coordinates
$Y_n(x)$	Bessel function of second kind and nth order
α	magnetic field factor [Eq. (2.5) of Chap. V]
β	wave number ω/v_0 (for example, $\beta_p = \omega_p/v_0$)
β	$m/(2kT_c)^{1/2}$ (Chap. VI)
Γ	transverse distance in rotating coordinates (Chap. III)
Γ	anode-lens correction factor (Chap. VI)
$\Gamma(x)$	gamma function
γ	$\hat{\phi}/\phi_0$ [Eq. (3.6) of Chap. V]
Δ, δ, ϵ	small quantities
∇, ∇	gradient operator
ϵ_0	permittivity of free space
ζ	$\xi + i\eta$ (Chap. VII)
η	$-q/m$
η	direction in complex variables (Chap. VII)
θ	angles in cylindrical and spherical polar coordinates
ϑ	$\int \omega_L dt$
κ	curvature
Λ	$P\Phi/T$ (Chapt. VI)
λ	wavelength
μ	dimensionless parameter for ratio of potentials
μ	magnification in rotating system [Eq. (5.22) of Chap. III]
μ_0	permeability of free space
ν	magnitude of displacement for unit transverse velocity in rotating system [Eq. (5.22) of Chap. III]
ξ	quantity related to γ [Chap. V, Eqs. (3.54), (4.14)]
ξ	normalized distance [Chap. VI, Eq. (2.29)]
ξ	coordinate along trajectories in complex variables (Chap. VII)
ρ	qn = space-charge density
σ	r/r_0 (Chaps. IV, V)
σ	surface charge, surface conductivity
σ	$N(kT_c/m)^{1/2}$ (Chap. VI)
τ	volume
τ_0	volume conductivity
Υ	normalized potential [Eq. (2.22) of Chap. VI]
Φ	potential on the ray axis for paraxial systems
Φ_A, etc.	potential of electrodes
ϕ	potential
Φ_0	work function
φ	angle in spherical polar coordinates
χ	complex potential $\phi + j\psi$ (Chap. VII)
Ψ	magnetic flux density
ψ	imaginary potential (Chap. VII)
ψ	angle between ray and axis of symmetry

Ω	magnetic scalar potential
ω	angular velocity
ω_H	cyclotron frequency ηB
ω_L	Larmor frequency $= \frac{1}{2}\eta B$
ω_n	characteristic transverse frequency of rippling
ω_p	plasma frequency $\sqrt{-\eta\rho/\epsilon_0}$

SUBSCRIPTS AND SUPERSCRIPTS

a_c	value of a at the cathode
a_e	equilibrium value of a (for example r_e = equilibrium radius)
a_e	value for electrons (restricted to m_e, η_e)
a_M	maximum value of a
a_m	minimum value of a
a_p	value for proton (restricted to m_p, η_e)
ω_p, etc.	plasma frequency (restricted to ω_p, λ_p, β_p)
a_{sc}	a due to space-charge (Chaps. VIII, IX)
a_T	value of a due to thermal effects (i.e., thermal velocity v_T)
$a_\square$	value per square (for example, $P_\square$ = perveance per square)
$a_\perp$	component of a transverse to z axis or paraxial axis
$\bar{a}$	average value of a
$\hat{a}$	root-mean-square value of a
a'	space derivative of a, along paraxial or z axis
$\dot{a}$	time derivative of a
$\lvert a \rvert$	modulus of a

SPACE-CHARGE FLOW

I

The General Dynamics of Steady Space-charge Flow

1. INTRODUCTION

1.1. The Space-charge-flow Problem. The design problems involved when high-charge densities are required are somewhat different from those involved in the design of focusing systems for weak beams, such as are required in cathode-ray tubes and electron microscopes. When the charge density in the beam is small, the motion of the individual charged particles can be determined by solving Laplace's equation to find the fields present within the electrode system, and then making use of the Lorentz force law. When the charge density is high, the field due to space charge becomes important. In this case, it is necessary to solve Poisson's equation rather than Laplace's equation to determine the fields. Thus Poisson's equation, the equation of continuity of charge, and the equations of motion must be solved in a self-consistent manner. The equations involved are nonlinear, and so such space-charge-flow problems tend to be of a highly complex nature. In an exact treatment, moreover, it would be necessary not only to be concerned with the effect of the charge on the electrostatic fields, but also to take into account the self-magnetic field due to the current flow. For nonrelativistic beams, however, with voltages less than about 150 kV, the forces due to the self-magnetic fields are normally negligible compared with the forces due to the electrostatic fields present.

Starting from Maxwell's equations and the Lorentz force law, we shall show that the equations of the flow can be simplified considerably by using certain assumptions. From the assumptions that a-c effects are ignored, the electric field may be considered static or quasi-static. By quasi-static, we mean that the fields do not change appreciably during the passage of a particle, so that the electric field can be derived from a scalar potential. We assume that no collisions occur between the charged particles and any other particle or the electrodes (until the particles impinge on the electrodes without reflection or secondary emission). With these assumptions, the total energy, kinetic plus potential, of each particle is conserved as it passes through the system. A further constant of the motion is the phase-space density (Sec. 3.3).

Under certain conditions, the equations describing the flow simplify considerably. One simplifying condition is that the flow is laminar; this means that all the particles at a particular position have the same velocity. A second slightly less restrictive condition is that the flow is quasi-laminar; this means that there are a finite number of laminar flows superposed. A third category is that of regular flows, in which the flow is laminar and each particle has the same total energy. Regular flows are comparatively simple to analyze, and are treated in much of this book. For regular flow, the particles must be emitted from an unipotential cathode with zero velocity.*

For laminar beams, there are certain conservation laws analogous to those used in hydrodynamics, e.g., Poincaré's invariant and Busch's theorem, which are fundamental to the work of much of this book. Some of these invariants, though derived more easily for laminar flows, are also true in nonlaminar beams (e.g., Busch's theorem). We shall show that the application of the conservation laws to regular flows allows yet further classifications of the flow, some of which simplify the process of determining their solutions.

1.2. The Contents of the Chapter. In Section 2 the basic equations and the underlying assumptions are stated. The hydrodynamic equation, which does not involve time explicitly, is deduced from the Lorentz force law. A hydrodynamic equation can always be deduced, but it is particularly useful only if the flow is laminar. From the hydrodynamic equations, the conservation of energy and vorticity are deduced (Section 3).

In Section 3, two invariants of the motion are deduced from the vorticity condition; these are analogous to those of Lagrange and Poincaré in hydrodynamics.[2-4] It is shown that Busch's theorem[1] for axially symmetric electron beams is a natural consequence of these invariants. We give some examples of the importance of this theorem. In addition, the concepts of phase-space density are presented, and its conservation, which is known as Liouville's theorem, is proved.

In Section 4 the important concepts of cyclotron frequency and Larmor frequency are defined.

In Section 5, we demonstrate how regular space-charge flows can be classified in terms of vorticity and the magnetic field at the cathode. We define a scalar function, the action function W, which can be regarded as a velocity potential. It is shown that a class of space-charge flows, which we call congruent flows, can be derived by employing this velocity potential and making use of the Hamilton-Jacobi equation of classical dynamics. The form of the space-charge-

*This condition is not strictly necessary, since the emission velocity could just compensate any drop in potential across the cathode, but such an assumption is physically unrealistic.

flow equations is then discussed for two classes of flow, congruent flow, with no normal component of magnetic field present at the cathode, and noncongruent flow, for which there is a normal component of magnetic field at the cathode. When space charge is negligible, the electrostatic potential satisfies Laplace's equation.

For all the solutions of space-charge flow, it is necessary to know what values the parameters of flow take at the cathode. The details of the determination of these values are given in later chapters, but the results are quoted in Section 6 in a concise form for later reference.

It is important to determine a gun design to be used for one voltage or frequency from a design already extant for other parameters. In most of this book we treat electron flow problems, although we should like to apply the solutions also to ion flow problems. For these reasons we consider also the scaling laws which must be obeyed by the parameters of the flow when the dimensions, potentials, charge, or mass of the particle is changed but the particle trajectories remain geometrically similar.

It is shown that the scaling laws alone lead to the law that, when the cathode is space-charge-limited, the current density is proportional to the three-halves power of the applied potential. From this law we define the perveance, which gives a normalized measure of the space charge in an electron beam. The special similarity laws which apply to transverse scaling of paraxial beams are also discussed. Under transverse scaling it is shown that the product of perveance and potential, divided by the cathode temperature, is preserved.

2. THE BASIC EQUATIONS

2.1. Introduction. Two sets of basic equations are required in space-charge flow. The first set consists of the equations obeyed by the electromagnetic field, assuming that the charge and current density distribution are known. The second set predicts the motion of the particles in given electromagnetic fields. The first set can be deduced from Maxwell's equations. When the flow is steady, the electromagnetic equations take a simpler form than the general one; these equations are presented and discussed in Sec. 2.2. The second set can be deduced from the Lorentz force law with the help of the electromagnetic equations, and is presented in Sec. 2.3. The definition of current density given in Sec. 2.2 is limited to flows in which either the beam is laminar, i.e., all particles at each point in space have the same velocity, or the beam is composed of a finite number of laminar flows. The limitation is only to simplify the equations presented. All the equations of Secs. 2.2 to 2.4 apply also to nonlaminar flow, unless specifically stated otherwise, and are derived without making use of laminarity. There is a distinction between the local derivative $\partial/\partial t$ of a vector field and the total derivative d/dt of that quantity, seen by a particle traveling in the field. Some conclusions are drawn from this difference in Sec. 2.4. If the flow is laminar, the velocity is a single-valued function of position, and a velocity field $\mathbf{v}(x,y,z)$ can be defined. For this case the Lorentz equation of motion is derived in a hydromagnetic form in Sec. 2.4. The extension to the case where there is a finite number of laminar beams is discussed also.

2.2. The Electromagnetic Field Equations. In this book only steady flows of charged particles are considered. The electric field **E** and the magnetic field **B** must obey Maxwell's equations, which take the form, for steady flows in vacuo,

$$\nabla \cdot \mathbf{E} = \frac{\rho}{\epsilon_0} \tag{2.1}$$

$$\nabla \times \mathbf{E} = 0 \tag{2.2}$$

$$\nabla \cdot \mathbf{B} = 0 \tag{2.3}$$

$$\nabla \times \mathbf{B} = -\mu_0 \mathbf{i} \tag{2.4}$$

In Eqs. (2.1) and (2.4), ρ and **i** are the charge density and current density, which are discussed below. The symbols $\nabla \cdot$ and $\nabla \times$ denote the divergence and curl of a vector. Expressions for $\nabla \cdot \mathbf{a}$, $\nabla \times \mathbf{a}$, and ∇a are given in Appendix A for various coordinate systems, where a and **a** denote arbitrary scalar and vector functions of the coordinates. Finally, ϵ_0 and μ_0 are constants, the dielectric constant of free space and the magnetic permeability. The numerical values of ϵ_0 and μ_0 are 8.854×10^{-12} and $4\pi \times 10^{-7}$.

We assume that the space-charge flow is made up of identical particles of one charge q. The number of particles is so large that it is meaningful to consider a distribution of particles. In the cube defined by

$$\begin{aligned} x_0 - \tfrac{1}{2}\delta x < x < x_0 + \tfrac{1}{2}\delta x \\ y_0 - \tfrac{1}{2}\delta y < y < y_0 + \tfrac{1}{2}\delta y \\ z_0 - \tfrac{1}{2}\delta z < z < z_0 + \tfrac{1}{2}\delta z \end{aligned} \tag{2.5}$$

there are $N\,\delta x\,\delta y\,\delta z$ particles, so that

$$\rho = qN \tag{2.6}$$

Thus ρ is measured in coulombs per cubic meter and N in particles per cubic meter. For brevity, we sometimes write $\rho(\mathbf{x})$, $N(\mathbf{x})$, etc., to denote $\rho(x,y,z)$, $N(x,y,z)$, etc. Usually, in this book, the particles are electrons, so that q is negative with magnitude 1.602×10^{-19}.

Often all the particles at (x,y,z) have the same velocity **v**. In this case the flow is laminar, and the current density **i** is given by

$$\mathbf{i} = -\rho\mathbf{v} \tag{2.7}$$

The minus sign is used because usually we deal with electrons, and it is convenient to treat current density and current as positive quantities. Sometimes there are a number of laminar beams passing through the same point. If the jth beam has current density ρ_j and velocity $\mathbf{v}_j$, then ρ and $\mathbf{i}$ are given by

$$\rho = \sum_j \rho_j \qquad \text{and} \qquad \mathbf{i} = -\sum_j \rho_j \mathbf{v}_j \tag{2.8}$$

This type of flow is called quasi-laminar in this book. The more general case, when the beam is completely nonlaminar and it is necessary to consider a velocity distribution of particles at each point, is treated in Sec. 3.3. However, the nonlaminarity affects only the definition of $\mathbf{i}$ and ρ; all the analyses of Secs. 2.2 and 2.3 are valid for nonlaminar flow unless stated otherwise.

From Eqs. (2.2) and (2.3) it is possible to define electric scalar and magnetic vector potentials ϕ and $\mathbf{A}$ so that

$$\mathbf{E} = -\nabla\phi \tag{2.9}$$

and

$$\mathbf{B} = \nabla \times \mathbf{A} \tag{2.10}$$

These ϕ and $\mathbf{A}$ are very convenient in the later analysis. The $\mathbf{A}$ defined by Eq. (2.10) is not unique; it is possible to add the gradient of any scalar to it without changing $\mathbf{B}$. Often it is convenient to apply the additional condition

$$\nabla \cdot \mathbf{A} = 0 \tag{2.11}$$

in which case $\mathbf{A}$ is defined almost uniquely. Equation (2.11) is not necessary, but often useful. With the ϕ of Eq. (2.9), it is possible to derive Poisson's equation from Eq. (2.1):

$$\nabla^2\phi = -\frac{\rho}{\epsilon_0} \tag{2.12}$$

If the space charge is negligible, Eq. (2.12) is called Laplace's equation, and takes the form

$$\nabla^2\phi = 0 \tag{2.13}$$

The electromagnetic field will be discussed further, when we have established the equations governing the motion of the particles in the field.

2.3. The Lorentz Force Law. The force $\mathfrak{F}$ on a particle in an electromagnetic field is

$$\mathfrak{F} = q(\mathbf{E} + \mathbf{v} \times \mathbf{B}) \tag{2.14}$$

where $\mathbf{v}$ is the velocity of the particle. Equation (2.14) is the Lorentz force law, and implies that acceleration of the particle is given by the Lorentz equation of motion

$$\frac{d\mathbf{v}}{dt} = -\eta(\mathbf{E} + \mathbf{v} \times \mathbf{B}) \tag{2.15}$$

Here η is defined by

$$\eta = -\frac{q}{m} \tag{2.16}$$

where q and m are the charge and mass of the particle. Equations (2.14) and (2.15) require modification for relativistic beams.

From Eq. (2.15) the acceleration and velocity of an electron are determined in terms of the fields in the system. The fields which affect the electron motion consist of two parts, those set up by the electrodes and external magnetic sources and those due to the electrons in the beam.

Although Eq. (2.4) is the exact equation obeyed by the magnetic field, it will be shown from Eq. (2.14) that, for nonrelativistic particle velocities, it is usually reasonable to neglect the self-magnetic field due to the beam itself; the magnetic forces on a particle are usually small compared with the space-charge force.

Consider, for example, a uniform cylindrical beam in which all the electrons have a uniform axial velocity v_0. By symmetry, there is a radial component of electric field E_r. It follows by using Gauss' theorem [Eq. (2.5) of Appendix A] and Eq. (2.1) that, at a radius r,

$$\int_S (\nabla \cdot E_r)\, dS = 2\pi r E_r = \int_S \frac{\rho}{\epsilon_0}\, dS \tag{2.17}$$

where S is the cross-sectional area of the beam within the radius r. Thus the electric field E_r is

$$E_r = \frac{Q}{2\pi r \epsilon_0} \tag{2.18}$$

where Q is the total charge per unit length within the radius r. Similarly, it follows by using Stokes' theorem [Eq. (2.7) of Appendix A] on Eq. (2.4) that the θ component of magnetic field due to the current flowing in the beam is

$$B_\theta = \frac{Q v_0 \mu_0}{2\pi r} \tag{2.19}$$

It follows from Eqs. (2.18) and (2.19) that the radial component of force $\mathfrak{F}_{sr}$ on an electron due to the space-charge field is

$$\mathfrak{F}_{sr} = \frac{Qq}{2\pi r \epsilon_0} \tag{2.20}$$

and the inward radial force $\mathfrak{F}_{mr}$ due to the self-magnetic field of the beam is

$$\mathfrak{F}_{mr} = \frac{\mu_0 Q q v_0^2}{2\pi r} \tag{2.21}$$

The ratio of the two forces is

$$\frac{\mathfrak{F}_{mr}}{\mathfrak{F}_{sr}} = \mu_0 \epsilon_0 v_0^2 = \frac{v_0^2}{c^2} \tag{2.22}$$

where c is the velocity of light. Thus, in this example, for nonrelativistic velocities, it is reasonable to neglect the force due to the self-magnetic field in comparison with the force due to space charge.

In general it is only necessary to evaluate the magnetic field by considering sources external to the beam; the contribution due to the current in the beam can be neglected. Consequently, we always use Eq. (2.4) in the form

$$\nabla \times \mathbf{B} = 0 \tag{2.23}$$

When the magnetic field obeys Eqs. (2.3) and (2.23), it is possible to define a magnetic scalar potential Ω so that

$$\mathbf{B} = -\mu_0 \nabla \Omega, \qquad \nabla^2 \Omega = 0 \tag{2.24}$$

It is sometimes more convenient to use the scalar potential Ω than the magnetic vector potential **A**.

It is possible to deduce one important property, the conservation of energy, directly from the Lorentz equation of motion. Taking the scalar product of Eq. (2.15) with **v**, that equation becomes

$$\mathbf{v} \cdot \frac{d\mathbf{v}}{dt} = -\eta \mathbf{v} \cdot \mathbf{E} \tag{2.25}$$

The magnetic term gives no contribution because $\mathbf{v} \times \mathbf{B}$ is perpendicular to the velocity **v**. From the definition of ϕ of Eq. (2.9),

$$\mathbf{v} \cdot \mathbf{E} = -\left(\frac{\partial \phi}{\partial x}\frac{dx}{dt} + \frac{\partial \phi}{\partial y}\frac{dy}{dt} + \frac{\partial \phi}{\partial z}\frac{dz}{dt}\right) = -\frac{d\phi}{dt} \tag{2.26}$$

Equation (2.26) follows because the flow is steady, so that ϕ does not depend on t explicitly. Equation (2.25) can be integrated directly, using Eq. (2.26) to give

$$v^2 - v_c^2 = 2\eta\phi \tag{2.27}$$

where v_c is the initial speed at $\phi = 0$, which is usually chosen at the cathode.

Equation (2.27) demonstrates that the total electron energy $\mathcal{H}$, kinetic plus potential energy, which is

$$\mathcal{H} = \frac{mv^2}{2} + q\phi = \frac{mv_c^2}{2} \tag{2.28}$$

where $q\phi$ is the potential energy, is conserved and is independent of the magnetic field. Moreover, if all the electrons are emitted from the cathode with the same speed v_c, the speed of an electron at any point is a single-valued function of the potential at that point. If the flow is also laminar, it is defined to be regular flow.

2.4. The Hydrodynamic Equations. In much of the work in this book we are concerned not so much with the motion of a single electron, but with the motion of many electrons. Moreover, we often do not require the position an electron reaches as a function of time; from its velocity as a function of its position, the electron trajectory can be determined. When the equation of motion can be written in such a hydrodynamic form, it can be used directly with Poisson's equation and the equation of continuity to determine all the parameters of the flow. In this section, a differential equation is derived which relates the electron velocity at any point to the coordinates of that point. It is usually possible to set up the equations in the hydrodynamic way only when the flow is laminar, i.e., when the velocity is a single-valued function of position [Eq. (2.7)]. It is sometimes possible to use these equations when the flow is composed of a small finite number of laminar beams [Eq. (2.8)]. This approach cannot be used in the general nonlaminar case.

When the flow is laminar, it is possible to treat the particle beam as a hydrodynamic fluid, in which the velocity vector $\mathbf{v}$ is a vector field which can be determined by solving a set of coupled differential equations. The procedure is to obtain, first, the equation of conservation of energy from Lorentz' equation of motion; by expressing the total differential d/dt in the Lorentz equation of motion in terms of partial differentials with respect to time and distance, an equation of motion is deduced, which we call the hydrodynamic equation of motion. This hydrodynamic equation implies that the curvature of the electron path in a pure electric field depends only on the components of the electric field normal to the path and the potential at the point of interest. More generally, in the presence of a magnetic field, we derive a relation between the potential, the curvature, and the components of electromagnetic fields normal to the path.

The Lorentz equation of motion, in the form given in Eq. (2.15), gives the variation in velocity $\mathbf{v}$ as seen by an observer moving with the particle along its trajectory. In this expression, the total derivative of the velocity, $d\mathbf{v}/dt$, with respect to time has been used. Consider the velocity of the particles in the stream passing a stationary observer. As a function of time, the rate of change of velocity as measured by the stationary observer will be given by the local derivative $\partial \mathbf{v}/\partial t$. If the flow is steady, this local derivative with respect to time will be zero. Thus a sharp distinction between the total derivative and the local derivative with respect to time must be drawn. More generally, if an observer changes his position within the flow from the point (x,y,z) to the point $(x + \delta x,\ y + \delta y,\ z + \delta z)$ and there is a time change from t to $t + \delta t$, he will observe the change in any vector $\mathbf{a}(x,y,z)$ to be $\delta\mathbf{a}$, where

$$\delta\mathbf{a} = \frac{\partial \mathbf{a}}{\partial t}\,\delta t + \frac{\partial \mathbf{a}}{\partial x}\,\delta x + \frac{\partial \mathbf{a}}{\partial y}\,\delta y + \frac{\partial \mathbf{a}}{\partial z}\,\delta z \qquad (2.29)$$

Dividing both sides of Eq. (2.29) by δt and taking the limit as $\delta t \to 0$, the total rate of change with respect to time of the vector **a** is

$$\frac{d\mathbf{a}}{dt} = \frac{\partial \mathbf{a}}{\partial t} + \frac{\partial \mathbf{a}}{\partial x}\frac{dx}{dt} + \frac{\partial \mathbf{a}}{\partial y}\frac{dy}{dt} + \frac{\partial \mathbf{a}}{\partial z}\frac{dz}{dt} \tag{2.30}$$

Equation (2.30) can be written more concisely in the vector form

$$\frac{d\mathbf{a}}{dt} = \frac{\partial \mathbf{a}}{\partial t} + (\mathbf{v} \cdot \nabla)\,\mathbf{a} \tag{2.31}$$

In this book, the flow is steady, the vector field does not depend on time explicitly, and Eq. (2.31) becomes

$$\frac{d\mathbf{a}}{dt} = (\mathbf{v} \cdot \nabla)\,\mathbf{a} \tag{2.32}$$

One special case of Eq. (2.32) has already been derived directly in Eq. (2.26). It is important to note that, in most coordinate systems, the jth component of $(\mathbf{v} \cdot \nabla)\,\mathbf{a}$ is not $(\mathbf{v} \cdot \nabla)\, a_j$. The general expressions for $(\mathbf{v} \cdot \nabla)\,\mathbf{a}$ in different coordinate systems are given in Appendix A. If, however, the coordinate system is chosen so that **v** has only one component in the s direction, then, from Eq. (2.12) of Appendix A,

$$(\mathbf{v} \cdot \nabla)\,\mathbf{a} = v_s \frac{\partial \mathbf{a}}{\partial s} \tag{2.33}$$

If the flow is laminar, so that **v** can be written **v**(x,y,z), substitution of Eq. (2.32) in Eq. (2.15) yields the following form of the Lorentz equation of motion:

$$(\mathbf{v} \cdot \nabla)\,\mathbf{v} = -\eta(\mathbf{E} + \mathbf{v} \times \mathbf{B}) \tag{2.34}$$

This expression does not contain time explicitly, and is in a form which is equivalent to a hydrodynamic equation of fluid flow. We call the equation of motion [Eq. (2.34)] the hydrodynamic equation of motion.

Even if the flow is nonlaminar, it is possible to define a coordinate system based on the particle trajectory, in which **v**(x,y,z) is defined for that particle. Of course, this **v**(x,y,z) has physical meaning only on the trajectory, but Eq. (2.34) has general validity. It is therefore necessary to preserve charge in any finite volume τ. If the velocity is single-valued,

$$\int_S \rho \mathbf{v} \cdot d\mathbf{S} = 0 \tag{2.35}$$

where S is the surface surrounding τ. Using Gauss' theorem, from Eq. (2.35) one obtains the equation of continuity:

$$\nabla \cdot \mathbf{i} = -\nabla \cdot (\rho \mathbf{v}) = 0 \tag{2.36}$$

Equations (2.34) to (2.36) are valid even if the flow is composed of a finite number of laminar streams, i.e., is quasi-laminar, although the velocity is then multivalued. However, the equations for the different streams must be written separately. Thus, if we denote the jth stream by the subscript j, Eq. (2.34) must be written in the form

$$(\mathbf{v}_j \cdot \nabla)\,\mathbf{v}_j = -\eta(\mathbf{E} + \mathbf{v}_j \times \mathbf{B}) \tag{2.37}$$

with the additional relation for a regular beam:

$$v_1^2 = v_2^2 = \cdots = v_j^2 = \cdots = v_c^2 + 2\eta\phi \tag{2.38}$$

because of conservation of energy.

Charge must be conserved in each stream, so that for each separate stream the current density is

$$\mathbf{i}_j = -\rho_j \mathbf{v}_j \tag{2.39}$$

and the equation of continuity, when the flow is steady, is

$$\nabla \cdot \mathbf{i}_j = 0 \tag{2.40}$$

Finally, the divergence equation for the electric field,

$$\nabla \cdot \mathbf{E} = \sum_j \frac{\rho_j}{\epsilon_0} \tag{2.41}$$

must be satisfied. The electric field depends on the total charge of all the streams. When the flow is laminar and there is only one stream, we omit the subscript j and the summation sign.

A physical example of regular flow which is quasi-laminar and to which Eqs. (2.37), (2.39), (2.40), and (2.41) apply when used properly is that of the beam in a cutoff magnetron. In Sec. 2.3 of Chap. II we treat a flow of this type from a planar cathode located along the $y = 0$ plane, as shown in Fig. 1.1, with an uniform magnetic field in the z direction. Individual electrons are assumed to be emitted from the cathode with zero velocity; they obtain a positive velocity in the y direction, and then proceed to a maximum distance from the cathode, and return to the cathode following a symmetrical path with respect to the y direction. At any point within the flow there are two

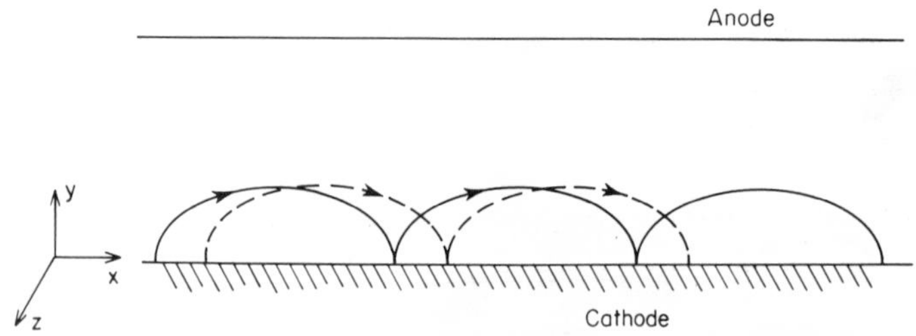

Fig. 1.1. An example of two stream flows in a cutoff magnetron.

streams, with one set of electrons moving away from the cathode and another set, equal in number, returning to it. The speed of the two streams of electrons at any point, from Eq. (2.38), is the same, but their velocities are in different directions.

Before proceeding further, we deduce an important relation between the radius of curvature of the electron trajectory and the applied field by making use of the hydrodynamic equation of motion [Eq. (2.34)]. We consider an electron traveling along the curved trajectory shown in Fig. 1.2; s is the distance along the path, and r is the distance from the trajectory along the principal normal to the path in a direction which is positive toward the center of curvature. In the (s,r,n) coordinates, the component of Eq. (2.34) in the r direction is, from Eq. (2.33),

$$v_s \frac{\partial v_r}{\partial s} = -\eta(E_r - v_s B_n) \tag{2.42}$$

where B_n is the component of magnetic field perpendicular to the path and to the r direction.

If an electron moves a distance δs along the path, the new principal normal to the path makes an angle $\delta\psi$ with the original principal normal, and the gain in radial velocity δv_r is, to first order, $v_s \delta\psi$. It follows that $\partial v_r/\partial s = v_s(\partial\psi/\partial s) = \kappa v_s$, where κ is the curvature of the path. Equation (2.42) can be written, therefore, in the form

$$\kappa v_s^2 = -\eta(E_r - v_s B_n) \tag{2.43}$$

This is the statement that the centrifugal force on an electron is balanced by the applied fields. By using the conservation-of-energy equation [Eq. (2.28)] and assuming that the initial velocity of an electron is zero, the curvature κ of the path is

$$\kappa = -\frac{E_r}{2\phi} + \left(\frac{\eta}{2\phi}\right)^{1/2} B_n \tag{2.44}$$

Thus the radius of curvature at any point of an electron path is en-

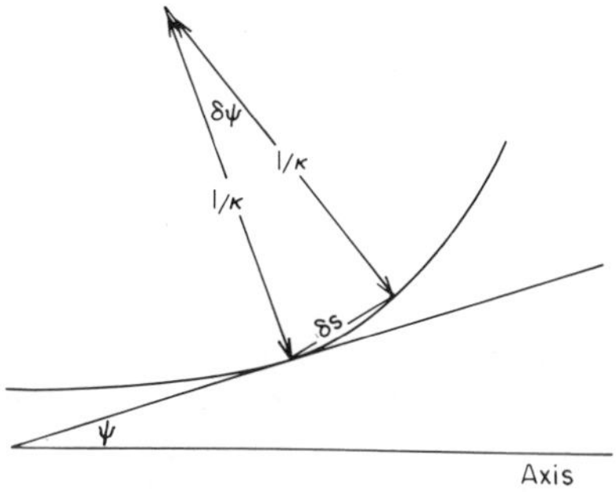

Fig. 1.2. Coordinate system for a curved trajectory.

tirely dependent on the potential and the fields normal to the path at that point.

Note that there is nothing in the derivation of Eq. (2.44) which requires that the flow be laminar. If it is not, then a different coordinate system, (s,r,n), has been implied for each particle. If the velocity of the particle at the cathode is $\mathbf{v}_c$, Eq. (2.44) has the general form

$$\kappa = -\frac{E_r}{2\phi + v_c^2\eta} + \left(\frac{\eta}{2\phi + v_c^2\eta}\right)^{1/2} B_n \tag{2.45}$$

It follows from Eq. (2.44) that a particle follows a rectilinear path ($\kappa = 0$) only if $E_r = (2\eta\phi)^{1/2} B_n$ at any point on the path. Moreover, if there is no magnetic field present, $E_r = 0$ on a rectilinear path, but E_r must be finite if the electron is to follow a curved path.

3. SOME INVARIANTS OF THE FLOW

3.1. Introduction. In Section 2 it was shown that the total energy of an electron is an invariant of its motion. In this section we discuss two other types of invariant. The first type depends on the vorticity w, defined by

$$\mathbf{w} = \nabla \times (\mathbf{v} - \eta\mathbf{A}) \tag{3.1}$$

We have already discussed that, whether the flow is laminar or not, it is always possible to define a velocity field $\mathbf{v}(x,y,z)$ for one particle. This $\mathbf{v}$ has a physical meaning, in general, only on the trajectory of the particle. Therefore most of the invariants based on $\mathbf{w}$ have meaning only if the velocity is a single-valued function of the coordinates (laminar flow) of if there are a finite number of such velocity functions (quasi-laminar flow). However, some of the integrals of $\mathbf{w}$ depend only on $\mathbf{v}$ itself; in this case the invariants are meaningful even if the flow is nonlaminar. These points are discussed in more detail with the invariants themselves in Sec. 3.2.

Another invariant which is significant is the phase-space density n of the flow, which is defined and discussed in Sec. 3.3. The concept of phase-space density is important only if the flow is nonlaminar and there is a velocity distribution of particles at each point of space. The invariance of n is called Liouville's theorem, and is proved also in Sec. 3.3.

3.2. The Lagrange Invariant, Poincaré Invariant, and Busch's Theorem. The invariant relations which we derive in this section are based on the w of Eq. (3.1). They have equivalents in hydrodynamic theory, and are called the Lagrange integral invariant and Poincaré invariant.[2-4] From these invariants we derive the important and much used Busch's theorem for axially symmetric beams. This theorem makes it possible to determine the angular component of electron velocity in an axially symmetric beam without having a detailed knowledge of the form of the electric fields present.

To derive the basic expression, we use the vector relation

$$(\mathbf{v} \cdot \nabla)\mathbf{v} = \tfrac{1}{2}\nabla(v^2) - \mathbf{v} \times (\nabla \times \mathbf{v})$$

and the expressions for **E** and **B** of Eqs. (2.9) and (2.10):

$$\mathbf{E} = -\nabla\phi \qquad \text{and} \qquad \mathbf{B} = \nabla \times \mathbf{A}$$

Equation (2.34) can then be written

$$\nabla(\tfrac{1}{2}v^2 - \eta\phi) - \mathbf{v} \times [\nabla \times (\mathbf{v} - \eta\mathbf{A})] = 0 \tag{3.2}$$

where **A** is the magnetic vector potential.

From the conservation-of-energy equation [Eq. (2.27)], the first term is always zero on the trajectory of a particle. It follows that

$$\mathbf{v} \times \mathbf{w} = \mathbf{v} \times [\nabla \times (\mathbf{v} - \eta\mathbf{A})] = 0 \tag{3.3}$$

Equation (3.3), which we call the vorticity relation, is very important. If the speed is known from the conservation-of-energy equation, Eq. (3.3) gives the additional information required about the direction of the velocity.

Equation (3.3) relates the velocity and the generalized velocity, $\mathbf{u} = \mathbf{v} - \eta\mathbf{A}$. From this equation either the curl of the generalized velocity vector **u** is parallel to the velocity vector **v** or it is zero. Again, by analogy with hydrodynamics, we call $\nabla \times \mathbf{u} = \mathbf{w}$ the vorticity of the flow.[5] Therefore the vorticity of the flow is zero or it is parallel to the velocity vector. In the subsequent analysis we assume the flow is quasi-laminar, so that the **v**, **u**, and **w** are functions of position for one stream. In hydrodynamics certain quantities remain invariant along the flow. Similarly for space-charge flow, certain analogous quantities remain invariant along an electron trajectory. To determine these invariants, we consider the trajectories in a stream passing through a closed curve $\mathcal{C}_1$, as shown in Fig. 1.3. This same set of trajectories passes through a second closed curve $\mathcal{C}_2$, and $\mathbf{S}_1$ and $\mathbf{S}_2$, with the vectors defined to be positive in the direction of **v**, are two surfaces which pass through the curves $\mathcal{C}_1$ and $\mathcal{C}_2$, respectively. The surface σ is the one traced out by the electron trajectories which pass between the two closed curves $\mathcal{C}_1$

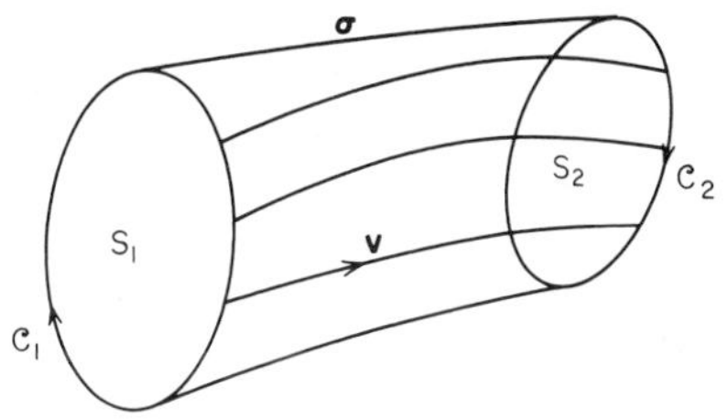

Fig. 1.3. Lagrange's invariant and Poincaré's invariant.

and $\mathcal{C}_2$, with the convention that σ is taken to be positive in the direction of the outward normal from the volume enclosed by $S_1 + S_2 + \sigma$. The two invariant relations which have hydrodynamic equivalents are Lagrange's integral invariant and Poincaré's invariant. Lagrange's integral invariant can be expressed as

$$\int_{S_1} [\nabla \times (\mathbf{v} - \eta \mathbf{A})] \cdot d\mathbf{S} = \int_{S_2} [\nabla \times (\mathbf{v} - \eta \mathbf{A})] \cdot d\mathbf{S} \tag{3.4a}$$

or equivalently,

$$\int_{S_1} \mathbf{w} \cdot d\mathbf{S} = \int_{S_2} \mathbf{w} \cdot d\mathbf{S} = \text{constant} \tag{3.4b}$$

Lagrange's integral invariant is a statement of the conservation of the vorticity of a beam.

Poincaré's invariant is the line-integral form of Lagrange's integral invariant, and is written

$$\oint_{\mathcal{C}_1} (\mathbf{v} - \eta \mathbf{A}) \cdot d\boldsymbol{\ell} = \oint_{\mathcal{C}_2} (\mathbf{v} - \eta \mathbf{A}) \cdot d\boldsymbol{\ell} = \text{constant} \tag{3.5}$$

These invariant relations can be proved by considering the volume integral of the vorticity $\mathbf{w}$ over the volume τ, enclosed by the surfaces $S_1 + S_2 + \sigma$. By using Gauss' theorem [Eq. (2.5) of Appendix A], it follows that

$$\begin{aligned} -\int_{S_1} [\nabla \times (\mathbf{v} - \eta \mathbf{A})] \cdot d\mathbf{S} + \int_{S_2} [\nabla \times (\mathbf{v} - \eta \mathbf{A})] \cdot d\mathbf{S} \\ + \int_{\sigma} [\nabla \times (\mathbf{v} - \eta \mathbf{A})] \cdot d\mathbf{S} = \int_{\tau} \nabla \cdot [\nabla \times (\mathbf{v} - \eta \mathbf{A})]\, d\tau \end{aligned} \tag{3.6}$$

The right-hand side of Eq. (3.6) must be zero, because the divergence of the curl of any vector is zero. Equation (3.3), the vorticity relation, implies that the vorticity, $\nabla \times (\mathbf{v} - \eta\mathbf{A})$, is either zero or it lies along a trajectory. Consequently, the third integral on the left-hand side of Eq. (3.6) is zero, proving Lagrange's invariant [Eq. (3.4)]. It is a simple matter to deduce Poincaré's invariant [Eq. (3.5)] by using Stokes' theorem [Eq. (2.7) of Appendix A].

It is possible to deduce another useful invariant form by using Stokes' theorem on only the $\nabla \times \mathbf{v}$ terms in Eq. (3.4), in order to obtain the expression

$$\oint_{\mathcal{C}_1} \mathbf{v} \cdot d\ell - \oint_{\mathcal{C}_2} \mathbf{v} \cdot d\ell = \eta \int_{S_1} \mathbf{B} \cdot d\mathbf{S} - \int_{S_2} \mathbf{B} \cdot d\mathbf{S} = \eta(\Psi_1 - \Psi_2) \tag{3.7}$$

where Ψ_1 and Ψ_2 are the total magnetic fluxes passing through the surfaces S_1 and S_2, respectively.

The most commonly used invariant relation, Busch's theorem for axially symmetric systems, follows from Eq. (3.7) by letting the two closed curves $\mathcal{C}_1$ and $\mathcal{C}_2$ become circles, with their planes perpendicular to the axis of symmetry of the system. We find that if the radii of the circles are r_1 and r_2, respectively, and the angular velocities of the electron at these planes are $\dot{\theta}_1$ and $\dot{\theta}_2$, respectively, then

$$r_1^2\dot{\theta}_1 - r_2^2\dot{\theta}_2 = \frac{\eta}{2\pi}(\Psi_1 - \Psi_2) \tag{3.8}$$

This relation, which is valid only for an axially symmetric system, is known as Busch's theorem. It is of great importance, because it makes it possible to determine the angular velocity of an electron about the axis of a symmetric system without requiring a detailed knowledge of the form of the electric fields. By analogy, we call Eq. (3.7) the generalized Busch's theorem.

Equation (3.8) is valid even when the flow is nonlaminar. This result will be proved independently, to express it in an alternative manner. When the flow is axially symmetric and there is no θ component of the magnetic field, the vector potential **A** in the (r,θ,z) system can be written from Eq. (2.19) of Appendix A:

$$\mathbf{A} = (0, A_\theta, 0) \tag{3.9}$$

The θ component of the Lorentz equation of motion is, using Eq. (3.4) of Appendix A and the **A** of Eq. (3.9),

$$r\ddot{\theta} + 2\dot{r}\dot{\theta} = -\eta\left[-\dot{z}\frac{\partial A_\theta}{\partial z} - \frac{\dot{r}}{r}\frac{\partial}{\partial r}(rA_\theta)\right] \tag{3.10}$$

Since A_θ does not depend on θ explicitly, Eq. (3.10) can be written, from the scalar form of Eq. (2.31),

$$\frac{d}{dt}(r^2\dot{\theta}) = \eta\frac{d}{dt}(rA_\theta) \tag{3.11}$$

In Eq. (3.11), $\dot{\theta}$ can be identified with the angular velocity, because it is required only on the trajectory. Therefore, for a single particle,

$$r^2\dot{\theta} = \eta r A_\theta = \text{constant} \tag{3.12}$$

Equation (3.12) is equivalent to Eq. (3.8); if $B_\theta = 0$, Ψ and A_θ are related by

$$\Psi = 2\pi r A_\theta \tag{3.13}$$

We consider now some applications of the usefulness of these invariant relations of Busch's theorem. For the first example, consider the surface S_1 to be the cathode. It follows from Busch's theorem that since $\dot{\theta}_1 = 0$ at the cathode, a beam can only be focused to a point, that is, $r_2 = 0$ if $\Psi_2 = \Psi_1$. Thus, if the magnetic flux passing through the cathode is zero, the magnetic flux passing through the focal point must also be zero. If, on the other hand, there is finite magnetic flux passing through the cathode, it is not possible to focus the beam to a point because this would require infinite magnetic field at the focal point of the beam.

A similar theorem for a strip beam also follows from the generalized Busch's theorem [Eq. (3.7)]. In this case, it is not possible to obtain a line-focused strip beam unless the magnetic flux passing through the cathode is zero.

Another example of the use of Busch's theorem is the determination of the minimum thickness of the beam emitted from a magnetron injection gun. In the magnetron injection gun, illustrated in Fig. 1.4, the beam is emitted from an axially symmetric cathode, usually conical in form; a hollow electron beam forms finally in a region of uniform magnetic field, with the axis of the beam in the same direction as the magnetic field. If the magnetic flux enclosed by the outer radius of the cathode is given by Ψ_b and the magnetic flux enclosed by the inner radius of the cathode is given by Ψ_a, it follows from Busch's theorem that the inner and outer radii of the final electron beam are r_o and r_i, respectively, with

$$r_o^2\dot{\theta}_o = \frac{\eta}{2\pi}(\pi r_o^2 B - \Psi_b) \tag{3.14}$$

$$r_i^2\dot{\theta}_i = \frac{\eta}{2\pi}(\pi r_i^2 B - \Psi_a) \tag{3.15}$$

where B is the value of magnetic field in the uniform field region. Equations (3.14) and (3.15) are valid even if the beam is nonlaminar, i.e., the electron trajectories cross each other. In the following treatment, we make the additional assumption that the beam is laminar; as a result, the electrons leaving from the point of maximum radius of the cathode are always at the outside surface of the beam. For this condition it is necessary that the magnetic flux enclosed by the cathode surface increase monotonically with radius. As the emitted beam is symmetrical, it follows from Gauss' theorem that the space-charge force on the inner electrons is zero. Consequently, for balanced flow, the angular velocity $\dot{\theta}_i$ of the inner electrons must

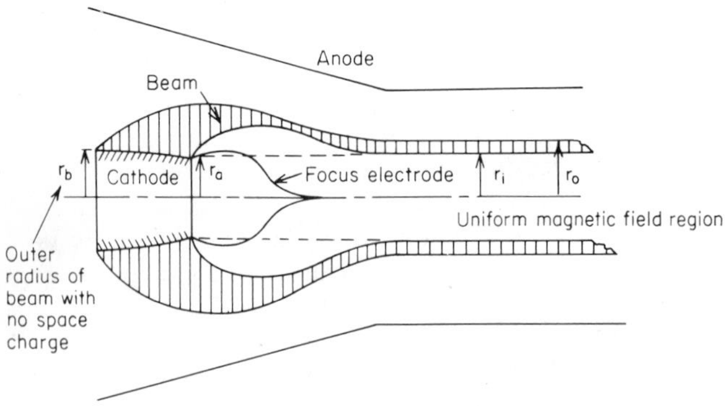

Fig. 1.4. Schematic of a magnetron injection gun.

be zero. In the extreme case, where the space-charge forces on electrons at the outside of the beam are also negligible, $\dot{\theta}_o$ must also be zero. From Eqs. (3.14) and (3.15), the outer and inner radii r_o and r_i are then given by

$$r_o^2 = \frac{\Psi_b}{\pi B} \tag{3.16}$$

$$r_i^2 = \frac{\Psi_a}{\pi B} \tag{3.17}$$

The outer radius given by this formula is the minimum possible radius for laminar flow. In the presence of space-charge forces, $\dot{\theta}_o$ is no longer zero, and the outer radius of the beam is larger than the value given by Eq. (3.16).

3.3. Liouville's Theorem. So far, we have considered invariants of the flow in which certain properties of one particular particle are conserved throughout its motion. Examples of this are the total energy and vorticity. Moreover, in many of the equations, such as Eq. (3.1), it is assumed that there exists a velocity vector field in which the velocity is a function of position, so that $(\nabla \times \mathbf{v})$ is defined. Sometimes, as in Eq. (2.8), it was assumed that there were a finite number of discrete flows. In this section we consider a more realistical description of a beam; at each point of space there is a continuous spectrum of velocities. In most of the applications treated in this book, the spectrum of velocities is so narrow that it can be approximated by a single-valued function. However, in some cases, of the type treated in Chap. VI, the spread of velocities at each point is important. If there is a spread of velocities at each point of space, the velocity no longer depends on position in each stream. Instead, it is necessary to define a distribution function $n(\mathbf{x};\mathbf{v})$ and discuss its variation in the six-dimensional space, of which three variables are position and three velocity.

The function n is defined as follows: The number of particles having velocity between $\mathbf{v} + d\mathbf{v}$ and in the region of space defined by $\mathbf{x}$ and $\mathbf{x} + d\mathbf{x}$ is $n(\mathbf{x};\mathbf{v})\, dx\, dy\, dz\, dv_x\, dv_y\, dv_z$, where

$$d\mathbf{x} = (dx, dy, dz) \qquad \text{and} \qquad d\mathbf{v} = (dv_x, dv_y, dv_z) \tag{3.18}$$

Usually, n is a function of $\mathbf{x}$, $\mathbf{v}$, and t, but in this book only steady flows are treated, so that all functions can be written independent of an explicit time dependence. Note that, for one particular particle, $\mathbf{v}$ and $\mathbf{x}$ depend on time; in general, however, the space variables $\mathbf{x}$ and velocity variables $\mathbf{v}$ are independent. It is usual, therefore, to write the variation of n in the six-dimensional phase space $\mathbf{x},\mathbf{v}$.

In this section the variation of n is discussed, and it is shown to be a constant of the motion. Let $\mathbf{x}_a$ be one point in space, with $n(\mathbf{x}_a, \mathbf{v}_a)$ particles in the range $\mathbf{v}_a$, $\mathbf{v}_a + d\mathbf{v}$, and $\mathbf{x}_b$ is another point with $n(\mathbf{x}_b, \mathbf{v}_b)$ in the range $\mathbf{v}_b$, $\mathbf{v}_b + d\mathbf{v}$.

If a particle with velocity $\mathbf{v}_a$ at $\mathbf{x}_a$ would at a later time reach $\mathbf{x}_b$ with velocity $\mathbf{v}_b$, we shall show that

$$n(\mathbf{x}_a;\mathbf{v}_a) = n(\mathbf{x}_b;\mathbf{v}_b) \tag{3.19}$$

We consider first the variation of the number of particles $n(x_1,x_2,x_3)$* contained in the box of Fig. 1.5 as a function of time. In this example, which is given for later generalization, the velocity $\dot{x}$ with components $(\dot{x}_1,\dot{x}_2,\dot{x}_3)$ is again considered a univalued function of position. The number of particles escaping across the surface $A_1A_2A_3A_4$ in time δt is then, to first order,

$$-\,n(x_1,x_2,x_3)\dot{x}_3(x_1,x_2,x_3)\;dx_1\;dx_2\;\delta t$$

Thus the sum of the particles escaping across the two surfaces $A_1A_2A_3A_4$ and $A_5A_6A_7A_8$ is δn_3, where

$$\delta n_3 = \frac{\partial}{\partial x_3}\left[n(x_1,x_2x_3)\dot{x}_3(x_1,x_2,x_3)\right]dx_1\;dx_2\;dx_3\;\delta t \tag{3.20}$$

The contributions escaping across the other sides may be paired similarly, so that the total change in the number of particles in the box, $\delta n\;dx_1\;dx_2\;dx_3$, is given by

$$\delta n\;dx_1\;dx_2\;dx_3 = \sum_i \frac{\partial}{\partial x_i}(n\dot{x}_i)\;dx_1\;dx_2\;dx_3\;\delta t$$

which can be written

$$\frac{\partial n}{\partial t} = \sum_j \frac{\partial}{\partial x_j}(n\dot{x}_j) \tag{3.21}$$

If the flow is assumed steady, so that n is explicitly time-independ-

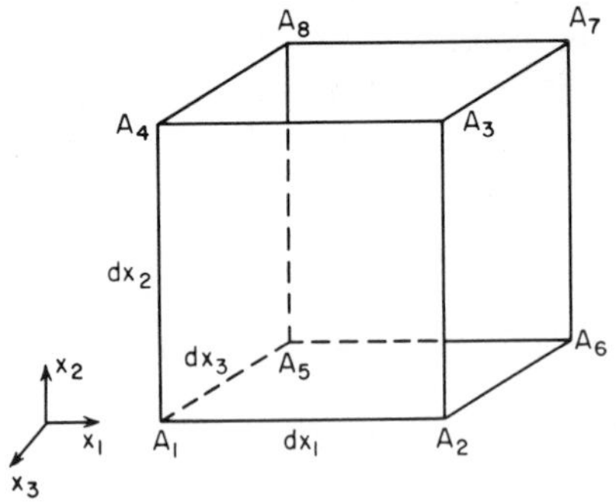

Fig. 1.5. Diagram of a three-dimensional box to illustrate the change of a quantity $n(x_1,x_2,x_3)$.

*For simplicity of notation, we denote (x,y,z) by (x_1,x_2,x_3) and use a similar notation for $\mathbf{v}$.

ent, then the left-hand side of Eq. (3.21) is zero. Now if n is identified with the space-charge density divided by electronic charge, ρ/q, $\dot{x}$ with the velocity **v**, and **x** with the usual position coordinate, Eq. (3.21) can be recognized as the usual conservation-of-charge equation, as in Eq. (2.36), for a single stream of flow.

Equation (3.20) could be deduced by considering the total flux of particles across the pair of bounding planes defined by x_3 = constant; Eq. (3.21) was derived from Eq. (3.20) by noting that n depended only on the three variables (x_1,x_2,x_3). If now n depends on six variables, $(x_1,x_2,x_3;\ v_1,v_2v_3)$, then equations like Eq. (3.20) can still be derived for the flux across the two defining planes x_3 = constant of a six-dimensional box (of course, the box is rather complicated to draw).

In exactly the same way as Eq. (3.21) is derived from Eq. (3.20), the change in n in time dt is given by

$$\delta n\, dx_1\, dx_2\, dx_3\, dv_1\, dv_2\, dv_3$$

$$= \left[\sum_j \frac{\partial}{\partial x_j}(n\dot{x}_j) + \sum_j \frac{\partial}{\partial v_j}(n\dot{v}_j)\right] dx_1\, dx_2\, dx_3\, dv_1\, dv_2\, dv_3\, \delta t$$

which can be written

$$\frac{\partial n}{\partial t} = \sum_j \frac{\partial}{\partial x_j}(n\dot{x}_j) + \frac{\partial}{\partial v_j}(n\dot{v}_j) \tag{3.22}$$

Again, if the flow is steady, n is time-independent, so that $\delta n/\delta t$ is zero, and Eq. (3.22) becomes

$$\sum_j \frac{\partial}{\partial x_j}(n\dot{x}_j) + \frac{\partial}{\partial v_j}(n\dot{v}_j) = 0 \tag{3.23}$$

Now the velocity $\dot{x}_j$ of a particle is independent, in six-dimensional phase space, of the position, because $\dot{x}_j$, x_j are independent coordinates, so that

$$\frac{\partial \dot{x}_j}{\partial x_j} = \frac{\partial v_j}{\partial x_j} = 0 \tag{3.24}$$

Also, $\dot{v}_j$ is related to $(\mathbf{x};\mathbf{v})$ by the Lorentz equation of motion [Eq. (2.15)], so that

$$\frac{\partial \dot{v}_j}{\partial \dot{x}_j} = \frac{\partial \dot{v}_j}{\partial v_j} = \frac{\partial}{\partial v_j}\{-\eta[\mathbf{E}(\mathbf{x}) + \mathbf{v} \times \mathbf{B}(\mathbf{x})]_j\} \tag{3.25}$$

Since **E** and **B** depend only on position and not on velocity, the only possible nonzero terms in Eq. (3.25) are $\partial(\mathbf{v} \times \mathbf{B})_j/\partial v_j$. The term with j = 1, for example, is

$$-\eta \frac{\partial}{\partial v_1}[v_2 B_3(\mathbf{x}) - v_3 B_2(\mathbf{x})]$$

Since v_2, v_3 are independent of v_1, this term is also zero; thus Eq. (3.25) can be written

$$\frac{\partial \dot{v}_j}{\partial v_j} = 0 \tag{3.26}$$

As a consequence of Eqs. (3.24) and (3.26), Eq. (3.23) can be written

$$\sum_j \left(\dot{x}_j \frac{\partial n}{\partial x_j} + \dot{v}_j \frac{\partial n}{\partial v_j} \right) = 0 \tag{3.27}$$

But if n is a function only of the six variables **x**, **v**, the left-hand side of Eq. (3.27) is exactly dn/dt; hence Eq. (3.27) shows that n is a constant of the motion; the phase-space density n about one particular particle as it moves in time obeys the relation

$$n(\mathbf{x};\mathbf{v}) = \text{constant} \tag{3.28}$$

This is exactly what we set out to prove at the beginning of this section, and it is called Liouville's theorem. The consequences of Eq. (3.28), always used in the form of Eq. (3.19), are far-reaching and form the basis of the whole of Chap. VI. Since six dimensions are difficult to imagine physically, it may be simpler to say that Eq. (3.28) means that in six dimensions the particles behave like an incompressible fluid.

With the phase-space density $n(\mathbf{x};\mathbf{v})$, we can complete the definition of space-charge density ρ and current density **i** of Sec. 2.2. To find $\rho(\mathbf{x})$, it is necessary to add up the contributions of all the particles which pass through **x**, so that

$$\rho(\mathbf{x}) = q \iiint_{\mathbf{V}} n(\mathbf{x};\mathbf{v})\, dv_1\, dv_2\, dv_3 \tag{3.29}$$

The range of integration in Eq. (3.29) is over all possible velocities **v**; in general, n is zero unless **v** falls within some finite limits. Similarly, the current $\mathbf{i}(\mathbf{x})$ is given by

$$\mathbf{i}(\mathbf{x}) = -q \iiint_{\mathbf{V}} \mathbf{v}\, n(\mathbf{x};\mathbf{v})\, dv_1\, dv_2\, dv_3 \tag{3.30}$$

It is easily verified that, in the laminar case, n is a delta function,[6] and the simpler expressions of Eq. (2.6) and (2.7) result. In most cases treated in this book, with the exception of Chap. VI, the flow is laminar, and the simpler equations can be used.

4. CYCLOTRON FREQUENCY AND LARMOR FREQUENCY

Certain frequencies are associated with the motion of an electron in a magnetic field. These frequencies, the cyclotron frequency and the Larmor frequency, are of great importance and are used throughout this book. We define them in this section and show why they are of importance in simple cases. Consider the motion of an electron in a uniform magnetic field B in the z direction, where space-charge forces are negligible and there is no applied electric field present. In rectangular coordinates, the equations of motion for an electron are

$$\frac{dv_x}{dt} = -\eta v_y B \tag{4.1a}$$

$$\frac{dv_y}{dt} = \eta v_x B \tag{4.1b}$$

$$\frac{dv_z}{dt} = 0 \tag{4.1c}$$

Equation (4.1a) can be substituted in Eq. (4.1b) to obtain the differential equation for v_x:

$$\frac{d^2v_x}{dt^2} + \eta^2 B^2 v_x = 0 \tag{4.2}$$

This has the solution

$$v_x = k \cos(\omega_H t + \alpha) \tag{4.3a}$$

with $$v_y = k \sin(\omega_H t + \alpha) \tag{4.3b}$$

where $$\omega_H = \eta B = -\frac{q}{m} B \tag{4.4}$$

and α and k are constants of integration. Equation (4.1c) can be integrated directly to give the result

$$v_z = v_{zo} = \text{constant} \tag{4.3c}$$

Equations (4.3) can be integrated, in turn, to yield the trajectories

$$x - x_o = \frac{k}{\omega_H} \sin(\omega_H t + \alpha) \tag{4.5a}$$

$$y - y_o = -\frac{k}{\omega_H} \cos(\omega_H t + \alpha) \tag{4.5b}$$

and $$z - z_o = v_{zo} t \tag{4.5c}$$

where x_o, y_o, and z_o are constants of integration. From Eqs. (4.5a) and (4.5b), the projection of the electron trajectory on the xy plane is the circle

$$(x - x_o)^2 + (y - y_o)^2 = \frac{k^2}{\omega_H^2} \tag{4.6}$$

The electron moves around a circle in the xy plane, center x_o, y_o, radius k/ω_H, in a period $2\pi/\omega_H$. This natural frequency of rotation of an electron about a magnetic field line, i.e., $(\omega_H/2\pi)$, is called the cyclotron frequency. The actual path is a helix with the axis $x = x_o$, $y = y_o$.

We consider now the motion of an axially symmetric beam emitted from a cathode shielded from the magnetic field, so that $\Psi = 0$. In a region where the magnetic field is uniform, it follows from Busch's theorem [Eq. (3.8)] that the angular velocity $\dot{\theta}$ of an electron, a distance r from the axis of the system, is given by

$$r^2\dot{\theta} = \frac{\eta}{2\pi}\Psi \tag{4.7}$$

where Ψ is the flux enclosed within the radius r. By writing $\Psi = \pi r^2 B$, we find that

$$\dot{\theta} = \frac{\eta B}{2} \tag{4.8}$$

Thus the natural frequency of rotation of an electron about the central axis is one-half of the cyclotron frequency. This frequency of rotation of an electron about the central axis of an axially symmetric beam is designated the Larmor frequency, and denoted by $\omega_L/2\pi$, where

$$\omega_L = \frac{\omega_H}{2} = \frac{\eta B}{2} \tag{4.9}$$

The difference between the cyclotron frequency and the Larmor frequency can be seen physically from the motion of a beam emitted from a shielded cathode. Space-charge forces are negligible in the region where there is a uniform magnetic field and there is no electric field present. Consequently, at some point on their path, by virtue of Busch's theorem, all electrons go through the axis. An individual electron rotates at the cyclotron frequency on a circular path which passes through the axis; the projection of its trajectory onto the xy plane is shown in Fig. 1.6. If the center of such a circle is radius r/2 from the axis, the maximum distance an electron moves from the axis will be r. If the instantaneous position of the electron is at the point P, the center of the circle is O, and the point where the circle intersects the axis is A, it can be shown by simple geometry that the angles in the figure shown are such that $\varphi = 2\theta$. But $\dot{\varphi} = \omega_H$; therefore the angular velocity $\dot{\theta} = \omega_H/2 = \omega_L$. Thus the electron is rotating about the axis at the Larmor frequency.

When there are electric fields present, it still follows from Busch's theorem that the rotation of the electron about the axis is at the Larmor frequency, but now the electrons no longer pass through the axis of the system. Physically, it is often easier to understand the form of the motion in such systems by considering the motion in a frame of reference which rotates at the Larmor frequency. In a circularly symmetric system, the equation of motion in the r direction is

$$\ddot{r} - r\dot{\theta}^2 = -\eta E_r \tag{4.10}$$

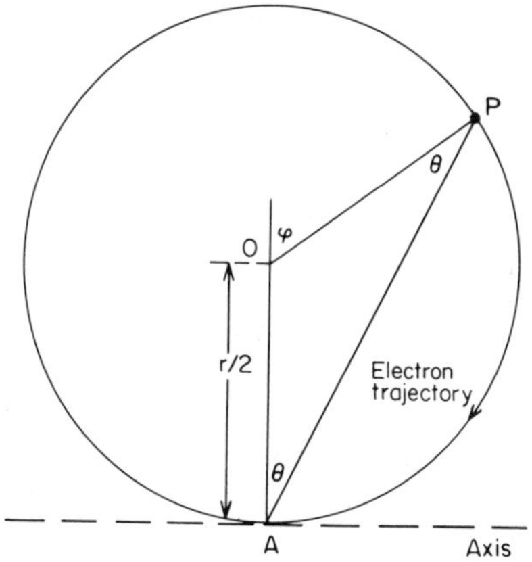

Fig. 1.6. An electron trajectory in the x,y plane of the beam emitted from a shielded gun in an axially symmetric system. The trajectory shown is in a region of uniform field.

In a system which rotates at the Larmor frequency, the angular velocity of an electron is zero. In the rest frame, the angular velocity of an electron is

$$\dot{\theta} = \omega_L \tag{4.11}$$

Thus, in a system rotating at the Larmor frequency, the Larmor frame, the electron appears to move radially, as if it were being accelerated by a field E_{rL}, where

$$E_{rL} = E_r - \frac{r\omega_L^2}{\eta} \tag{4.12}$$

If $E_{rL} = 0$, the electrons move neither inward nor outward, provided they enter the field with zero velocity in the radial direction. The electrons revolve about the axis at a constant radius. The type of beam which has this motion is called a Brillouin beam, and is dealt with more fully in Chapter IV.

The definitions of ω_H and ω_L of Eqs. (4.4) and (4.9) are quite general, and are useful even if the magnetic field is nonuniform. Several examples of the advantages of working in the Larmor frame are given later (Section 5 of Chap. III, for example).

5. THE CLASSIFICATION OF ELECTRON BEAMS

5.1. Introduction. The invariant relations of Sec. 3.2 are meaningful, in most cases, only when the flow is quasi-laminar. Although in one integral form (Busch's theorem) useful results are obtained for single particles, this is the only such instance. In this section we describe the whole flow in terms of a small number of vector fields. Therefore the flow is restricted throughout this section to laminar flow. It is possible, though not very profitable, to extend the analysis to quasi-laminar flow. This extension is not carried out in this book. Here, **v** is a single-valued function of position, so that expressions like $\nabla \times \mathbf{v}$, etc., have a unique meaning.

In Sec. 5.2 we categorize the different forms of laminar flow, based on the properties of $\nabla \times \mathbf{v}$. It is shown that, when the normal component of magnetic field at the cathode is zero, the velocity is related to the gradient of a scalar function W; the type of flow which results is called congruent flow. In Sec. 5.3 the electromagnetic equations are combined with the Lorentz equation of motion to derive a nonlinear differential equation for W when the flow is congruent. Finally, in Sec. 5.4, the equations for noncongruent space-charge flow are discussed.

5.2. Congruent and Noncongruent Flow. The application of the invariant relations given in Sec. 3.2 and of the vorticity relation $\mathbf{v} \times \mathbf{w} = 0$ makes it possible to classify the different types of space-charge flow. This classification is based entirely on the form of the magnetic field at the cathode surface.

We consider the form taken by Lagrange's integral invariant [Eq. (3.4)] when S_1 is the cathode surface and the component of velocity tangential to the cathode surface is zero. In this case, the component of $\nabla \times \mathbf{v}$ perpendicular to the cathode surface must also be zero, and Eq. (3.4) becomes

$$\int_{S_2} \mathbf{w} \cdot d\mathbf{S} = \int_{S_2} [\nabla \times (\mathbf{v} - \eta \mathbf{A})] \cdot d\mathbf{S} = \int_{S_1} [(\nabla \times \mathbf{v}) - \eta \mathbf{B}] \cdot d\mathbf{S} = -\eta \int_{S_1} B_{nc}\, dS \tag{5.1}$$

where B_{nc} is the component of magnetic field normal to the cathode surface. The vorticity relation $\mathbf{v} \times \mathbf{w} = 0$ implies that the component of the vorticity **w** perpendicular to an electron trajectory must be zero. At the cathode, therefore, the component of the vorticity parallel to the surface of the cathode must be zero. It follows from the preceding arguments that if there is no magnetic field perpendicular to the surface of the cathode, the vorticity **w** is zero everywhere in the beam. In particular, when there is no magnetic field present, $\nabla \times \mathbf{v} = 0$ anywhere within the beam. Conversely, if there is a normal component of magnetic field at the cathode, the vorticity is in general finite throughout the beam.

We can now classify the different types of space-charge flow according to the behavior of $\nabla \times \mathbf{v}$. It was shown in Sec. 3.2 that Busch's theorem implies that if the magnetic field is zero everywhere, it is possible to focus the beam to a point. Moreover, if $\mathbf{B} \equiv 0$ everywhere, then $\nabla \times \mathbf{v} = 0$ everywhere. In this case we can express the velocity as a gradient of the scalar function W as follows:

$$\mathbf{v} = \nabla W \tag{5.2}$$

so that the surfaces of constant W are at right angles to the velocity vectors **v** which cut them, as shown in Fig. 1.7. Space-charge flows of this type are called normal congruent flows in analogy with the similar definition in optics.[3,4]

In classical dynamics a function similar to the above W is used, called the action function.[2] In order that the definition may be valid for motion at relativistic velocities, the momentum $\mathbf{p} = m\mathbf{v}$, rather than the velocity, is normally expressed as the gradient of the action function. For convenience, because relativistic beams are not treated here, we call W the action function. It is related to the commonly used action function of classical dynamics by a simple scaling factor when the motion is nonrelativistic. The action function W used in this book is a velocity potential. When such a function can be defined and is known, all the parameters of the flow are determined.

In the more general case when $B_{cn} = 0$ but $\mathbf{B} \neq 0$ in the beam, $\mathbf{w} = \nabla \times (\mathbf{v} - \eta\mathbf{A}) = 0$ everywhere, and it is still possible to focus the beam to a point. The generalized velocity **u** can now be expressed in terms of a scalar function W as follows:

$$\mathbf{u} = \mathbf{v} - \eta\mathbf{A} = \nabla W \tag{5.3}$$

Thus the velocity **v** is given by the expression

$$\mathbf{v} = \nabla W + \eta\mathbf{A} \tag{5.4}$$

A flow of this type is called a skew-congruent flow. For such a beam the velocity vectors **v** do not cut the surfaces of constant action, W = constant, at right angles. However, the generalized velocity vectors **u** do cut these surfaces at right angles.

In order to understand skew-congruent flow more clearly, we consider an axially symmetric system with no flux intersecting the cathode, $\Psi_c = 0$. In this case, as was shown in Sec. 3.2, in a region where there is a uniform axially directed magnetic field, the electrons rotate about the axis at the Larmor frequency ω_L. Moreover, when space-charge fields are negligible, all electrons pass through the axis at some point of their trajectory. With the correct axial velocities, therefore, it is possible to focus this beam to a point. The θ component of velocity of the electrons in the uniform field

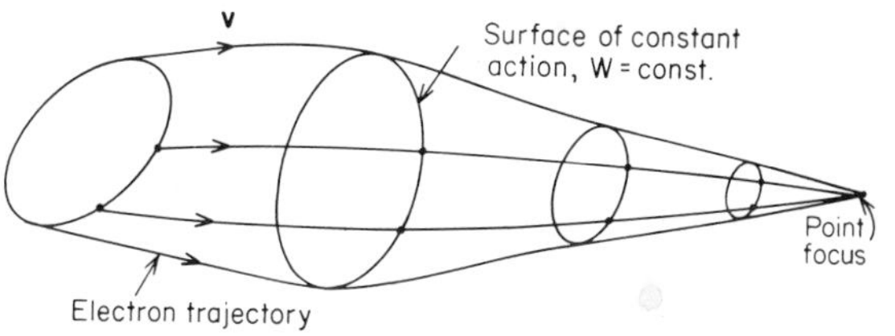

Fig. 1.7. A normal congruent electron beam focused to a point.

region is $v_\theta = r\omega_L = \eta rB/2$. We can find the generalized velocity, $\mathbf{u} = \mathbf{v} - \eta\mathbf{A}$, by considering the form of the magnetic vector potential. In a uniform field region, this is $A_\theta = rB/2$. Consequently, the θ component of the generalized velocity is

$$u_\theta = v_\theta - \eta\mathbf{A}_\theta = 0 \tag{5.5}$$

Thus, in this axially symmetric skew-congruent flow, the generalized velocity has components only in the axial and radial directions. The generalized electron velocity is the velocity of an electron in the rotating Larmor frame of reference. When all electrons have the same axial velocity and zero radial velocity, that is, $v_r = 0$, $v_\theta = 0$, and v_z = constant, as would be the case for Brillouin flow (Chap. IV), the surfaces of constant action are planes perpendicular to the axis.

When there is no component of magnetic field normal to the cathode, the determination of electron trajectories can be simplified greatly by the use of the action function. In terms of the action function W, the conservation-of-energy equation [Eq. (2.28)] can be written

$$(\nabla W)^2 = 2\eta\phi \tag{5.6}$$

when $v_c = 0$. This equation is known as the Hamilton-Jacobi equation in classical dynamics.

At this point it is necessary to digress slightly. In classical mechanics the Hamilton-Jacobi formulation can be used always, whereas here we have stated that the analysis is confined to laminar flow. This apparent contradiction is resolved by the fact that it is always possible to construct a velocity field $\mathbf{V}(x,y,z)$ which takes particular values $\mathbf{v}$ on one trajectory and yet is the gradient of a scalar W. In general, however, this $\mathbf{V}$ would have no relation, at a point in space off the particular trajectory, with the velocity of particles at that point. This means that it is necessary to construct a different action function W, in general, for each particle in the flow. The important property of congruent flow is that the same action function W applies to all the particles in the flow. Not only is Eq. (5.6) valid for one particle, as it is in classical mechanics, but it is valid for the whole flow.

Equation (5.6) can be generalized to the case of $\mathbf{v}_c \neq 0$; it is necessary, however, that $\mathbf{v}_c$ be uniform in magnitude and normal to the cathode. If the electrostatic potential is known a priori, Eq. (5.6) can be solved to find W at any point; hence the velocity and electron trajectories can be deduced anywhere within the flow. This procedure can be simpler than the solution of three separate equations of motion for the different components of velocity. A more important property is that, with this approach, it is easier to recognize possible analytic solutions. It has been shown by Gabor[7] that it is possible to devise fairly simple graphical techniques for the determination of trajectories, based on the fact that the velocity vectors must be perpendicular to the surfaces of constant W.

The more complicated case of skew-congruent flow can be treated in a similar manner. For this type of flow, with $\mathbf{v}_c = 0$, the generalized Hamilton-Jacobi equation, which is also convenient for analysis and graphical methods of solution, has the form

$$(\nabla W + \eta \mathbf{A})^2 = 2\eta\phi \tag{5.7}$$

When there is a component of magnetic field normal to the cathode, we call the flow noncongruent.

An example of noncongruent flow is the flow in the magnetron injection gun treated in Sec. 3.2. We consider the simple case of a conical cathode in a uniform axially directed magnetic field B, as shown in Fig. 1.8. In this case, if the space-charge fields are negligible, it was shown in Sec. 3.2 that, in a unipotential region, there is a possibility of obtaining a beam of constant radius, the outer radius of the beam being the outer radius of the cathode r_o and the inner radius of the beam being the inner radius of the cathode r_i. With negligible space-charge fields, the angular velocity of all electrons is zero. Thus $v_\theta = 0$ in a unipotential region and, because $A_\theta = rB/2$,

$$u_\theta = v_\theta - \eta A_\theta = -\frac{\omega_H r}{2} \tag{5.8}$$

and the vorticity is

$$\mathbf{w} = \nabla \times \mathbf{v} = -\frac{\omega_H}{|B|}\mathbf{B} \tag{5.9}$$

In this particular case, it is possible to find planes which intersect the electron trajectories at right angles. However, where there are space-charge forces, the angular velocity of the outer electrons is no longer zero, the vorticity is different, and it is not possible to find planes which intersect either the electron trajectories or the generalized velocity vectors at right angles.

For noncongruent flow it is not possible to express the velocity at every point of the flow in terms of one simple scalar function. Instead, it is possible to express the velocity in terms of a set of

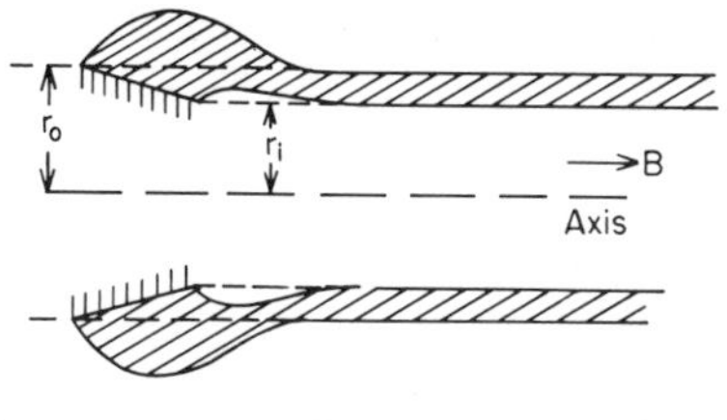

Fig. 1.8. Schematic of noncongruent flow from a conical cathode in an axially symmetric system with a uniform axial magnetic field B.

scalar functions, known as Clebsch variables in hydrodynamics.[8] Since it is extremely difficult to find solutions for the electron motion by means of this formalism, we do not treat this procedure in this book. With noncongruent-flow problems, it is most convenient to work directly with the hydrodynamic equation of motion [Eq. (2.34)] or the Lorentz equation of motion for single particles [Eq. (2.15)]. Particle flow problems will be solved by these methods in the following chapters.

5.3. The Equations of the Space-charge Field for Congruent Flow. In the preceding sections we dealt with various possible forms of the equations of motion for an electron beam which are convenient for analysis. It is not enough to deal only with the equations of motion. When the beam is tenuous, or the effect of space charge on the potential field is small, the electrostatic potential must obey Laplace's equation. More commonly, in most of the flow problems of this book, the effect of space charge is not negligible. The electrostatic potential within the beam is dependent on the space charge present, which is itself dependent on the applied potential, and the whole problem of determining the electron trajectories becomes much more complicated.

First we set up a flow problem when the effect of space charge is negligible. In this case, Laplace's equation for the applied potential fields,

$$\nabla^2\phi = 0 \tag{5.10}$$

must be satisfied, in addition to the equations of motion. When there is no magnetic field present and the flow is of a normal congruent type, the equations of motion can be stated in terms of the action function W by means of the Hamilton-Jacobi equation [Eq. (5.6)]. On substitution of this equation in Eq. (5.10), the following partial differential equation for W is deduced:

$$\nabla^2(\boldsymbol{\nabla} W)^2 = 0 \tag{5.11}$$

The solution of this single partial differential equation for W, with the correct boundary conditions, gives all the possible sets of electron trajectories which would satisfy Laplace's equation for the electrostatic potential.

When the space-charge fields are not negligible, it is necessary for the potential to obey Poisson's equation,

$$\nabla^2\phi = -\frac{\rho}{\epsilon_0} \tag{5.12}$$

rather than Laplace's equation.

In addition, the equation of continuity for space-charge flow,

$$\nabla \cdot \mathbf{i} = 0 \tag{5.13}$$

must be satisfied, taking into account the relation between current density $\mathbf{i}$ and charge density ρ, since the flow is laminar.

$$\mathbf{i} = -\rho\mathbf{v} \tag{5.14}$$

Thus the problem of solving for trajectories becomes that of satisfying Eqs. (5.12) to (5.14) simultaneously, with a form of the equation of motion. As in the case of negligible space-charge effects, it is convenient to work with the action function when the flow is of a normal congruent or skew-congruent type. For such problems, all the relevant equations can be expressed in terms of the action function W by the substitution $\mathbf{v} = \nabla W + \eta\mathbf{A}$, and the following unwieldy partial differential equation for W can be derived:

$$\nabla \cdot \{(\nabla W + \eta\mathbf{A})\,\nabla^2[(\nabla W + \eta\mathbf{A})^2]\} = 0 \tag{5.15}$$

The solutions of this equation yield all the possible congruent laminar-flow solutions which satisfy Poisson's equation. However, it is usually more convenient to work with the separate equations rather than with the complete partial differential equation (5.15) for the flow.

5.4. The Equations of the Space-charge Field for Noncongruent Flow. When the flow is noncongruent, it is not possible to make use of the action-function formalism. Instead, we must work directly with either the Lorentz equation of motion,

$$\frac{d\mathbf{v}}{dt} = -\eta(\mathbf{E} + \mathbf{v} \times \mathbf{B}) \tag{5.16}$$

the hydrodynamic equation of motion,

$$(\mathbf{v} \cdot \nabla)\,\mathbf{v} = -\eta(\mathbf{E} + \mathbf{v} \times \mathbf{B}) \tag{5.17}$$

or, if the flow is regular and the emission velocity is normal to the cathode, the equation of conservation of energy,

$$v^2 = v_c^2 + 2\eta\phi \tag{5.18}$$

with the vorticity condition

$$\mathbf{v} \times [\nabla \times (\mathbf{v} - \eta\mathbf{A})] = 0 \tag{5.19}$$

In practice, it is more convenient to work with either Eq. (5.16) or (5.17). These equations are used in combination with the equation of continuity [Eq. (5.13)] and the relation between current density and charge density [Eq. (5.14)]. In addition, it is necessary to satisfy the divergence equation

$$\nabla \cdot \mathbf{E} = \frac{\rho}{\epsilon_0} \tag{5.20}$$

Where space-charge effects are negligible, we can put $\rho \equiv 0$ in Eq. (5.20), simplifying the analysis. The simultaneous solution of one of the forms of the equations of motion with Eq. (5.20), under the appropriate boundary conditions at the cathode, gives all possible flows. If space-charge effects are not negligible, the equation of motion and the other relevant space-charge-flow equations must be satisfied in a self-consistent manner. When these equations are solved in combination with the boundary conditions at the cathode, all possible laminar flows can be determined.

6. BOUNDARY CONDITIONS AT AN EMITTER

It is not within the scope of this book to consider the behavior of electrons at the surface of a cathode. The subject is treated in several review articles, in particular in an excellent one by Nottingham.[9] It is important for us, however, to specify the variation of current density, velocity distribution, and potential, near such a cathode, as initial conditions for the flows treated later. In most of the book, with the exception of Chap. VI and a few other isolated instances, it will be assumed that space-charge-limited emission occurs; this means that the charge density is so distributed that the electric field is zero near the cathode. This is not an a priori boundary condition and is not satisfied for all conditions; there may not be enough electrons emitted to counteract completely the applied electric field at the cathode. The behavior near the cathode is dominated by thermal effects. The charge distribution exerts a retarding field and, in the applications to electron-beam devices of this book, produces a potential minimum in front of the cathode. Only those particles with sufficient energy to cross this potential minimum are available for the electron beam.

In this section we state without proof the result for the two-dimensional parallel-plane diode, including thermal-velocity effects. A simplified parallel-plane diode is treated in Sec. 2.2 of Chap. II as one of the exact space-charge-flow solutions; the complete problem is treated in Section 2 of Chap. VI. The arguments of this section are given here, so that the conclusions may be used to specify boundary conditions for the later chapters. All the justifications for the statements in this section are given in Section 2 of Chap. VI.

The condition which occurs most frequently in electron-beam devices is that flow is either thermally limited or space-charge-limited. In the former case the emitted current density i_c is independent of the applied voltage and is given by Richardson's law,[9] i.e.,

$$i_c = i_{cM} = AT^2 \exp - \left[\frac{11{,}600\Phi_0}{T_c}\right] \tag{6.1}$$

where A depends on the material but usually has a value of about 1.2×10^6 in mks units, Φ_0 is the work function of the material, and T_c the cathode temperature in degrees Kelvin. The initial velocity of the emitted particles has a Maxwellian distribution, but the mean value of the initial velocity is $\overline{v_{Tc}}$, where, in the thermally or space-charge-limited cases, $\overline{v_{Tc}}$ is given by Eq. (2.8) of Chap. VI, i.e.,

$$\overline{v_{Tc}} = 2 \times 10^5 \left(\frac{T_c}{1000}\right)^{1/2} \quad \text{m/sec} \tag{6.2}$$

In Eq. (2.8) of Chap. VI, several mean velocities, $\overline{v_{Tc}}$, $(\overline{v_{Tc}^2})^{1/2}$, $\overline{v_{Tcz}}$, etc., are defined. These all play slightly different roles, but differ from each other by less than a factor of 3. Equation (6.2) gives the order of magnitude of the initial velocity.

In the space-charge-limited case, there is a minimum of potential at a short distance from the cathode. Between the cathode and this potential-minimum plane, the electrons flow in two directions, some toward and some away from the minimum; some electrons therefore flow back to the cathode. Only those electrons with velocity normal to the cathode greater than $(2q\phi_m/m)^{1/2}$, where $-\phi_m$ is the potential at the potential-minimum plane, pass through the potential minimum and proceed to the anode. Electrons which are emitted with a velocity normal to the cathode, with less than this value, return to the cathode. The mean velocity of the emitted particles measured at the potential-minimum plane is still given by Eq. (6.2). The depth of the potential minimum, and the current that can pass through it, now depend on the applied voltage. The electric field is given by

$$\mathbf{E} = 0 \quad \text{at the potential minimum} \tag{6.3}$$

The actual distance of the potential minimum from the cathode can be deduced from the equations of Sec. 2.5 of Chap. VI. It is usually considerably less than 0.1 mm. In most of the examples given in this book, it is assumed that the potential minimum, which can be regarded as a virtual cathode, and the cathode coincide; therefore Eq. (6.3) is taken to hold at the cathode. To check the validity of this assumption in any particular case, the reader should consult Section 2 of Chap. VI.

If (q_1,q_2,q_3) form an orthogonal curvilinear coordinate system so that the virtual cathode is $q_1 = 0$, then the phase-space density at the potential minimum $n(0,q_2,q_3;v)$ is

$$n(0,q_2,q_3;\mathbf{v}) = -\frac{i_c(q_2,q_3)}{q}\,\frac{2}{\pi}\left(\frac{m}{2kT_c}\right)^2 \exp -\left(\frac{mv^2}{2kT_c}\right) \tag{6.4}$$

where i_c is the current density passing through the potential minimum and is directed along the q_1 direction.

From Eq. (6.4), it is possible to deduce the mean velocities $\overline{v_{Tc}}$, etc., at the cathode (potential-minimum surface). These mean velocities are evaluated in Eq. (2.8) of Chap. VI. In that equation the $\overline{v_{Tc}}$, etc., are evaluated directly at the emitter. By comparing the $n(\mathbf{x};\mathbf{v})$ at the emitter and the potential minimum, however, it can be shown that the same formulas apply to the mean velocity at the potential minimum. For example,

$$\left(\overline{v_{sTc}^2}\right)^{1/2} = \left(\frac{kT_c}{m}\right)^{1/2} \quad \text{and} \quad \left(\overline{v_{\perp Tc}^2}\right)^{1/2} = \left(\frac{2kT_c}{m}\right)^{1/2} \tag{6.5}$$

where $(\overline{v_{sTc}^2})^{1/2}$ denotes the root mean square of the longitudinal velocity, due to thermal effects, at the cathode (potential-minimum plane), and $(\overline{v_{\perp Tc}^2})^{1/2}$ is the corresponding transverse quantity. One reason why $(\overline{v_{\perp Tc}^2})^{1/2}$ is used instead of $\overline{v_{\perp Tc}}$ is that the latter is zero; also, $\overline{v_{\perp Tc}^2}$ is a measure of the mean energy in the transverse direction. Usually, kT_c/m is sufficiently small so that it is accurate enough to replace the boundary conditions of Eqs. (6.4) and (6.5) by

$$\mathbf{v}_c = 0 \tag{6.6}$$

The formula for i_{cM} of Eq. (6.1) is valid only for electrons from a thermionic cathode. All the other equations of this section, however, apply equally to electrons or ions emitted from a gas discharge or other similar source.

7. SCALING LAWS

7.1. Introduction. It is of great interest to evaluate how the performance of an electron gun or focusing system changes when the applied potentials or dimensions are changed. In general, such criteria can be determined only by carrying out detailed trajectory solutions for each individual condition of interest, which is by no means an easy task. However, if the restriction is made that the trajectories of particles in the system either remain invariant or at least are scaled geometrically, it is possible to deduce certain general scaling laws which are of great help to the tube designer.

In Sec. 6.2, general scaling laws are derived for changing the linear dimensions, applied potentials, particle mass, and particle charge. These scaling laws are valid even when thermal-velocity effects are taken into account. In Sec. 7.3, a further scaling factor is introduced, but the resulting scaling laws are valid only for a restricted class of beams.

7.2. General Scaling. In order for a set of scaled parameters to represent a possible flow, these parameters must satisfy the differential equations of the flow and the boundary conditions. We first discuss the differential equations which govern the flow. These are the Lorentz equation of motion [Eq. (2.15)],

$$\frac{d\mathbf{v}}{dt} = -\eta(\mathbf{E} + \mathbf{v} \times \mathbf{B}) \tag{7.1}$$

the defining equation for velocity,

$$\frac{d\mathbf{x}}{dt} = \mathbf{v} \tag{7.2}$$

the divergence relation [Eq. (2.1)],

$$\nabla \cdot \mathbf{E} = \frac{\rho}{\epsilon_0} \tag{7.3}$$

the continuity equation [Eq. (3.27)],

$$\sum_j \left(v_j \frac{\partial n}{\partial x_j} + \frac{dv_j}{dt} \frac{\partial n}{\partial v_j} \right) = 0 \tag{7.4}$$

the divergence and curl equations for the magnetic field [Eqs. (2.3) and (2.23)],

$$\nabla \cdot \mathbf{B} = 0 \qquad \text{and} \qquad \nabla \times \mathbf{B} = 0 \tag{7.5}$$

and the defining equation for ρ [Eq. (3.29)],

$$\rho = q \iiint_{\mathbf{v}} n(\mathbf{x};\mathbf{v})\, dv_1\, dv_2\, dv_3 \tag{7.6}$$

These equations govern the flow.

First we consider how the various parameters of space-charge flow change when the applied potential is changed by a factor μ but all electrode positions remain fixed. It is convenient to begin by examining the Lorentz equation of motion. When the potential ϕ at the point (x_1,y_1,z_1) is changed by a factor μ, where it is assumed, for the moment, that μ is constant (independent of $\mathbf{x}$), it follows that, when all dimensions are unaltered, $\mathbf{E}$ also changes by μ. For the left-hand side of Eq. (7.1), since $d\mathbf{v}/dt = (\mathbf{v} \cdot \nabla)\mathbf{v}$, it is seen that $d\mathbf{v}/dt \propto v^2$, under these conditions, so that $\mathbf{v}$ changes by $\mu^{1/2}$. Again, because $\mathbf{v}$ changes by $\mu^{1/2}$ and $\mathbf{E}$ by μ, it follows from Eq. (7.1) that $\mathbf{B}$ must change by $\mu^{1/2}$. We may now apply this argument to the divergence equation (7.3); since it is linear, Eq. (7.3) implies that ρ changes by μ. It follows that, for laminar flow, $\mathbf{i} = -\rho\mathbf{v}$ changes by $\mu^{3/2}$. If the trajectories remain unchanged, it is still possible to satisfy the equation of continuity. Thus, when the applied potential Φ is changed, the electron trajectories remain invariant and the current density $\mathbf{i}$ varies as $\Phi^{3/2}$.

This argument assumes that μ can be chosen so that it is constant throughout the system. This fact will now be proved, and at the same time scaling laws for changes in linear dimensions and particle mass will be deduced.

We assume that η, $\mathbf{B}_1(\mathbf{x})$, $\mathbf{E}_1(\mathbf{x})$, and $\rho_1(\mathbf{x})$ are one set of electromagnetic quantities which satisfy Eqs. (7.1) to (7.6), and $\mathbf{x} = \mathbf{x}_1(t_1)$ and $\mathbf{v} = \mathbf{v}_1(t_1)$ are the position and velocity of a particular particle as a function of transit time t. The fields seen by this particle are $\mathbf{B}_1[\mathbf{x}_1(t_1)]$ and $\mathbf{E}_1[\mathbf{x}_1(t_1)]$, and space-charge densities and phase-space densities are $\rho_1[\mathbf{x}_1(t_1)]$ and $n_1[\mathbf{x}_1(t_1);\ \mathbf{v}_1(t_1)]$.

We try first to find constant scaling factors so that, for one particular particle, the position $\mathbf{x}_2(t_2)$, transit time t_2, etc., are given by

$$
\begin{aligned}
&\mathbf{x}_2(t_2) = \gamma\ \mathbf{x}_1(t_1) \\
&t_2 = at_1 \\
&\mathbf{v}_2(t_2) = b\mathbf{v}_1(t_1) \\
&\mathbf{E}_2[\mathbf{x}_2(t_2)] = c\ \mathbf{E}_1[\mathbf{x}_1(t_1)] \\
&\mathbf{B}_2[\mathbf{x}_2(t_2)] = d\ \mathbf{B}_1[\mathbf{x}_1(t_1)] \\
&m_2 = \nu m_1 \\
&n_2[\mathbf{x}_2(t_2);\ \mathbf{v}_2(t_2)] = e\ n_1[\mathbf{x}_1(t_1);\ \mathbf{v}_1(t_1)] \\
&\rho_2[\mathbf{x}_2(t_2)] = f\ \rho_1[\mathbf{x}_1(t_1)]
\end{aligned}
\tag{7.7}
$$

For Eq. (7.7) to be possible, the condition that $\mathbf{v}_2(t_2)$, $\mathbf{x}_2(t_2)$, etc., still satisfy the equations of the flow [Eqs. (7.1) to (7.6)] imposes relations on the constant scaling factors a,b,c,d, etc. For example, from Eq. (7.2),

$$\frac{d\mathbf{x}_2}{dt_2} = \frac{\gamma}{a}\frac{d\mathbf{x}_1(t_1)}{dt_1} = \mathbf{v}_2(t_2) = b\ \mathbf{v}_1(t_1) = b\frac{d\mathbf{x}_1(t_1)}{dt_1} \tag{7.8}$$

Thus $ab = \gamma$ (7.9)

Equations (7.4) and (7.5) are satisfied by the parameters of Eq. (7.7), though for the latter equation, Eq. (7.9) is required again. From Eq. (7.7), it is clear that $\eta_2 = (1/\nu)\eta_1$, and

$$\frac{d\mathbf{v}_2}{dt_2} = \frac{b}{a}\frac{d\mathbf{v}_1}{dt_1} = -\frac{b}{a}\eta_1(\mathbf{E}_1 + \mathbf{v}_1 \times \mathbf{B}_1) \tag{7.10a}$$

and

$$-\eta_2(\mathbf{E}_2 + \mathbf{v}_2 \times \mathbf{B}_2) = -\frac{1}{\nu}\eta_1\{c\ \mathbf{E}_1[x_1(t_1)] + bd\ \mathbf{v}_1 \times \mathbf{B}_1\} \tag{7.10b}$$

Equation (7.1) requires that the left sides of Eqs. (7.10a) and (7.10b) be equal, so that

$$\frac{b}{a} = \frac{c}{\nu} \qquad \text{and} \qquad \frac{b}{a} = \frac{bd}{\nu} \tag{7.11}$$

In the same way, for Eq. (7.3) to be satisfied, it is necessary that

$$\frac{\rho_2[\mathbf{x}_2(t_2)]}{\epsilon_0} = f\,\frac{\rho_1[\mathbf{x}_1(t_1)]}{\epsilon_0} = f\nabla\cdot\mathbf{E}_1[\mathbf{x}_1(t_1)] = \frac{f\gamma}{c}\nabla\cdot\mathbf{E}_2[\mathbf{x}_2(t_2)] \tag{7.12}$$

so that $f\gamma = c$ (7.13)

Finally, for Eq. (7.6) to be satisfied, it is necessary that

$$f = eb^3 \tag{7.14}$$

Equations (7.9), (7.11), (7.13), and (7.14) are satisfied if

$$
\begin{aligned}
a &= c^{-1/2}\gamma^{1/2}\nu^{1/2} \\
b &= c^{1/2}\gamma^{1/2}\nu^{-1/2} \\
d &= c^{1/2}\gamma^{-1/2}\nu^{1/2} \\
e &= c^{-1/2}\gamma^{-5/2}\nu^{3/2} \\
f &= c\gamma^{-1}
\end{aligned}
\qquad (7.15)
$$

If Eq. (7.15) is satisfied, then as far as the differential equations of the flow for one particle are concerned, a scaling of the physical parameters of the flow according to Eq. (7.7) is possible. All the quantities in Eq. (7.15) are constants, independent of the particle considered, so that the scale factors hold for every particle in the flow.

If $\mathbf{E}_2$ and $\mathbf{x}_2$ satisfy Eq. (7.7), the potential $\phi_2(\mathbf{x}_2)$ is given, since $\nabla\phi = -\mathbf{E}$, by

$$\phi_2(\mathbf{x}_2) = c\gamma\phi_1[\mathbf{x}_1(t_1)] \qquad (7.16)$$

It is more usual to scale potentials than fields, so that, if $\mu \equiv c\gamma$, then μ, γ, and ν are taken as the fundamental scaling parameters. In terms of μ, γ, and ν, Eq. (7.15) becomes

$$
\begin{aligned}
a &= \mu^{-1/2}\gamma\nu^{1/2} \\
b &= \mu^{1/2}\nu^{-1/2} \\
c &= \mu\gamma^{-1} \\
d &= \mu^{1/2}\gamma^{-1}\nu^{1/2} \\
e &= \mu^{-1/2}\gamma^{-2}\nu^{3/2} \\
f &= \mu\gamma^{-2}
\end{aligned}
\qquad (7.17)
$$

Before it is possible to assert that the parameters of Eq. (7.7) represent a possible flow, it is necessary to consider the initial values of the parameters at the boundaries. For these we require the current density $i_2(x_2)$, which is given, from Eq. (3.30), by*

$$
\begin{aligned}
\mathbf{i}_2 &= -q \iiint_{V_2} \mathbf{v}_2(\mathbf{x}_2)\, n_2(\mathbf{x}_2;\mathbf{v}_2)\, dv_{21}\, dv_{22}\, dv_{23} \\
&= -(b^4 e)\, q \iiint_{V_1} \mathbf{v}_1(\mathbf{x}_1)\, n_1(\mathbf{x}_1;\mathbf{v}_1)\, dv_{11}\, dv_{12}\, dv_{13} \\
&= \mu^{3/2}\gamma^{-2}\nu^{-1/2}\mathbf{i}_1
\end{aligned}
\qquad (7.18)
$$

For space-charge-limited flow, the boundary conditions between the emitter and the potential minimum are complicated and do not scale. However, if by cathode we mean the virtual cathode at the

*We use the obvious notation that v_{ij} is the jth component of $\mathbf{v}_i$.

potential minimum, the boundary conditions are, from Eqs. (6.3) and (6.7),

$$n_c(x_c, v_c) = -\frac{i_c}{q}\frac{2}{\pi}\frac{m^2}{(2kT_c)^2}\exp -\left(\frac{mv^2}{2kT_c}\right), \qquad E_c = 0 \tag{7.19}$$

and at the electrodes $\mathcal{C}$

$$\phi = \Phi \qquad \text{on } \mathcal{C} \tag{7.20}$$

For the physical parameters of Eqs. (7.7), (7.15), (7.17), and (7.18) to satisfy Eq. (7.20), it is necessary that

$$\Phi_2(\mathbf{x}_2) = \mu\Phi_1(\mathbf{x}_1) \tag{7.21}$$

If we assume that

$$T_{c2} = gT_{c1} \tag{7.22}$$

then it follows that

$$\frac{m_2 v_2^2}{T_{c2}} = \frac{b^2\nu}{g}\frac{m_1 v_1^2}{T_{c1}} = \frac{\mu}{g}\frac{m_1 v_1^2}{T_{c1}} \tag{7.23a}$$

and

$$-\frac{i_{c2}}{q}\frac{m_2^2}{(2kT_{c2})^2} = -\frac{\mu^{7/2}\gamma^{-2}\nu^{3/2}}{g^2}\frac{i_{c1}m_1^2}{q(2kT_{c1})^2} \tag{7.23b}$$

In Eq. (7.23b) it has been assumed that i_{c1} scales according to Eq. (7.18). If n_{c1} is to scale according to Eq. (7.7) and Eq. (7.17), it is necessary, from Eqs. (7.22) and (7.23a), that

$$\mu = g \tag{7.24}$$

If Eq. (7.24) is satisfied, then, from comparing Eqs. (7.19) and (7.23b), n_{c1} scales according to Eqs. (7.7) and (7.17).

Thus we have shown that, by suitable choice of scaling factors, it is possible to set up new physical parameters which obey both the differential equations of the flow [Eqs. (7.1) to (7.6)] and the boundary conditions [Eqs. (7.19) and (7.20)]. Note that it has been necessary to assume that i_{c1} scales the same way as $\mathbf{i}_1$. For thermally limited emission, this would require, from Eq. (6.1), a particular variation of Φ_0, the work function of the material. Usually, however, the flow is space-charge-limited, and it is adequate to consider the flow only beyond the potential minimum; in this case i_c is governed almost entirely by the applied fields, and the scaling laws on i_{c2} are given by Eq. (6.4). These are consistent with Eq. (7.18).

If the scaling laws of Eqs. (7.7), (7.17), (7.18), (7.21), (7.22), and (7.24) are satisfied, by substitution in the appropriate defining equations, the scaling laws of all the other parameters of the flow can be evaluated. These are summarized in Table 1.1. In that table, a further possible scale change in parameters has been included, the possibility that the charge of the particle q changes by

Table 1.1. Scaling Factors for Geometrically Similar Beams

$x_2 = \gamma x_1$, $\phi_2(x_2) = \mu\sigma\phi_1(x_1)$, $m_2 = \nu m_1$, $q_2 = \sigma q_1$

Any parameter χ is scaled by $\mu^{c_1}\gamma^{c_2}\nu^{c_3}\sigma^{c_4}$

Parameter	Scaled by factor with:			
	c_1	c_2	c_3	c_4
Applied potential Φ	1	0	0	1
Dimension L	0	1	0	0
Potential at any point ϕ	1	0	0	1
Charge q	0	0	0	1
Mass m	0	0	1	0
Charge to mass ratio $q/m = -\eta$	0	0	−1	1
Electrostatic field **E**	1	−1	0	1
Magnetic field **B**	1	−1	1/2	0*
Cyclotron frequency $\omega_H = \eta B$	1/2	−1	−1/2	0
Total magnetic flux Ψ	1/2	1	1/2	0*
Magnetic vector potential **A**	1/2	0	1/2	0*
Velocity **v**	1/2	0	−1/2	1†
Mean initial speed v_c (where applicable)	1/2	0	−1/2	1†
Space-charge density ρ	1	−2	0	1
Plasma frequency $\omega_p = (-n\,\rho/\epsilon_0)^{1/2}$	1/2	−1	−1/2	2*
Current density **i**	3/2	0	−1/2	2*
Total current emitted from gun I	3/2	0	−1/2	2*
Perveance $P = \lvert I\rvert/\lvert\phi\rvert^{3/2}$	0	0	−1/2	1†
Perveance per square $P_\square$ (Chap. II)	0	0	−1/2	−1†
Action function W (when applicable)	1/2	1	−1/2	1†
Transit time between two points t	−1/2	1	−1/2	−1†
Emitter temperature T_c (when applicable)	1	0	0	0
Phase-space density n (when applicable)	−1/2	−2	3/2	−3†
Power density $i\phi$	5/2	−2	−1/2	3
Power $I\phi$	5/2	0	−1/2	3

*For negative values of σ, this parameter also changes sign.

†For negative values of σ, $|\sigma|$ is used so that the sign of the parameter is unchanged.

$$q_2 = \sigma q_1 \tag{7.25}$$

The parameter σ can be negative, unlike μ, γ, or ν. The inclusion of σ allows the scaling from electrons to positive ions (including multiply ionized ions).

It is interesting to examine some of the conclusions we can draw from these simple scaling laws. We see that $\mathbf{i} \propto \mu^{3/2}\gamma^{-2}$, provided that the trajectories remain similar and the type of particle is not changed. Thus, when the emitter is capable of supplying the current dictated by the space-charge-flow solutions, the current density is proportional to the three-halves power of the applied potential, and inversely proportional to the square of the dimensions of the system. Therefore the current density at the cathode of a given gun is critically dependent on its scale, and there must be a minimum size for each type of gun, limited by the capabilities of the emitter. Moreover, if there is a magnetic field present, the condition $\mathbf{i} \propto \mu^{3/2}\gamma^{-2}$ is pertinent only if $\mathbf{B}$ is varied as $\mu^{1/2}\gamma^{-1}$. So again an ultimate limit to a gun design is reached by the practical limit on the magnetic field obtainable.

The total current I passing through the system is proportional to $\Phi^{3/2}$. The ratio $I/\Phi^{3/2}$ is not dependent on the scale of the system and depends only on its geometrical shape. The ratio $I/\Phi^{3/2}$, which is usually called the perveance of the system, is an important criterion of performance. It is convenient to define a unit of perveance as the perv P, where $P = I/\Phi^{3/2}$. Because this unit is very much larger than the practical values used, it is normal to work in terms of micropervs, i.e., units of 10^{-6}P. It is common practice to use the microperv as the basic unit and to refer to a perveance of unit as being $P = 10^{-6}$ amp/volts$^{3/2}$. A convenient figure to remember is that unit perveance corresponds to 1 amp at 10 kv for electrons. Then, if two geometrically similar guns were designed, one using electrons and one using cesium ions, $\nu^{-1/2} = 500$, $\sigma = -1$, the ratio of their perveances would be 1/500. Thus, at 10 kv, only 2 ma would be emitted from a cesium-ion gun of the same size as a unit-perveance electron gun.

7.3. Transverse Scaling. We have already seen, in Sec. 7.2, how it is possible to scale all the dimensions of a focusing system of gun uniformly, so as to determine a new space-charge-flow solution. In general, it is not possible to scale only one of these dimensions at a time. However, useful and informative properties for determining one flow from another may be found by scaling only the transverse dimensions if the electric and magnetic fields have a linear transverse variation.

We shall consider only a system with a rectilinear axis in this section. The axis of this system is taken to be the z axis of the coordinate system, the transverse coordinates being x, y, respectively. If the electrode system is a perfect lens, the fields vary linearly out to the electrodes. In most real lenses, and in the paraxial beams described in Chap. III, the transverse electric and magnetic fields vary linearly from the axis in the vicinity of the axis, where the beam is located. In this case, the scaling laws we shall derive are valid for the parameters of the flow in the beam. Unlike the situation in Sec. 7.2, the electrodes outside the beam do not scale. In this case it is necessary to show that the physical parameters scale by constant scale factors in the beam and obey the correct boundary conditions at the cathode (potential minimum). At the cathode, the effect of longitudinal thermal-velocity spreads is neglected, but it is shown that the phase-space-density scales correctly for the transverse velocities.

In the beams to be discussed in this section, the electric and magnetic fields are assumed to be such that $E_x \propto x$, $E_y \propto y$, $B_x \propto x$, $B_y \propto y$. It is also assumed that the variation of E_z and B_z with respect to x and y may be neglected or regarded as of second order in x and y. These assumptions apply to the paraxial beams of Chap. III with a rectilinear axis. It follows that, if an electron is emitted along the z axis, it will continue to move along the z axis. Consequently, to first order, the components of the Lorentz equation of motion [Eq. (7.1)] become

$$\frac{dv_z}{dt} = -\eta[E_z + (\mathbf{v} \times \mathbf{B})_z] \qquad (7.26a)$$

$$\frac{d\mathbf{v}_\perp}{dt} = -\eta[\mathbf{E}_\perp + (\mathbf{v} \times \mathbf{B})_\perp] \qquad (7.26b)$$

where the subscript $\perp$ denotes the transverse component. We carry through an analysis similar to Sec. 7.2 and assume it is possible to scale a particular trajectory so that the longitudinal dimensions and the transit time remain unchanged but the transverse dimensions scale by a constant factor $\gamma_\perp$. This means that, if $x_1(t)$, $y_1(t)$, $z_1(t)$, $\phi_1[x_1(t), y_1(t), z_1(t)]$, etc., are physical parameters of the flow encountered by one particular particle in the system, we assume that it is possible to find $x_2(t)$, $y_2(t)$, etc., such that

$$x_2(t) = \gamma_\perp x_1(t) \qquad y_2(t) = \gamma_\perp y_1(t) \qquad z_2(t) = z_1(t) \qquad (7.27)$$

where t is the transit time. In this case the velocity components are given by

$$v_{2x}(t) = \gamma_\perp v_{1x}(t), \qquad v_{2y}(t) = \gamma_\perp v_{1y}(t) \qquad v_{2z}(t) = v_{1z}(t) \qquad (7.28)$$

Substituting Eq. (7.28) into Eq. (7.26b), it is seen that the $\mathbf{v}_{2\perp}$ can represent possible trajectories only if

$$\mathbf{E}_{2\perp} = \gamma_\perp \mathbf{E}_{1\perp}, \qquad \mathbf{B}_{2\perp} = \gamma_\perp B_{1\perp} \qquad B_{2z} = B_{1z} \qquad (7.29)$$

From Eq. (7.26a), the $\mathbf{B}_{2\perp}$, $\mathbf{E}^2{}_\perp$, and $\mathbf{v}_{2\perp}$ of Eqs. (7.28) and (7.29) can represent parameters of the flow only if the component $\mathbf{v}_\perp \times \mathbf{B}_\perp$ is neglected. This assumption is valid for the paraxial flows of Chap.

III, where the particles deviate only a short distance from the axis.

By similar considerations with the divergence and continuity equations [Eqs. (7.3) and (7.4)], it is found that the $\mathbf{v}_2$, $\mathbf{E}_2$, etc., represent possible parameters of the flow if

$$\rho_2[\mathbf{x}_2(t)] = \rho_1[\mathbf{x}_1(t)] \tag{7.30}$$

Of the relations Eq. (7.5), the divergence equation for the magnetic field is automatically satisfied; $\nabla \times \mathbf{B}_2 = 0$ is also true, because we have assumed that the terms $\partial B_z/\partial x$ are negligible. Although by a suitable scaling law it is possible to satisfy Eq. (7.6), there would be trouble with the boundary conditions. At the cathode the initial velocity distribution is isotropic; for this reason scaling is possible only if the phase-space density is integrated over the longitudinal velocity spread, and longitudinal velocity effects are ignored. In this case Eq. (7.6) becomes

$$\rho = q \iint_{\mathbf{v}_\perp} n_\perp(\mathbf{x};\mathbf{v}_\perp)\, dv_x\, dv_y \tag{7.31}$$

where $$n_\perp = \left(\frac{m}{2kT_c}\right)^{1/2} \int_{v_z} n(\mathbf{x};\mathbf{v})\, dv_z \tag{7.32}$$

The $n_{\perp 2}$ represents a possible physical parameter of the flow, from Eqs. (7.28), (7.30), and (7.31), if

$$n_{\perp 2}[\mathbf{x}_2(t);\ \mathbf{v}_{2\perp}(t)] = \gamma_\perp^{-2}\, n_{\perp 1}[\mathbf{x}_1(t);\mathbf{v}_{1\perp}(t)] \tag{7.33}$$

With the scaling laws of Eqs. (7.28), (7.29), (7.30), and (7.33), the parameters $\mathbf{x}_2$, $\mathbf{v}_2$, etc., satisfy all the differential equations of the flow for the one particle. The appropriate potentials and current density of the particle $\phi_2[\mathbf{x}_2(t)]$ and $\mathbf{i}_2[\mathbf{x}_2(t)]$ are given by

$$\phi_2[\mathbf{x}_2(t)] = \phi_1[\mathbf{x}_1(t)]$$

$$i_{2z}[\mathbf{x}_2(t)] = i_{1z}[\mathbf{x}_1(t)] \tag{7.34}$$

and $$\mathbf{i}_{2\perp}(t) = \gamma_\perp \mathbf{i}_{1\perp}(t)$$

where terms in $\mathbf{E}_\perp \cdot \mathbf{x}_\perp$ have been ignored to obtain ϕ.

Since all the scaling factors are constants, the same laws hold for every particle in the flow and, provided the boundary conditions are satisfied appropriately, the whole flow has been proved to scale.

If the flow is space-charge-limited, since ϕ remains unchanged, it is reasonable to assume that $\mathbf{i}_c$, which is only in the z direction, also remains unaltered on transverse scaling. At the cathode (potential minimum), E_z is always zero, and $n_{\perp c}$ is given by integrating Eq. (7.19) over v_z to give at the cathode

$$n_{\perp c}(\mathbf{x}_c;\mathbf{v}_\perp) = \frac{\rho_c}{\pi q}\,\frac{m}{2kT_c}\,\exp -\left(\frac{mv_\perp^2}{2kT_c}\right) \tag{7.35}$$

where ρ_c is the space-charge density at the potential minimum. It is necessary to write $n_{\perp c}$ in the form of Eq. (7.35) with ρ_c rather

Table 1.2. Transverse Scaling Laws for Geometrically Similar Paraxial Beams

$x_2 = \gamma_\perp x_1,\ y_2 = \gamma_\perp y_1,\ z_2 = \gamma z_1,$ and $\phi_2(x_2, y_2, z_2) = \mu\phi_1(x_2, y_2, z_2)$

Any parameter χ is scaled by $\mu^{c_1}\gamma_\perp^{c_2}\gamma_2^{c_3}$.

Parameter	Scaled by factor with:		
	c_1	c_2	c_3
Applied potential Φ	1	0	0
Longitudinal dimension z	0	0	1
Transverse dimensions x, y	0	1	0
Longitudinal component of electric field E_z	1	0	−1
Transverse component of electric field $\mathbf{E}_\perp$	1	1	−2
Longitudinal component of magnetic field B_z	1/2	0	−1
Transverse component of magnetic field $\mathbf{B}_\perp$	1/2	1	−2
Total magnetic flux Ψ through z = constant (where applicable)	1/2	2	−1
Longitudinal component of velocity v_z	1/2	0	0
Transverse component of velocity $\mathbf{v}_\perp$	1/2	2	−1
Space-charge density ρ	1	0	1
Current density i_z	3/2	0	−2
Total current I_z	3/2	1	−2
Action function W (where applicable)	1/2	1	0
Transit time between two points t	−1/2	0	1
Perveance P	0	2	−2
Emitter temperature T_c (transverse velocity components only, when applicable)	1	2	−2
Power density $i_z\phi$	5/2	0	−2
Power $I_z\phi$	5/2	2	−2

than i_c, because integration over v_z does not scale appropriately, and such an integration is required for i_c. Since ρ_c does not change, this $n_\perp$ scales according to Eq. (7.33) if and only if

$$T_{C2} = \gamma_\perp^2 T_{C1} \tag{7.36}$$

Thus all the boundary conditions scale appropriately at the cathode, and the whole flow scales transversely.

Several approximations have been made. In any case, the scaling applies only to the parameters of the beam. In general, the electrodes do not scale, since the assumptions we have made are not valid far from the axis, where the electrodes are situated.

The other parameters of the flow can be deduced in the same way as in Sec. 7.2 by substitution in the appropriate equations. The results can be generalized by using Table 1.1 and by supposing that all longitudinal dimensions are changed by a factor γ_Z, transverse dimensions by a factor $\gamma_\perp$, and the applied potential by a factor μ. This is equivalent to carrying out three operations in turn: (1) changing all dimensions by a factor γ_Z, (2) changing the ratio of the transverse to longitudinal dimensions by a factor $\gamma_\perp/\gamma_Z$, (3) changing the applied potential by a factor μ. We summarize the results of such scaling in Table 1.2.

In Sec. 7.2, it was shown that the perveance $P = |I|/|\Phi|^{3/2}$ was invariant under scaling of dimensions and potential. The perveance P is not, from Table 1.2, invariant under transverse scaling. However, a related parameter, $\Lambda = P\Phi/T_C$, is invariant under scaling of potential, transverse dimensions, and longitudinal dimensions. This invariance, although very important, is only an approximation, because the effects of longitudinal thermal-velocity spreads have been ignored. As one example of the use of this invariance, Danielson et al.[10] presented a larger number of sets of curves for the properties of a converging beam from a spherical cathode, including thermal-velocity effects. Herrman[11] has shown that these curves can be reduced to one set by use of the invariance of $P\Phi/T_C$.

Scaling laws may be derived in the same manner for paraxial strip beams, paraxial hollow beams, and paraxial beams with curvilinear axes. It is also possible, by restricting the magnetic field to having only a z component, to scale separately with respect to x and y; the properties of an elliptic beam can then be derived from that of a circular cylindrical beam.

REFERENCES FOR CHAPTER I

1. Pierce, J. R.: "Theory and Design of Electron Beams," D. Van Nostrand Company, Inc., Princeton, N. J., 1954.
2. Goldstein, H.: "Classical Mechanics," Addison Wesley Publishing Company, Inc., Cambridge, Mass., 1951.
3. Sturrock, P. A.: "Static and Dynamic Electron Optics," Cambridge University Press, London, 1955.
4. Gabor, D.: Dynamics of Electron Beams, *Proc. IRE*, vol. 33, p. 792, 1945.
5. Milne-Thomson, L. N.: "Theoretical Hydrodynamics," Macmillan & Co., Ltd., London, 1938.

6. Morse, P. M., and H. Feshbach: "Methods of Theoretical Physics," vol. 1, McGraw-Hill Book Company, New York, 1953.
7. Gabor, D.: Mechanical Tracer for Electron Trajectories, *Nature*, vol. 139, p. 373, 1937.
8. Butcher, P. N.: A Variational Formulation of the Multi-stream Electrodynamic Field Equations, *Phil. Mag.*, ser. 7, vol. 44, p. 971, 1953.
9. Nottingham, W. D.: Thermionic Emission, *Handbuch der Physik*, vol. 21, Springer Verlag OHG, Berlin, 1956.
10. Danielson, W. E., J. S. Rosenfeld, and J. A. Saloom: A Detailed Analysis of Beam Formation with Electron Guns of the Pierce Type, *Bell System Tech. J.*, vol. 35, p. 325, 1956.
11. Herrman, G.: Transverse Scaling of Electron Beams, *J. Appl. Phys.*, vol. 28, p. 474, 1957.

PROBLEMS

1. A regular electron beam is emitted from a cylindrical cathode, radius r_c, immersed in a uniform axial magnetic field B. Find the angular velocity of an electron which reaches a radius r, and the generalized velocity u_0 at radius r. What type of flow is this, and what is its vorticity **w**? Suppose the beam finally flows in a drift tube with $v_r = 0$. Find the inner radius of this beam when (a) the value of B is the same as at the cathode, and (b) when the value of B is twice its value at the cathode.

Note: Assume laminar flow.

2.

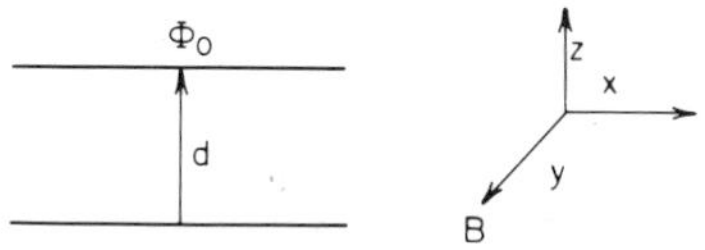

An infinite plane magnetron has an anode-cathode spacing d, the potential applied to the anode being Φ_0 and the magnetic field B. By using the equation of conservation of energy and Busch's theorem in the cartesian form, or the vorticity relation, find the condition for cutoff.

Hint: Find the potential below which v_x at the anode, given by Busch's theorem, is such that the kinetic energy of the electrons at the anode must be greater than the potential energy available.

3.

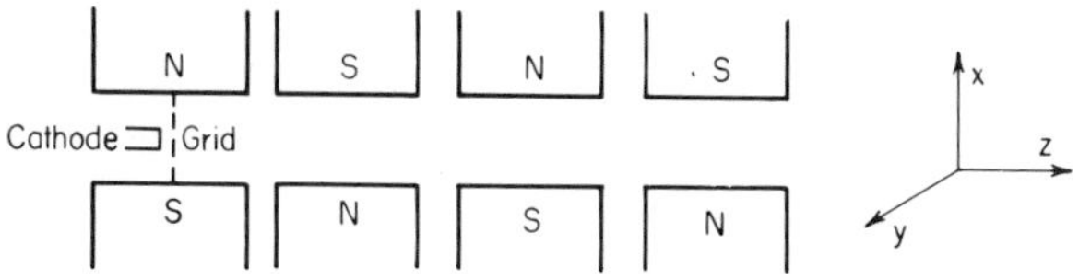

An infinite system of magnets is arranged as shown. The transverse component of magnetic field along the axis of this strip beam system is

$$B_x = B_0 \cos \frac{\pi z}{L}$$

Electrons are emitted from a strip cathode at $z = 0$, where $B_z = 0$, and are suddenly accelerated to a potential Φ_0 by a closely spaced grid. If the potential is Φ_0 everywhere else in the system, find the motion of the electrons along the central axis; i.e., find v_y and then, from conservation of energy, v_z. What is the potential below which electrons must return to the cathode?

4. Find a set of transverse scaling relations equivalent to those of Table 1.2 which make it possible to scale separately with respect to x and y. Assume that there is only a z component of magnetic field, the initial velocity of electrons leaving the cathode is zero, and the system is space-charge-limited.

5. From Poisson's equation find the potential and charge density within the Brillouin beam described in Section 4. Find the electron velocity components, charge density, electric field components, and potential at any point within an equivalent elliptically shaped Brillouin beam by using the scaling relations derived in Prob. 4.

II

Exact Space-charge-flow Solutions

1. INTRODUCTION

This chapter is devoted to a description of the methods used to obtain exact space-charge-flow solutions, in which the electrons leave the cathode either with zero velocity or with a uniform, but finite, velocity. It is of great importance to find laminar space-charge-flow solutions valid in a beam of infinite extent, which can serve as the basis of an electron-gun design. It is shown in Chap. VII that if an infinite-beam space-charge-flow solution is known, a finite portion of such a beam can be used as the beam in an electron gun; electrodes can be found to synthesize the boundary conditions at the edge of this portion of the beam. This is the Pierce-gun design procedure. Unfortunately, only a limited number of such exact space-charge-flow solutions are suitable for use in electron guns. The plane-diode, spherical-diode, and cylindrical-diode solutions, the latter two of which are described in Appendix E, have formed the basis of many useful gun designs. Certain other exact solutions for flow in a magnetic field have proved suitable for use in the design of crossed-field electron guns and magnetron injection guns. These flows are described in this chapter.

The basic method of analysis used in this chapter is to reduce the equations of space-charge flow to ordinary differential equations. We review the various mathematical techniques which are possible and indicate some of the flows which have proved useful in practice. We then develop a basic set of solutions which can be used also as a check on less exact, but more flexible, design techniques.

These methods of solution all depend on reducing the partial differential equations of the flow to ordinary differential equations. Without the use of such a technique, it has not been possible to solve the space-charge-flow problems in analytical form. Numerical procedures are available which make it possible to solve the full set of partial differential equations describing the flow directly. This approach to the problem, which is extremely complicated, is an elaboration of the analytical electrode design techniques described in Section 5 of Chap. VII; it has been used by Harker. The method is not described in this book; the reader may consult Refs. 1 and 2.

In Section 2, several space-charge-flow solutions are derived by direct use of the Lorentz equation of motion. This derivation depends on the fact that all parameters of the flow are functions of only one of the coordinates, usually the coordinate direction normal to the cathode. Several technically important solutions suitable for gun design are obtained by this technique.

In Section 3 we examine an approach to space-charge-flow problems which involves the use of an orthogonal curvilinear coordinate system; one set of the coordinates is the trajectories of the flow, and the other set, the surfaces of constant action. Although, by this method, it is possible to reduce the equations of flow to an ordinary differential equation, the determination of the correct coordinate systems to use involves solving a set of partial differential equations, and so no great simplification has been made. However, certain general properties of the flow can be determined by this method; in particular, the relation between the flow configuration in the region of the cathode and the current-density variation at the cathode can be determined. As an illustration of the method, a flow with circular trajectories is obtained.

The great advantage of the use of the action function is that it is a scalar variable. Consequently, the vector parameters of the flow, the velocity and current density, can be stated in terms of a scalar quantity, the action function. The equations of flow can then be reduced to a partial differential equation with one dependent variable, the action function. By the method of separation of variables, the partial differential equation can be reduced to a set of ordinary differential equations. This method, which is extended to take account of skew-congruent flow, is not necessarily the only approach. In Section 5, the full set of vector equations is solved directly by the method of the separation of variables.

The difficulties which occur in the numerical solutions of the resulting ordinary differential equations are due to one of the derivatives of a parameter of interest becoming infinite, either at the cathode or at some point within the flow. It is shown how such problems can be eliminated by the direct use of Lorentz's force law and the employment of the transit time of an electron along its trajectory as the independent variable.

2. ONE-DIMENSIONAL SPACE-CHARGE-FLOW SOLUTIONS

2.1. Introduction. A number of space-charge-flow solutions can be found by making direct use of the Lorentz equation of motion. In these solutions the parameters of the flow, such as the potential, velocity, and charge density, vary with only one of the coordinates. Consequently, there is a one-to-one relationship between this coordinate and the time it takes an electron to move to a given point. All the parameters of the flow can be expressed in terms of one independent variable, the time an electron takes to move along its trajectory. In this section we give a number of examples of such flows.

In Sec. 2.2 a detailed description of the solution for the plane diode is derived, with special attention to the boundary conditions at the cathode. The boundary conditions of space-charge-limited flow and of zero or finite initial electron velocity are of importance and fundamental to the study of all space-charge-flow solutions. One reason for the importance of the plane-diode solutions is that all other space-charge-flow solutions behave similarly in regions very near the cathode.

The treatment of Sec. 2.2, which ignores the effects of the spread of velocities emitted from the cathode, should be compared with the exact treatment of Section 2 of Chap. VI. There it is shown that the solution of Sec. 2.2 is the limiting form of the flow valid for zero cathode temperature, i.e., zero velocity spread.

In Sec. 2.3 we generalize the treatment to cover the case of the crossed-field diode in which there is a magnetic field parallel to the cathode but where the potential, velocity, etc., depend only on the coordinate normal to the cathode, and hence the time along a trajectory. This solution has formed the basis for two different types of crossed-field electron-gun designs.

In Sec. 2.4 the solutions for flow in a magnetic field are generalized further to take account of a uniform magnetic field which is directed at an angle to the cathode. Once more, it is assumed that the parameters of the flow vary only in the direction normal to the cathode.

2.2. Rectilinear Flow in a Planar Diode. As a first example, we consider the plane diode in which all parameters of the flow depend only on one coordinate z, the distance from the cathode. This example not only illustrates the direct use of the Lorentz force equation, but is also a basis for a discussion of the boundary conditions which are common to all space-charge-flow problems.

For this one-dimensional problem, the Lorentz force equation reduces to the simple form

$$\frac{dv_z}{dt} = -\eta E_z \tag{2.1}$$

where $\eta = -q/m$. The equation of continuity is

$$\frac{di_z}{dz} = 0 \tag{2.2}$$

which can be integrated to give the physically obvious result i_z = constant = i_0, the current density at the cathode. Because

$$i_z = i_0 = -\rho v_z \tag{2.3}$$

it follows that the charge density ρ at any point of the flow is

$$\rho = -\frac{i_0}{v_z} \tag{2.4}$$

Poisson's equation, which has the one-dimensional form

$$-\frac{d^2\phi}{dz^2} = \frac{dE_z}{dz} = \frac{\rho}{\epsilon_0} = -\frac{i_0}{\epsilon_0 v_z} \tag{2.5}$$

must also be satisfied; here d/dz is used instead of $\partial/\partial z$, since the solution depends explicitly on only the independent variable z.

Two equations, Eqs. (2.1) and (2.5), relate E_z to v_z; one differential equation is stated in terms of time, the other being stated in terms of the coordinate z. However, the z coordinate to which an electron moves is related directly to the time elapsed in its motion from the cathode by the expression

$$\frac{d}{dt} \equiv v_z \frac{d}{dz} \tag{2.6}$$

Equations (2.5) and (2.6) can be combined to give

$$\frac{dE_z}{dt} = -\frac{i_0}{\epsilon_0} \tag{2.7}$$

This equation can be integrated to show that

$$E_z = -\frac{i_0}{\epsilon_0} t + E_c \tag{2.8}$$

at any point on the trajectory of an electron, where t is the time which it takes the electron to reach a point distance z from the cathode, and E_c is the electric field at the cathode.

It is necessary to consider now the boundary conditions for the electric field at the cathode. In this book, it is usually assumed that the flow is space-charge-limited. The term space-charge-limited flow is defined as a type of flow in which the current drawn from the cathode is independent of the maximum emission current from the cathode; it depends only on the potentials applied to the electrodes of the system, and hence on the space charge itself. If the field E_c at the cathode is finite and positive, electrons will initially be accelerated toward the cathode; unless there is a finite velocity of emission, no current will be drawn from it. On the other hand, if E_c is negative, there will be a force tending to draw electrons from the cathode and increase the emitted current and the space-charge density in front of the cathode, and so decrease the magnitude of E_c. Thus, if the cathode is capable of supplying sufficient current and if the initial electron velocity is zero, E_c becomes zero and the emission is space-charge-limited. The term E_c can remain finite and negative only if the cathode is incapable of supplying sufficient current for the space-charge-limited flow condition to occur.[3] In this book, unless a statement is made to the contrary, we always assume that the flow is space-charge-limited and that E_c is zero at the cathode, or at a practically coincident virtual cathode.

Equation (2.8) can be substituted in Eq. (2.1) to obtain the differential equation of motion

$$\frac{dv_z}{dt} = \frac{\eta i_0}{\epsilon_0} t - \eta E_c \tag{2.9}$$

This equation can be integrated to find the expression for the velocity of an electron v_z as a function of time, namely,

$$v_z = \frac{\eta i_0}{\epsilon_0} \frac{t^2}{2} + v_c - \eta E_c t \tag{2.10}$$

where v_c is the velocity of emission of electrons from the cathode.

We must consider now what value to place on v_c. For a thermally emitting cathode, electrons are emitted, not with zero velocity, but with a half-Maxwellian distribution of velocities. It is shown in Section 2 of Chap. VI that, when the flow is space-charge-limited, there is a minimum of potential at a plane a small distance from the cathode. Between the cathode and this potential-minimum plane, the electrons flow in two directions, some toward the minimum and some away from the minimum, i.e., back to the cathode. The electrons which are emitted from the cathode with a velocity normal to the cathode greater than $(-2\eta\phi_m)^{1/2}$, where ϕ_m is the negative potential at the potential-minimum plane, pass through the potential minimum and proceed to the anode. On the other hand, electrons which are emitted with a smaller velocity normal to the cathode return to the cathode. Thus, with sufficient emission current, the potential minimum adjusts itself until a space-charge-limited condition is reached. It is then a convenient physical approximation to regard the potential-minimum plane, where $E_c = 0$, as being a virtual cathode; for purposes of gun design the real physical cathode and the virtual cathode may be regarded as coincident. In the Langmuir-Fry model of the plane diode, described in Chap. VI, the electrons leave the potential-minimum plane with a half-Maxwellian distribution of normal velocities of the same root-mean-square value $\overline{v_{zTc}^2}$ as that of those leaving the cathode. It is shown in Eq. (2.8) of Chap. VI that $\overline{v_{zTc}^2}$ has the value $(kT_c/m)^{1/2}$. For an oxide-coated cathode with a temperature of 1050°K, $\overline{v_{zTc}^2}$ is approximately 4.2×10^5 m/sec, which corresponds to the velocity of an electron accelerated by a potential ϕ_T of about 0.5 volt. As this potential ϕ_T is very small compared with the potentials normally applied to an electron gun, it is common practice to assume that the initial velocity of electrons, v_c, is zero. It should be noted, however, that the choice $v_c = 0$ is arbitrary and is chosen only for convenience. As an alternative, for certain flows in a magnetic field discussed in Sec. 2.3, a more convenient form of analytic space-charge-flow solution can be derived by taking v_c to be small but finite. Such an assumption is just as reasonable, and may be more accurate than the choice of $v_c = 0$, if the value of v_c is taken to be comparable with the root-mean-square thermal velocity $\overline{v_{zTc}^2}$.

It should be noted that the types of assumptions described here are suitable only for electron guns in which the anode potential is considerably greater than the potential ϕ_T. For instance, in a discussion of the properties of a plane-diode thermionic generator, thermal velocities are all-important, and the velocity distribution of the electrons must be taken into account.

Returning to the plane-diode solution, we write $E_c = 0$, $v_c = 0$ in Eqs. (2.8) and (2.9) and find that

$$E_z = -\frac{i_0}{\epsilon_0}t \quad \text{and} \quad v_z = \frac{\eta i_0}{2\epsilon_0}t^2 \tag{2.11}$$

A further integration gives the distance z traveled by the electron from the cathode to be

$$z = \frac{\eta i_0}{\epsilon_0}\frac{t^3}{6} \tag{2.12}$$

The corresponding potential at the plane z is found by writing

$$\phi = -\int_0^z E_z dz = -\int_0^t E_z v_z dt \tag{2.13}$$

Substitution of Eqs. (2.11) and (2.12) in Eq. (2.13) yields the result

$$\phi = \frac{\eta i_0^2}{\epsilon_0^2}\frac{t^4}{8} \tag{2.14}$$

It is often more convenient to express the various parameters of the flow in terms of the coordinate z rather than the time t. One equation which is required later in the book is the differential equation for ϕ. If $v_c = E_c = 0$, it can be shown from Eqs. (2.5), (2.10), and (2.14) that this equation is

$$\frac{d^2\phi}{dz^2} = \frac{i_0}{(2\eta)^{1/2}\epsilon_0}\phi^{-1/2} \tag{2.15}$$

with the initial conditions

$$\phi = \frac{d\phi}{dz} = 0 \quad \text{at } z = 0 \tag{2.16}$$

The explicit dependence of the potential on time can be obtained by integrating Eq. (2.15) with the boundary conditions of Eq. (2.16). A much simpler method is to substitute Eq. (2.12) into Eq. (2.14) to give

$$\phi = \left(\frac{81}{32\eta\epsilon_0^2}\right)^{1/3} i_0^{2/3} z^{4/3} \tag{2.17a}$$

The other parameters of the flow can be expressed in terms of z in the same way. Equation (2.17a) yields the result that, for a diode of length z_0, to which is applied a potential ϕ_0 at the anode, the current density i_0 is

$$i_0 = \tfrac{4}{9}(2\eta)^{1/2}\epsilon_0 \frac{\phi_0^{3/2}}{z_0^2}$$

$$= 2.335 \times 10^{-6} \frac{\phi_0^{3/2}}{z_0^2} \quad \text{for electrons} \qquad (2.17b)$$

This solution for rectilinear flow in a plane diode is a basic one, to which we often refer. It is the space-charge-flow solution used by Pierce[4] in his first paper describing the design of the Pierce gun. The potential distribution of Eq. (2.17a) is called the Langmuir distribution, or the four-thirds-power law. A knowledge of this solution is extremely useful for comparison with more complicated flows. One of the main purposes in having this solution available for reference is that, because the space-charge density ρ is infinite at the cathode, it is not easy to carry out numerical solutions for a space-charge flow on a computer; the singularity in ρ causes trouble with the computation in the neighborhood of the cathode. To obviate this difficulty, it may be convenient to use an approximate form of the space-charge-flow solution near the cathode. The approximate form normally chosen is the plane-diode solution. Alternatively, a derivation of the space-charge-flow solution directly from the Lorentz equation of motion, and its expression in terms of the transit time of an electron along its trajectory, eliminates the need for starting a computation with an approximate solution. The above example and others given in Secs. 2.3 and 2.4 show that the space-charge density itself need never enter into the defining equations of the problem; all the other parameters of interest are finite near the cathode, so that computations can be started at the cathode itself.

2.3. Space-charge Flow in Crossed Electric and Magnetic Fields. The Lorentz equation of motion can be used directly to derive simple analytical space-charge-flow solutions for electrons flowing in a magnetic field. As in the plane-diode problem, which was solved in the preceding section, all the flow parameters are dependent on only one coordinate. As a first example of this procedure, we treat a crossed-field space-charge-flow solution which has been used as the basis of a crossed-field gun design by Kino.[5,6]

The flow is from a plane cathode $y = 0$, in the presence of a uniform magnetic field $-B$ directed along the z axis. All parameters of the flow are assumed to depend only on the y coordinate. As the potential is a function only of y, E_y is the only component of the electric field different from zero. Consequently, the Lorentz equation of motion [Eq. (2.15) of Chap. I], resolved into its separate components, takes the form

$$\ddot{x} = -\omega_H \dot{y} \tag{2.18a}$$

$$\ddot{y} = \omega_H \dot{x} - \eta E_y \tag{2.18b}$$

$$\ddot{z} = 0 \tag{2.18c}$$

where the superscript ($\dot{}$) denotes differentiation with respect to time, and $\omega_H = \eta B$ is the cyclotron frequency of an electron in the magnetic field (Section 4 of Chap. I). As E_y and i_y are assumed to be functions only of y, it follows from the treatment in Sec. 2.2 that $i_y = i_c$, the current density at the cathode, and that for a space-charge-limited flow, Eq. (2.11), which is repeated here for convenience,

$$E_y = -\frac{i_0}{\epsilon_0} t \tag{2.19}$$

still holds in the presence of a magnetic field.

Equations (2.18a) and (2.19) can be substituted into the derivative, with respect to time, of Eq. (2.18b) to obtain the differential equation

$$\ddot{v}_y + \omega_H^2 v_y = \frac{\eta i_0}{\epsilon_0} \tag{2.20}$$

where v_y is the y velocity. All velocity components are similarly defined, i.e.,

$$\dot{x} = v_x, \qquad \dot{y} = v_y \qquad \dot{z} = v_z \tag{2.21}$$

The linear differential equation (2.20) can be solved to yield a solution for the space-charge flow. Different choices of boundary conditions give different solutions of technical importance. If, as a first choice, the boundary conditions at the cathode are

$$v_x = v_y = v_z = 0, \qquad x = 0, \qquad y = y_0, \qquad z = z_0 \qquad \text{at } t = 0$$

the solutions are

$$\begin{aligned} v_x &= -C(T - \sin T) \\ v_y &= C(1 - \cos T), \qquad v_z = 0 \end{aligned} \tag{2.22a}$$

and

$$\begin{aligned} x &= x_0 - \frac{C}{\omega_H}\left(\frac{T^2}{2} + \cos T - 1\right) \\ y &= \frac{C}{\omega_H}(T - \sin T), \qquad z = z_0 \end{aligned} \tag{2.22b}$$

where T and C are normalization parameters:

$$C = \frac{\eta i_0}{\epsilon_0 \omega_H^2} \qquad \text{and} \qquad T = \omega_H t \tag{2.23}$$

Thus T is a normalized time.

The potential can be found by integrating Eq. (2.19); the procedure is identical with that used in deriving the potential of Eq. (2.14) from the E_z of Eq. (2.11) in Sec. 2.2. The resultant potential is

$$\phi = \frac{C^2}{\eta}\left(\frac{T^2}{2} - T \sin T + 1 - \cos T\right) \tag{2.24}$$

This expression is deduced more simply from the conservation-of-energy expression, $2\eta\phi = v^2 - v_c^2$, of Eq. (2.12) of Chap. I.

A plot of a typical electron trajectory and the potential along this trajectory are given in Fig. 2.1. In contrast to the electrostatic plane-diode problem discussed in Sec. 2.2, it is not possible here to eliminate the parameter time and to state the various parameters of the flow in an analytic form directly in terms of the coordinates. However, a parametric solution stated as a function of time gives all the information required.

Certain peculiarities of this solution should be noted. From Eq. (2.22b), $v_y = 0$ and $\rho = \infty$ at the points $T = 2n\pi$; in addition, the acceleration $\dot{v}_y$ of an electron in the y direction is also zero at these points. Consequently, when $T = 2n\pi$, the electron trajectories pass through points of inflection, and there is some uncertainty as to whether an electron will proceed beyond one of these points in a direction away from the cathode or whether it will turn back toward the cathode. There is a distinction between the solutions for a finite electron beam and those for an infinite electron beam. The solutions which have been derived here are those for an infinite electron beam. However, in the Pierce-gun design procedure, which is described in Chaps. VII and VIII, a finite beam is produced by using a finite length of cathode, and the flow from this cathode is considered as a portion of an infinite beam. Electrodes are designed to give fields and potentials along the edge of this finite beam, which would be the same as those due to the rest of the infinite beam if it were present. Consequently, the fields and potentials in the beam region remain the same as those for an infinite beam (Sec. 3.6 of Chap. VII) for details of the electrode design. For the finite-beam crossed-field-gun solution, there is no uncertainty regarding the points of inflection,

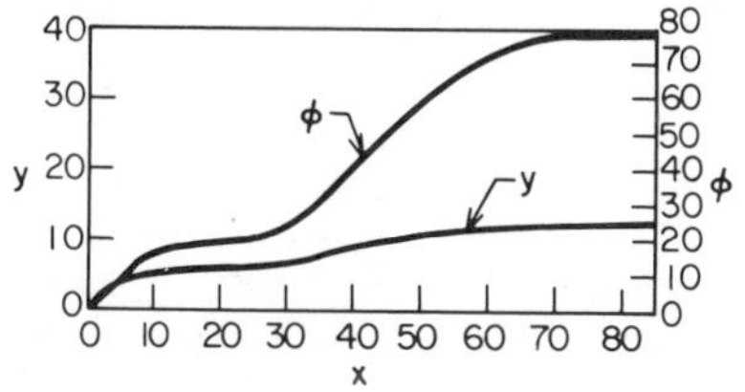

Fig. 2.1. A plot of a typical electron trajectory in a crossed-field diode. The potential at any point along the electron path is also given.

because the electrodes are designed to match the beam for which electrons move upward through the points of inflection. If the electrons tended to move downward from the points of inflection, the electrode design would not be correct, and the necessary conditions for the existence of such a beam would not be satisfied.

From Eq. (2.22b) the points on the trajectory given by $T = 2n\pi$ lie on the curve

$$x = x_0 - \frac{C}{\omega_H}\frac{T^2}{2} \quad \text{and} \quad y = \frac{C}{\omega_H} T \tag{2.25}$$

which is a parabola. Therefore the curve given by Eq. (2.22b) undulates around a parabola. A gun designed to make use of this space-charge-flow solution would be very difficult to construct if, within the gun, T became much larger than 2π, for it is shown in Sec. 3.6 of Chap. VII that it is not possible to synthesize the edge potentials of such a beam using only one positive electrode. Consequently, this beam is suitable for use only in what we call a short gun, in which the electron trajectories are of a length such that T is not much greater than 2π. In practice, it is convenient to construct a short crossed-field gun as in the schematic of Fig. 2.2, so that an electron emitted from the center of the cathode has a transit time of approximately $2\pi/\omega_H$. In this case the beam flows nearly parallel to the cathode at the exit plane of the gun and is considerably thinner than at the cathode. As with many types of gun designs, however, the beam which is theoretically produced at the exit plane of the gun does not fulfill all the criteria for the ideal beam required.

It is shown in Section 7 of Chap. IV that, for the Brillouin flow beam required in a crossed-field device, the electron trajectories must be parallel; the charge density ρ in the beam must be uniform, with a value such that the plasma frequency, defined by $\omega_p = (-\eta\rho/\epsilon_0)^{1/2}$, equal to ω_H.

The short-gun space-charge-flow solution given here cannot satisfy all the requirements at the exit of the gun. Near the point $T = 2\pi$, the beam space-charge density is higher than that of a

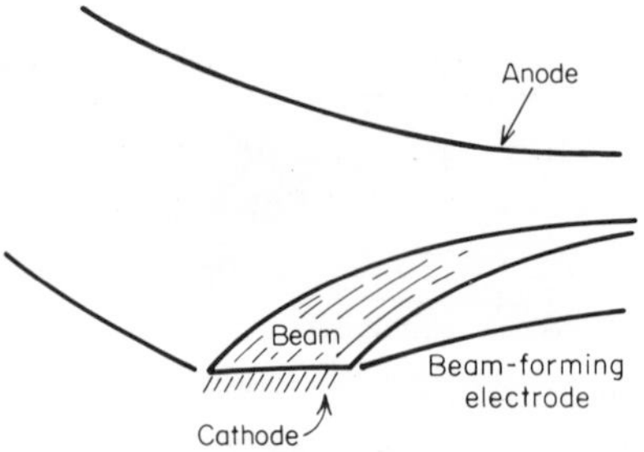

Fig. 2.2. Schematic of the "short" crossed-field electron gun.

Brillouin beam. In addition, the beam trajectories are not exactly parallel. One approach would be to modify this design by making use of the paraxial methods described in Chap. III. In practice, however, the effect of the thermal velocities of the electrons at the cathode changes the shape and charge density of the beam at the exit of the gun. Consequently, without a consideration of thermal effects, these more sophisticated methods would not necessarily yield a better-focused beam.

For practical guns, a design procedure has been developed empirically. The exit plane is placed at the theoretical point of minimum thickness of the beam; generally, this minimum beam thickness is less than that for Brillouin flow. The effect of thermal velocities is to increase the beam thickness in the gun above its designed non-thermal value, and so help with the matching to the Brillouin-beam focusing condition. Finally, the potentials in the drift region are adjusted to accelerate the beam velocity by a few per cent over its value at the gun exit plane. This procedure produces a slight lens effect which, with optimum focusing, cancels out errors that cannot easily be taken into account in the theoretical design. Experimentally, an excellent beam, only slightly thicker than that for ideal Brillouin flow, can usually be obtained by these techniques.[7]

For many purposes, sufficient convergence is not obtained in this type of gun when the exit is taken at a point corresponding to a $T = 2\pi$ transit time in the gun. In the discussion of the planar diode, it was shown that the boundary condition $v_c = 0$ at the cathode was not the only possible one which could be used. Obviously, if a solution could be found in which the electrons were to move along parabolic trajectories, rather than undulating about a parabolic path, this would be convenient for an analytical gun design. As the undulations are associated with the trigonometric terms in the trajectory solution, it is useful to consider the solution of Eq. (2.20), for which the trigonometric terms are zero. The particular solution of Eq. (2.20) is one for which the velocity v_y is uniform and of value

$$v_y = v_c = \frac{\eta i_0}{\epsilon_0 \omega_H^2} \equiv C \qquad (2.26)$$

Here C is the same constant as in Eq. (2.23).

This solution is one in which the initial velocity of electrons emitted from the cathode is assumed to be finite and given by Eq. (2.26). With the application of the additional boundary conditions $v_x = v_z = 0$, $x = x_0$, $y = 0$, $z = z_0$ at the cathode, Eqs. (2.18) and (2.19) yield the following parabolic trajectory solution:

$$x = x_0 - \frac{C}{\omega_H}\frac{T^2}{2}, \qquad y = \frac{C}{\omega_H} T, \qquad z = z_0 \qquad (2.27a)$$

with $$\phi = \frac{C^2}{\eta}\frac{T^2}{2} \qquad (2.27b)$$

It is necessary to examine under what conditions this result is physically reasonable. The required initial velocity v_c depends upon the current density at the cathode and the value of the magnetic field. This initial velocity is equivalent to accelerating an electron through a potential

$$\phi_e = \frac{\eta i_0^2}{2\epsilon_0^2 \omega_H^4} \tag{2.28}$$

With strong magnetic fields and the current densities used in practice, this initial potential is very small. For instance, with a field of B = 1500 gauss and a current density at the cathode of i_0 = 300 ma/cm^2, the initial potential $\phi_e \approx 0.02$ volt, a potential which gives a velocity of the order of the average thermal velocity of emission. Consequently, in this range, the parabolic solution, or long-gun solution, is at least as close to the true physical situation as the short-gun design which assumes zero velocity of emission. The electrode design for a gun to produce this beam is discussed in Sec. 3.5 of Chap. VII.

In practice, both solutions have a useful range of validity. The solution for zero velocity of emission is used with low magnetic fields and high current densities. For instance, with B = 750 gauss and i_0 = 2 amp/cm^2, ϕ_e = 16 volts, well above the potential corresponding to thermal velocities; for these parameters only the short-gun design is suitable. However, for a highly convergent gun, for which the transit time in the gun must be many cycles of the cyclotron frequency, a high magnetic field is normally required. In this range, the long-gun, or finite-initial-velocity solution, is the most suitable type to use.

A further feature of this type of crossed-field flow can be observed from the infinite-plane crossed-field diode. In the derivation for the short gun, it was shown that the electron trajectories passed through points of inflection at $T = 2n\pi$. When current flows to the anode of the infinite diode, the solution which should be used is that already discussed. There is also the possibility of a diode being cut off; i.e., no current flows to the anode. In this case, all current which is emitted from the cathode returns to it; at any point there are two streams of current flowing, one stream away from the cathode, and the other toward the cathode, as shown in Fig. 2.3. Expressions for this type of flow can be derived from the same assumptions about the field variations as before. However, if the current emitted from the cathode is i_0, there is an equal component of current i_0 returning to the cathode. Equations (2.18b) is satisfied as before; consequently, on integration, it is found that, for either stream,

$$v_x = -\omega_H y \tag{2.29}$$

It follows from conservation of energy that the velocities in the y

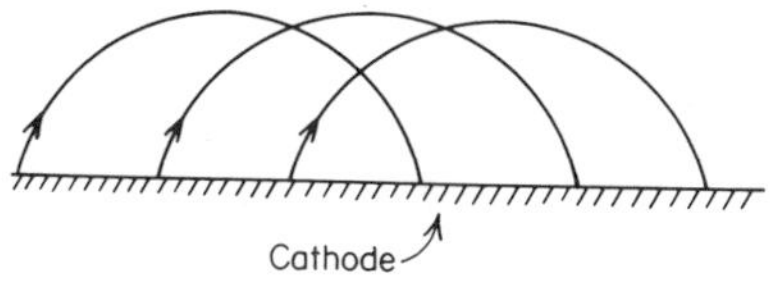

Fig. 2.3. Electron trajectories for the two-stream solution of a crossed-field diode.

direction of the two separate streams are equal and opposite. Thus the total change density at any point is now

$$\rho = -\frac{2i_0}{v_y} \tag{2.30}$$

where v_y is the velocity of the stream leaving the cathode. Consequently, in all the expressions that we have used heretofore for the short-gun solution, it is only necessary to replace i_0 by $2i_0$ to find a solution for the infinite-cutoff diode. This solution will not be discussed further, because it is not useful for the purpose of gun design; it was derived only because it is a very simple example of a two-stream solution. Few of these are known; as far as an exact gun design is concerned, such solutions are not of much practical value, because a portion of a two-stream solution for an infinite beam cannot be cut off to yield a finite beam. Under such conditions, it is no longer a two-stream solution.

Solutions similar to the ones derived here have also been found for the flow from a circular cathode. Although the solutions can be expressed parametrically in terms of time, they are not analytic in form. Nevertheless, reasonable and useful analytic approximations to them can be found[8] by assuming that the radius of the cathode is large compared with the distance traveled by an electron in time $t = 2\pi/\omega_H$.

2.4. Solutions with a Component of Magnetic Field Normal to the Cathode. The crossed-field solutions described in the last section can be generalized still further, to take account of a component of magnetic field normal to the cathode. We consider now a planar cathode in the xz plane, with components of magnetic field in both the z and y directions, as shown in Fig. 2.4. As before, we assume that all parameters of the system depend only on the y coordinate, so that there is only a component of electric field in the y direction. The equations of motion for an electron in this system are

$$\ddot{x} = \omega_{Hy}\,\dot{z} - \omega_{Hz}\,\dot{y} \tag{2.31a}$$

$$\ddot{y} = -\eta E_y + \omega_{Hz}\,\dot{x} \tag{2.31b}$$

$$\ddot{z} = -\eta\dot{x}\,\omega_{Hy} \tag{2.31c}$$

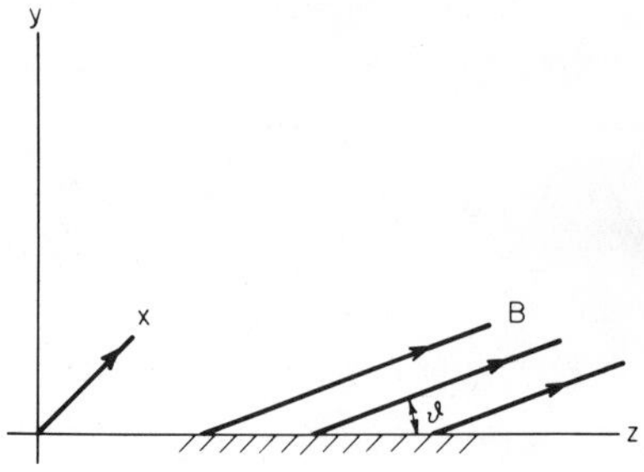

Fig. 2.4. The coordinate system for the planar-diode form of the magnetron injection gun.

where $\omega_{Hy} = \eta B_y$ and $\omega_{Hz} = \eta B_z$ (2.32)

As before, Eq. (2.11) is valid and can be substituted in Eq. (2.31b) to obtain an ordinary differential equation with t as the independent variable. This equation, in combination with Eqs. (2.31a) and (2.31c), can be solved by elementary methods. As in the case of the crossed-field gun, two sets of boundary conditions can be imposed; the velocity of emission from the cathode can be assumed zero or finite. Because of its simplicity, the finite-initial-velocity solution is the one which is the most useful. We consider, therefore, only the case for which the initial velocity v_{yc} is given by

$$v_{yc} = \frac{\eta i_0}{\epsilon_0 \omega_H^2} \approx C \tag{2.33}$$

where $\omega_H^2 = \omega_{Hy}^2 + \omega_{Hz}^2$ (2.34)

With this condition, the solution of Eqs. (2.31) and (2.19) gives the trajectory from the point $(x_0, 0, z_0)$ to be

$$\begin{aligned} x &= x_0 - \frac{C}{\omega_H}\frac{T^2}{2}\cos\vartheta \\ y &= \frac{C}{\omega_H}\left(T + \frac{T^3}{6}\sin^2\vartheta\right) \\ z &= z_0 + \frac{C}{\omega_H}\frac{T^3}{6}\sin\vartheta\cos\vartheta \end{aligned} \tag{2.35}$$

where $\tan\vartheta = \dfrac{\omega_{Hy}}{\omega_{Hz}}$ (2.36)

It follows, by using the same methods as before, that the potential at any point of the trajectory is given by

$$\phi = \frac{C^2}{\eta}\left(\frac{T^2}{2} + \frac{T^4}{8}\sin^2\vartheta\right) \tag{2.37}$$

The solution given here would not be used directly in a plane-gun design. It is important because it provides a good approximate solution from which to design a hollow-beam gun.[8] Thus, if we consider a conical cathode in a uniform magnetic field, as shown in Fig. 2.5, distances along a generator of the conical cathode can be regarded as equivalent to the z direction; distances normal to the surface of the cone are equivalent to the y direction, and distances in the θ direction are equivalent to the x direction. For small θ, the beam which is emitted from this cathode hugs the cathode quite closely, and a cathode of fairly large radius can be approximated well by this plane design. The design of electrodes for this system can also be based on the plane solution. The procedure is discussed for the other crossed-field flows in Secs. 3.5 and 3.6 of Chap. VII.

In order to synthesize still better the properties of the beam emitted from a conical cathode, it is possible to carry out a modified version of the plane-diode theory. This method takes account of the fact that when electrons move in an angular direction around the cathode, there is a component of centrifugal force radially outward, causing particles to leave the cathode somewhat faster than is predicted by the simple plane-diode theory. It is assumed that the average radius of the conical cathode is r_c and the distance of any point on the electron path from the axis is approximately r_c. This implies that there is an extra component of centrifugal force on the electron directed radially outward of magnitude $mr_c\dot{\theta}^2$. In the equivalent plane-diode system, this extra force has components of value

$$\mathcal{F}_y = \frac{m\dot{x}^2}{r_c}\cos\vartheta \tag{2.38a}$$

in the y direction and

$$\mathcal{F}_z = -\frac{m\dot{x}^2}{r_c}\sin\vartheta \tag{2.38b}$$

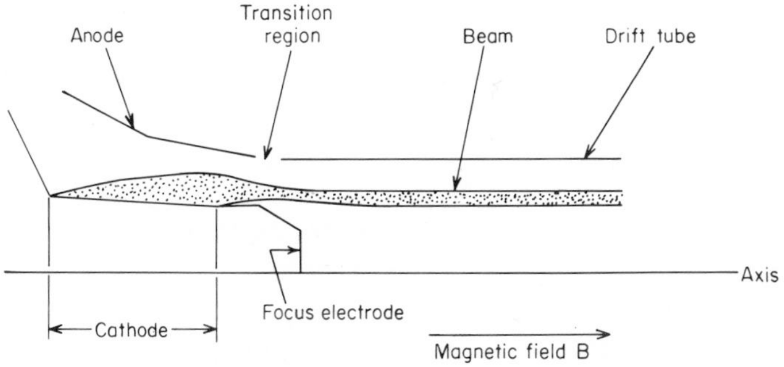

Fig. 2.5. The conical form of the magnetron injection gun.

in the z direction. This procedure has been carried out by Okoshi,[9] who has used it to design a magnetron injection electron gun.

In Section 5 we describe a completely different procedure, which makes use of the method of separation of variables to derive the flow from a conical cathode in a magnetic field, without making approximations of this kind. The advantage of the procedures given in this section are that they are at least semianalytical in nature, and the results can be obtained in analytical form, eliminating a great amount of numerical work. The advantages of the more exact procedures are obvious, in that they provide a solution closer to the truth. However, they can in practice be difficult to apply, especially in designing electrodes which must be used with such a beam.

One feature of crossed-field guns, and of guns of the above type, is that the emitted beam from the gun need not necessarily be the final beam which is required. For instance, if a gun with a conical cathode is designed using this prescription for the space-charge flow, the emitted beam requires a component of electric field both inside and outside the beam. Such a beam can be used in an injected-beam type of magnetron, but is not appropriate for the hollow beam of a traveling-wave tube or klystron. In this type of device, the electron beam passes through a drift region where the radial fields are small. It was shown in Sec. 3.2 of Chap. I that Busch's theorem implies that the drift-tube hollow beam should have fields which are zero on its inside surface. The emitted beam from the gun produces the type of hollow beam required if, after the exit of the gun proper, the electrodes are slowly tapered to allow the field in the beam region to decrease to its final value.[7]

Theoretically, the taper must be slow, so that the fractional change in the beam radius over a distance of one cyclotron wavelength λ_H is small compared with unity. With such a slow taper an adiabatic change of the beam radius will occur, and the taper itself will induce only small rippling of the final beam radius.

In practice, it is found that relatively fast tapering can be entirely acceptable, since it is often not necessary that beam rippling should be at an absolute minimum. A discussion of adiabatic tapering of electron beams is given in Sec. 9.4 of Chap. IV and in Sec. 2.5 of Chap. V. If, in an actual device, adiabatic tapering leads to an electron gun which is objectionably long, the designer is advised to resort to detailed ray tracing on a computer as an aid to a more practical design.

3. ORTHOGONAL CURVILINEAR COORDINATE SYSTEMS BASED ON THE STREAMLINES OF THE FLOW

3.1. Introduction. One approach to finding space-charge-flow solutions is to use a coordinate system in which one set of the coordinate lines forms the trajectories of the flow.[10,11] For normal congruent flow, from Eq. (5.6) of Chap. I, the velocity of an electron along its trajectory can be expressed in terms of an action function in the form

$$\mathbf{v} = \nabla W \tag{3.1}$$

Thus the surfaces perpendicular to the trajectory lines are the surfaces of constant action, W = constant, so that along a trajectory, W is a function of only one of the coordinates. At first sight it might seem that the derivation of space-charge-flow solutions would be considerably simplified by the choice of an orthogonal curvilinear coordinate system based on the flow pattern. Therefore, in Sec. 3.2, one set of coordinate lines is chosen to be the trajectories of the flow, and the intersections of the other two sets of coordinate lines trace out the surfaces of constant action. Although the equations of space-charge flow can be reduced to a set of ordinary differential equations by this method, the difficulty lies in determining suitable coordinate systems; in general, the choice of such coordinate systems depends on solving a set of partial differential equations. The method is useful, however, for obtaining certain general results which are difficult to obtain by other means, such as general existence theorems on possible flow systems; these theorems are not presented here, because they seem to have no practical applications. Two important results are obtained, however, in Sec. 3.2. One is that the variation of potential very near the cathode generally follows the four-thirds-power law (when emission velocities are neglected); the second is a general formula for the dependence of the cathode current-density variation on the curvature of the trajectories in the neighborhood of the cathode. These results are of considerable importance as a guide for the design of electron guns. Most of the analysis is restricted to congruent flows, where the magnetic field is zero at the cathode surface. It is shown in Sec. 3.3 that the last two results apply also if the magnetic field is parallel to the cathode in the neighborhood of the cathode.

In Sec. 3.4 we determine, by the methods of this section, an analytic solution in which the electron trajectories are circles. This solution can be obtained by other means also.

3.2. Normal Congruent Flow. The parameters of the flow are defined in a three-dimensional orthogonal curvilinear coordinate system (q_1,q_2,q_3) with scale factors h_1,h_2,h_3 so that the increment of length $d\ell$ in this system is given by the relation

$$d\ell^2 = d\ell_1^2 + d\ell_2^2 + d\ell_3^2 \tag{3.2a}$$

where $d\ell_1 = h_1 dq_1, \qquad d\ell_2 = h_2 dq_2, \qquad d\ell_3 = h_3 dq_3$ (3.2b)

It is assumed that the electron flow is such that the trajectories cut the surfaces of constant q_1 at right angles. Thus, for normal congruent flow, W is only a function of q_1, and the cathode must lie on a surface given by q_1 = constant. The velocity of an electron at any point of the flow is, therefore, from Eq. (3.1),

$$\mathbf{v} = (v_1, 0, 0) \tag{3.3}$$

where
$$v_1 = \frac{1}{h_1}\frac{dW(q_1)}{dq_1} \tag{3.4}$$

To obtain Eq. (3.4) from Eq. (3.1), the expression for the gradient of Eq. (2.4) of Appendix A has been used. From the equation of the conservation of energy [Eq. (2.12) of Chap. 1], which is $v^2 = 2\eta\phi$ when the velocity of emission at the cathode is assumed to be zero, the potential at any point of the flow is

$$2\eta\phi = \frac{1}{h_1^2}\left(\frac{dW}{dq_1}\right)^2 \tag{3.5}$$

In the analysis of this section, the action function W does not appear explicitly; reference is made only to its derivative. It is convenient, therefore, to define a new variable Q by

$$Q(q_1) = \frac{dW}{dq_1} \tag{3.6}$$

The potential ϕ and velocity $\mathbf{v}$ can be written, from Eqs. (3.3), (3.4), (3.7), and (3.8), as

$$\mathbf{v} = (v_1, 0, 0) = \left(\frac{Q}{h_1}, 0, 0\right) \tag{3.7}$$

and
$$2\eta\phi = \frac{Q^2}{h_1^2} \tag{3.8}$$

The charge density at any point of the flow can be found by expressing Poisson's equation in its orthogonal curvilinear coordinate form. From the expression for the Laplacian of Eq. (2.11) of Appendix A and the expression for ϕ of Eq. (3.8), Poisson's equation, $\nabla^2\phi = -\rho/\epsilon_0$, becomes

$$\rho = -\frac{\epsilon_0}{2\eta h_1 h_2 h_3}\left\{\frac{\partial}{\partial q_1}\left(\frac{h_2 h_3}{h_1}\frac{\partial}{\partial q_1}\frac{Q^2}{h_1^2}\right) + Q^2\left[\frac{\partial}{\partial q_2}\left(\frac{h_3 h_1}{h_2}\frac{\partial}{\partial q_2}\frac{1}{h_1^2}\right) + \frac{\partial}{\partial q_3}\left(\frac{h_1 h_2}{h_3}\frac{\partial}{\partial q_3}\frac{1}{h_1^2}\right)\right]\right\} \tag{3.9}$$

The current density $\mathbf{i}$ has only one component i_1 given from Eqs. (3.7) and (3.9) by

$$i_1 = -\frac{Q}{h_1}\rho \tag{3.10}$$

Using the expression for the divergence of Eq. (2.6) of Appendix A, the conservation-of-charge equation, $\nabla \cdot \mathbf{i} = 0$, becomes

$$\frac{\partial}{\partial q_1}\left(\frac{h_2 h_3}{h_1} Q\rho\right) = 0$$

which can be integrated to give

$$i_1 = \frac{\epsilon_0}{2\eta} \frac{F(q_2,q_3)}{h_2 h_3} \tag{3.11}$$

where $F(q_2,q_3)$ is an arbitrary function of q_2 and q_3. It follows, using Eq. (3.10), that ρ can be written in the form

$$\rho = -\frac{\epsilon_0}{2\eta} \frac{h_1}{h_2 h_3} \frac{F(q_2,q_3)}{Q} \tag{3.12}$$

Consequently, Poisson's equation [Eq. (3.9)] becomes

$$F(q_2,q_3) = \frac{Q}{h_1^2}\left\{\frac{\partial}{\partial q_1}\left(\frac{h_2 h_3}{h_1} \frac{\partial}{\partial q_1} \frac{Q^2}{h_1^2}\right) + Q^2\left[\frac{\partial}{\partial q_2}\left(\frac{h_3 h_1}{h_2} \frac{\partial}{\partial q_2} \frac{1}{h_1^2}\right) + \frac{\partial}{\partial q_3}\left(\frac{h_1 h_2}{h_3} \frac{\partial}{\partial q_3} \frac{1}{h_1^2}\right)\right]\right\} \tag{3.13}$$

If a coordinate system could be found in which it were possible to satisfy the conditions of Eq. (3.13), all the parameters of the flow could be found by substitution in the relevant formulas. The choice of h_1, h_2, and h_3 is by no means arbitrary, however, for these scaling parameters must be chosen so as to represent a real coordinate system. The necessary condition for the coordinate system to be real, the Einstein condition,[12] involves a series of partial differential equations which, if they could be solved in combination with Eq. (3.13), would yield possible coordinate systems for the flow. However, these partial differential equations are too complicated to be useful in solving space-charge-flow problems of this kind.

Nevertheless, if it is assumed that there is a space-charge-flow solution in the given coordinate system, Eq. (3.13) can provide useful general information. In particular, we derive expressions for the potential variation near the cathode. In addition, the variation of current density over the cathode surface is shown to be related to the geometric shape of the electron trajectory near the cathode.

We assume that the cathode is a surface on which h_1, h_2, and h_3, regarded as functions of q_1, do not have poles or zeros. For convenience, and without loss of generality, we take the cathode to be the surface $q_1 = 0$. At points very near the cathode, it is possible to write Eq. (3.13) in the simplified form

$$F(q_2,q_3) = \frac{h_2 h_3}{h_1^5} Q \frac{d^2}{dq_1^2}(Q^2) \tag{3.14}$$

To obtain Eq. (3.14), it has been assumed that Q and $dQ/dq_1 \rightarrow 0$ and $Q(d^2Q/dq_1^2) \rightarrow \infty$ as $q_1 \rightarrow 0$. The first two assumptions follow from Eq. (3.8) and the condition that $\mathbf{v}$ and $\mathbf{E} \rightarrow 0$ as $q_1 \rightarrow 0$, and the third is necessary to obtain a finite emission density at the cathode. From Eq. (3.14) it follows that, near $q_1 = 0$,

$$F(q_2, q_3) = k^3 \frac{h_2 h_3}{h_1^5} \tag{3.15}$$

where k is a constant. Hence Eq. (3.14) becomes

$$Q \frac{d^2}{dq_1^2} (Q^2) = k^3 \tag{3.16}$$

Equation (3.16) has the form of Eq. (2.15), with $Q^2 = \phi$, and it can be verified that the solution is

$$Q = \left(\frac{3}{2}\right)^{2/3} k\, q_1^{2/3} \qquad \text{near } q_1 = 0 \tag{3.17}$$

Since the h_i have neither poles nor zeros near $q_1 = 0$, in the immediate neighborhood of the cathode it is possible to express the h_i as h_{ic}, the values at $q_1 = 0$. Substitution of the Q of Eq. (3.17) into Eqs. (3.8), (3.9), and (3.11) gives the expressions for the parameters of the flow near the cathode, namely,

$$\begin{aligned} v_1 &= \left(\frac{3}{2}\right)^{2/3} \frac{k}{h_{1c}} q_1^{2/3} \\ \phi &= \left(\frac{81}{16}\right)^{1/3} \frac{k^2}{2\eta h_{1c}^2} q_1^{4/3} \qquad \text{near } q_1 = 0 \end{aligned} \tag{3.18}$$

and

$$i_{1c} = \frac{\epsilon_0}{2\eta} \frac{k^3}{h_{1c}^5} \tag{3.19}$$

where i_{1c} is the value of i_1 at the cathode.

The expressions of Eq. (3.18) are only approximations, but are the justification for treating the flow from any electrostatic space-charge-limited system near the cathode as if it were a plane diode. This property is used often in this and later chapters. The expression for i_{1c} is exact and shows that, because of the dependence on h_{1c}, for any congruent, electrostatic, space-charge-limited solution, the variation in current density over the surface of the cathode depends only on the nature of the trajectories in the neighborhood of the cathode.

The cathode current-density variation of Eq. (3.19) can be related directly to the initial curvature of the trajectory from the point $(0, q_2, q_3)$. The pertinent parameter for the determination of the variation of i_{1c} in the q_2 direction is μ_2, the fractional variation of i_{1c} with distance, defined by

$$\mu_2 = \frac{1}{i_{1c}} \frac{\partial i_{1c}}{\partial \ell_2} = \frac{1}{h_{2c} i_{1c}} \frac{\partial i_{1c}}{\partial q_2} \tag{3.20}$$

where $d\ell_2 = h_2\, dq_2$, the element of length in the q_2 direction. Substitution of Eq. (3.19) in Eq. (3.20) yields the following expression for the current uniformity factor μ_2:

$$\mu_2 = -\frac{5}{h_{1C}h_{2C}} \frac{\partial h_{1C}}{\partial q_2} \tag{3.21}$$

It can be shown[12] that $-(\partial h_1/\partial q_2)/h_1h_2$ is precisely the curvature κ_2 of the q_2 = constant, q_3 = constant line in the direction normal to q_3 = constant surface, i.e., the curvature κ_2 of the electron trajectory in the plane q_3 = constant. Consequently, the uniformity factor μ_2 is given by

$$\mu_2 = 5\kappa_{2C} \tag{3.22}$$

where κ_{2C} is the curvature of the electron trajectory in the q_1, q_3 surface passing through the point $(0,q_2,q_3)$ on the cathode. A similar result may be found for the rate of change of current density in the q_3 direction. Thus the uniformity of current density at the cathode depends only on the curvature of the trajectories of the electrons as they leave the cathode.

The physical meaning of this result and its significance in gun design is illustrated by reference to flow from a planar cathode. We assume that there is no motion in the z direction parallel to the cathode, and the cathode is the plane x = 0. If the electron trajectories leaving the cathode have zero curvature, as in Fig. 2.6a, the current density should, from Eq. (3.22), be uniform. This result is certainly true for the planar diode. If the trajectories have zero curvature near the cathode, then $E_y = 0$. Hence, as

$$\nabla \times \mathbf{E} = 0 \tag{3.23}$$

it follows that

$$\frac{\partial E_x}{\partial y} = \frac{\partial E_y}{\partial x} = 0 \tag{3.24}$$

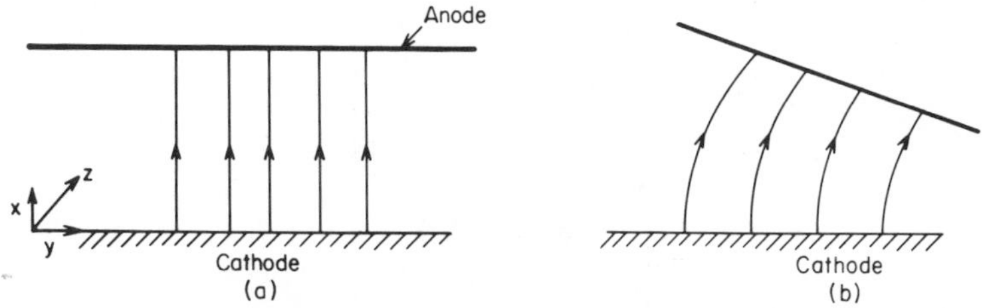

Fig. 2.6. Electron trajectories from a plane cathode. (a) Rectilinear trajectories from a plane cathode are illustrated for the case where the current density is uniform. (b) It is shown that the electron trajectories form positive curvature when the current density near the edge of the cathode is greater than that in the middle.

Therefore, just in front of the cathode, E_x is uniform so that the current density at the cathode should be uniform. If the electron trajectories in front of the cathode have a positive curvature κ_c as shown in Fig. 2.6b, it follows from Eq. (2.44) of Chap. I that

$$E_y \simeq E_r = -2\kappa_c\phi \tag{3.25}$$

just in front of the cathode. Thus E_y is negative if the curvature of the path is positive. Since $E_y = 0$ at the cathode, from Eq. (3.24), $\partial E_x/\partial y$ is negative. But E_x is itself a negative quantity; it follows that the magnitude of E_x increases with y. The current density at the cathode increases, therefore, with y; this result is consistent with Eqs. (3.20) and (3.22).

Conversely, the control of the current density at the cathode can have a profound effect on the nature of the electron trajectories in the neighborhood of of the cathode. For example, in order to modify the design of a rectilinear-flow Pierce gun to make the beam converge within the gun, a beam configuration somewhat like that in Fig. 2.7 might be used. Here the electron trajectories for positive y have negative curvature in the neighborhood of the cathode, and vice versa. It follows that the current density at the cathode would need to decrease away from the plane of symmetry of the flow. This is the type of flow illustrated in Fig. 2.8, which occurs in one section of a planar triode with a grid at negative potential.

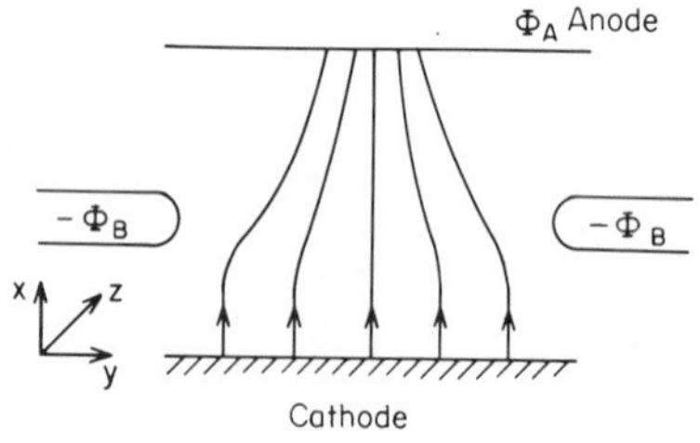

Fig. 2.7. An illustration of the electrode configuration; the beam converges as it leaves the cathode.

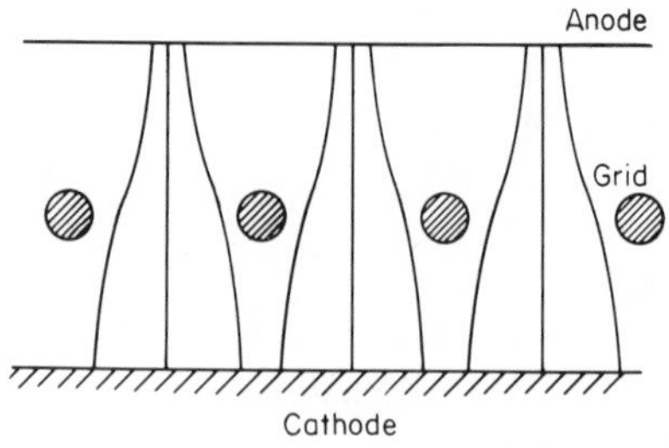

Fig. 2.8. An illustration of a curvature of the electron in a plane triode in which the grid wires are at a negative potential.

3.3. A Solution in Cylindrical Polar Coordinates. It has already been pointed out that it is not easy to find suitable coordinate systems which will satisfy the conditions of Eq. (3.13). Certain general solutions in two dimensions can be derived by these methods by putting other limitations on the flow. One possible restriction is that the flow lines should be along the level lines of a harmonic function. With this restriction, it is possible to find certain solutions for plane flow. These flows, however, and others not obtainable by the methods of this section, could be found much more easily by the method of separation of variables (Sections 4 and 5). The formalism of Eq. (3.14) can be used as the basis for deriving paraxial equations of flow. In Chap. III, simpler and more direct methods of attack are developed for this purpose.

As an illustration of this formalism, we derive an analytic form for space-charge flow in which the trajectories are circular lines. In a two-dimensional cylindrical coordinate system, with $q_1 = \theta$, $q_2 = r$, $h_1 = r$ and $h_2 = 1$. Equation (3.13) then takes the form

$$F(r) = \frac{Q}{r^5}\left[\frac{d^2}{d\theta^2}(Q^2) + 4Q^2\right] \tag{3.26}$$

For Eq. (3.26) to be valid, it follows that

$$F(r) = \frac{C}{r^5} \tag{3.27}$$

where C is an arbitrary constant, and

$$Q\left[\frac{d^2}{d\theta^2}(Q^2) + 4Q^2\right] = C \tag{3.28}$$

The solution of Eq. (3.28) can be derived by elementary methods, and is of the form

$$Q = C^{1/3}\left[\sin\left(\frac{3}{2}\theta\right)\right]^{2/3} \tag{3.29}$$

This solution satisfies the boundary conditions for space-charge flow, $Q = \partial Q/\partial\theta = 0$ at $\theta = 0$. The other parameters of the flow can be derived from this solution by using Eqs. (3.7) to (3.10) to show that

$$\begin{aligned}
v_\theta &= \frac{C^{1/3}}{r}\Theta \\
\phi &= \frac{C^{2/3}}{2\eta r^2}\Theta^2 \\
\rho &= \frac{-\epsilon_0 C^{2/3}}{2\eta r^4}\Theta^{-1} \\
i_\theta &= \frac{\epsilon_0 C}{2\eta r^5}
\end{aligned} \tag{3.30}$$

where $$\Theta = \left[\sin\left(\frac{3}{2}\theta\right)\right]^{2/3} \tag{3.31}$$

By eliminating C from these equations, it can be shown that

$$i_\theta = (2\eta)^{1/2}\frac{\epsilon_0\phi^{3/2}}{r^2\Theta^3} \tag{3.32}$$

so that the current is proportional to $\phi^{3/2}$, as it should be in all space-charge-limited flows. It should be noted that

$$\frac{1}{i_\theta}\frac{\partial i_\theta}{\partial r} = -\frac{5}{r} \tag{3.33}$$

a result which agrees exactly with Eq. (3.19).

This space-charge-flow solution differs from the plane-diode solution in one important respect. In this solution, the potential and the velocity rise to a maximum value at $\theta = \theta_M = \pi/3$ and decrease once more to zero at $\theta = 2\pi/3$. A solution of this type can be particularly important in gun design because it makes possible the design of a gun with a nonintercepting anode. An electrode outside a finite beam of this nature, which has a potential greater than any point in the beam, cannot pass through any region in the beam, and is therefore a nonintercepting electrode. In other words, at the point $\theta = \theta_M = \pi/3$, the potential is maximum, and the electric field in the direction of the trajectory is zero; therefore, at the beam edge, the only component of electric field is radial. Consequently, an electrode designed to form this beam is an equipotential surface parallel to the beam at $\theta = \pi/3$, and can be designed not to intercept the beam. It is shown in Section 3 of Chap. VII that, by using an analytic form of solution such as this one, it is possible to use the method of analytical continuation in complex variables to carry out the electrode design entirely by analytic means.

There are other interesting applications for a beam solution of this kind. There is much interest in the problems of designing a gun to produce an ion beam for ion-propulsion purposes. If a plane diode is considered for this purpose, the analysis indicates that, for the currents and potentials involved, the diode spacing must be extremely small, which is equivalent to the perveance per unit area being very high. One solution to this problem is to use what is called an accel-decel system; here the beam potential rises to a much higher value within the gun than the potential at the gun exit orifice. With this scheme, it is possible to increase the spacings by a considerable factor. A circular-beam solution of the type described here could form the basis of such a gun design, but would not be quite suitable for the purpose because of the rapid variation of current density over the cathode surface. This solution can be regarded only as a basic one, which might be used as a guide to a suitable gun design. The solution could be modified by making the curvature of the beam smaller near the cathode to yield uniform current density and to obtain a minimum of potential other than zero at the point where the beam is emitted, so that the final decelerating electrode would also be a nonintercepting one. Such design can be handled by the paraxial methods described in Chap. III* or numerically.

4. THE USE OF THE SEPARATION OF VARIABLES WITH THE ACTION FUNCTION

4.1. Introduction. The space-charge flow solutions found in Sections 2 and 3 were of a particularly simple type, in which all the parameters of the flow depended on only one coordinate. A far more general class of space-charge-flow solutions can be derived by assuming that the parameters of the flow depend on more than one coordinate. The first step in this procedure is to consider the case of normal congruent flow.

For normal congruent flow, all parameters can be expressed in terms of an action function W, and so all possible normal congruent flow can be found by solving the partial differential equation [Eq. (5.15) of Chap. I] for W:

$$\nabla \cdot \left[(\nabla W)\, \nabla^2 (\nabla W)^2\right] = 0 \tag{4.1}$$

Equation (4.1) is extremely difficult to solve directly, even with the use of modern computing facilities. Consequently, to obtain exact solutions for the flow, it is convenient to make assumptions concerning the form of W. The powerful method of separation of variables, which is used in potential theory and in classical dynamics for solving the Hamilton-Jacobi equation, can also be applied to problems of this kind.[13,14] Such an approach makes it possible to reduce the partial differential equation [Eq. (4.1)] to a set of ordinary differential equations, which can either be solved analytically or by relatively simple numerical means.

In this section it is shown how the use of the action-function formalism makes it possible to derive a large class of solutions for normal congruent flow and skew-congruent flow by carrying out the separation in terms of real variables.

The method of separation of variables, as applied to space-charge-flow problems, is by no means as powerful or as general as when applied to deriving the solutions of Maxwell's equations. The defining equations for space-charge flow are nonlinear; consequently, individual solutions obtained by the method of separation of variables generally cannot be added to form further solutions. Nevertheless, a large number of useful solutions can be determined by these techniques.[15,16]

*See, for example, Sec. 9 of Chap. III.

The use of the action function to solve space-charge-flow problems is analogous to the use of a scalar potential to solve the static forms of Maxwell's equations. When a scalar function, rather than a vector function, is used, the analytical procedures are considerably simpler and provide convenient illustrations of the methods involved. However, just as in the case of the solutions of Maxwell's equations, the equations of space-charge-flow can be set up in their full vector form, and all the individual vector parameters, e.g., current density and velocity, can be expressed in separable form. The complete set of vector equations can be solved directly by the method of separation of variables without reference to the use of an action function. This procedure is more general, because the action function can be applied only to normal congruent and skew-congruent flows.

In Sec. 4.2 the use of the action function to obtain separable solutions in an additive form is illustrated. We show that such procedures do not yield space-charge-flow solutions from a real cathode, except in the degenerate case where the parameters depend only on one coordinate of the system. The flow derived by this method occurs in a rectangular coordinate system, where the electrons flow in hyperbolic trajectories and the equipotentials are circles.

In Sec. 4.3 the more important method of separation of variables in product form is applied to the case of a normal congruent flow. It is shown in this section that a large class of flows from cylindrical cathodes, conical cathodes, and cathodes in the form of a spiral can be derived. Some illustrations of the trajectories, potentials, etc., relevant to these flows are given.

In Sec. 4.4 the methods of Sec. 4.3 are generalized to make use of the action function to derive skew-congruent flows, i.e., flows in a magnetic field where there is no normal component of magnetic field at the cathode surface. Perhaps the most important application of this flow is to a crossed-field gun, a solution derived by simpler methods in Section 2. Flows of this kind are not likely to be of much use in the design of guns to produce cylindrical beams, because of the complexity of the required magnet structure.

4.2. Normal Congruent Flow with the Separation in Additive Form. In classical dynamics, the Hamilton-Jacobi equation has been solved[13] by writing the action function W in the separable form

$$W = W_1(q_1) + W_2(q_2) + W_3(q_3) \tag{4.2}$$

where (q_1,q_2,q_3) are the coordinates in the system of interest.

If the coordinate system is restricted to be orthogonal and curvilinear, the velocities in the directions of the three coordinates are, respectively,

$$v_1 = \frac{W_1'}{h_1}, \qquad v_2 = \frac{W_2'}{h_2} \qquad v_3 = \frac{W_3'}{h_3} \tag{4.3}$$

where a prime (′) denotes differentiation with respect to the variable of interest.

The assumption of normal congruent flow implies that all electrons must be emitted with zero velocity from the cathode. Consequently, the cathode must lie along a surface where

$$W_1'(q_1) = W_2'(q_2) = W_3'(q_3) = 0 \tag{4.4}$$

Equation (4.4) defines the coordinates of a point (q_1,q_2,q_3). Therefore the cathode must be a point source, or a finite number of discrete points. This type of space-charge-flow solution is therefore not of great interest for electron-gun design. Nevertheless, for completeness, we consider one example of this method of attack, a simple solution for a flow with hyperbolic trajectories.

In a cartesian coordinate system, W is taken to have the form

$$W = C_1x^2 + C_2y^2 + C_3z^2 \tag{4.5}$$

It follows that the velocity at any point of the flow is

$$\mathbf{v} = 2(C_1x,\ C_2y,\ C_3z) \tag{4.6}$$

From the equation of conservation of energy it follows that the potential at any point of the flow is

$$\eta\phi = 2(C_1^2x^2 + C_2^2y^2 + C_3^2z^2) \tag{4.7}$$

From Poisson's equation it can be shown that the space-charge density is uniform and of value

$$\rho = -\frac{4\epsilon_0}{\eta}(C_1^2 + C_2^2 + C_3^2) \tag{4.8}$$

Equations (4.6) and (4.8) imply that the current density at any point of the flow is

$$\mathbf{i} = \frac{8\epsilon_0}{\eta}(C_1^2 + C_2^2 + C_3^2)(C_1x,\ C_2y,\ C_3z) \tag{4.9}$$

The equation of continuity of current, $\nabla \cdot \mathbf{i} = 0$, therefore yields the result

$$(C_1 + C_2 + C_3)(C_1^2 + C_2^2 + C_3^2) = 0 \tag{4.10}$$

Equation (4.10) is the condition for the flow to exist; from that equation we find either the condition

$$C_1 + C_2 + C_3 = 0 \tag{4.11}$$

or the trivial conditions $C_1 = C_2 = C_3 = 0$.

From Eq. (4.6), the coordinate directions can be chosen so that $C_3 = 0$ and $C_1 = -C_2 = -1$, without any restriction on the generality of the solutions. In this case the flow is two-dimensional, and the equipotentials are the circles

$$\phi = \frac{2}{\eta}(x^2 + y^2) \tag{4.12}$$

The trajectories of the electrons can be found from the differential equation

$$\frac{v_y}{v_x} = \frac{dy}{dx} = -\frac{y}{x} \tag{4.13}$$

The trajectories are therefore the hyperbolas

$$xy = \text{constant} \tag{4.14}$$

The resultant flow is illustrated in Fig. 2.9. This is an example of one of the limited class of space-charge-flow solutions which can be found by assuming W to be separable in the form of Eq. (4.2).

4.3. Normal Congruent Flow with the Separation in Product Form. A fruitful approach to obtaining a large class of space-charge-flow solutions is to choose W to be separable in the product form:

$$W = W_1(q_1)\, W_2(q_2)\, W_3(q_3) \tag{4.15}$$

The three velocity components are therefore

$$v_1 = \frac{W_1'W_2W_3}{h_1}, \qquad v_2 = \frac{W_1W_2'W_3}{h_2}, \qquad v_3 = \frac{W_1W_2W_3'}{h_3} \tag{4.16}$$

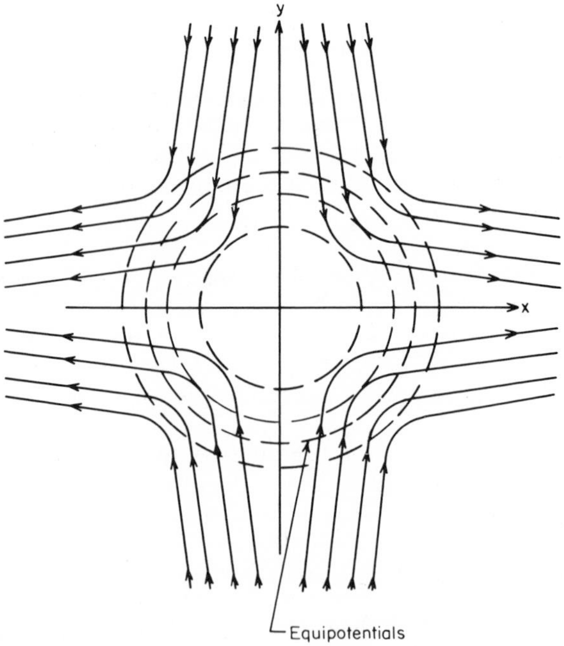

Fig. 2.9. Schematic of electron flow in hyperbolic trajectories with circular equipotentials.

where, as before, a prime denotes differentiation with respect to the variable of interest. It then follows that if, for instance, W_1 and W_1' are zero at some surface q_1 = constant, all the velocity components are zero on the surface. Thus one necessary condition for such a surface to be a space-charge-limited cathode is established.

Let us consider the application of this method of solution to a cylindrical polar coordinate system (r,θ,z). We choose W to have the form

$$W = W_1(r)\, W_2(\theta)\, W_3(z) \tag{4.17}$$

so that the velocity at any point of the flow is

$$\mathbf{v} = W_1W_2W_3\left(\frac{W_1'}{W_1}, \frac{W_2'}{rW_2}, \frac{W_3'}{W_3}\right) \tag{4.18}$$

The potential at any point of the flow is given by the expression

$$2\eta\phi = W_1^2W_2^2W_3^2\left[\left(\frac{W_1'}{W_1}\right)^2 + \frac{1}{r^2}\left(\frac{W_2'}{W_2}\right)^2 + \left(\frac{W_3'}{W_3}\right)^2\right] \tag{4.19}$$

Even when there is no space charge present and the potential obeys Laplace's equation, the only simple solutions for the potential are in the separable form. It is reasonable, therefore, to assume that when space-charge forces are not negligible, the potential ϕ can be written in the separable form

$$\phi = \phi_1(r)\, \phi_2(\theta)\, \phi_3(z) \tag{4.20}$$

In order for both Eqs. (4.19) and (4.20) to be valid, it follows that the sum of the terms inside the parentheses of Eq. (4.19) must either be constant or a function of only one variable. If now we assume the function inside the parentheses to be a function of r, we must take

$$\frac{W_3'}{W_3} = \text{constant} = m \qquad \frac{W_2'}{W_2} = \text{constant} = n \tag{4.21}$$

where m and n are arbitrary real constants (not necessarily positive).* Equation (4.21) has the simple solution

$$W_3 = e^{mz}, \qquad W_2 = e^{n\theta} \tag{4.22}$$

so that both W and ϕ are separable functions if W is chosen to have the form

$$W = \exp\,(mz + n\theta)\, W_1(r) \tag{4.23}$$

with $\phi = \exp 2(mz + n\theta)\, \phi_1(r)$ (4.24)

The crux of this method of analysis is to reduce all the parame-

*The parameters m and n must be real, because the governing set of equations for the flow is nonlinear. Complex values of m and n would only lead to solutions in the complex plane, which would not be physically useful.

ters of the flow, i.e., the action function, the velocity components, the potential, the charge density, and the components of current density, in turn, to separable forms. By this approach to the problem, the nonlinear partial differential equation (4.1), which W obeys, is reduced to a set of ordinary nonlinear differential equations which can be solved in general by numerical methods. There are other possible choices for W in this coordinate system. Thus we might have chosen W to have the form $W = W_1(z) \exp mr$. This form satisfies the conditions on separability for W and ϕ, but it can be shown that $\nabla^2\phi$, and therefore the continuity equation, are not separable. Consequently, the only possible choice for W in this coordinate system is that of Eq. (4.23).

We consider, first, the flow solutions for the case where the space-charge density is extremely small and has a negligible effect on the potentials present. Under these conditions the potential anywhere in the system obeys Laplace's equation. It follows from Eq. (4.24), if we assume rotationally symmetric solutions for simplicity, that Laplace's equation implies the following form for the potential:

$$\phi = \exp(2mz)\left[C_1J_0(2mr) + C_2Y_0(2mr)\right] \tag{4.25}$$

where C_1 and C_2 are arbitrary constants, and J_0, Y_0 are the Bessel functions of the first and second kind, respectively. It then follows from Eqs. (4.19) and (4.25) that W_1 obeys the ordinary differential equation

$$W_1'^2 + 4m^2W_1^2 = 2\eta\phi_1 \tag{4.26}$$

where, for a Laplacian potential field, $\phi_1 = C_1J_0(2mr) + C_2Y_0(2mr)$. The cathode position is at $\phi = 0$, i.e., where

$$C_1J_0(2mr) + C_2Y_0(2mr) = 0 \tag{4.27}$$

Thus the cathode has the form r = constant, which represents a cylinder. The electron trajectories may be found from the solution of Eq. (4.26) by finding the slope of a trajectory. The expression for this slope is

$$\frac{dr}{dz} = \frac{v_r}{v_z} = \frac{W_1'}{mW_1} \tag{4.28}$$

By integration, it follows that the trajectory from the point ($z = z_0$, $r = r_0$) on the cathode is of the form

$$z - z_0 = \int_{r_0}^{r} \frac{mW_1}{W_1'}\,dr \tag{4.29}$$

Thus one trajectory may be derived from another by a translation in the z direction.

This example illustrates an important result of the separation-of-variables technique, namely, that a simple trajectory equation, such as Eq. (4.29), essentially defines all trajectories of the flow. In the example given above all trajectories are identical in size and shape, differing only in their points of origin; in later examples we shall see that it is possible also for trajectories to differ by a magnification factor, and yet a single trajectory equation still suffices.

We consider now the form of the solution when the space-charge forces are not negligible. In this case, the potential ϕ must satisfy Poisson's equation. With the form of potential of Eq. (4.25), we can write Poisson's equation to give the following separable form for the charge density ρ:

$$\frac{\rho}{\epsilon_0} = -\exp(2mz)\left[\frac{1}{r}\frac{d}{dr}\left(r\frac{d\phi_1}{dr}\right) + 4m^2\phi_1\right] \tag{4.30}$$

Because the expressions involved are rather complicated, it is convenient to use a simplifying notation, defined as

$$\sigma(r) \equiv mW_1 r\left[\frac{1}{r}\frac{d}{dr}\left(r\frac{d\phi_1}{dr}\right) + 4m^2\phi_1\right] \tag{4.31a}$$

$$\tau(r) \equiv W_1' r\left[\frac{1}{r}\frac{d}{dr}\left(r\frac{d\phi_1}{dr}\right) + 4m^2\phi_1\right] \tag{4.31b}$$

In terms of these new parameters, $\sigma(r)$ and $\tau(r)$, the current density at any point is

$$\mathbf{i} = \frac{\exp 3mz}{r}(\tau, 0, \sigma) \tag{4.32}$$

It follows that the equation of continuity, $\nabla \cdot \mathbf{i} = 0$,

$$\tau' + 3m\sigma = 0 \tag{4.33}$$

We have now reduced the original partial differential equation for W, Eq. (4.1), to a set of simultaneous ordinary differential equations, Eqs. (4.26), (4.31), and (4.33). The solution of these differential equations can be carried out numerically for all real values of the parameter m. When the flow is space-charge-limited, the boundary conditions are that at the cathode, that is $r = r_0$, the potential and total electric field vectors vanish, which implies that $W_1 = W_1' = \phi_1' = 0$ at the cathode.

For purposes of computation, it is usually convenient to normalize the dimensions of the system to the cathode radius r_0, by substituting

$$M = \frac{m}{r_0}, \qquad r = r_0 R, \qquad z = r_0 Z \tag{4.34}$$

where M is a real number, not necessarily a positive integer, and R and Z are the dimensionless coordinates of interest. In this case, the equations of the flow then assume the following forms:

$$W = \exp(MZ)W_1(R), \qquad \mathbf{v} = \exp(MZ)\mathbf{v}_1(R),$$
$$\phi = \exp(2MZ)\phi_1(R), \qquad \mathbf{E} = \exp(2MZ)\mathbf{E}_1(R) \qquad (4.35)$$
$$\rho = \exp(2MZ)\rho_1(R), \qquad j = \exp(3MZ)j_1(R)$$

In addition, from Eq. (4.29), the equation for a normalized trajectory transforms to

$$Z - Z_0 = \int_1^R \frac{MW_1}{W_1'}\,dR \qquad (4.36)$$

All the possible flows which can be derived from this solution are found by changing the value of the parameter M. When $M = 0$ the flow reduces to the rectilinear flow between coaxial cylinders (Appendix E). Otherwise, the flow will be curvilinear, and the trajectories are found from Eq. (4.36). A number of possible trajectories for flow inward from the cathode toward the axis are shown in Fig. 2.10. Another possibility, not illustrated here, consists of flow outward from the cathode.

Certain features of these solutions are of interest. For $M < 1.55$, it is possible for the electron trajectories to cross the axis. When this occurs, the method of solution becomes invalid because electron trajectories cross, a fact not consistent with the laminar-flow assumption. If the flow is cut off before reaching the axis, however, the solutions are valid. For $M > 1.55$, the electron trajectories do not reach the axis, but become parallel to the axis at some point.

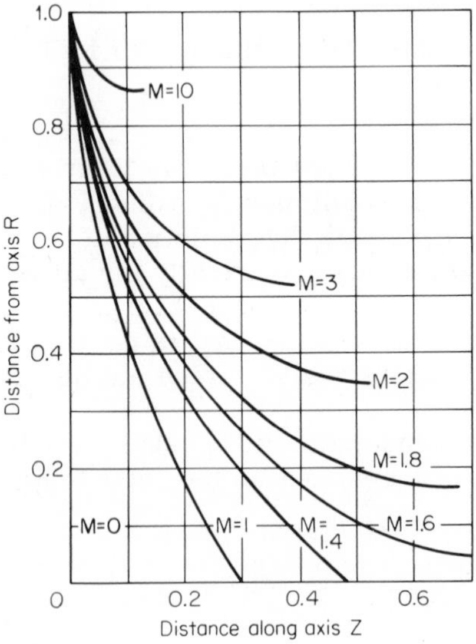

Fig. 2.10. Electron trajectories on the inside of a cylindrical cathode for different values of M. (Reproduced from Ref. 15, courtesy of the American Institute of Physics.)

Beyond this point, they tend to turn back toward the cathode. Once again, there would be the possibility of crossing electron trajectories, because neighboring trajectories are generated by a displacement in Z and would cross after the point $dR/dZ = 0$; the solutions are valid only if the trajectories are terminated before the crossover point. It should be noted that this restriction does not apply to the zero-space-charge solutions discussed above, because for them the potential is a single-valued function, so that the electron motion can still be computed. The reason for the breakdown of the space-charge-flow solutions at the crossover is the breakdown of the relation between current and charge, $\mathbf{i} = -\rho\,\mathbf{v}$, a problem which does not appear in the zero-space-charge solutions discussed above. In this discussion it is not necessary to refer to negative values of M, for such solutions are merely the positive-M solutions reflected in the $Z = 0$ plane, as the reader may easily demonstrate.

The space-charge flows derived above are, with certain limitations which we have discussed, those for an infinite beam. For an electron gun a finite beam is required; consequently, a finite portion of one of these space-charge-flow solutions is taken as the basic finite beam for an electron gun. For such a beam the potentials and fields along the two bounding surfaces are obtained by using Eq. (4.37); an electrode system exterior to the beam is designed to give the correct values of potential and field at these surfaces. Because the flow is curvilinear, a component of electric field exists normal to the edge surfaces of the beam, and the design procedure for electrodes is not as simple as that for rectilinear-flow guns. Details of the many possible electrode design procedures are given in Chaps. VII and VIII.

In order to design an electron gun, it is necessary to calculate how the current density varies across the cathode, and the expected value of total current. Moreover, the most efficient usage of the cathode requires that the current-density variation over the cathode must be small. Consequently, a choice of beam for a gun using this flow is normally limited to such values of M that the current density over the cathode varies only by a specified amount F, where $F = \exp 3M\delta$, and δ is the normalized length of the cathode. For large M, δ must be small, whereas for large cathode widths, M must be small.

A finite beam which can be derived from the universal trajectories of Fig. 2.10, with $M = 1.8$, is shown in Fig. 2.11, where edge trajectories are plotted for two cathode widths. Solid lines represent trajectories, and dotted lines, equipotentials. From Fig. 2.10 it can be seen that the minimum diameter of this beam would be that of a cylinder of radius 0.17 of the cathode radius and that the convergence could be extremely large, although, in practice, limited by thermal velocities. However, the high convergence of such a beam is not necessarily as useful as it might appear, because the perveance may

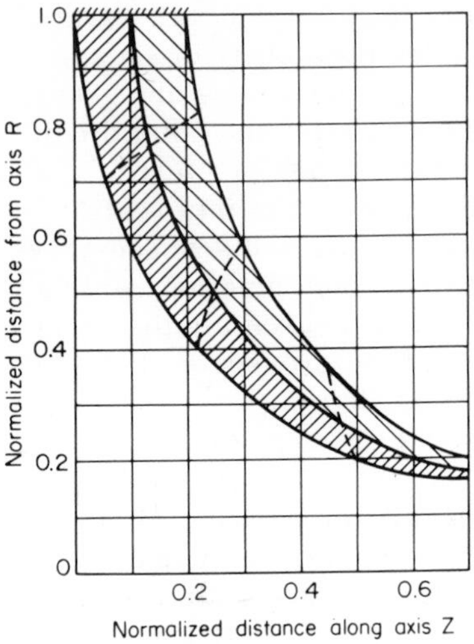

Fig. 2.11. Schematic of the finite beam emitted from a cylindrical cathode with M = 1.8. (Reproduced from Ref. 15, courtesy of the American Institute of Physics.)

be small. From Eqs. (4.35) it is seen that the perveance density p at any point of the flow is

$$p = \frac{|i|}{\phi^{3/2}} = \frac{|i_1(R)|}{\phi_1^{3/2}(R)} \tag{4.37}$$

If the beam is traveling almost parallel to the z axis, as would be required near the exit point of the gun, r is almost constant, and so also is p. Hence the total perveance is inversely proportional to the area convergence. Therefore electron-gun designs based on these solutions do not necessarily yield a high-perveance beam. However, the gun may find utility in low-power applications; an outstanding advantage is the simplicity of the cathode form.

Some typical results for M = 1.8 are given in Table 2.1; the notation for the table is illustrated in the schematic of Fig. 2.12. For a perveance of unity and a change in current density over the cathode length of 1.7:1, the area convergence is 7.2. Further results for this type of solution can be found in Refs. 15 to 17.

If the cathode is chosen to lie between the planes $z = z_0$ and $z = z_0 + \delta r_0$, and i_{1r} is the current density flowing in the radial direction, at z = 0, then

$$\begin{aligned} I_c &= 2\pi r i_{1r}(R) \int_{z_0}^{z_1} \exp(3mz)\, dz \\ &= \frac{2\pi}{3M} r_0^2 R i_{1r}(R) \exp \frac{3Mz_0}{r_0} [\exp(3M\delta) - 1] \end{aligned} \tag{4.38}$$

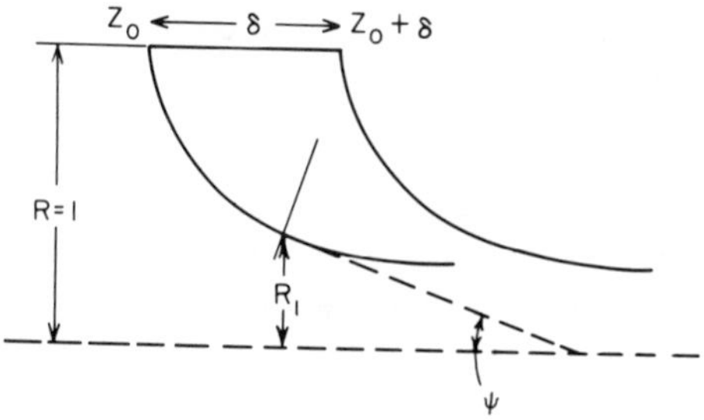

Fig. 2.12. The nomenclature used for the finite beam emitted from a cylindrical cathode.

Because current must be conserved, $Ri_{1r}(R)$ is constant and equal to its value at the cathode $i_c = i_{rc}(R)$. This relation can be used either as a useful check on a numerical computation or to compute the current density directly. Equation (4.38) shows that the cathode should not be excessively long, because, if the maximum current density at the cathode is a predetermined quantity, the addition of extra length will yield only a small increment to the total current. On the other hand, if the cathode is big enough to make the minimum current density only a small fraction of the maximum, the task of designing electrodes sufficiently accurate for practical utilization of the gun is made much easier.

The choice of W in the product form of Eq. (4.15) also yields space-charge-flow solutions in coordinate systems other than the cylindrical polar system used as an example here. It can be shown that the only circularly symmetric coordinate systems to which this method of solution can be applied are the cylindrical and the spher-

Table 2.1. Characteristics of Beams from a Cylindrical Cathode with M = 1.8

Normalized final beam radius R_1	Variation of current density across cathode, $i_c(Z_0 + \delta)/i_c(Z_0)$	Normalized cathode width δ	Area convergence	Micro perveance Eq. (4.37)	Final angle of beam ψ (Fig. 2.12)
0.75	1.7	0.1	1.4	22	75°
0.75	2.9	0.2	1.4	14	75°
0.5	1.7	0.1	2.4	3.8	58°
0.5	2.9	0.2	2.4	2.7	58°
0.25	1.7	0.1	7.2	1.0	34°
0.25	2.9	0.2	7.2	0.7	34°
0.18	1.7	0.1	27	0.5	10°
0.18	2.9	0.2	27	0.35	10°

ical polar systems. In a spherical polar coordinate system, W is taken to have the form[15,16]

$$W = r^n \exp(m\varphi)\, W_2(\theta) \tag{4.39}$$

The solutions of most interest are of course the axially symmetrical ones for which m = 0. With this space-charge flow, the cathode is in the form of a cone, and electrons can be emitted from the outside or the inside of the cone.

Certain solutions in which the electrons are emitted from the outside of the cone have been evaluated; one of particular interest[18,19] is that for n = 0. In this case, the radial component of velocity is zero, so that the electrons flow on great circles along the surfaces of spheres. There is one important feature of this type of flow which is not observed with simple rectilinear flow; like the circular flow discussed in Sec. 3.4, the potential may pass through a maximum along the trajectory of an electron and then decrease again to a minimum or to zero. This is still true for other values of n near zero, but it is not true for general values of n.[20] Such solutions can have certain advantages for gun design, which will be discussed in Sec. 3.4 and Section 5 of Chap. VIII.

It can be shown that the solutions to the flow from a cylindrical cathode are special cases of the solutions of flow from a conical cathode. This fact is related to the result that a cylindrical cathode is the limiting form of a conical cathode for which the cone angle $\theta_0 \rightarrow 0$.

There are a number of possible space-charge-flow solutions in two-dimensional coordinate systems. In cartesian coordinates,[15,16] for instance, W is taken to have the form

$$W = \exp(\alpha x)\, W_2(y) \tag{4.40}$$

the cathode being a plane surface. Two types of solution in a two-dimensional cylindrical polar coordinate system are possible,[15,16] namely,

$$W = \exp(m\theta)\, W_2(r) \tag{4.41}$$

and

$$W = r^n W_2(\theta) \tag{4.42}$$

For the first type of solution, the cathode is in the form of a cylinder; for the second type, the cathode is in the form of a plane.

Finally, it is possible to obtain solutions in a more general coordinate system than either of the last two discussed, one in which the cathode is in the form of an equiangular spiral. In this system, the two coordinate lines are formed by the two sets of equiangular spirals,[15,16] as illustrated in Fig. 2.13:

$$r \exp\left(\frac{b_1}{b_2}\theta\right) = \text{constant} \qquad r \exp\left(-\frac{b_2}{b_1}\theta\right) = \text{constant} \tag{4.43}$$

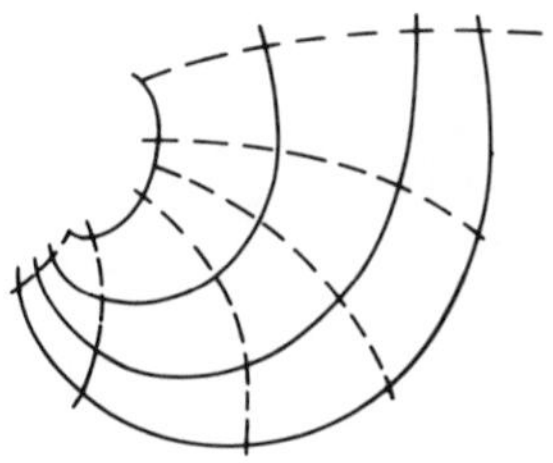

Fig. 2.13. The equiangular spiral coordinate system.

If q_1 and q_2 are the coordinates of two intersecting equiangular spiral coordinate lines, the relation between r, θ and q_1, q_2 is

$$\theta = b_1q_2 - b_2q_1 \qquad r = \exp(b_1q_1 + b_2q_2) \tag{4.44}$$

with $h_1 = h_2 = \exp(b_1q_1 + b_2q_2)$ (4.45)

The general form of W which yields a solution is

$$W = \exp(mq_1)\, W_2(q_2) \tag{4.46}$$

Sample trajectories for this type of solution have been derived in Refs. 15 to 17.

As there is a wide choice for b_1/b_2 and m, a wide range of solutions for W, and hence the flow, can be derived by this method. A correct choice of the two arbitrary parameters allows the design of highly convergent sheet beams. Particular choices generate some of the simple solutions already described. For instance, if $b_1 = b_2 = 0$, W assumes the cartesian form of Eq. (4.40). On the other hand, if only $b_2 = 0$, W assumes the form of Eq. (4.41) or (4.42). Consequently, the spiral metric can be regarded as a more general form than either the cartesian or the cylindrical polar coordinate metrics.

4.4. Skew-congruent Flow. The action-function method of solution, which was discussed in Secs. 4.2 and 4.3, can be generalized to give skew-congruent solutions. As before, it is useful to take W in product form.

As an illustration of the method, we derive one of the simpler solutions in the cylindrical polar coordinate system (r, θ, z). The action function W is chosen to have the form

$$W = r^2W_2(\theta) \tag{4.47}$$

which is a special case of

$$W = r^nW_2(\theta) \tag{4.48}$$

It was shown in Eq. (5.4) of Chap. I that the velocity at any point of the skew-symmetric flow is given by the relation

$$\mathbf{v} = \nabla W + \eta \mathbf{A} \tag{4.49}$$

When W is expressed as in Eq. (4.49), one form of the vector potential for which **v** is separable is

$$\mathbf{A} = (0, \frac{rB}{2}, 0) \tag{4.50}$$

where B is constant. This **A** corresponds to a magnetic field (0,0,B).* Such a choice of **A** allows the velocity to be expressed in the separable form

$$\mathbf{v} = r(2W_2, W_2' + \frac{\omega_H}{2}, 0) \tag{4.51}$$

where $\omega_H = \eta B$. More generally, when W is expressed in the form of Eq. (4.48), **A** has the form

$$\mathbf{A} = r^{n-1}[A_1(\theta), A_2(\theta), 0] \tag{4.52}$$

With the **v** of Eq. (4.51), the potential is given by

$$\phi = r^2 \phi_2(\theta) \tag{4.53}$$

$$\text{where} \quad \phi_2 = \left(W_2' + \frac{\omega_H}{2}\right)^2 + 4W_2^2 \tag{4.54}$$

When the space-charge density is small and the effect on the potential due to space charge is negligible, Laplace's equation implies that

$$\phi_2 = C_1 \cos(2\theta) + C_2 \sin(2\theta) \tag{4.55}$$

where C_1 and C_2 are arbitrary constants. Thus, with no space charge, the equipotentials are hyperbolic surfaces. To complete the zero-space-charge solution, Eq. (4.55) is substituted in Eq. (4.54), which is solved to find W_2. The trajectories are then determined from the relation

$$\frac{1}{r}\frac{dr}{d\theta} = \frac{v_r}{v_\theta} = \frac{4W_2}{2W_2' + \omega_H} \tag{4.56}$$

This equation yields the integral

$$r = r_0 \exp\left(\int_0^\theta \frac{4W_2}{2W_2' + \omega_H}\, d\theta_1\right) \tag{4.57}$$

where the cathode is taken to be the surface $\theta = 0$. From Eq. (4.57), for all solutions given by an action function of the type of Eq. (4.47), one trajectory can be derived from another by magnification, be-

*This choice of **A** is not unique for the magnetic field (0,0,B). Another choice, $\mathbf{A} = (-B\theta/r, 0, 0)$, is also possible, but less useful for the separation of variables. This **A** must be used, however, to apply the method of Sec. 3.4.

cause for a given θ the radial coordinates on two trajectories remain in a constant ratio.

The solution given here is one which was first derived by Poritsky[21] by direct integration of the Lorentz equation of motion in cartesian coordinates. The results are similar to those for electron motion in uniform crossed electric and magnetic field, where the electron trajectories would be cycloidal. Here the electron trajectories are cycloidal or trochoidal in character, but with a diminishing amplitude of undulation as they leave the cathode. Two trajectories from different parts of the cathode may cross, but this causes no difficulty since the space charge has been assumed negligible.

If there is space charge present and the solution is space-charge-limited at the cathode, the procedure used in Sec. 4.3 can be followed to find separable forms for all the physical parameters of the flow. It is possible to solve the resultant nonlinear differential equations for W_2 and to deduce the trajectories of the flow. When this is done, it is found that the flow is very similar to the crossed-field flow described in Sec. 2.3. In fact, for very large r, the two flows are identical. The flow in Sec. 2.3 could also have been found using this method of solution, if W and **A** had been taken as

$$W = W(x) \qquad \text{and} \qquad \mathbf{A} = (0, Bx, 0) \tag{4.58}$$

Thus, by choosing the solution to be of the cylindrical polar type given here, we have introduced an additional parameter, the value of r at the cathode; with a given magnetic field, this parameter can be varied to alter the form of the flow.

More general solutions can be derived in each one of the coordinate systems in which it is possible to derive normal congruent space-charge-flow solutions. Of particular interest are solutions with constant magnetic field in a spiral coordinate system, which should yield suitable flows for a crossed-field gun.

Only the solutions with uniform magnetic field have, so far, appeared to be of much practical importance. The reason for the lack of practical application of the others can be seen by considering some examples. For the skew-congruent axially symmetric flow from a cylindrical cathode, the normal magnetic field must be zero at the cathode. It follows that, except for the magnetron, in which the magnetic field is uniform and parallel to the axis of the cylinder, the magnetic field must have radial components at points both inside and outside the cathode; this situation is illustrated in Fig. 2.14. To obtain such a flow, it is necessary to have pole pieces both inside and outside the cathode. Such configurations are not very convenient to construct. In another example, a two-dimensional system with a nonuniform magnetic field, there are components of magnetic field tending to move the electrons in the beam so that they "slip" past each other. Consequently, a beam leaving a rectangular cathode would assume a trapezoidal shape and the electrons would have

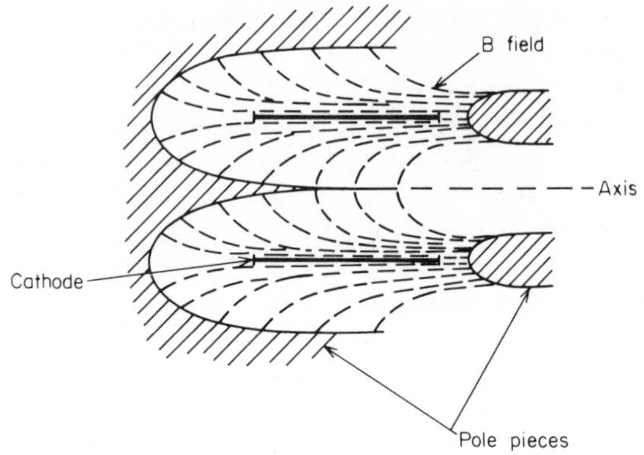

Fig. 2.14. The magnetic field configuration required to produce skew-congruent flow from a cylindrical cathode.

components of velocity which would cause the resultant beam to be a difficult one to inject into most focusing systems. Thus this type of beam is not very suitable for use in a strip-beam electron gun.

5. THE SEPARATION OF VARIABLES AND THE LORENTZ FORCE LAW

5.1. Introduction. In the action-function method of finding space-charge-flow solutions, all the parameters of the flow can be expressed in terms of one scalar variable W. Just as electromagnetic fields satisfying Maxwell's equations cannot always be expressed in terms of a scalar potential, so the space-charge-flow solutions are not always derivable. However, the method of the separation of variables can be used to find space-charge-flow solutions even when the flow is noncongruent, and the parameters of the flow must be expressed in terms of the velocity vector. In this case it is necessary to use the hydrodynamic equation of motion

$$(\mathbf{v} \cdot \nabla)\,\mathbf{v} = -\eta(\mathbf{E} + \mathbf{v} \times \mathbf{B}) \tag{5.1}$$

derived in Eq. (2.34) of Chap. I, or the Lorentz equation of motion,

$$\frac{d\mathbf{v}}{dt} = -\eta(\mathbf{E} + \mathbf{v} \times \mathbf{B}) \tag{5.2}$$

In Sec. 5.2 the hydrodynamic equation of motion [Eq. (5.1)] is used directly for the determination of noncongruent space-charge flows by the method of separation of variables. For simplicity, the method of separation of variables is illustrated in a cartesian coordinate system. When space-charge forces are negligible, Laplace's equation can be used; otherwise Poisson's equation and the equation of continuity must be used. The most important solutions of this type which have been derived are those in a spherical polar coordinate system.

The use of these methods in this coordinate system and an important practical application to the design of the magnetron injection gun are described in Sec. 5.2. The numerical solution of the flows derived by the method of separation of variables is discussed in Sec. 5.3. It is shown that it is often more convenient to work directly with the Lorentz equation of motion than the hydrodynamic equation of flow. In this case, instead of reducing all the parameters of the flow to a set of ordinary differential equations with an independent variable which is also one of the coordinates, all the equations of the flow are reduced to a set of ordinary differential equations with the transit time of an electron along its trajectory as the independent variable.

In some situations, this can simplify the numerical analysis; in particular, it is often useful where the electron trajectories approach a turning point. For example, in the flow from a cylindrical cathode, the electron trajectory is almost parallel to the axis. Using the r coordinate as the independent variable can provide computational difficulties. Using time as the independent variable is one way of obviating these difficulties, and provides a close relationship to the earlier forms of solution derived in Section 2. The techniques developed here are a generalization of those described in Section 2.

5.2. The Hydrodynamic Equation of Motion. We consider as an example the solution of Eq. (5.1) in cartesian coordinates. The governing nonlinear partial differential equations for problems of this kind cannot easily be solved directly. Instead, it is usually necessary to choose some form for the parameters of interest, so that these equations are reduced to a set of ordinary differential equations. We assume that all vector components of the velocity, electric field, and magnetic field can be expressed in product forms which are self-consistent with each other. In a cartesian coordinate system, the velocity vector is written as

$$\mathbf{v} = \exp(my + nz)[v_x(x),\ v_y(x),\ v_z(x)] \tag{5.3}$$

where m and n are arbitrary real constants. In order for **E** and **B** to be separable and for Eq. (5.1) to be self-consistent, it follows that the fields must assume the forms

$$\mathbf{E} = \exp(2my + 2nz)[E_x(x),\ E_y(x),\ E_z(x)] \tag{5.4}$$

$$\mathbf{B} = \exp(my + nz)[B_x(x),\ B_y(x),\ B_z(x)] \tag{5.5}$$

The following set of three equations relating the components of **v**, **E**, and **B** can then be derived from Eq. (5.1):

$$v_x \frac{\partial v_x}{\partial x} + m v_y v_x + n v_z v_x = -\eta(E_x + v_y B_z - v_z B_y) \tag{5.6a}$$

$$v_x \frac{\partial v_y}{\partial x} + m v_y^2 + n v_z v_y = -\eta(E_y + v_z B_x - v_x B_z) \tag{5.6b}$$

$$v_x \frac{\partial v_z}{\partial x} + m v_y v_z + n v_z^2 = -\eta(E_z + v_x B_y - v_y B_x) \tag{5.6c}$$

There are, in addition, two constraints on **E** and **B**:

$$\nabla \times \mathbf{E} = 0 \tag{5.7}$$

$$\nabla \times \mathbf{B} = 0 \tag{5.8}$$

Consequently, **E** and **B** must be of the form

$$\mathbf{E} = -\nabla\phi \tag{5.9}$$

and $$\mathbf{B} = -\nabla\Omega \tag{5.10}$$

where ϕ and Ω are the electrostatic and magnetic potentials within the system. Because

$$\nabla \cdot \mathbf{B} = 0 \tag{5.11}$$

it follows that Ω obeys Laplace's equation and has the form of Eq. (5.5); i.e.,

$$\Omega = \exp(my + nz)[C_1 \sin(\ell x) + C_2 \cos(\ell x)] \tag{5.12}$$

where $$m^2 + n^2 - \ell^2 = 0 \tag{5.13}$$

and C_1 and C_2 are arbitrary constants. If space-charge forces are negligible, ϕ is given by the relation

$$\phi = \exp(2my + 2nz)[D_1 \sin(2\ell x) + D_2 \cos(2\ell x)] \tag{5.14}$$

where D_1 and D_2 are arbitrary constants. More generally, when the space-charge fields are not negligible, ϕ must be written as

$$\phi = \exp(2my + 2nz)\,\phi_2(x) \tag{5.15}$$

Following the previous analyses in this chapter, it is possible to find separable forms for the charge density and the current density. By this process a set of ordinary differential equations in the variable x can be derived, and the flow determined.

Most of the solutions in cartesian coordinates have not been computed numerically. One solution is of some interest; this is the very simple one for $m = n = 0$, which is identical with that derived by other methods in Sec. 2.4. It is apparent that there are often many different ways to derive the same space-charge solutions.

The solutions which have generated practical interest for gun-design purposes are those derived in spherical polar coordinates (r, θ, φ) for flow from a conical cathode. Some care in using Eq. (5.1) must be taken with this coordinate system because $(\mathbf{v} \cdot \nabla)\mathbf{v}$ cannot be written by inspection, as it can in a cartesian coordinate system. The reason for this difficulty is that the unit vectors change their direction as the coordinate is changed. Consequently, in the differential $(\mathbf{v} \cdot \nabla)\mathbf{v}$, there are contributions from the change in direction of the vectors. In Appendix A, $(\mathbf{v} \cdot \nabla)\mathbf{v}$ is derived in a general orthogonal curvilinear coordinate system, and in spherical polar and cylindrical polar coordinates in particular.

We can examine the form of the solutions for the flow in spherical polar coordinates without carrying out the detailed differentiations. By analogy with the derivations for normal congruent flow and skew-congruent flow, **v** is assumed to have the form

$$\mathbf{v} = r^n[v_1(\theta),\ v_2(\theta),\ v_3(\theta)] \tag{5.16}$$

for axially symmetric flow. It follows that, if **E** is to be expressed in separable form, it must be written in the form

$$\mathbf{E} = r^{2n-1}[E_1(\theta),\ E_2(\theta),\ 0] \tag{5.17}$$

This is so because differentiation with respect to any of the coordinates reduces the order of the variables by one power of r. It should be noted that E_φ vanishes because of the assumption of axial symmetry. Similarly, it follows that the magnetic field **B** must take the form

$$\mathbf{B} = r^{n-1}[B_1(\theta),\ B_2(\theta),\ 0] \tag{5.18}$$

The magnetic scalar potential obeys Laplace's equation, and so it must be of the form

$$\Omega = r^n[C_1P_n(\cos\theta) + C_2Q_n(\cos\theta)] \tag{5.19}$$

where C_1 and C_2 are arbitrary constants, and P_n and Q_n are Legendre polynomials of the first and second kind of order n. Similarly, from the equation of conservation of energy, Poisson's equation, and the equation of conservation of charge in this coordinate system, other parameters of interest can be written:

$$\phi = r^{2n}\,\phi_2(\theta), \qquad \rho = r^{2n-2}\,\rho_2(\theta)$$

and $$\mathbf{j} = r^{3n-2}[j_1(\theta),\ j_2(\theta),\ j_3(\theta)] \tag{5.20}$$

The electron trajectories corresponding to this solution are found in the same way as in earlier examples by writing

$$\frac{1}{r}\frac{dr}{d\theta} = \frac{v_r}{v_\theta} = \frac{v_1(\theta)}{v_2(\theta)} \tag{5.21}$$

and $$\sin\theta\,\frac{d\varphi}{d\theta} = \frac{v_\varphi}{v_\theta} = \frac{v_3(\theta)}{v_2(\theta)} \tag{5.22}$$

so that $$r = r_0 \exp \int_{\theta_0}^{\theta} \frac{v_1}{v_2}\,d\theta_1 \tag{5.23}$$

and $$\varphi = \varphi_0 + \int_{\theta_0}^{\theta} \frac{1}{\sin\theta_1}\,\frac{v_3}{v_2}\,d\theta_1 \tag{5.24}$$

Here r_0, θ_0, and φ_0 are the cathode coordinates of the electron trajectory of interest. It is seen that any one trajectory can be derived from another by magnification in r.

This method of solution for the flow yields a very wide range of trajectories. There are three independent parameters, namely, n, the angle of the cone θ_0, and the strength of the magnetic field. In addition, the ratio C_1/C_2 can be varied to change the form of the magnetic field and its angle to the cathode. As in the case of skew-symmetric flow, the solutions with $C_2 \neq 0$ are not of much practical interest, because they presuppose that the value of magnetic field on the axis is infinite or that it is necessary to put a pole piece inside the cathode. Consequently, all the solutions that have been calculated so far are those for $C_2 = 0$.

One type of solution which has yielded very useful practical results is that for the magnetron injection gun.[20,22,23] The type of flow obtained is very similar to that derived in Sec. 2.4. When the cathode magnetic field is almost parallel to the cathode, the electrons move in almost circular paths, hugging the cathode closely, with a small component of axial velocity. The two solutions of most importance are those for $n = 1$ and $n = 2/3$. When $n = 1$, Eq. (5.18) shows that there must be a uniform magnetic field parallel to the axis of the cone, and Eq. (5.20) indicates that the current density at the cathode is proportional to r. When $n = 2/3$, Eq. (5.20) implies that the current density at the cathode is uniform, although the magnetic field is not. The emitted beam can be used in the manner described in Sec. 2.4, and electrodes for such beams can be designed by the methods given in Chaps. VII and VIII. The plane solution and the modification which takes the centrifugal force into account were given in Sec. 2.4. These solutions can be expressed in a very simple analytic form, and yield an analytic method for designing the electrodes, which are often satisfactory for a practical gun. Guns with cathodes four times the length of their average diameter have been made, based on this planar solution, the uniformity of current density over the cathode being within 20 per cent.

The full solution from a conical cathode must be used if the radius of the cathode has a large variation over its length. One important application of this method is to design guns of small diameter from a conical cathode. If the apex of the cone is not included, an electrode, which may be difficult to construct, would be required inside the beam. For this reason the use of the full conical cathode may be necessary. Very successful low-noise, low-voltage guns have been made by this procedure.[23]

It should be pointed out that, as with the plane-diode solutions, the choice of zero initial velocity or finite initial velocity is possible. When zero initial velocity is used, the trajectories of the flow are not perfectly smooth, but have small ripples with a period of the cyclotron frequency ω_H. This ripple can cause difficulty, not only with the numerical calculations of the flow, but also in the electrode design. The electrodes, if analytically designed, can have many branch points, or cross over themselves, making the electrodes physically unrealizable (Sec. 3.6 of Chap. VII). It is therefore important to obtain a smooth flow. With a uniform magnetic field, it has been found[20] that, if the initial velocity v_c of the electrons at the cathode is taken to be

$$v_c = \frac{\eta i_0}{\epsilon_0 \omega_H^2} \tag{5.25}$$

a smooth flow can be obtained and the electrode design considerably simplified. This procedure can be analytically justified by reference to perturbation theories; it was demonstrated for a plane cathode in Secs. 2.3 and 2.4.

5.3. Numerical Methods and the Direct Application of the Lorentz Equation of Motion. The method of the separation of variables yields a large number of possible space-charge-flow solutions. Most of these solutions cannot be written in analytic form, but must be determined numerically, usually on a digital computer because of the accuracy obtainable. In this section we discuss how such problems are set up for computational purposes, using as an example the normal congruent flow in cylindrical polar coordinates derived in Sec. 4.3. However, the methods described and the problems encountered are common to all space-charge-flow solutions which are obtained numerically. An alternative technique, which makes use of the direct application of the Lorentz equation of motion, is also described. This method obviates the difficulties which occur in regions where the space charge becomes infinite; is convenient to apply in complicated coordinate systems; and can be used to determine any of the space-charge flows discussed earlier in this chapter.

As a first step to obtain a space-charge-flow solution numerically, it is convenient to express the parameters of the flow in a normalized form. As the differential equations involved are of fourth order, there are four boundary conditions to be satisfied. For normal congruent flow from a cylindrical cathode, for instance, three of these boundary conditions require that W, $\partial W/\partial r$, and $\partial^2 W/\partial r^2$ be zero at the cathode. The fourth is determined from the required current density at a reference point on the cathode. Thus, after normalization of the coordinate system as discussed in Sec. 4.3, it is usually convenient to normalize in terms of the current density at the cathode, or more generally, in terms of the perveance or perveance per unit area. Such normalization procedures are standard and are a matter of individual preference. Consequently, we do not treat these in detail.[15-17]

Let us examine now how the solution for normal congruent flow may be formulated for computational purposes. In Sec. 4.3, we obtained the parameters of the flow in a cylindrical polar system in the normalized form [Eq. (4.35)], repeated below for convenience:

$$W = \exp(MZ)\, W_1(R), \qquad \mathbf{v} = \exp(MZ)\, \mathbf{v}_1(R),$$
$$\phi = \exp(2MZ)\, \phi_1(R), \qquad \mathbf{E} = \exp(2MZ)\, \mathbf{E}_1(R), \tag{4.35}$$
$$\rho = \exp(2MZ)\, \rho_1(R), \qquad \mathbf{i} = \exp(3MZ)\, \mathbf{i}_1(R)$$

To analyze the flow numerically, it is convenient to work with only first-order differential equations. Consequently, we use the set of equations (4.35) to represent the flow and employ the equations governing space-charge flow to determine the following differential relations between the parameters denoted by the subscript 1.

$$Z' = \frac{v_{1Z}}{v_{1R}}, \qquad W_1' = v_{1R}, \qquad \phi_1' = -E_{1R}$$
$$E_{1R}' = -2ME_{1Z} + \frac{\rho_1}{\epsilon_0} - \frac{E_{1R}}{R} \tag{5.26}$$
and $$i_{1R}' = -3Mi_{1Z} - \frac{i_{1R}}{R}$$

with the defining relations

$$v_{1Z} = M\, W_1$$
$$E_{1Z} = -2M\phi_1$$
$$\rho_1 = -\frac{i_{1R}}{v_{1R}} \tag{5.27}$$
$$i_{1Z} = \frac{v_{1Z}}{v_{1R}}\, i_{1R}$$

In Eq. (5.26) the prime denotes differentiation with respect to R; the subscript 1 indicates that the Z variation has been removed as in Eq. (4.35). It is now necessary to examine the boundary conditions. Because v_{1R} and v_{1Z} are zero at the cathode, W_1 and W_1' are zero there. Again, for space-charge-limited flow, E_{1R} is zero at the cathode, as is ϕ_1, but for finite emission, i_{1R} is finite. Consequently, it follows that ρ_1 must be infinite at the cathode; since E_{1Z} and ϕ are zero there, E_{1R}' is infinite at the cathode. Because of the boundary condition on E_{1R}, the set of differential equations (5.26) cannot be solved directly on the computer; the requirement of a derivative of one of the parameters being initially infinite causes too many difficulties. To work with these equations, it is necessary to use an approximate analytical solution in the neighborhood of the cathode to start the computation. The approximate solution in this case is essentially the plane-diode solution of Sec. 2.2, because it can be deduced from Eq. (3.17) that near the cathode

$$W_1' \propto |R - 1|^{2/3} \tag{5.28}$$

Therefore this analytic solution is used to determine the initial values for the numerical solution, which is started at a point a short distance from the cathode.

This procedure can often cause difficulties. As a first step, a series form for the space-charge-flow solution in the neighborhood of the cathode is required. The solution needed in the foregoing illustration of the method is not difficult to obtain; nevertheless, its use is somewhat tedious and requires several extra steps in the computation. With more complicated solutions, for instance, those for noncongruent flow, it is necessary to determine the first few terms of each series for the different parameters of the flow and to use these in the initial-value problem. With a coordinate system such as the spherical polar one, the process of determining the necessary series is tedious. In addition, it is difficult to determine the range of validity of the series expansion.

Another difficulty which can occur in the computation is that at some point the electron trajectory may almost coincide with one of the coordinate surfaces; for instance, in the example discussed above, the electron trajectory may become almost parallel to the axis of the system. In such a case Z' and ρ would both become extremely large and give rise to very large errors in a calculation by finite-difference methods. One remedy for this difficulty, namely, making the steps of the computation extremely small, would cause the time of computation to become indefinitely long; this is because Z is found as a function of R rather than R as a function of Z or S, the normalized distance along the trajectory. To sum up, both at the cathode and farther along the trajectory, the reason for the basic difficulties which occur is that, with the independent variable used, a derivative of one of the parameters of interest can becomes excessively large, or even infinite.

In Sec. 2.4, by using the transit time of an electron along its trajectory as the independent variable, a number of space-charge-flow solutions were obtained from the Lorentz equation of motion. An important property of these solutions was that all the derivatives of the potential ϕ with respect to time were finite. Consequently, if the method of separation of variables could be applied directly to the Lorentz equation with time as the independent variable, it might be expected that a space-charge-flow solution would not lead to the usual difficulties in a numerical computation.

For simplicity, the previous example of normal congruent flow in a cylindrical polar coordinate system is used to illustrate the application of the separation-of-variables method to the Lorentz equation of motion. It will become apparent as the analysis is carried out that no assumptions are made which limit the technique to normal congruent flow, and that it is a simple matter to generalize the method to find any of the space-charge flows determined earlier in this chapter.

It was shown in Eq. (2.31) of Chap. I that if a is any scalar and **a** any vector function of the coordinates,

$$\frac{da}{dt} = (\mathbf{v} \cdot \nabla)a \qquad \text{and} \qquad \frac{d\mathbf{a}}{dt} = (\mathbf{v} \cdot \nabla)\mathbf{a} \tag{5.29}$$

Here d/dt means the rate of change following a trajectory, and the fact that the flow is steady has been used to eliminate the term in $\partial/\partial t$. If a and **a** do not depend on θ, and if **v**, **a**, have no θ component, Eqs. (5.29) become, using Eq. (3.4) of Appendix A in cylindrical polar coordinates,

$$\frac{da}{dt} = v_r \frac{\partial a}{\partial r} + v_z \frac{\partial a}{\partial z} \tag{5.30a}$$

and $$\frac{d\mathbf{a}}{dt} = v_r \frac{\partial \mathbf{a}}{\partial r} + v_z \frac{d\mathbf{a}}{dz} \tag{5.30b}$$

If $v_\theta \neq 0$, or **a** has a θ component, Eq. (5.30b) is modified, but a similar relation can be obtained. However, in the differential equation derived when the parameters of the flow have the form of Eq. (4.35), Eq. (5.30) is always satisfied, and any partial differential with respect to r can be written as

$$\frac{\partial}{\partial r} \equiv \frac{1}{v_r}\frac{d}{dt} - \frac{v_z}{v_r}\frac{\partial}{\partial z} \tag{5.31}$$

From the form of the solution given in Eq. (4.35), or its unnormalized form, the variation with z of the parameters of interest is known. Consequently, partial differentiation with respect to r can always be expressed in terms of total differentiation with respect to time t. The Lorentz equations of motion for this problem are

$$\frac{dv_z}{dt} = -\eta E_z \qquad \text{and} \qquad \frac{dv_r}{dt} = -\eta E_r \tag{5.32}$$

If all the parameters of interest are considered functions of time along the trajectory, it follows from Eq. (5.31) that

$$E_z = -\frac{\partial \phi}{\partial z} = -2m\phi \tag{5.33a}$$

and $$E_r = -\frac{\partial \phi}{\partial r} = -\frac{1}{v_r}\frac{d\phi}{dt} + \frac{2mv_z}{v_r}\phi \tag{5.33b}$$

By the same process, Poisson's equation, or the divergence equation, is written as

$$2mE_z + \frac{1}{v_r}\frac{dE_r}{dt} + \frac{E_r}{r} - \frac{2mv_z}{v_r}E_r = \frac{\rho}{\epsilon_0} \tag{5.34}$$

The equation of continuity can be transformed in much the same manner. However, because the integration is along a trajectory, it is more convenient to use the continuity equation in the form of Eq. (4.38) to write

$$r i_r = r_c i_{rc} \tag{5.35}$$

where i_{rc} is the cathode current density at the intersection r_c of the trajectory of interest with the cathode. Since

$$i_r = -\rho v_r \tag{5.36}$$

Eq. (5.34) can be written in the form

$$2mE_z v_r r + \frac{dE_r}{dt} + \left(\frac{v_r}{r} - 2mv_z\right) E_r = \frac{r_c i_{rc}}{\epsilon_0} \tag{5.37}$$

To complete the defining equations of the flow, we write

$$v_r = \frac{dr}{dt} \quad \text{and} \quad v_z = \frac{dz}{dt} \tag{5.38}$$

The set of first-order ordinary differential equations and algebraic equations is suitable for solution on a computer and allows determination of all the parameters of interest. It can be shown by comparison with the solutions in Section 2, or by substitution in the set of equations (5.32) to (5.38), that near the cathode the potential variation is quadratic with respect to time; i.e.,

$$\phi \propto t^2 \tag{5.39}$$

It follows that all the derivatives of ϕ with respect to time t are finite or zero. This is true for all the other parameters involved in the computation. Consequently, with this type of solution, after normalization, numerical integrations can be performed directly from the cathode. This method of analysis is applicable to the more complicated type of solutions for skew-congruent and noncongruent flow. Moreover, in complicated coordinate systems, the equations of motion in terms of time are far simpler than their equivalent equations in terms of distance. Consequently, the process of deriving these equations becomes much simpler, mistakes are far less liable to occur* and there is now no necessity to carry out complicated algebraic analyses to find the series form of the solution near the cathode. If the trajectory becomes parallel to one of the coordinate lines of the system, there is no difficulty with numerical integration.

The separation-of-variables solution in terms of time along the trajectory is only one of many possible ways of finding suitable forms for a numerical solution. For instance, it is possible to

*Particular care should be taken in deriving the equation analogous to Eq. (5.30b); $(\mathbf{v} \cdot \nabla)\mathbf{a}$ does not, in general, have components $(\mathbf{v} \cdot \nabla) a_i$ [Eq. (2.12) of Appendix B].

formulate the equations of flow in terms of distance along the trajectory rather than in terms of time along the trajectory. This method of solution can obviate the difficulties with turning points on the trajectory, but not those which are due to infinite space charge at the cathode. It is therefore the opinion of the authors that the method of integration with respect to time is, in general, by far the most important and convenient approach to all space-charge-flow problems.

REFERENCES FOR CHAPTER II

1. Kino, G. S., and K. J. Harker: Space Charge Theory for Ion Beams, *Microwave Lab. Rept.* 779, Stanford University, Stanford, Calif., 1961.
2. Harker, K. J., and D. S. Colburn: Exact Solutions of the Equations of Space Charge Limited Flow, *Microwave Lab. Rept.* 858, Stanford University, Stanford, Calif., 1961.
3. Childs, C. D.: Discharge from Hot CaO, *Phys. Rev.*, vol. 32, p. 495, 1911.
4. Pierce, J. R.: Rectilinear Flow in Electron Beams, *J. Appl. Phys.*, vol. 11, p. 548, 1940.
5. Kino, G. S.: A New Type of Crossed-field Gun, *Trans. IRE*, vol. ED-7, p. 179, 1960.
6. Midford, T. A., and G. S. Kino: Some Experiments with a New Type of Crossed-field Gun, *Trans. IRE*, vol. ED-8, p. 324, 1961.
7. Midford, T. A., and G. S. Kino: Experiments with a New Type Adiabatic Crossed-field Gun, *Trans. IRE*, vol. ED-9, p. 431, 1962.
8. Kino, G. S., and N. Taylor: Design and Performance of a Magnetron Injection Gun, *Trans. IRE*, vol. ED-9, p. 1, 1962.
9. Okoshi, T.: An Improved Design Theory of a Magnetron Injection Gun, *Trans. IEEE*, vol. ED-11, p. 349, 1964.
10. Rosenblatt, J.: Three-dimensional Space Charge Flow, *J. Appl. Phys.*, vol. 31, p. 1371, 1960.
11. Meltzer, B.: Single-component Space Charge Flow, *J. Electronics*, vol. 2, p. 118, 1956.
12. Eisenhart, L. P.: "Treatise on the Differential Geometry of Curves and Surfaces," Dover Publications, Inc., New York, 1960.
13. Goldstein, I.: "Classical Mechanics," Addison-Wesley Publishing Company, Inc., Cambridge, Mass., 1950.
14. Gabor, D.: Dynamics of Electron Beams, *Proc. IRE*, vol. 33, p. 792, 1945.
15. Kirstein, P. T., and G. S. Kino: A Solution to the Equations of Space Charge Flow by the Method of Separation of Variables, *J. Appl. Phys.*, vol. 29, p. 1758, 1958.
16. Kirstein, P. T.: Curvilinear Space Charge Flow with Application to Electron Guns, *Microwave Lab. Rept.* 440, Stanford University, Stanford, Calif., 1958.
17. Kirstein, P. T., R. Kantor, and J. Szego: Numerical Solution to the Space Charge Limited Flow Obtained by the Separation of Variables Method, *Microwave Rept.* 714, Stanford University, Stanford, Calif., 1960.
18. Kino, G. S., and K. J. Harker: Space Charge Theory for Ion Beams, *Progr. in Astronautics and Rocketry*, vol. 5, *Electrostatic Propulsion*, Academic Press Inc., New York, 1961.
19. Waters, W. E.: Azimuthal Electron Flow in a Spherical Diode, *J. Appl. Phys.*, vol. 30, p. 368, 1959.
20. Dryden, V.: Exact Solutions to Space-charge Flow in Spherical Coordi-

nates with Application to Magnetron Injection Guns, *J. Appl. Phys.*, vol. 33, p. 3118, 1962.
21. Poritsky, H., and R. P. Jerrand: An Integral Case of Electron Motion in Electric and Magnetic Fields, *J. Appl. Phys.*, vol. 23, p. 928, 1952.
22. Kirstein, P. T.: Some Solutions to the Equations of Steady Space Charge Flow in Magnetic Fields, *J. Electronics and Control*, vol. 7, p. 417, 1959.
23. Waters, W. E.: A Theory of Magnetron Injection Guns, *Trans. IEEE.*, vol. ED-10, p. 226, 1963.

PROBLEMS

1. Assume that all electrons are emitted from a cathode with uniform initial velocity v_{Tc} normal to the cathode. Suppose that a planar diode with such an electron source were run space-charge-limited. Then a virtual cathode would establish itself at a distance z_m from the real cathode. From $z = 0$ to $z = z_m$ there would be two-stream flow. From $z = z_m$ to $z = z_0$, the diode spacing, there would be single-stream flow. Assuming that $\phi = -\phi_m$ at $z = z_m$, the potential minimum; $\phi = \phi_0$ at $z = z_0$; and the saturation current density of the cathode is i_c: find an expression for the anode current density i_0 in terms of ϕ_0 and v_{Tc}. Also, find expressions relating x_m and ϕ_m to ϕ_0, i_0, and v_{Tc}. For $i_c = 0.5$ amp/cm^2, $z_0 = 1$ cm, $\phi_0 = 500$ volts, $v_T = 1.5 \times 10^7$ cm/sec, find z_m and ϕ_m. This value of v_{Tc} is of the right order for a cathode temperature of 800°C.

Hint: Let $i_0/i_c = \alpha$. First find ϕ_m, z_m in terms of α and i_0. This may be done by solving only for the region $0 < x < x_m$. In order to find the numerical result required, it is reasonable to assume that $\phi_m \ll \phi_0$ and $z_m \ll z_0$.

2. Derive the equations for rectilinear flow in a planar diode assuming that there is an initial velocity v_c and that the field at the cathode E_c is not zero (thermally limited emission). Show that far from the cathode the potential still varies as $z^{4/3}$. Consider the space-charge-limited case with $E_c = 0$. Show that the solution can be written in the form

$$i_0 = {}^4\!/_9\, \epsilon_0\, (2\eta)^{1/2} \frac{\phi^{3/2}}{z^2}\, F\left(\frac{\phi_c}{\phi}\right)$$

where

$$2\eta\phi_c = v_{Tc}^2$$

and

$$F\left(\frac{\phi_c}{\phi}\right) = \left[1 - \left(\frac{\phi_c}{\phi}\right)^{1/2}\right]\left[1 + 2\left(\frac{\phi_c}{\phi}\right)^{1/2}\right]^2$$

Plot $F(\phi_c/\phi)$ as a function of ϕ_c/ϕ and show that the current found by assuming $\phi_c/\phi = 0.001$ is 10 per cent higher than it would be with the assumption $\phi_c = 0$.

3. The two sets of orthogonal equiangular spirals

$$r \exp k\theta = \exp\,[(k^2 + 1)q_2] \qquad r \exp(-\theta/k) = \exp\left(\frac{k^2+1}{k}\, q_1\right)$$

form a suitable set of coordinates for a space-charge flow in which the electron trajectories are the curves q_2 = constant and the surfaces of constant action are $W(q_1)$ = constant. Find q_1 and q_2 in terms of θ and r. By writing $(d\ell)^2 = (r\,d\theta)^2 + (dr)^2 = h_1^2 dq_1^2 + h_2^2 dq_2^2$, show that $h_1 = h_2 = \exp(kq_1 + q_2)$. Find a suitable differential equation for $Q = \partial W/\partial q_1$, and show how the current density at the cathode varies with q_2.

4. Show, by working in an orthogonal curvilinear coordinate system, that the usual planar-diode approximation of Eq. (3.17) is valid near the cathode when the flow is skew-congruent. Why is this result still true when there is a normal magnetic field at the cathode? It is convenient to choose the vector potential **A** so that it has the form $\mathbf{A} = (A_1, 0, 0)$ near the cathode.

5a. Consider a skew-congruent flow in a uniform magnetic field B. Assume that the action function W may be expressed in the additive form $W = \alpha x^2 + \beta y^2 + 2\gamma xy + \delta y + v_0 z$, where α, β, γ, δ, and v_0 are constants. By taking the form of the vector potential to be $\mathbf{A} = (0, Bx, 0)$, show that the charge density in this type of flow is uniform, and find its value in terms of α, β, γ, δ, and $\omega_H = \eta B$. Find the condition between α and β, γ, δ, v_0, and ω_H for which this flow reduces to one with electron trajectories which are circles in the xy plane. This is known as Brillouin flow, and is discussed in Chap. IV.

5b. Determine conditions for the flow to reduce to that of a crossed-field beam with the electrons flowing parallel to the cathode $x = 0$ (take $v_0 = 0$).

5c. Express the parabolic flow from a cathode (with an initial velocity) in terms of the W given here.

5d. Show that there are generalizations of this flow in which the electron trajectories in the xy plane are conic sections and the charge density is constant.

6. By using the Lorentz equation of motion directly, determine the motion of electrons in a potential field of the form $\phi = Cxy = (C/2)r^2 \sin 2\theta$ and a uniform magnetic field in the z direction. From your result find an analytic form for the action function W of the space-charge-free flow of Eqs. (4.47) and (4.54).

7. It is known that there is a possible normal congruent flow from a conical cathode ($\theta = \theta_0$) in which the electrons flow along the surface of a sphere. Using the method of separation of variables, write down the form of the action function W for this case. Find a differential equation for W or $\partial W/\partial\theta$. Show that this is precisely the differential equation for the flow that you would obtain by working in an orthogonal curvilinear coordinate system based on the electron trajectory surfaces.

8. For the conditions of Prob. 7, determine an ordinary differential equation for the velocity of an electron along its trajectory, with the time of flight along the trajectory as an independent variable.

9a. Derive an expression relating the electron-plasma frequency and the cyclotron frequency for the crossed-field flow discussed in subsection 2.3.

9b. Show that the particular initial velocity given by Eq. (2.26) [or that given by Eq. (5.25) in the case of flow from a conical cathode] makes the plasma frequency and the cyclotron frequency equal at the cathode.

III

Paraxial-ray Equations

1. INTRODUCTION

The exact solutions of static space-charge-flow configurations of Chap. II are limited in number and scope. Practical electron-gun and focusing systems require design control over a number of competing properties simultaneously, but it is seldom that all the properties of the exact solutions are optimum for any given application. In addition, the mathematical procedures used to derive the exact solutions do not allow the estimation of the consequences of permitting a flow pattern to deviate in some small detail from the mathematical ideal.

In this chapter, first-approximation formulas, suitable for analyzing certain perturbations in guns or focusing systems, are developed. These formulas are referred to as paraxial-ray equations. In later chapters, these equations will be applied to a detailed study of focusing systems, and it will be shown also how these same equations may be used to obtain approximate gun designs, having certain desirable prescribed properties.

The basic approach of paraxial-ray analysis is to work in terms of a coordinate system based on one trajectory of the flow. For a round solid beam, this would be the central axis. In other cases, the central trajectory of the flow is not rectilinear, and thus forms a curvilinear axis. It is assumed in paraxial-ray theory that the electron trajectories are such that electron velocities in a direction normal to the ray axis are small compared with velocities parallel to the ray axis. In addition, it is usually convenient to express the solution of Poisson's and Laplace's equations for the scalar magnetic potential in terms of the values of the electrostatic potential and magnetic field on the ray axis. To do this an expansion procedure is used in which it is assumed that distances normal to the ray axis are small and therefore only first-order terms in this quantity are required. Although the results obtained by this procedure are only approximate, it is possible to obtain certain useful relations between the flow parameters. Thus a final paraxial-ray equation is obtained which relates the thickness of the beam, the current in the beam, the curvature of the ray axis, and the potential variation along the ray axis. Any three of these quantities may be specified; the fourth then follows from the solution of the paraxial-ray equations. A great deal of flexibility can be obtained, therefore, in design procedures based on the use of paraxial-ray equations.

Paraxial-ray theory may be applied to electron beams from two rather different points of view. First, solutions of the paraxial-ray equation applicable to a given focusing system may be taken to represent the extreme boundary of the entire beam; in this case, the paraxial equation may be considered to be the approximate equation of motion of electrons moving on the bounding surface of the beam. A second type of paraxial approximation may be considered as the equation of motion of a single electron moving inside an established beam, where by inside we mean in the region occupied by the electrons of the established beam. Both types of paraxial equation are discussed in this chapter.

The outstanding advantage of the paraxial method is that it is ideally suited to the study of perturbations in a beam, particularly of the effects created by varying the initial conditions of a space-charge flow at some selected entrance plane of a focusing system. The outstanding weakness is that the paraxial method is only approximate, and it is usually difficult to establish the range of validity of the equation when applied to a particular focusing system.

Section 2 is devoted to the derivation of the paraxial equation for the bounding surface of an axially symmetric solid beam, including both space charge and an axially symmetric magnetic field. The development is based upon the use of Lagrange's equation, a direct and rigorous method for deriving equations of motion, independent of the congruence or noncongruence of the flow. In Section 3 a similar treatment is given for sheet beams in a two-dimensional magnetic field.

Of great importance in paraxial theory is an idealization of a physical beam, known as the laminar-beam model. According to this model, all trajectories in a beam for which paraxial analysis is assumed valid are geometrically similar. This, and related items, are discussed in Section 4.

In Section 5, the paraxial equation applicable to the inside of a solid axially symmetric beam is derived. Solutions of this equation are discussed in terms of a 2×2 matrix, a formalism developed still further in later chapters. In Section 6 the paraxial-ray equation for crossed-field curvilinear sheet beams is derived. Section 7 is concerned with hollow (i.e., annular) beams. Electron lenses are discussed in Section 8 from a phenomenological point of view, supplemented by the derivation of certain properties of electron lenses, based upon paraxial theory.

The use of paraxial theory as applied to electron-gun design is discussed in Section 9. Three examples are discussed in detail; these are the radial space-charge flow between coaxial cylinders, the radial space-charge flow between concentric spheres, and an axially symmetric electrostatic flow in which it is assumed that the beam converges exponentially with respect to axial position. Finally, in Section 10, a simple, but very useful, solution is given for a drifting round solid beam and a drifting sheet beam in a region devoid of both magnetic fields and axial-potential variations. The solutions of these problems lead to universal beam-spread curves for beams drifting in a field-free region.

2. PARAXIAL EQUATION FOR THE BOUNDING SURFACE OF A ROUND SOLID BEAM WITH A RECTILINEAR AXIS

2.1. Mathematical Preliminaries. In Section 5 of Chap. I, it was shown that the action-function formalism is valid only if the flow is congruent. Although the presence of flux through the cathode introduces vorticity into the flow, and as a result the mathematical treatment is considerably complicated, paraxial equations are still useful for the analysis of trajectories moving near to a reference trajectory. The paraxial equations may be derived elegantly from Lagrange's equations, which are independent of the value of the normal component of magnetic flux at the cathode.* In this section, Lagrange's equations are used to derive the paraxial equations for an axially symmetric solid beam. The magnetic field need not be uniform; a finite flux density may appear at the cathode; and the only restriction imposed upon the ray-axis-potential variation is that it be positive and twice-differentiable.

The Lagrangian for a conservative electromagnetic system may be stated in the form

$$\mathfrak{L} = \mathfrak{T} - q\phi + q\mathbf{v} \cdot \mathbf{A} \tag{2.1}$$

where $\mathfrak{T}$ = kinetic energy, $q\phi$ = potential energy, $\mathbf{A}$ = vector potential, whose curl represents the applied axially symmetric magnetic field.

It is assumed that both the potential ϕ and the charge density ρ may be expanded in the vicinity of the ray axis in an infinite power series. Axial symmetry is also assumed, leading to the conclusion that both ϕ and ρ are even functions of the off-axis radius r. Thus we are led to the relations

$$\phi(r,z) = a_0(z) + r^2 a_2(z) + r^4 a_4(z) + \cdots \tag{2.2}$$

and

$$\rho(r,z) = b_0(z) + r^2 b_2(z) + r^4 b_4(z) + \cdots \tag{2.3}$$

*An analysis based on Lagrange's equations can be used also to derive rigorously higher order equations, which can be used to calculate lens aberrations; this subject is not discussed in this book.

where z is distance along the axis, and the a's and b's are functions of z to be determined such that ϕ and ρ satisfy Poisson's equation. In the axially symmetric system of Fig. 3.1 being considered, this equation has the form

$$\frac{1}{r}\frac{\partial}{\partial r}\left(r\frac{\partial\phi}{\partial r}\right)+\frac{\partial^2\phi}{\partial z^2}=-\frac{\rho}{\epsilon_0} \tag{2.4}$$

Upon inserting Eqs. (2.2) and (2.3) into Eq. (2.4) and collecting the coefficients of each power of r, one is led to the result

$$\left(4a_2 + a_0'' + \frac{b_0}{\epsilon_0}\right)+r^2\left(16a_4 + a_2'' + \frac{b_2}{\epsilon_0}\right)+\cdots \tag{2.5}$$

where the double prime (″) denotes d^2/dz^2.

If Eq. (2.5) is to be true at any arbitrary radius r, the coefficient of each power of r must vanish, leading to the relations

$$a_2 = -\tfrac{1}{4}\left(a_0'' + \frac{b_0}{\epsilon_0}\right) \tag{2.6}$$

and $$a_4 = -\tfrac{1}{16}\left(a_2'' + \frac{b_2}{\epsilon_0}\right) \tag{2.7}$$

Referring to Eqs. (2.2) and (2.3), it is clear that, on the ray axis, r = 0, the potential is given by

$$\phi(0,z) = a_0(z) \equiv \Phi(z) \tag{2.8}$$

and the charge density is given by

$$\rho(0,z) = b_0(z) \equiv \rho_0(z) \tag{2.9}$$

These two equations define $a_0(z)$ and $b_0(z)$. Using Eqs. (2.6) to (2.9) in Eqs. (2.2) and (2.3), the expressions for $\phi(r,z)$ and $\rho(r,z)$ become

$$\phi(r,z) = \Phi(z) - \frac{r^2}{4}\left[\Phi''(z) + \frac{\rho_0(z)}{\epsilon_0}\right] \tag{2.10}$$

and $$\rho(r,z) = \rho_0(z) \tag{2.11}$$

In these relations all terms needed in the first-order paraxial theory have been included. It is important to note that only the axial value

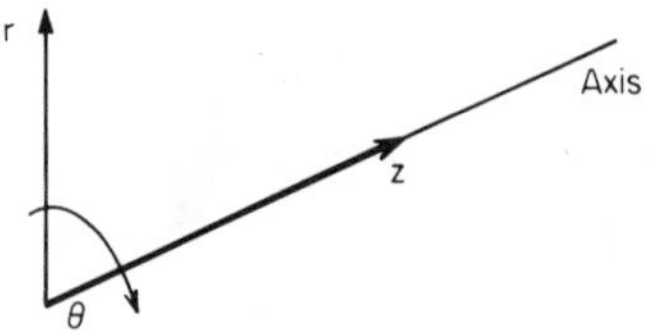

Fig. 3.1. The cylindrical coordinate system for round beams.

of the charge density is required. Stated otherwise, first-order paraxial theory makes no use of off-axis charge-density variations, though, as we shall see, the charge density may be allowed to vary, and in general will vary, from point to point along the ray axis. In the (r,θ,z) coordinate system of Fig. 3.1, we assume that there is no θ component of magnetic field. Using Eq. (2.19) of Appendix A, the magnetic vector potential **A** can be written $(0,A,0)$, and has the form*

$$\mathbf{A} = \left(0, \frac{r}{2}\,\mathcal{B}(z) - \frac{r^3}{16}\,\mathcal{B}''(z) + \cdots, 0\right) \tag{2.12a}$$

Here $\mathcal{B}(z)$ is the magnetic field flux density on the axis

$$\mathcal{B}(z) \equiv B_z(0,z) \tag{2.12b}$$

Usually the argument is dropped, and $\mathcal{B}(z)$ is written $\mathcal{B}$.

2.2. Detailed Derivation of the Paraxial Equation. If x_i is any one of the coordinates of the system, Lagrange's equation for the ith equation of motion is

$$\frac{d}{dt}(\partial\mathcal{L}/\partial\dot{x}_i) - \partial\mathcal{L}/x_i = 0 \tag{2.13}$$

In Eq. (2.13), the x_i is any one of the coordinates (r,θ,z) of Fig. 3.1. Applying Lagrange's equation first to the z coordinate, we have

$$\frac{d}{dt}\frac{\partial\mathcal{L}}{\partial\dot{z}} - \frac{\partial\mathcal{L}}{\partial z} = 0$$

where $\mathcal{L} = \frac{1}{2}\,m(\dot{r}^2 + \dot{z}^2 + r^2\dot{\theta}^2) - q(\phi - r\dot{\theta}A)$. This equation leads to the equation of motion in the z direction,

$$\ddot{z} - \eta\left(\frac{\partial\phi}{\partial z} - r\,\dot{\theta}\,\frac{\partial A}{\partial z}\right) = 0 \tag{2.14}$$

where z pertains to the paraxial electron. Suppose we let $z_0(t)$ represent the motion of an electron which moves on the ray axis, and $z_1(t)$ represent the axial perturbation of the paraxial electron at corresponding times; that is, let $z = z_0 + z_1$. Note also, that the partial derivatives appearing in Eq. (2.14) are to be evaluated at the position of the paraxial electron; these derivatives may be obtained in the form of a power series expansion about the unperturbed position $(0,z_0)$. Thus one obtains the expression

$$\frac{\partial\phi}{\partial z} = \left(\frac{\partial\phi}{\partial z}\right)_{z_0} + \left(\frac{\partial^2\phi}{\partial z^2}\right)_{z_0} z_1 + \left(\frac{\partial^2\phi}{\partial z\,\partial r}\right)_{z_0} r + \cdots \tag{2.15}$$

where "$(\ )z_0$" denotes "evaluated at z_0 on the ray axis." Similar expressions can be derived for the derivatives of A.

*It can be verified from the equations of Appendix A, or Ref. 2, that for this form of **A** the components of $\nabla \times \mathbf{B}$ are zero.

Upon using Eq. (2.12), it is seen that $\partial A/\partial z = r\mathcal{B}'/2 + \ldots$, so that $r\dot{\theta}(\partial A/\partial z)$ is of the second order in r, and hence will be neglected.

From the zero-order terms, we obtain the relation

$$\ddot{z}_0 - \left(\eta \frac{\partial \phi}{\partial z}\right)_{z_0} = 0 \tag{2.16}$$

which simply states that the acceleration of an electron along the ray axis is governed only by the axial electric field.

Next, the first-order terms may be combined to yield the result,

$$\ddot{z}_1 - \eta\left[\left(\frac{\partial^2 \phi}{\partial z^2}\right)_{z_0} z_1 + r\left(\frac{\partial^2 \phi}{\partial z \partial r}\right)_{z_0}\right] = 0$$

but upon using Eq. (2.10), we find that, at $r = 0$, $\partial^2\phi/(\partial z \partial r) = 0$, and therefore the perturbed equation is

$$\ddot{z}_1 - \eta z_1 \Phi'' = 0 \tag{2.17}$$

where $\Phi(z)$ is the potential and $\rho_0(z)$ the charge density on $r = 0$.

A similar derivation may be used to obtain the r equation of motion. When necessary, $\partial\phi/\partial r$ is expanded in a series about the unperturbed position. There are no zero-order terms in this expansion, and so we are led to the result

$$\ddot{r} - r\,\dot{\theta}^2 + \eta\, r\left(\mathcal{B}\dot{\theta} + \tfrac{1}{2}\Phi'' + \frac{\rho_0}{\epsilon_0}\right) = 0 \tag{2.18}$$

where Φ means ϕ on the ray axis, $\phi\,(0,z)$, and the double prime denotes d^2/dz^2. In the same way, ρ_0 denotes ρ on the ray axis. This equation shows a coupling between the radial and azimuthal motion, due to the centrifugal-force components and the $\mathbf{v} \times \mathbf{B}$ forces. This problem cannot completely be solved until an expression for the azimuthal motion is obtained. Therefore Lagrange's equations must be used a third time, letting $x_i = \theta$.

In making use of Lagrange's formalism, so far only zero- and first-order terms have been retained. In the θ equation, however, there are no zero- or first-order terms, and therefore the second-order terms must be retained. This may seem artificial, since second-order terms have not been retained previously. But whatever the order, the lowest-order terms for the perturbed motion have been retained, and just this will be done for the θ equation.

The Lagrangian is independent of θ because of the axial symmetry, and $\partial\mathcal{L}/\partial\dot{\theta}$ is given by the expression

$$\frac{\partial \mathcal{L}}{\partial \dot{\theta}} = mr^2\dot{\theta} + qrA \approx mr^2\dot{\theta} + qr^2\mathcal{B}/2$$

Hence Eq. (2.13) becomes

$$\frac{d}{dt}\left(mr^2\dot{\theta} + \frac{qr^2\mathcal{B}}{2}\right) = 0 \tag{2.19}$$

which is immediately integrable. The initial conditions are taken to be that $\dot{\theta} = 0$ where $r = r_0$ and $B(0,z) = B_0$. For example, the initial point may be at the cathode, but it is not essential to choose the initial coordinates in this fashion. The integral of Eq. (2.19) then may be written

$$\dot{\theta} = \frac{\eta}{2}\left(\mathcal{B} - \frac{\mathcal{B}_0 r_0^2}{r^2}\right) \tag{2.20}$$

a result which also follows from Busch's theorem [Eq. (3.8) of Chap. I].

A useful substitution is obtained upon making use of the energy equation to eliminate the axial potential Φ in terms of the axial velocity V; it is also to be noted that, in a short time interval dt, an electron will move an axial distance $dz = V\,dt$. Substitution of this relation, the energy relation $V^2 = 2\eta\Phi$, and Eq. (2.20) into Eq. (2.18) leads to the paraxial equation

$$\ddot{r} + \frac{r\ddot{V}}{2V} + \frac{\eta^2}{4}\left(r\mathcal{B}^2 - \frac{\mathcal{B}_0^2 r_0^4}{r^3}\right) + \frac{\eta\, r\rho_0}{2\epsilon_0} = 0 \tag{2.21}$$

A second useful substitution is obtained upon eliminating t explicitly in terms of z. A second application of the relation $dz = V\,dt$ allows the transformation

$$\frac{d^2F}{dt^2} = V\frac{d}{dz}\left(V\frac{dF}{dz}\right) \tag{2.22}$$

where F is any function of t, and hence z. Application of the energy equation results in the expression

$$\frac{d^2F}{dt^2} = \eta\left(2\Phi\frac{d^2F}{dz^2} + \frac{d\Phi}{dz}\frac{dF}{dz}\right) \tag{2.23}$$

where, as usual, Φ denotes ϕ on the ray axis.

Upon substituting Eqs. (2.20) and (2.23) into Eq. (2.18), one obtains the paraxial equation

$$2r''\Phi + r'\Phi' + \frac{r}{2}\left(\Phi'' + \frac{\rho_0}{\epsilon_0} + \frac{\eta\mathcal{B}^2}{2}\right) - \frac{\eta B_0^2 r_0^4}{4r^3} = 0 \tag{2.24}$$

It is convenient to express ρ in terms of the beam current I, the radius r, and either the axial potential Φ or the axial velocity V. It has been shown that, within the first-order paraxial approximation, the charge density ρ may be taken to be a constant at any cross-section plane z = constant. The axial current density may therefore be approximated by $\rho_0 V = -I/\pi r^2$, where I is the magnitude of the total current enclosed within the radius r, and the minus sign has been introduced because the sign of electron current density in the direction of motion of the electrons is negative. Upon solving for ρ_0

from the above relation, the final form of the paraxial equation is obtained; i.e.,

$$2r''\Phi + r'\Phi' + r\left(\frac{\Phi''}{2} + \frac{\eta \mathcal{B}^2}{4}\right) - \frac{\eta \mathcal{B}_0^2 r_0^4}{4r^3} - \frac{I}{2\pi\epsilon_0(2\eta\Phi)^{1/2}r} = 0 \qquad (2.25)$$

The same substitution for ρ_0 in Eq. (2.21) leads to the paraxial-equation form

$$\ddot{r} + \frac{r\ddot{V}}{2V} + \frac{\eta^2}{4}\left(r\mathcal{B}^2 - \frac{\mathcal{B}_0^2 r_0^4}{r^3}\right) - \frac{I}{2\pi\epsilon_0 r V} = 0 \qquad (2.26)$$

2.3. Discussion of Paraxial Forces. In an axially symmetric focusing system of the type described and analyzed in the preceding paragraphs, there are four off-axis forces acting in the radial direction:

1. An electric-lens force, proportional to Φ''. The radial electric force is simply qE_r. However, because the potential must satisfy either Laplace's or Poisson's equation, it is found that, for small radial displacements, the radial electric field E_r at a given axial position is proportional to the axial value of Φ'' at the same axial position. To the extent that E_r increases linearly with r, the electric-lens force will be proportional to $r\Phi''$.

2. A centrifugal force mv_θ^2/r, acting always to accelerate the paraxial electron away from the ray axis, i.e., in the positive r direction. Because of Eq. (2.20), the centrifugal force is

$$\mathfrak{F}_{\text{centrifugal}} = \frac{q^2}{4m}\left(r\mathcal{B}^2 - \frac{2\mathcal{B}\mathcal{B}_0 r_0^2}{r} + \frac{\mathcal{B}_0^2 r_0^4}{r^3}\right) \qquad (2.27)$$

3. The Lorentz magnetic force $q(\mathbf{v} \times \mathbf{B})_r = qv_\theta B_z$. It is then easily found that the Lorentz force is given by

$$\mathfrak{F}_{\text{Lorentz}} = -\frac{q^2}{4m}\left(2r\mathcal{B}^2 - \frac{2\mathcal{B}\mathcal{B}_0 r_0^2}{r}\right) \qquad (2.28)$$

4. The space-charge force $qr\rho_0/\epsilon_0$. For a given value of ρ_0 the space-charge force increases linearly with r, up to the beam boundary. The beam boundary by definition surrounds a constant current I, so that ρ_0 must vary as r^{-2}. Thus, for a given beam current, the space-charge force itself, at the outer beam boundary, is inversely proportional to r.

A fact of substantial importance in magnetic focusing systems is that the resultant of the centrifugal force, i.e., the sum of Eqs. (2.27) and (2.28), contains only terms in which the square of the magnetic fields $\mathcal{B}$ and $\mathcal{B}_0$ occurs. Also, the resultant is just half the Lorentz force itself, and is always directed toward the radius

$r = r_0[|\mathcal{B}_0/\mathcal{B}|]^{1/2}$. Thus the net restoring force due to the magnetic field is insensitive to the signs of either the cathode field $\mathcal{B}_0$ or the off-cathode field $\mathcal{B}$. However, inspection of Eq. (2.20) reveals that the angular velocity is in fact very sensitive to a reversal of the sign of either $\mathcal{B}$ or $\mathcal{B}_0$. More will be said of this matter in Chap. IV.

2.4. Assumptions Inherent in Paraxial Theory. Throughout the derivation of the basic paraxial equation (2.21), terms involving $\dot{r}^2$, and all higher-order terms in $\dot{r}$, were neglected. Now, if the total speed of an electron is v and the radial speed is $\dot{r}$ (Fig. 3.2), the sine and cosine of the slope angle ψ, relative to the ray axis, are $\dot{r}/v$ and $(v^2 - \dot{r}^2)^{1/2}/v$; the latter is approximately $1 - \frac{1}{2}(\dot{r}^2/v^2)$. At this point we must be consistent in neglecting terms in $\dot{r}^2$ and conclude that the cosine of the slope angle is nearly unity. To this approximation the sine of ψ is small compared with unity, and the axial velocity V equals the total velocity v.

In summary, paraxial theory contains two underlying assumptions:

1. Throughout the focusing system, the slope of a paraxial electron, relative to the ray axis, is sufficiently small so that the axial velocity is perturbed only to second order by the presence of the radial velocity.

2. The paraxial electron is always sufficiently close to the ray axis so that the electric-lens force is proportional to the radial position r; the force due to space charge is the same as if the transverse space-charge distribution were uniform, at least as far from the axis as the radial position of the electron. Comparison of Eq. (2.20) and the general form of Busch's theorem [Eq. (3.8) of Chap. I] also implies that, in the paraxial theory, the axial magnetic flux density at a given axial position is assumed to be essentially independent of radial position, at least out to the paraxial position r.

These restrictions must be kept in mind when the paraxial-ray equation is applied to an analysis of any focusing system. From a mathematical point of view, correct solutions of a given paraxial equation may always be obtained in principle, regardless of the choice made for the off-axis position r or the slope r′ at some reference plane. However, before such solutions may be said to represent accurately the paraxial behavior of electrons, it must be verified that the restrictions underlying the paraxial equation itself have not been violated.

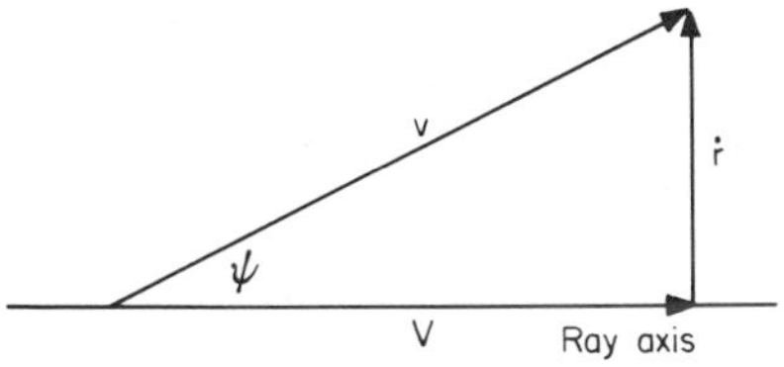

Fig. 3.2. Diagram of radial, axial, and total velocities.

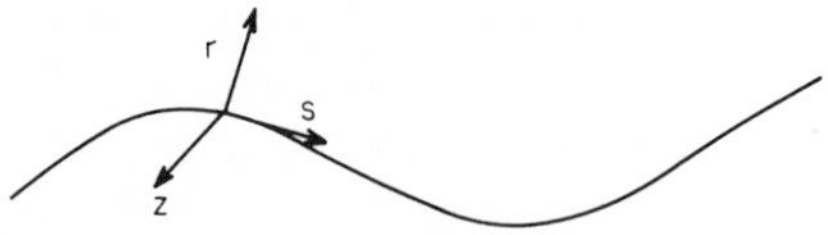

Fig. 3.3. Rectangular coordinate system for sheet beams.

3. PARAXIAL EQUATION FOR THE BOUNDING SURFACE OF SHEET BEAMS

Let us now proceed to the derivation of the paraxial equation for the sheet-beam equivalent of the problem considered in Section 2, again making use of Lagrange's equations.

The geometrical arrangement for the sheet beam with a variable axial magnetic field is shown in Fig. 3.3. Here the coordinates are (s,r,z) and the magnetic field has components B_r and B_s, but not B_z. Using Eq. (2.19) of Appendix A, the magnetic vector potential **A** has the form*

$$\mathbf{A} = \left[0,\ 0,\ r\,\mathcal{B}(s) - \frac{r^3\mathcal{B}''(s)}{6} + \cdots\right] \tag{3.1}$$

and the value of B_s on the axis is $\mathcal{B}(s)$, which is usually written $\mathcal{B}$.

The magnetic field is symmetric with respect to the ray axis, and the kinetic energy is $(m/2)(\dot{r}^2 + \dot{s}^2 + \dot{z}^2)$. A derivation similar to that which led to Eq. (2.10) yields the potential series

$$\phi(r,s) = \Phi(s) - \frac{r^2}{2}\left[\Phi''(s) + \frac{\rho_0}{\epsilon_0}\right] + \cdots \tag{3.2}$$

where $\Phi(s)$ is the potential $\phi(r,s)$, and ρ_0 is the space-charge density on the axis $r = 0$.

Upon using Lagrange's equation for the s component, the following zero- and first-order expressions are obtained:

$$m\,\ddot{s}_0 + q\Phi' = 0 \tag{3.3}$$

$$m\,\ddot{s}_1 + q\left[\left(\frac{\partial^2\phi}{\partial s^2}\right)_{s_0} s_1 - r\,\dot{z}\,\mathcal{B}'\right] = 0 \tag{3.4}$$

For the r component, one obtains

$$m\,\ddot{r} - q\left[r\left(\Phi'' + \frac{\rho_0}{\epsilon_0}\right) + \mathcal{B}\,\dot{z}\right] = 0 \tag{3.5}$$

There is no zero-order equation pertaining to the r motion.

Proceeding as in Section 2, where the θ equation was derived, the equation for the z motion is found; this equation is integrable, subject to the assumed initial condition that $\dot{z} = 0$ where $r = r_0$ and

*It can be verified from the equations of Appendix A, or Ref. 2, that for this form of **A** the components of $\nabla \times \mathbf{B}$ are zero.

$\mathcal{B} = \mathcal{B}_0$. Neither zero-order nor first-order terms are found. One therefore obtains

$$\dot{z} = \eta(r\,\mathcal{B} - r_0\,\mathcal{B}_0) \tag{3.6}$$

This may be substituted into Eq. (3.5) to eliminate $\dot{z}$. Also, use may be made again of Eq. (2.23). The charge density may be eliminated in terms of the total current I per unit beam width to yield the final paraxial equation

$$2r''\Phi + r'\Phi' + r(\Phi'' + \eta\,\mathcal{B}^2) - \eta r_0 \mathcal{B}\mathcal{B}_0 = \pm\frac{I}{2\epsilon_0(2\eta\,\Phi)^{1/2}} \tag{3.7}$$

It is to be noted that, unlike Eq. (2.25), Eq. (3.7) appears to be linear in r, regardless of the presence of either magnetic flux at the cathode or a finite current. This appearance is deceptive, however. If Eq. (3.7) is considered to be the equation of motion of an electron on an outer extremity of the beam, recognition must be made of the fact that the space-charge force is always directed away from the ray axis. Therefore, on opposite sides of the ray axis, the algebraic sign of the space-charge term must be reversed. In using Eq. (3.7) to follow a given electron, the space-charge term must be taken with a + sign where $r > 0$, and with a − sign where $r < 0$; thus, although Eq. (3.7) is piecewise-linear, it has most of the characteristics of a nonlinear equation.

4. THE LAMINAR-BEAM MODEL

The paraxial equations which were derived in the preceding sections pertained explicitly to those electrons moving on a beam boundary. Under certain conditions, the same equations may be used to describe the motion of electrons within the beam boundaries; these conditions are considered in this section. In addition, the permissible transverse variation of the charge density is discussed.

The most important equations of the derivation in Section 2, Eqs. (2.24) and (2.25), are to be interpreted as the equations of motion of an electron which moves in the vicinity of the ray axis, such that the paraxial approximation is a valid representation of its motion. In deriving the equations, however, it was not necessary to single out any particular electron; the equation applies to any electron sufficiently close to the axis and moving always at a small angle relative to the axis.

As it stands, Eq. (2.24) is applicable to an electron which has the coordinate r_0 at the cathode. If the equation is divided by r_0 and a new symbol μ is introduced in place of r/r_0, a universal equation, independent of the initial coordinate r_0, results, provided I varies suitably with radius. This new equation is therefore applicable to <u>all</u> electrons for which the paraxial method itself is valid. If μ is the solution of the normalized paraxial equation, subject to a given set of initial conditions, the solution for any particular electron is just $r_0\mu$, which is proportional to r_0. Thus all trajectories may be represented by the same function, multiplied by a scale parameter r_0. This is a way of stating that all trajectories described by the paraxial equation will be geometrically similar, once the initial conditions of a single electron of the beam are prescribed. A consequence of this condition is that the slope of any electron, at any position z, is proportional to the displacement r of that electron from the ray axis. A further consequence is that crossing of trajectories is not permissible, except at a point lying on the ray axis. Of course, to be permissible solutions in this sense, the initial slopes of the different trajectories must also be proportional to r.

A further implication of the above statement is pertinent. Consider a layer of the beam which, at some position z_1, has an inner bound r_1 and an outer bound $r_1 + \Delta r_1$. Consider at the same time the layer which has the bounds $r_1 + \Delta r_1$ and $r_1 + 2\Delta r_1$, respectively. At some point s_2 further along the beam, these layers will have moved so that their "thicknesses" have changed from the initial value Δr_1 to some new value $k\,\Delta r_1$. It follows that each of the two layers must carry a constant current, for the geometrical similarity of the trajectories precludes the possibility that electrons from a given layer can move into any other layer. Therefore, from the fact that the layer thicknesses have changed by the same factor, it follows that, however the charge density varies across the beam at the initial position, the same variation must hold at any other position. The absolute value of the charge density may vary from point to point along the ray axis, as the potential on the axis is allowed to vary, but the transverse variation of the charge density must always be represented by the same function of r.

In the derivation which led to Eq. (2.25) [or Eq. (3.7)], it was shown that only the axial term for ρ was needed. Therefore the effect of transverse variations in space-charge density on the electric field are ignored to the paraxial approximation. Thus we are led to the conclusion that the beam must have geometrically similar trajectories, relative to the ray axis, and a constant charge density with regard to any transverse variation. The motion of particles within a beam which is paraxially thin, but not laminar in the sense of the above definition, is treated in the next section.

A final word concerning the space-charge term in the various paraxial equations is in order. In these equations, in the form of Eq. (2.25), it is the total current of the beam which appears in the space-charge terms, and the equations per se pertain to an electron at a beam boundary. It has been noted that the same equations also pertain to an electron moving between the axis and the outer edge. Therefore, if a particle distant r_1 from the axis initially is being studied, a current $(r_1^2/r_0^2)I$ is required for the space-charge term in axially symmetric solid beams, and $(r_1/r_0)I$ in sheet beams.

5. THE PARAXIAL EQUATIONS INSIDE A SOLID AXIALLY SYMMETRIC BEAM

5.1. Introduction. In Sections 2 and 3, the paraxial equations were derived for the beam boundary of a paraxially thin beam. To the same approximation, in Section 4, the similar equations were shown to hold for particles inside the beam, provided the initial slope had a prescribed dependence on initial distance from the axis. In this section this last condition is relaxed; we assume the existence of a particular solution of Eq. (2.25) and derive an approximate equation; its solutions may be taken to represent the possible trajectories of a single electron moving within the boundaries of the particular beam. It is shown that the paraxial equation to be derived is linear, and hence its solutions may be represented in terms of a simple 2×2 matrix. This formulation is very useful in later chapters.

5.2. Derivation of the Equations. Since we will be concerned with rotation of the paraxial electron, as well as its radial and axial motion, it is necessary to derive equations for all three components of the motion. It is particularly convenient to proceed with the derivation in cartesian coordinates (x,y,z). Only the lowest-order terms needed in each step of the derivation are retained.

From Eq. (2.10) it is easily verified that the vector electric field is given by the relation

$$\mathbf{E} = (x\Psi,\ y\Psi,\ -\Phi') \tag{5.1}$$

where $$\Psi = \tfrac{1}{2}\left[\phi''(0,0,z) + \frac{\rho(0,0,z)}{\epsilon_0}\right] = \tfrac{1}{2}\left(\Phi'' + \frac{\rho_0}{\epsilon_0}\right) \tag{5.2}$$

where Φ and ρ_0 are again the values of ϕ and ρ on the axis. Also, from Eq. (2.12), it may be verified that the vector magnetic field is given by

$$\mathbf{B} = [-\tfrac{1}{2}\, x\,\mathcal{B}'(z),\ -\tfrac{1}{2}\, y\mathcal{B}'(z),\ \mathcal{B}(z)] \tag{5.3}$$

where, as usual, a prime denotes d/dz. It is assumed that, from the particular solution of Eq. (2.25), the charge density is a known function of axial position z. We write the function $\mathcal{B}(z)$ usually as $\mathcal{B}$.

Upon substituting Eqs. (5.1) and (5.3) into the Lorentz force equation [Eq. (2.15) of Chap. I], expanding in cartesian coordinates, and using the following relations for the Larmor frequency ω_L,

$$\omega_L = \frac{\eta\mathcal{B}}{2} \qquad \dot{\omega}_L = \frac{d\omega_L}{dt} = \frac{\eta\dot{z}\mathcal{B}'}{2} \tag{5.4}$$

the following forms of the x and y equations of motion are obtained:

$$\ddot{x} = -\eta x\Psi - 2\dot{y}\omega_L - y\dot{\omega}_L \tag{5.5}$$

$$\ddot{y} = -\eta y\Psi + 2\dot{x}\omega_L + x\dot{\omega}_L \tag{5.6}$$

The s equation is not required.

The complex substitution

$$w = x + jy \tag{5.7}$$

transforms Eqs. (5.5) and (5.6) into the combined equation

$$\ddot{w} = (-\eta\Psi + j\dot{\omega}_L)\, w + 2j\omega_L \dot{w} \tag{5.8}$$

As it has been defined, w is the complex transverse position of a paraxial electron.

It will be convenient to work in a frame of reference rotating at the Larmor frequency ω_L. Consequently, we put

$$w = x + jy = \Gamma e^{j\vartheta} = (\xi + j\chi)\, e^{j\vartheta} \tag{5.9}$$

where $$\vartheta = \int_0^z \omega_L \, dt \tag{5.10}$$

We note that, to the limits of accuracy of the paraxial approximation,

$$\vartheta = \int_0^z \frac{\omega_L}{(2\eta\Phi)^{1/2}} \, dz \tag{5.11}$$

In the rotating system, Eq. (5.8) can be written

$$\ddot{\Gamma} + \Gamma(\eta\Psi + \omega_L^2) = 0 \tag{5.12}$$

It is seen that, in the rotating coordinate system, the electron behaves as if there is a restoring force toward the axis of value $\Gamma\omega_L^2/\eta$, in addition to the forces due to the electric field.

The transverse velocity in the rotating coordinate system is u, where

$$u = \dot{\Gamma} \tag{5.13}$$

and from Eq. (5.12),

$$\dot{u} = -\Gamma\,(\eta\Psi + \omega_L^2) \tag{5.14}$$

These equations may also be expressed in terms of the z coordinate and written as follows:

$$\Gamma' = Vu \tag{5.15}$$

and $$u' = -V(\eta\Psi + \omega_L^2)\Gamma \tag{5.16}$$

where V is the velocity on the axis $(2\eta\Phi)^{1/2}$.

Equations (5.13) and (5.14) and Eqs. (5.15) and (5.16) are pairs of first-order equations, which are linear whether or not there is flux threading the cathode, i.e., whether or not $\omega_{Lc} \neq 0$ at $s = 0$. On the contrary, the paraxial equation defining the beam boundary [Eq. (2.25)] is nonlinear whenever there is flux present at the cathode or there is space charge in the beam. The equations developed here are quite different, however, for they only define the motion of electrons inside the beam; moreover, they are for the complex displacements and velocities Γ, u.

5.3. The Matrix Formulation. The pairs of linear first-order equations, Eqs. (5.13) and (5.14) and Eqs. (5.15) and (5.16), have two independent solutions. Suppose we denote these by Γ_1, u_1 and Γ_2. u_2, respectively. Then it may easily be shown by substitution in either Eqs. (5.13) and (5.14) or Eqs. (5.15) and (5.16) that

$$\frac{d}{dt}(\Gamma_1 u_2 - \Gamma_2 u_1) = 0 \qquad (5.17)$$

It follows, therefore, upon integration that the Wronskian

$$\Gamma_1 u_2 - \Gamma_2 u_1 = \text{constant} \qquad (5.18)$$

throughout the beam.

It is convenient to choose two linearly independent principal solutions of Eqs. (5.13) and (5.14). These are given, respectively, by the initial conditions

$$\Gamma_1(0) = 1 \qquad u_1(0) = 0 \qquad (5.19)$$

and $$\Gamma_2(0) = 0 \qquad u_2(0) = 1 \qquad (5.20)$$

In writing Eqs. (5.19) and (5.20), the initial plane (0) is any reference plane; it is often convenient to choose this plane to coincide with the cathode surface, but such a choice is not necessary.

We denote the principal solutions, then, by

$$\Gamma_1(t) = \mu(t) \qquad u_1(t) = \dot{\mu}(t)$$

and $$\Gamma_2(t) = \nu(t) \qquad u_2(t) = \dot{\nu}(t) \qquad (5.21)$$

It will be seen that $\mu(t)$ is the magnification of the beam and $\nu(t)$ is related to the stiffness of the beam, defined in Chap. IV. Since the coefficient of Γ in Eq. (5.14) is real, $\mu, \nu, \dot{\mu}, \dot{\nu}$ are all real functions of time.

The complete solution for any choice of initial conditions can be obtained by linear superposition. For the initial conditions $\Gamma = \Gamma(0)$, $u = u(0)$, the solution is most conveniently expressed in the matrix form

$$\begin{bmatrix} \Gamma \\ u \end{bmatrix} = \begin{bmatrix} \mu & \nu \\ \dot{\mu} & \dot{\nu} \end{bmatrix} \begin{bmatrix} \Gamma(0) \\ u(0) \end{bmatrix} \qquad (5.22)$$

It follows from Eqs. (5.18), (5.19), and (5.20) that the matrix in Eq. (5.22) must have a unit determinant, i.e., that the Wronskian for μ and ν is

$$\mu\dot{\nu} - \dot{\mu}\nu = 1 \qquad (5.23)$$

Because the ray axis of this paraxial system is rectilinear, the change in transverse position due to small changes in the initial longitudinal velocity v_z will be of the order $v_z\Gamma$, $v_z u$. Consequently, this can be neglected to first order in Γ. However, if the ray axis were curved, the longitudinal-velocity terms would become of importance. In this case it follows by linear superposition that the matrix-transformation laws would take the form

$$\begin{bmatrix}\Gamma\\ u\end{bmatrix} = \begin{bmatrix}\mu & \nu\\ \dot{\mu} & \dot{\nu}\end{bmatrix}\begin{bmatrix}\Gamma(0)\\ u(0)\end{bmatrix} + \begin{bmatrix}\Omega\\ \dot{\Omega}\end{bmatrix} v_s \tag{5.24}$$

where Ω and $\dot{\Omega}$ are quantities which depend on s, the distance along the ray axis, through the curvature and the form of the electromagnetic fields. For hollow beams or sheet beams with a straight ray axis, $\Omega = \dot{\Omega} = 0$, but $\mu, \dot{\mu}, \nu, \dot{\nu}$ are related to the fields through slightly different formulas than those defined above. However, the form of the matrix formula is that of Eq. (5.22).

For the cylindrical beam dealt with above, Eq. (5.9) may be used with Eq. (5.22) to find w. It follows from Eq. (5.9) that

$$\dot{w} = v_w = (u + j\omega_L\Gamma)\, e^{j\vartheta} \tag{5.25}$$

where $\quad v_w = v_x + jv_y$

or in matrix form,

$$\begin{bmatrix}w\\ v_w\end{bmatrix} = e^{j\vartheta}\begin{bmatrix}1 & 0\\ j\omega_L & 1\end{bmatrix}\begin{bmatrix}\Gamma\\ u\end{bmatrix} \tag{5.26}$$

$$\begin{bmatrix}\Gamma\\ u\end{bmatrix} = e^{-j\vartheta}\begin{bmatrix}1 & 0\\ -j\omega_L & 1\end{bmatrix}\begin{bmatrix}w\\ v_w\end{bmatrix} \tag{5.27}$$

where $v_w = \dot{w}$.

It follows from Eqs. (5.22), (5.24), and (5.27) that

$$\begin{bmatrix}w\\ v_w\end{bmatrix} = e^{j\vartheta}\begin{bmatrix}1 & 0\\ j\omega_L & 1\end{bmatrix}\begin{bmatrix}\mu & \nu\\ \dot{\mu} & \dot{\nu}\end{bmatrix}\begin{bmatrix}1 & 0\\ -j\omega_{L0} & 1\end{bmatrix}\begin{bmatrix}w(0)\\ v_w(0)\end{bmatrix} \tag{5.28}$$

where ω_{L0} is the Larmor frequency at the plane z = 0. After taking the products of the matrices, we find that

$$\begin{bmatrix}w\\ v_w\end{bmatrix} = \begin{bmatrix}(\mu - j\omega_{L0}\nu)\, e^{j\vartheta} & \nu\, e^{j\vartheta}\\ \frac{d}{dt}\left[(\mu - j\omega_{L0}\,\nu)\, e^{j\vartheta}\right] & \frac{d}{dt}(\nu\, e^{j\vartheta})\end{bmatrix}\begin{bmatrix}w(0)\\ v_w(0)\end{bmatrix} \tag{5.29}$$

The solution with $v_w(0) = 0$ and $w(0) = 1$ is $w = (\mu - j\omega_{L0}\nu)\, e^{j\vartheta}$. It is convenient to define two new quantities given by

$$\mathfrak{M} = (\mu - j\omega_{L0}\nu)\, e^{j\vartheta}$$
$$\mathfrak{N} = \nu\, e^{j\vartheta} \tag{5.30}$$

where $|\mathfrak{M}| = M = (\mu^2 + \omega_{L0}^2\nu^2)^{1/2}$
$$|\mathfrak{N}| = N = \nu \tag{5.31}$$

Consequently, Eq. (5.28) may be written in the simple form

$$\begin{bmatrix} w \\ v_w \end{bmatrix} = \begin{bmatrix} \mathfrak{M} & \mathfrak{N} \\ \dot{\mathfrak{M}} & \dot{\mathfrak{N}} \end{bmatrix} \begin{bmatrix} w(0) \\ v_w(0) \end{bmatrix} \tag{5.32}$$

Thus the quantity M corresponds to the magnification of a beam leaving the plane z = 0 with zero transverse velocity. Similarly, the solution with $v_W(0) = 1$, $w(0) = 0$ is $w = \mathfrak{N}$. The distance from the axis after time t of an electron leaving the axis with unit initial transverse velocity is therefore $|w| = r = N(t)$, and is related to the stiffness of the beam.

It is to be noted that, in general, the principal solutions of Eq. (5.32) yield complex values of w, even though the μ, ν are real. This implies that the trajectory is undergoing a rotation about the ray axis. It is often required to know the Wronskian of the transformation of Eq. (5.32). It follows from Eqs. (5.23) and (5.30) that

$$\mathfrak{M}\dot{\mathfrak{N}} - \dot{\mathfrak{M}}\mathfrak{N} = \exp(2j\vartheta) \tag{5.33}$$

5.4. An Illustrative Example. As an example of the use of the theory developed above, let us consider an axially symmetric system in which the potential has the constant value ϕ_0, the magnetic field has the constant value B_0, and the current vanishes. Then, from Eq. (5.2), $\Psi = 0$; from Eq. (5.10), $\vartheta = \omega_L t$. Equations (5.13) and (5.14) therefore yield the principal solutions

$$\mu = \cos\omega_L t \qquad \dot{\mu} = -\omega_L \sin\omega_L t$$
$$\nu = \frac{1}{\omega_L}\sin\omega_L t \qquad \dot{\nu} = \cos\omega_L t \tag{5.34}$$

The matrix equation (5.22) therefore becomes

$$\begin{bmatrix} \Gamma(t) \\ u(t) \end{bmatrix} = \begin{bmatrix} \cos\omega_L t & \frac{1}{\omega_L}\sin\omega_L t \\ -\omega_L\sin\omega_L t & \cos\omega_L t \end{bmatrix} \begin{bmatrix} \Gamma(0) \\ u(0) \end{bmatrix} \tag{5.35}$$

By using the transformation of Eq. (5.29), it follows that

$$\begin{bmatrix} w(t) \\ v_W(t) \end{bmatrix} = \begin{bmatrix} 1 & \frac{j}{2\omega_L}(1 - \exp 2j\omega_L t) \\ 0 & \exp 2j\omega_L t \end{bmatrix} \begin{bmatrix} w(0) \\ v_W(0) \end{bmatrix} \tag{5.36}$$

Equation (5.36) represents the undamped oscillation of the individual electrons at a radian frequency $2\omega_L$, that is, at the cyclotron frequency of the magnetic field. This is the behavior to be expected of a unipotential round beam in a uniform magnetic field; the theory of this type of beam will be developed in great detail in Chap. IV. The solution for the motion of individual electrons given by Eq. (5.36) is exact: with uniform magnetic field and no space charge, the assumptions used in paraxial analysis have not been invoked.

6. CURVILINEAR SHEET BEAMS

6.1. Introduction. The paraxial-ray equation for a sheet beam possessing a rectilinear ray axis and including a two-dimensional magnetic field was derived from Lagrange's equation in Section 3. This section is concerned with the paraxial equation for a more general sheet-beam configuration. In the derivation to follow, the magnetic field is assumed uniform and perpendicular to the plane containing any given trajectory. In addition, the restriction that the ray axis is rectilinear is removed, and instead we impose the much less stringent condition that the curvature of the ray axis must be an analytic function of arc length along the axis (Fig. 3.4).

There are many specialized focusing systems to which the paraxial equation to be derived in this section is applicable. Among these may be listed:

1. Planar crossed-field focusing, in which the ray axis is assumed to be a rectilinear equipotential
2. Electrostatic deflection focusing, in which the ray axis is assumed to be an equipotential and the curvature is assumed to be a periodic oscillatory function of arc length
3. Centrifugal electrostatic focusing, in which the ray axis is assumed to be an equipotential circle
4. Cyclotron focusing, in which the ray axis is assumed to be circular and a uniform magnetic field is present
5. Periodic electrostatic systems with a rectilinear ray axis

Because of the length of the derivation, only an outline is presented here; however, sufficient detail is given so that the interested reader should experience no fundamental difficulty in supplying the missing steps.

6.2. Establishment of the Metric. The focusing system for which

Fig. 3.4. A curvilinear sheet beam with a crossed magnetic field.

the ray equation is to be derived is assumed to be uniform in one spatial direction, designated by the coordinate z. The magnetic field is assumed to be uniform and entirely in the z direction. Because the potential is independent of z, the field component E_z vanishes. One may therefore show, from the Lorentz equation of motion, that d^2z/dt^2 vanishes; hence an electron will drift with constant velocity in the z direction. With no loss in generality the drift velocity is ignored in the following paragraphs.

The type of beam being considered is one in which each electron executes a trajectory in an (r,s) plane which is normal to the magnetic field. In the paraxial derivation the existence of a reference trajectory, or ray axis, is assumed. A second-order differential equation of motion is obtained, solutions of which represent the trajectory of a second electron relative to the ray axis.

In general, the ray axis is curvilinear. It is convenient to construct a curvilinear orthogonal coordinate system such that one coordinate axis lies along the ray axis, the second axis is normal to the first, and the third is normal to the first two and coincides with the magnetic field direction (Fig. 3.5). Distances along, and normal to, the ray axis are designated by s and r, respectively.

The point O is a reference point on the ray axis; O′ is an off-axis point lying a distance r from O; point P is separated by distances ds′ and dr in the s and r directions, respectively, from O′. Point Q is the center of curvature of the ray axis at O; the distance OQ = R = $1/\kappa$, where R is the radius of curvature at O, and κ is the curvature itself. R and κ are positive if O lies in the positive r direction from O, and negative otherwise.

It is clear that $(d\ell)^2 = (ds')^2 + (dr)^2$. Furthermore,

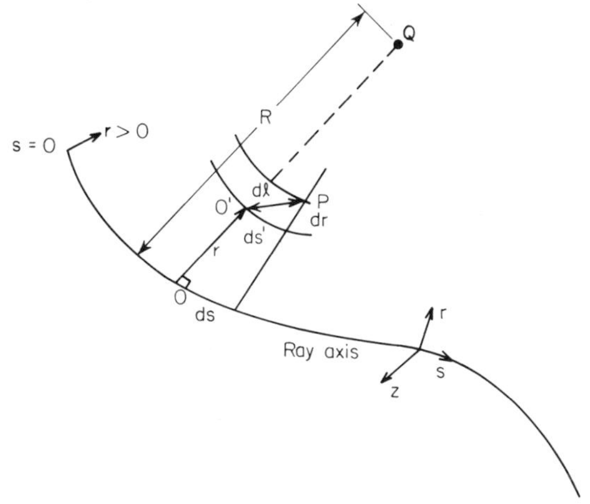

Fig. 3.5. Diagram of the coordinate system for curvilinear sheet beams.

$ds'/ds = (R - r)/r = 1 - \kappa r$, or $ds' = ds\,(1 - \kappa r)$. From these considerations it follows that the metric equation is

$$(d\ell)^2 = (ds)^2(1 - \kappa r)^2 + (dr)^2 + (dz)^2 \tag{6.1}$$

where we have included the condition that the planes containing O′ and P′ are separated by a distance dz in the z direction. Thus in general orthogonal curvilinear coordinates $dq_1 = ds$, $dq_2 = dr$, $dq_3 = dz$ and $h_1 = 1 - \kappa r$, $h_2 = 1$, $h_3 = 1$. Equation (6.1) can be used to formulate Lagrange's equation in the (s,r,z) coordinate system. In addition, we shall need Poisson's equation and the vector curl relation **B** = curl **A**. The expressions for these in general curvilinear coordinates are derived in Appendix A.

6.3. Lagrange's Equation for r. Lagrange's equation was presented in Section 2, in Eq. (2.13). It may be verified from Eq. (2.9) of Appendix A that the vector potential in the (s,r,z) coordinate system of Fig. 3.5,

$$\mathbf{A} = \left(-\frac{B_Z r}{2}, \frac{B_Z s}{2}, A_Z\right) \tag{6.2}$$

where B_Z = constant and A_Z is independent of z, represents the most general magnetic field uniform in the z direction. The components of the magnetic field **B** are

$$\mathbf{B} = \left(\frac{\partial A_Z}{\partial r}, -\frac{1}{1-\kappa r}\frac{\partial A_Z}{\partial s}, B_Z\right) \tag{6.3}$$

It is this **B** which is used in the subsequent analysis.

The kinetic energy $\mathfrak{I}$ is $(m/2)(d\ell/dt)^2$, or, from Eq. (6.1),

$$\mathfrak{I} = \frac{m}{2}\left[\dot{s}^2(1 - \kappa r)^2 + \dot{r}^2 + \dot{z}^2\right] \tag{6.4}$$

where the dot ($\dot{}$) signifies d/dt; the potential energy is $q\phi(s,r)$, where the electric potential ϕ is some continuously differentiable function of both s and r. Finally, it is easy to show that

$$\mathbf{v}\cdot\mathbf{A} = \frac{B_Z}{2}\left[s\dot{r} - r\dot{s}(1 - \kappa r)\right] + \dot{z}\,A_Z$$

The Lagrangian may now be written as

$$\mathfrak{L} = \frac{m}{2}\left[\dot{s}^2(1 - \kappa r)^2 + \dot{r}^2 + \dot{z}^2\right] - q\phi(s,r) - q\,\frac{B}{2}\left[r\dot{s}(1 - \kappa r) - s\dot{r}\right] + q\dot{z}A_Z \tag{6.5}$$

From Eqs. (2.13) and (6.5), three equations of motion for s, r, and z may be obtained. The z equation of motion is, using the $\mathfrak{L}$ of Eq. (6.5) in Eq. (2.13), and letting $x_i = z$,

$$\frac{d}{dt}(\dot{z} - \eta A_Z) = 0$$

which can be integrated to give

$$\dot{z} = \eta\, A_Z \tag{6.6}$$

Provided there is no magnetic field normal to the cathode, A_Z can be chosen to be zero on this surface, so that the constant of integration in Eq. (6.6) is zero. Equation (6.6) is the two-dimensional version of Busch's theorem [Eq. (3.12) of Chap. I].

The r equation of motion is

$$\ddot{r} + [\dot{s}^2\,\kappa(1-\kappa r) - \eta B_Z \dot{s}(1-\kappa r)] + \eta\dot{z}\,\frac{\partial A_Z}{\partial r} - \eta\,\frac{\partial \phi}{\partial r} = 0 \tag{6.7}$$

where the functions inside the brackets are evaluated at an arbitrary point (s,r,z); refer to Fig. 3.6. The values of these functions on the ray axis at s are known, and will be little changed at the point (s,r,z). Therefore we express the parameters as a power series in r, namely,

$$\begin{aligned}
\phi &= \Phi(s) + r\,\Phi_1(s) + \tfrac{1}{2}r^2\,\Phi_2(s) + \cdots \\
A_Z &= \mathcal{A}(s) + r\,\mathcal{A}_1(s) + \tfrac{1}{2}r^2\,\mathcal{A}_2(s) + \cdots \\
\dot{s} &= V(s) + r\,\dot{s}_1(s) + \cdots \\
\kappa &= \kappa_0(s) + r\,\kappa_1(s) + \cdots \\
\rho &= \rho_0(s) + r\,\rho_1(s) + \cdots
\end{aligned} \tag{6.8}$$

Here all the functions Φ_i, A_i, etc., depend only on s, and Φ, $\mathcal{A}$, V, κ_0 are the values of the appropriate functions on the ray axis.

From Poisson's equation, using the expression for the Laplacian of Eq. (2.11) of Appendix A, ρ is given by

$$-\frac{\rho}{\epsilon_0} = \frac{1}{1-\kappa r}\left\{\frac{\partial}{\partial s}\left(\frac{1}{1-\kappa r}\,\frac{\partial \phi}{\partial s}\right) + \frac{\partial}{\partial r}\left[(1-\kappa r)\,\frac{\partial \phi}{\partial r}\right]\right\} \tag{6.9}$$

Substituting from Eq. (6.8) and keeping only terms in r^0, Eq. (6.9) gives

$$\phi_2 = \kappa_0\,\Phi_1 - \Phi'' - \frac{\rho_0}{\epsilon_0} \tag{6.10}$$

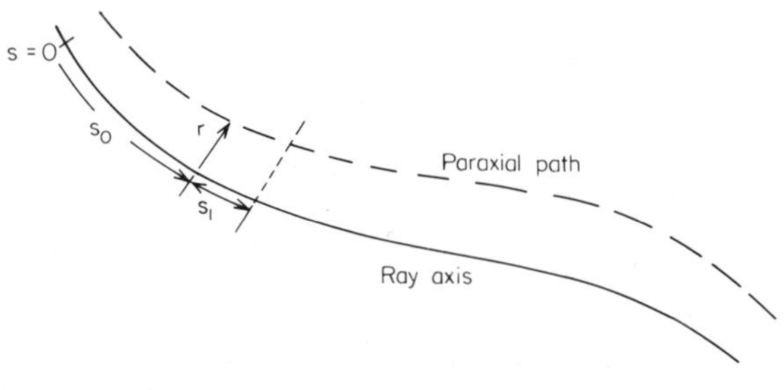

Fig. 3.6. Schematic of ray axis and off-axis trajectories.

Similarly, from $(\nabla \times \mathbf{B})_z = 0$, using the expression for $\nabla \times$ of Eq. (2.9) of Appendix A,

$$\mathcal{A}_2 = \kappa_0 \mathcal{A}_1 - \mathcal{A}'' \tag{6.11}$$

From Eqs. (6.3) and (6.8), the magnetic field **B** has components on the ray axis,

$$(\mathbf{B})_{r=0} = (\mathcal{A}_1, -\mathcal{A}', B_z) \tag{6.12}$$

The conservation-of-energy equation is

$$(1 - \kappa r)^2 \dot{s}^2 + \dot{r}^2 + \dot{z}^2 - 2\eta\phi = 0 \tag{6.13}$$

Comparing terms of order r^0 and r and using Eqs. (6.6) and (6.8), one obtains the result

$$V^2 + \eta^2 \mathcal{A}^2 = 2\eta\Phi \tag{6.14}$$

and $$V \dot{s}_1 - \kappa_0 V^2 + \eta^2 \mathcal{A}\mathcal{A}_1 = \eta\Phi_1 \tag{6.15}$$

The substitution of Eqs. (6.6), (6.8), and (6.15) into Eq. (6.7) and the collection of terms in r^0 give

$$V^2 \kappa_0 - \eta B_z V + \eta^2 \mathcal{A}\mathcal{A}_1 = \eta\Phi_1 = -\eta E_{r0} \tag{6.16}$$

where E_{r0} is the normal field on the ray axis. Equation (6.16) is the condition that the ray axis is a possible trajectory, and was derived, for $\mathcal{A} = 0$, in Eq. (2.43) of Chap. I. From the terms of order r in Eq. (6.7), using Eqs. (6.6), (6.8), (6.10), (6.11), (6.15), and (6.16), we obtain the following relation

$$\ddot{r} + r\left(2 V^2 \kappa_0^2 - 2\eta\kappa_0 V B_z + \eta^2 B_z^2 + \eta\Phi'' + \eta^2\mathcal{A}_1^2 - \eta^2 \mathcal{A}\mathcal{A}'' + \frac{\eta\rho_0}{\epsilon_0}\right) = 0 \tag{6.17}$$

Several substitutions will convert Eq. (6.17) into a more useful form. From Eq. (2.22), we may write that $\ddot{r} = V^2 r'' + VV' r'$, and the charge density ρ_0 may be eliminated in terms of the current I carried by a sheet beam of thickness 2r and (constant) width ℓ (Fig. 3.4). The beam carries a total current $I = 2i_0 r\ell$; also, $i_0 = -\rho_0 V$, so that

$$\rho_0 = -\frac{I}{2\ell V r} \tag{6.18}$$

Upon substituting these quantities into Eq. (6.17), the final form of the paraxial equation is obtained, namely,

$$V^2 r'' + VV' r' + r(2V^2\kappa^2 - 2\eta\kappa V B_z + \eta^2 B_z^2 + \eta\Phi'' + \eta^2\mathcal{A}_1^2 - \eta^2\mathcal{A}\mathcal{A}'') = \frac{\eta I}{2\epsilon_0 \ell V} \tag{6.19}$$

where the subscript o has been dropped, since it is understood that

κ refers to the ray axis. It is important to note that the space-charge term appearing in the right-hand side of Eq. (6.19) is a constant independent of r [see discussion following Eq. (3.7)]. When $\mathfrak{a}$ is zero, that is, B_r is zero on the ray axis, V in Eq. (6.19) can be replaced by $(2\eta\Phi)^{1/2}$.

6.4. Discussion of the Paraxial-ray Equation. Equation (6.17), or its alternative form, Eq. (6.19), reveals the presence of seven off-axis force terms which act independently to accelerate a paraxial electron toward or away from the ray axis; it is obvious that six terms increase linearly with off-axis coordinate r, and the last, the space-charge term, is independent of r.

The space-charge term, $-\eta\rho_0 r/\epsilon_0$, in Eq. (6.17) or the right hand-side of Eq. (6.19), arises from the mutual repulsions of the electrons constituting the beam. It has already been mentioned that in a sheet beam the space-charge force on an edge-of-the-beam electron is independent of the beam thickness 2r.

The fourth off-axis term is the electric-lens force $\eta r\Phi''$. This term appears when the longitudinal field at the ray axis varies; this force tends to diverge the beam when $\Phi'' < 0$ and to converge it otherwise. The term in $2V^2\kappa_0^2$ is due to the balance between the centrifugal force and the off-axis variation of the electric force qE_r. This force is convergent whatever the curvature. If a magnetic field normal to the plane of the trajectory is present, it is necessary to give further consideration to the off-axis rate of variation of the Lorentz magnetic force, $q\mathbf{v}\times\mathbf{B}$; inclusion of this force accounts for the term $2\kappa_0 V\eta B_z r$ in Eq. (6.17).

The purely magnetic term $(\eta B_z)^2 r$ represents a pseudoforce. It may be noted that this term does not explicitly involve either ray-axis curvature or the ray-axis velocity. In order to explain this term, let us consider the planar motion of two electrons 1 and 2 in a uniform magnetic field directed normal to the plane of motion as represented in Fig. 3.7; it is assumed that the potential is uniform over the plane, so that E_{r0} vanishes everywhere, and that V is v_0 a constant. Then, from Eq. (6.16), the ray axis must be a circle having radius $r_H = \omega_H/v_0$. The length r_H is known as the cyclotron radius of the first electron, and its trajectory is the ray axis. The nearby electron (trajectory 2 in Fig. 3.7) must also move in a circular path having the same radius r_H; the uniformity of the potential and the magnetic field ensures that the trajectories may differ only in the displacement of their centers of curvature.

An observer on the ray axis, moving with velocity v_0, will observe that the off-axis electron oscillates about the ray axis; relative to the ray axis, there is a restoring force acting on the off-axis electron. Detailed analysis shows that, for values of displacement small compared with r_H, the restoring force is $r(\eta B_z)^2$, and is always directed toward the ray axis.

The term in $\mathfrak{a}_1^2$ is always focusing and is, from Eq. (6.12), the

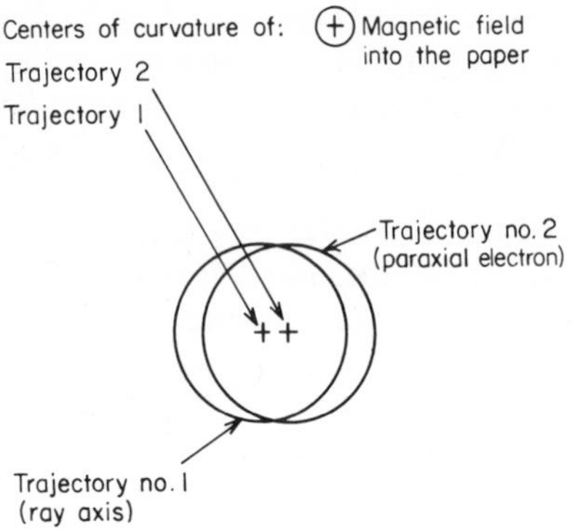

Fig. 3.7. The trajectories of electrons on an equipotential plane in a uniform magnetic field.

focusing due to the longitudinal magnetic field. The term in $\mathcal{A}\mathcal{A}''$ is related, from Eqs. (6.12) and (6.13), to $\dot{z}\ (\partial B_r/\partial s)$. It is focusing or defocusing, depending on the sign of $\dot{z}\ (\partial B/\partial s)$. The former of these two is used in periodic permanent magnet focusing (Section 2 of Chap. V), and the second in deflection focusing (Section 4 of Chap. V).

To see the significance of the other terms, it is convenient to transform coordinates to a set which allows for the change in velocity of the particle. Writing

$$S = \int V ds \qquad \text{and} \qquad R = Vr \tag{6.20}$$

the first term of Eq. (6.17) becomes

$$\ddot{r} = V^2 r'' + VV'r' = V^2\left(\frac{d^2R}{dS^2}V - R\frac{d^2V}{dS^2}\right) \tag{6.21}$$

Using Eqs. (6.14) and (6.21), Eq. (6.17) becomes, dropping the subscript o on κ,

$$\frac{d^2R}{dS^2} + \frac{R}{V^4}\left(2V^2\kappa^2 - 2\eta\kappa VB_Z + \eta^2 B_Z^2 + \right.$$
$$\left. + \eta^2\mathcal{A}_1^2 + \eta^2\mathcal{A}'^2 + 2V'^2 + \frac{\eta\rho_0}{\epsilon_0}\right) = 0 \tag{6.22}$$

With the exception of the term in ρ_0 and κB_Z, all the other terms are focusing. The form of Eq. (6.22) is particularly significant when it is remembered that the three quadratic terms in B_Z and $\mathcal{A}$ are exactly, from Eq. (6.12), $\eta^2 B^2$. Thus all magnetic field components are equally significant, and all focus with the square of their amplitude. It is this fact which leads to the importance of periodic, or deflection, focusing. In these forms of focusing, $B_Z = 0$, and in the (R,S) coordinate system, ηB_S, ηB_r, and V' are equally effective at compensating for space-charge defocusing. Of course, the curvature is related to the magnetic and electric fields by Eq. (6.16); that equation shows that the fields related to $\mathcal{A}$ can produce additional focusing due to curvature. This is the reason for the strength of the focusing produced by the deflection focusing of Section 4 of Chap. V.

Finally, a note concerning a restriction on the ray-axis curvature: Except in rare instances, the potential and all the derivatives of the potential on the ray axis in particular E_{r0}, must be analytic functions of arc length. From Eq. (6.10) it follows that the curvature of the axis itself must be an analytic function of s.

6.5. The Paraxial Equations Inside a Curvilinear Sheet Beam. It is possible to obtain expressions for the motion of a particle in strip beams which are identical in form with those derived in Section 5 for solid axially symmetric beams. Instead of using Eqs. (5.6) and (5.7), the motion of a particle inside a curvilinear beam is given by Eq. (6.17), which may be written

$$\ddot{r} + \left(4\eta\Phi\kappa^2 - 2\eta\kappa(2\eta\Phi)^{1/2}B_z + \eta^2 B_z^2 + \eta\Phi'' + \eta^2\mathcal{A}_1^2 - \eta^2\mathcal{A}\,\mathcal{A}'' + \frac{\eta\rho_0}{\epsilon_0}\right) r = 0 \tag{6.23}$$

To obtain Eq. (6.23), V^2 has been replaced by $2\eta\Phi$ and the subscript 0 has been dropped from the κ. The ρ_0 is given, from Eq. (6.18), by

$$\rho_0 = -\frac{I}{2\ell(2\eta\Phi)^{1/2} r_e} \tag{6.24}$$

where $r = r_e$ denotes the beam edge.

The analysis follows exactly the same course as that of Sec. 5.2. Equation (6.23) is linear in r and therefore has two linear solutions, $\mathfrak{M}$ and $\mathfrak{N}$, subject to the initial conditions $r(0) = 1$, $v_r(0) = 0$ and $r(0) = 0$, $v_r(0) = 1$, where $v_r = \dot{r}$. Thus, in the same way as in Section 5, it is possible to express r(t) and $v_r(t)$ in the form

$$\begin{pmatrix} r \\ v_r \end{pmatrix} = \begin{pmatrix} \mathfrak{M} & \mathfrak{N} \\ \dot{\mathfrak{M}} & \dot{\mathfrak{N}} \end{pmatrix} \begin{pmatrix} r(0) \\ v_r(0) \end{pmatrix} \tag{6.25}$$

Unlike Eq. (5.29), the $\mathfrak{M}$ and $\mathfrak{N}$ are now real. The symbols $\mathfrak{M}$ and $\mathfrak{N}$ are still retained; their numerical values are denoted by M and N, as in Eq. (5.31), so that

$$|\mathfrak{M}| = M \qquad \text{and} \qquad |\mathfrak{N}| = N \tag{6.26}$$

Since the $\mathfrak{M}$ and $\mathfrak{N}$ are already real, it is not necessary to introduce the μ and v required in Section 5. The formalism developed there may be used identically, provided ϑ and ω_{L0} are put zero in the relevant formulas.

Thus, for example, instead of Eq. (5.33), we find

$$\mathfrak{M}\dot{\mathfrak{N}} - \dot{\mathfrak{M}}\mathfrak{N} = 1 \tag{6.27}$$

The expressions are so similar to those of Section 5 that no further discussion is required.

7. ANNULAR BEAMS

7.1. Space-charge Fields in a Cylindrical System. Consider a long, cylindrically symmetric distribution of charged particles, such as electrons; the charge density may be a function of r. From the symmetry the electric field may be taken to be entirely radial at any point. In order to evaluate the field at a given radius r, Poisson's equation may be integrated over a cylindrical volume of radius r and length L, concentric with the charge distribution. Thus, by the use of Gauss' law, one obtains

$$\int_\tau \nabla \cdot \mathbf{E}\, d\tau = \frac{1}{\epsilon_0}\int_\tau \rho\, d\tau = \int_S \mathbf{E} \cdot d\mathbf{S}$$

where S is the surface of the volume of integration, and the positive direction of **S** is taken to be the positive r direction. If Q_L is the charge per unit length enclosed within radius r, one obtains the result

$$E_r = \frac{Q_L}{2\pi\epsilon_0 r} \tag{7.1}$$

Two implications of this expression are of great importance. First, Eq. (7.1) implies that at any radius of a long cylindrical electron beam, the space-charge field E_r is determined only by the total charge per unit length contained within that radius. Second, inside a hollow beam $Q_L = 0$, so that the hollow region is free of electric fields. Round electrostatic focusing systems, and round magnetic focusing systems in which the cathode is completely shielded from magnetic flux, are unsatisfactory for hollow beams. The reason is that these types of focusing systems produce a net inward force on the innermost electrons of the beam. Because this force is not balanced by a space-charge force, the inner radius of the beam will eventually collapse to zero. Thus a beam which is initially hollow on injection into the focusing system will not remain hollow. The outer beam radius will adjust itself so that, on the average, the space charge will be balanced by focusing forces.

The presence of a center rod completely changes the picture. Surface charges on the rod produce an electric field at the inner radius of an annular beam. Thus, if a center rod is acceptable or even desirable, many more types of annular-beam focusing systems are possible than if the region interior to the beam must be completely empty.

7.2. Paraxial-ray Equations for Annular Beams. If there is no electrode inside a round annular beam, Eq. (2.25) may be used to calculate the paraxial behavior of various electrons in the beam. In using Eq. (2.25), however, the current must be adjusted in accordance with the considerations discussed in Sec. 7.1; the space-charge term of the paraxial equation may include only the current enclosed by a circle having the radius of the electron under consideration.

Thus, for the electrons forming the inner boundary surface of the beam, Eq. (2.25) must be taken with I = 0. Similarly, for the outer boundary, the current I must be the total current carried by the beam.

There is nothing inherent in Eq. (2.25) which will necessarily prevent off-axis crossing of trajectories. Consequently, a hollow beam which is initially laminar may not remain so. Let us assume that, when Eq. (2.25) is used for the analysis of a hollow beam, the equation is to be solved simultaneously for N distinct regions of the beam carrying N distinct fractions of the total current. So long as no two trajectories cross, the calculations may proceed. However, if crossing of any two trajectories does occur, then beyond the crossover the currents in each of the N subbeams must be readjusted; the current term for any particular electron may be only that current enclosed by a circle having the radius of the electron.

Although it is possible to derive a paraxial-ray equation for round annular beams containing a center rod, the derivation is tedious, and the number of applications rather limited.* Provided the radius of the beam measured from the axis is large compared with either the radial thickness or the local radius of curvature of the beam, the sheet-beam equation (3.7) or (6.19) may be employed with good accuracy.

8. PHYSICAL ACTION OF A LENS

8.1. Phenomenological Description. We now consider in detail the action which takes place in a single electrostatic lens of axial symmetry. In order to simplify the discussion, space charge will be ignored. The lens depicted in Fig. 3.8 consists of two equal-diameter concentric cylinders, one being maintained at a potential Φ_a and the other at a lower potential, Φ_b. A short gap appears between the two cylinders. Figure 3.8 also includes a sketch of the potential on the axis of the system.

The acceleration of an electron moving close to the ray axis is proportional to Φ''. To the left of the gap, Φ'' is negative, so that the electron accelerates away from the axis. After passing the gap center, Φ'' becomes positive, and the electron accelerates toward the axis. Hence the lens consists of a divergent region, the region on the high-potential side of the gap center, and a convergent region, the region on the low-potential side of the gap center.

The space integral of the acceleration†, $\int \Phi''\,ds$, is almost zero. However, the potential is higher, on the average, in the divergent

---

*Such derivations, suitable for application to periodic focusing systems of various types, are carried out in Chap. V.

†In this section we denote distance along the ray axis by s irrespective of whether it is in a cylindrical or sheet-beam geometry.

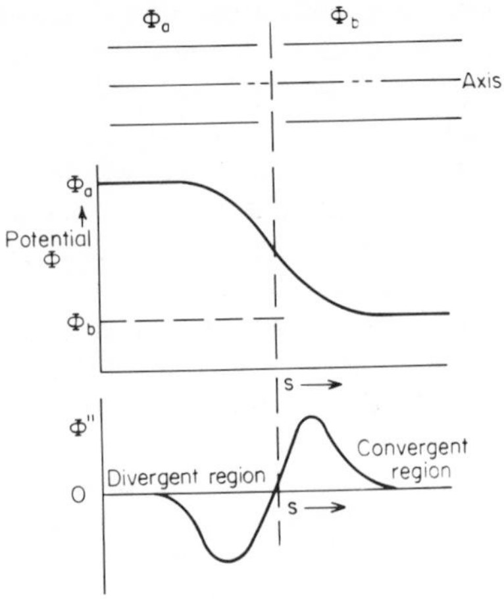

Fig. 3.8. A two-cylinder electrostatic lens, the axial potential $\Phi(z)$, and $\Phi''(z)$.

region, and lower in the convergent region. Therefore, in view of the energy equation, the electron moves faster in the axial direction while it is in the divergent region and slower while in the convergent region. Because these two regions are of nearly equal length, it follows that the acceleration is directed toward the axis for a longer time than away from the axis. It is therefore necessary to use a time-average acceleration rather than a space-average, and it follows that the time-average effect is one of convergence. In order to facilitate the understanding of this phenomenon, an actual trajectory is depicted in Fig. 3.9. The short arrows on the trajectory represent the force which accelerates the electron toward or away from the axis.

It is important to observe that a net convergent effect does not necessarily guarantee that an electron entering the lens with an arbitrary radial velocity will be moving toward the ray axis upon emerging from the lens; however, a particle entering the lens system will be deflected toward the axis.

8.2. Paraxial-ray Analysis of a Lens. It is instructive to consider the action described in the preceding section from the paraxial-

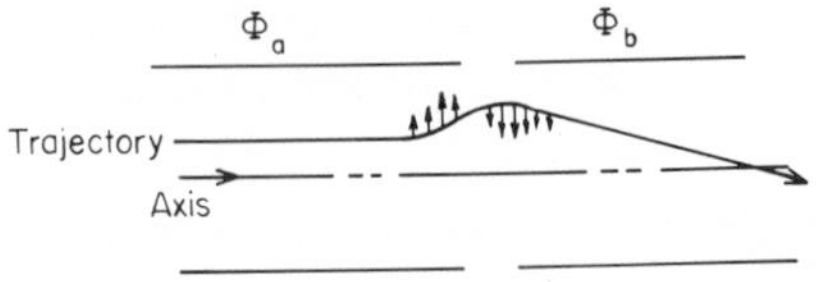

Fig. 3.9. Schematic representation of a trajectory in the two-cylinder lens. The arrows represent the radial force on the trajectory, and $\Phi_b < \Phi_a$.

equation point of view. For convenience, the appropriate equation is repeated here:

$$2\Phi r'' + \Phi' r' + \Phi'' \frac{r}{2} = 0 \tag{2.24}$$

If the substitution $R = r\Phi^{1/4}$ is made, Eq. (2.24) will transform into the equation

$$R'' = -\frac{3}{16}\left(\frac{\Phi'}{\Phi}\right)^2 R \tag{8.1}$$

Provided the lens is sufficiently weak so that r remains of one sign, e.g., positive, as the electron progresses through the lens, R will remain positive throughout the lens, since the energy equation precludes the possibility that Φ can be negative. Therefore the righthand side of Eq. (8.1) is negative throughout the lens, and the first integral requires that

$$R'_B - R'_A < 0 \tag{8.2}$$

where R'_B, R'_A are the initial and final slopes of an electron trajectory.

Let it be supposed that the lens begins and ends at axial points P and Q, at which Φ' vanishes, as shown in Fig. 3.10. The axial distance P – Q is known as the length, or thickness, of the lens. Then $R'_P = r'_P \Phi_P^{1/4}$, and $R'_Q = r'_Q \Phi_Q^{1/4}$, so that the following inequality holds:

$$r'_Q \Phi_Q^{1/4} - r'_P \Phi_P^{1/4} < 0 \tag{8.3}$$

We conclude that, if $\Phi_Q > \Phi_P$, a space-charge-free electrostatic lens is always convergent. It should be noted, however, that the assumption has been made that the motion of an electron is between field-free points. In contrast, if the space-charge forces are not negligible or the motion of the electron is not between field-free points, the lens is not necessarily convergent.

There are two important solutions of Eq. (2.24). The first class is one where the electrons enter the lens system parallel to the axis so that $r'_P = 0$ independent of r_P. It follows from Eq. (8.3) that all

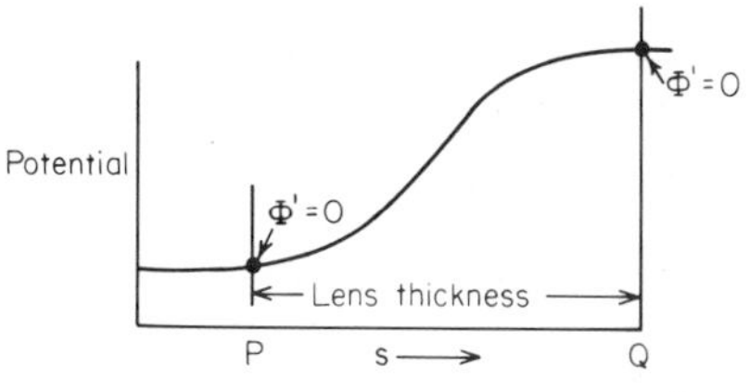

Fig. 3.10. At the end planes of a lens the axial field Φ' vanishes. In the two-cylinder lens the axial field remains zero outside the PQ region.

electrons which enter the system parallel to the axis must have a trajectory with a negative slope when they leave the lens; i.e., all such rays must bend toward the axis in passing through the lens.

It is important to note that Eq. (8.3) does not imply that the lens action is convergent at every point in the lens, but only that the net effect is convergent.

The second class represents all electrons which exit from the lens moving parallel to the axis. Again according to Eq. (8.3), all trajectories of the second class must possess a positive slope at the entrance plane P, and again, all trajectories of this class must have been bent toward the axis. Conversely, electrons entering the lens in the opposite direction with trajectories parallel to the axis are bent toward the axis. Trajectories of the two classes are illustrated in Fig. 3.11.

Equation (2.24) is a linear second-order equation in r; it is particularly convenient to define two principal solutions r_1 and r_2 of that equation by the following initial conditions:

$$\begin{aligned} r_1(0) &= 1 \qquad r_1'(0) = 0 \\ r_2(0) &= 0 \qquad r_2'(0) = 1 \end{aligned} \tag{8.4}$$

Then the linear nature of Eq. (2.24) permits the construction of the general solution and its first derivative as follows:

$$\begin{aligned} r(s) &= r(0)\, r_1(s) + r'(0)\, r_2(s) \\ r'(s) &= r(0)\, r_1'(s) + r'(0)\, r_2'(s) \end{aligned} \tag{8.5}$$

which may be put into a matrix form similar to Eq. (5.32), i.e.,

$$\begin{bmatrix} r(s) \\ r'(s) \end{bmatrix} = \begin{bmatrix} r_1(s) & r_2(s) \\ r_1'(s) & r_2'(s) \end{bmatrix} \begin{bmatrix} r(0) \\ r'(0) \end{bmatrix} \tag{8.6}$$

Suppose there exists a plane $s = F_1$ at which $r_1(F_1) = 0$. Then, from Eq. (8.5), if $r'(0) = 0$, $r(F_1) = 0$. Thus all electrons (carrying negligible current) which enter the lens flowing parallel to the axis, pass through the axial point $s = F_1$. The point $s = F_1$ is known as a

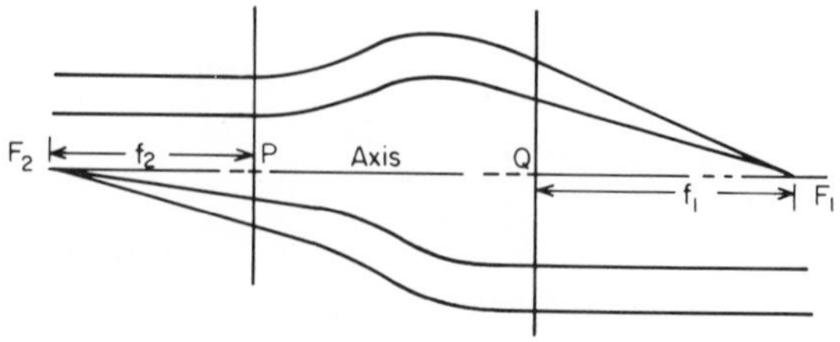

Fig. 3.11. All trajectories are deflected toward the axis in passing through an electrostatic lens.

principal focus, or focal point, of the lens. Every electron lens is characterized by two paraxial focal points which lie on opposite sides of the lens, since an initially parallel flow beam may approach the lens from either direction.

If the lens is not too strong, the focal points will lie in the field-free region outside the axial segment P – Q mentioned earlier. In the field-free region the electrons must approach the axis along straight-line paths. Any of these paths may be projected backward to its intersection with the projection of the original path, which was parallel to the axis; this is shown in Fig. 3.12. The point of intersection is known as a principal plane of the lens; it is clear that there are two principal planes, one for each direction of approach of the original beam.

The principal planes correspond directly with their light-optics counterparts. The axial distance separating a given principal plane and the corresponding focal point is known as the focal length of the lens. Lenses for which the focal length is large compared with the axial thickness are known as thin lenses.

In general, the two focal lengths of a lens are unequal. Although the principal planes do not coincide in general, it may be shown that both principal planes always lie between the axial end points P and Q. Another set of planes important in the theory of lenses are those for which $r_2(s)$ vanishes, i.e., the planes where an electron entering the lens at an axial point again passes through the axis. There are two such planes, also, distinguished by the direction of approach of the beam. Let there be a plane $s = G_2$ such that $r_2(G_2) = 0$. Then, according to Eq. (8.5), $r(G_2) = r(0)\, r_1(G_2)$. This relation implies that the radius of a ray on this plane is independent of the initial slope of the ray and is also proportional to the initial radius r(0). Therefore all rays leaving the initial plane at a radius r_1 (known as the object plane) arrive at the same radius r in the plane $s = G_2$ (known as the image plane); this behavior is illustrated in Fig. 3.13. The ratio $r/r_1 = r(0)$ is known as the magnification of the lens. The focal planes, at which $r_1(s) = 0$, and the image planes, at which $r_2(s) = 0$, are distinct.

The separation of an image plane from its corresponding principal planes is known as the image distance of the lens; the separation

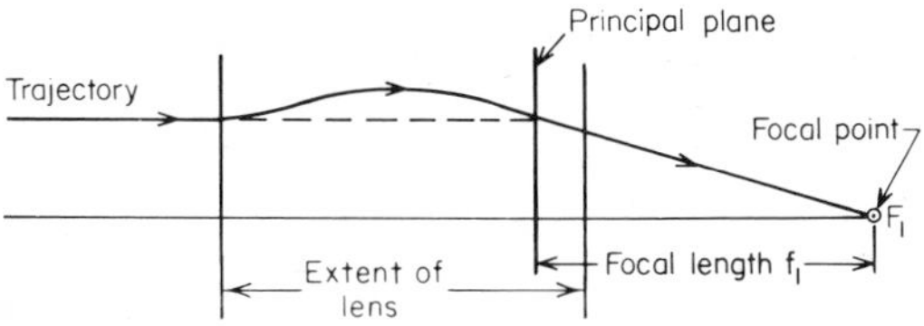

Fig. 3.12. Illustrating how the principal plane is determined, and how the focal length is defined.

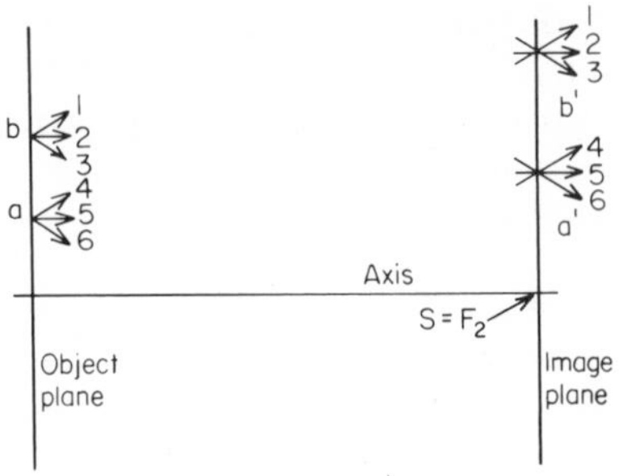

Fig. 3.13. Illustrating how an image of a source on the object plane is obtained on the image plane. The small numbers 1 to 6 refer to individual trajectories.

of the initial plane from the same principal plane is known as the object distance. The reader should consult any standard text on either light optics or electron optics to obtain detailed relations among such quantities as the object distance, image distance, focal length, and separation of the principal planes and for discussion of lens aberrations.[3,4]

The reader is warned not to read into Eq. (8.3) a meaning which is not intended. It has not been concluded that the lens action is one of convergence at every point within the lens, but only that the net action is that of convergence. In part of the lens a trajectory may well bend away from the axis, but the remainder of the lens will overcome this divergence and reduce the exit slope of the trajectory to a value less than the entrance slope.

It has been assumed in the above discussion that the lens is "not too strong." By this it is meant that the trajectory never crosses the axis within the lens. Unfortunately, it is difficult, if not impossible, to give an inviolable criterion which may be used to determine if a given lens is in fact too strong to meet this test. The only way to be absolutely certain is to integrate Eq. (2.24) or its equivalent, Eq. (8.1), through the lens. Equation (8.1) is a paraxial approximation and may not give the true answer to the strength of the lens; if a particular solution of that equation predicts a crossover within the lens, however, the evidence is persuasive that the lens is in fact too strong. The lens may still have a net convergent effect, but the proof after Eq. (8.1) is no longer valid. More will be said concerning lens strengths when periodic focusing systems are discussed in Chap. V; in periodic systems the question of lens strength is extremely important.

The conclusion concerning the convergent nature of an electrostatic lens, as deduced from the paraxial-ray equation, is in complete accord with the conclusion reached by the qualitative discussion of the physical action of the lens. The lens properties sketched in this section, i.e., two focal points, two principal planes, etc., are very general; they depend only on the linear form of the electromagnetic fields, and also apply if there are crossovers inside the lens and in different geometric configurations. It is left as an exercise for the reader to establish these results, for planar electrostatic or magnetic lenses, and to show that lenses which begin and end at field-free points are always convergent; the effect of image rotation in magnetic lenses should also be examined.

8.3. The Thin Lens. In optical theory, it is often convenient to make the assumption that the lens is thin. We define, similarly, a thin lens in the present context as one in which the fields are finite only in a region small compared with the focal distances f_1 and f_2. This implies that, in the lens, $\underline{r = \text{constant}}$ is a reasonable approximation, and that the two principal planes must be coincident. It then follows from Eq. (8.1) that if an electron enters the thin lens with an initial trajectory slope r'_P and a final trajectory slope r'_Q, the relation between r'_Q and r'_P is

$$\Phi_Q^{1/4}\, r'_Q - \Phi_P^{1/4}\, r'_P = -\frac{3r}{16}\int_P^Q \Phi^{1/4}\left(\frac{\Phi'}{\Phi}\right)^2 ds \tag{8.7}$$

After leaving the thin lens, the electrons travel along a rectilinear trajectory. Consequently, an electron leaving the lens reaches the axis at a point distance s from its center, given by $s = -r/r'_Q$. It follows that, if an electron enters the lens parallel to the axis, the distance z at which it crosses the axis corresponds to the focal length f_1. Similarly, when an electron enters parallel to the axis from the other side of the lens, the distance to the point where it crosses the axis is f_2. It follows from Eq. (8.7) that

$$\frac{f_2}{f_1} = \left(\frac{\Phi_P}{\Phi_Q}\right)^{1/4} \tag{8.8}$$

Thus, unlike its optical counterpart, the electrostatic lens does not, in general, have equal focal lengths. This is because of the difference in potentials on each side of the lens, and hence the difference in the velocity of the electrons, a situation which does not occur in the optical counterpart. The following generalized form of the usual optical focusing formula also follows from Eq. (8.7):

$$f_1 = \frac{16\Phi_Q^{1/4}}{3\int_P^Q \Phi^{1/4}\left(\frac{\Phi'}{\Phi}\right)^2 ds} \tag{8.9}$$

If an electron leaves the axis at a point $s = -s_1$ and meets it again after passing through the lens at a point $s = s_2$, it follows that $r'_P = r/s_1$ and $r'_Q = r/s_2$. Therefore we find that

$$\frac{1}{s_2} + \frac{1}{s_1}\left(\frac{\Phi_P}{\Phi_Q}\right)^{1/4} = \frac{1}{F_1} = \frac{1}{F_2}\left(\frac{\Phi_P}{\Phi_Q}\right)^{1/4} \tag{8.10}$$

This reduces to the usual optical formulas when $\Phi_P = \Phi_Q$.

8.4. The Aperture Lens. An important form of lens often used in electron guns is the aperture lens. This consists of a circular aperture with a field gradient Φ'_P on the side through which the electrons enter it and a field gradient Φ'_Q on the side through which the electrons leave it, as illustrated in Fig. 3.14.

The focal length of this lens can be determined on the assumptions that it is thin, so that r does not change through the lens region, and that r' and Φ' are finite throughout the lens region. As the thickness of the lens is reduced, both r'' and Φ'' tend to become very large within the aperture. Consequently, we can integrate Eq. (2.24) from one side to the other of the lens to obtain the result

$$\Phi(r'_Q - r'_P) = -\frac{r}{4}(\Phi'_Q - \Phi'_P) \tag{8.11}$$

Thus the focal length of the lens is

$$f = \frac{4\Phi}{\Phi'_Q - \Phi'_P} \tag{8.12}$$

An important example of the aperture lens is that formed by the hole in the anode of an electron gun. In this case, the field lines on the left-hand side of the aperture are virtually those given by the theory for an infinite diode. On the other hand, if the beam exits into a drift tube, potential gradient on the output side of the lens is essentially zero. Because the field lines in the neighborhood of the anode hole are not parallel to the axis, there is a net focusing action on the beam. If $\Phi'_Q = 0$, the hole behaves like divergent lens.

We consider, as an example, the plane diode with an aperture in the anode, illustrated in Fig. 3.15. For the plane diode the potential variation in the beam is given by

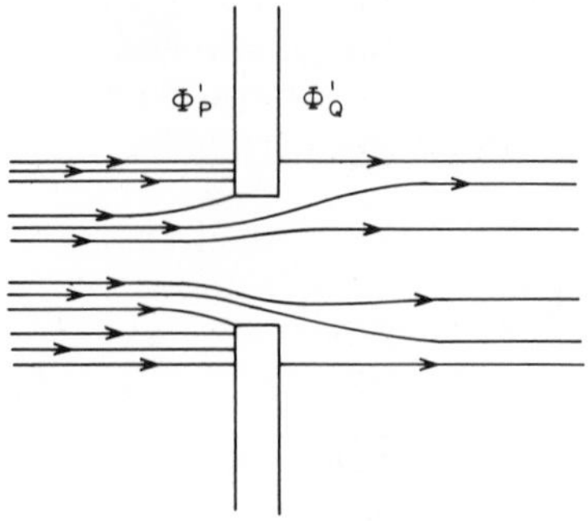

Fig. 3.14. Schematic of an aperture lens.

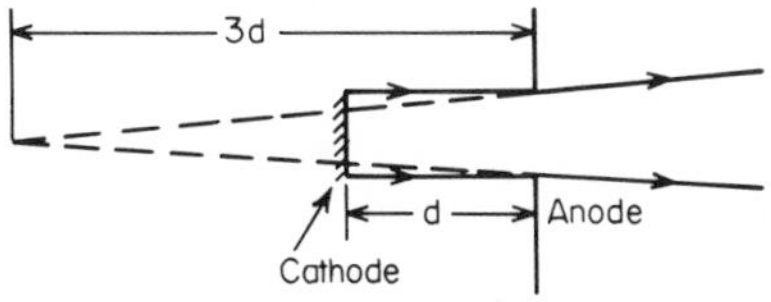

Fig. 3.15. Schematic of a planar diode with a hole in the anode.

$$\Phi = C\, s^{4/3} \quad \text{and} \quad \Phi' = \frac{4}{3} C\, s^{1/3} \tag{8.13}$$

We assume that the beam leaving the diode enters into a drift region where $\Phi'_Q = 0$. The focal length of the aperture in the anode is then given approximately by the formula

$$f = -3d \tag{8.14}$$

where d is the length of the diode. Thus the beam leaving a diode of this kind diverges and appears to have been emitted from a point distance 3d behind the anode.

The focusing effect of a hole in the anode would not be present if the anode were itself a perfect grid. This is, basically, because the potential fields do not obey Laplace's equation at the grid. On the other hand, for a true grid, each hole in the grid tends to behave as a separate lens of focal length given by Eq. (8.12). Thus the slope of the trajectory of an electron leaving the grid is given by the formula

$$r'_Q = -\frac{r\Phi'_Q}{4\Phi} \tag{8.15}$$

where r is now the radius of the hole in the grid. The smaller this radius, the smaller the divergence of the individual beamlet after passing through a grid hole. Thus, as the mesh of the grid is made finer, the grid behaves more like a perfect grid, and the emergent beam becomes parallel. With a real grid, there is a tendency, then, for the beam to become nonlaminar after it has left the grid because of the divergence of the individual beamlets.

9. THE USE OF PARAXIAL THEORY FOR ELECTRON-GUN DESIGN

Historically, paraxial equations have found their greatest utility for the analysis of electron-optical systems in which the potential and applied magnetic field are specified, e.g., in particle accelerators. In this section, we outline a method for utilizing paraxial equations in a distinctly different manner, namely, for the synthesis of an electron gun having a prescribed space-charge-limited flow pattern.

The exact design of an electron gun usually consists of the following two major phases:

1. Statements concerning symmetry of the trajectories and the applied magnetic field. These symmetries permit the partial differential equations of the flow to be reduced to one or more ordinary differential equations, which are solved analytically or by approximate methods. From the solutions all flow parameters, such as the trajectories, potential along a given trajectory, charge density, etc., may be derived.

2. Calculation of a set of electrodes which will actually produce the prescribed flow.

The use of paraxial theory enormously increases the flexibility of prescribing the geometrical shape of the space-charge-flow lines or the nature of the potential variation in the beam, or both. The penalty to be paid for the increased flexibility is uncertainty of the range of validity of the method.

It is clear that Eqs. (2.25) and (3.7) are ordinary differential equations relating the axial potential Φ, the axial magnetic field $\mathcal{B}$, and the radius (or half thickness) r. If two of these three quantities are specified as functions of axial position, the third may be calculated. In the usual electron optical problem one specifies Φ and $\mathcal{B}$ and calculates r. For the purpose of designing an electron gun, r and $\mathcal{B}$ are specified, and then the paraxial equation is used for the calculation of Φ.

As the first example, consider Eq. (2.25) subject to the conditions $\mathcal{B} = \mathcal{B}_0 = 0$ and $r = r_0 =$ constant. The equation then reduces to

$$\Phi'' = \frac{i_0}{\epsilon_0(2\eta\Phi)^{1/2}} \tag{9.1}$$

where $i_0 = I/\pi r_0^2$, the constant beam current density.

Equation (9.1) is the standard potential equation for a planar diode, and its solution has been discussed at considerable length in Sec. 2.2 of Chap. II. The solution for such a space-charge-limited diode is from Eq. (2.17a) of Chap. II,

$$\Phi = [\tfrac{9}{4}\,\epsilon_0(2\eta)^{1/2}\,i_0]^{2/3}\,z^{4/3} \tag{9.2}$$

A rather different form of solution of Eq. (9.1), applicable in the screen-grid anode region of beam power tetrodes, is given by Haeff[5] and by Fay et al.[6]

In a second example, the paraxial theory is applied to the linear convergence of an electrostatic sheet beam. The requisite paraxial equation is Eq. (3.7), with $B = B_0 = 0$. The beam is prescribed to converge linearly, so that $r = r_0(1 - s/s_0)$, where s_0 is the axial focal point (Fig. 3.16).

It is convenient to transform the origin to the focal point through the substitution $R = s_0 - s$. It is also convenient to develop the theory in terms of the total current I_r per unit length emitted from an

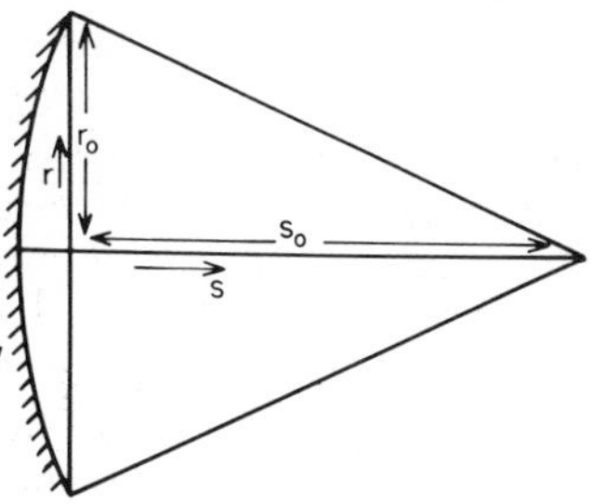

Fig. 3.16. Schematic of a linearly converging round beam.

imaginary cathode of radius s_0. In this case, if the convergence angle is small, $I = I_r r_0/\pi s_0$.

When these considerations are applied to Eq. (3.7), the following standard potential equation for cylindrical electrode space-charge flow is obtained:

$$\frac{d}{dR}\left(R\frac{d\Phi}{dR}\right) = \frac{I_r}{2\pi\epsilon_0(2\eta\Phi)^{1/2}} \tag{9.3}$$

Solutions of this equation are discussed in Appendix E.

Still a third example concerns the linear convergence of an electrostatic round solid beam. In this case, the potential equation is that for the radial space-charge flow between concentric spheres. It is left as an exercise for the reader to demonstrate that Eq. (2.25) leads to the correct potential equation as given in Appendix E.

In the three examples discussed above, paraxial theory leads to potential equations known to be exactly correct. The reason for this is that each of the three flow patterns is one-dimensional, in a coordinate system for which an exact analysis is possible. The exact analysis reveals that the variation of any parameter of the flow in a direction normal to the trajectories is zero. By far the more frequent type of flow is characterized by a variation of any or all of the flow parameters normal to the trajectories. It is for this class of space-charge flows that the range of validity of the paraxial method is most difficult to estimate.

Other difficulties arise with the breakdown of the paraxial method when the radial velocity components become too large relative to the axial velocity. As an example, it is usually necessary, in order to allow exit of the beam, to cut a hole in the anode of a gun designed on the basis of the examples given above. It follows from the work in Section 8, that this hole will give rise to a divergent lens action which must be considered in the design of such a gun. If the hole diameter is only two or three times the anode-cathode spacing, i.e., the beam has a high perveance, paraxial theory tends to yield underestimates of the lens strength. Moreover, because the field strength at the edge of the anode hole can, in this case, be much larger than on the axis, the lens itself tends to be strong and the radial velocity components relatively large. This gives rise to aberrations which in turn leads to a nonlaminar beam. Yet another difficulty is associated with the change in perveance of the beam associated with the introduction of the hole in the anode. The current density tends to become lower near the axis because of the lower axial potential due to the presence of the hole. Thus, the charge density is no longer uniform across the beam and the validity of the paraxial theory becomes difficult to estimate. However, none of these problems should be severe in a low-perveance gun where the anode-cathode spacing is several times the hole diameter. Methods of dealing with difficulties of this kind and estimating their effect are discussed in Chap. IX.

As an example of a flow pattern which may readily be treated by the paraxial method, but for which no exact solution is known, let us consider an exponentially converging electrostatic round solid beam, as depicted in Fig. 3.17. The paraxial equation (2.25) becomes

$$2r''\Phi + r'\Phi' + \frac{r\Phi''}{2} = \frac{I}{2\pi\epsilon_0(2\eta\Phi)^{1/2}r} \tag{9.4}$$

The beam radius r is prescribed to decrease exponentially; i.e.,

$$r = r_0\, e^{-\gamma z} \tag{9.5}$$

If the substitutions $\Phi = K^{2/3}\, Y \exp(4\gamma z/3)$, where

$$K = \frac{I}{\pi\epsilon_0(2\eta)^{1/2}\gamma^2 r_0^2}$$

and $X = \gamma z$, are made in Eq. (9.4), the following universal potential equation is obtained:

$$Y'' + \tfrac{2}{3}Y' + \tfrac{28}{9}Y - Y^{-1/2} = 0 \tag{9.6}$$

where a prime denotes d/dX.

This equation has been solved on a digital computer* subject to initial conditions which make the flow space-charge-limited ($\Phi = \Phi' = 0$ at the cathode; see Section 6 of Chap. I).

From this solution a curve of potential versus z may be plotted. It is more convenient to deal with a normalized potential, $(16K/7)^{2/3}\,\Phi$,

---

*It is convenient to introduce a variable v such that $Y = v^2$ and a variable t such that $dX = v\,dt$. Letting a dot denote d/dt, Eq. (9.6) transforms into

$$\ddot{v} + \frac{2}{3}\dot{v}v + \frac{14}{9}v^3 = \frac{1}{2}$$

This transformation avoids, as in Section 2 of Chap. II, the singularity at the cathode which characterizes Eq. (9.6). For space-charge-limited flow the appropriate initial conditions are $v = \dot{v} = 0$ at $t = 0$.

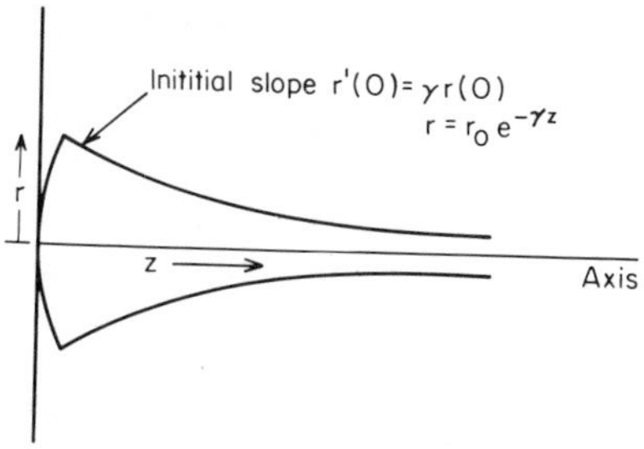

Fig. 3.17. Schematic of an exponentially converging round beam.

as a function of γz, and a curve relating these variables is presented in Fig. 3.18, along with the radius convergence factor $\exp \gamma z$.

It is evident that at $\gamma z = 1.94$ the potential passes through a maximum; at this point the radius and slope have been decreased to 0.144 of their values at the cathode, and the area convergence is 48.3. It is convenient to define the beam perveance in terms of the maximum potential ϕ_M; that is, $P = I/\phi_M^{3/2}$. The beam perveance reduces to

$$P = 0.928\ (\gamma r_0)^2 \qquad \text{micropervs} \tag{9.7}$$

A further substitution makes the development more meaningful. The scale parameter γ may be expressed in terms of the initial radius r_0 and the slope at the cathode $r'(0)$. From Eq. (9.5) one finds that $\gamma r_0 = -r'(0)$, so that the perveance expression becomes

$$P = 0.928\,[r'(0)]^2 \qquad \text{micropervs} \tag{9.8}$$

where the initial slope is in radians. For an initial slope of 20°, the microperveance is approximately 0.10. Since one of the underlying assumptions of paraxial theory is that the slope of trajectories relative to the ray axis is small (the slope in radians is much less than unity), the validity of the paraxial theory for a slope as large as 20° is open to question. Thus it is evident that the type of exponentially

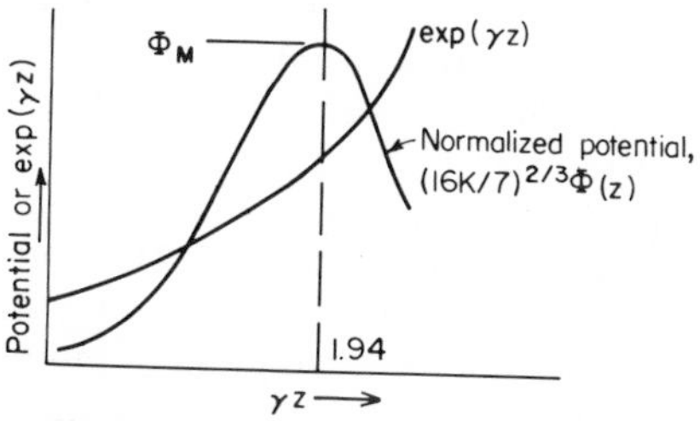

Fig. 3.18. Normalized potential and radial convergence factor for an exponentially convergent round beam.

convergent gun under discussion is limited to rather low perveance applications.

The curvature of the trajectories requires the existence of a component of electric field normal to the trajectories. This field component may be calculated with the aid of Eq. (2.43) of Chap. I. Finally, the normal field may be integrated to the boundary, whence a second application of Eq. (2.43) of Chap. I will yield the normal component of field on the boundary. The resulting potential and normal component of the field constitute the necessary and sufficient boundary values needed for determination of suitable electrodes.

Two other features of the exponentially convergent flow pattern are of interest. First, it may be noted that Eq. (9.6) is the equation of a damped harmonic oscillator. Because of the damping term $2Y'/3$, the function Y will oscillate with decreasing amplitude, eventually converging to the value $(9/28)^{2/3} = 0.470$ for large values of γz. It is found that the complete potential expression for Φ, which included the factor exp $(4\gamma z/3)$, also exhibits the oscillatory character. This type of behavior of the potential function is frequently encountered in space-charge-flow problems.

It is important that at certain values of γz the slope of the axial potential Φ' vanishes. Of particular interest is the point of maximum potential depicted in Fig. 3.18. The fact that this is a true point of maximum potential, and not merely an inflection point, may be shown to lead to the conclusion that equipotential surfaces in the vicinity of the maximum will not intersect the beam. Therefore a theoretically correct anode, which will contain an aperture sufficient for passage of the beam, may be designed; and this anode will (theoretically) intercept no current. Thus the anode-hole effect (discussed in detail in Section 5 of Chap. VIII), which is the source of considerable design difficulty when the electron gun is based upon the linearly convergent flow between concentric spheres, may be completely avoided. The same is true even if the potential is taken to be a constant, equal to Φ_M, for values of γs greater than 1.94. The lack of the anode-hole problem is of interest for a gun designed for the injection of a convergent beam into a constant-potential drift tube, such as a traveling-wave-tube interaction circuit.

It should be noted that the introduction of an anode hole can also be regarded as a method which tends to introduce a maximum of potential. For instance, when a hole is cut in the anode of a plane diode and there is a drift tube at the same potential as the anode beyond the hole, the potential on the axis increases from cathode to anode, rising to a maximum far down the drift tube. Thus, the slope of the axial potential Φ' is very small on the exit side of the anode, as is the radial field E_r. It follows that the equipotentials near the beam are almost parallel to the axis and may not intersect the beam until some distance beyond the anode. If some type of focusing is introduced before the beam diverges and hits the drift tube (an equipotential surface) the anode will then be a nonintercepting one. However, in high perveance guns, the beam tends to diverge even before it reaches the anode plane or, at best, too soon after it passes through the anode hole.

The same analytical techniques can be used to design other types of paraxial flow guns. A wide range of strip-beam guns which have curvilinear central axes can be designed by employing Eq. (6.19). In this case, Eq. (6.19) gives a relation between the beam thickness, the potential variation along the beam, the magnetic field, and the curvature of the central axis. If any three of these parameters are specified, in addition to the boundary conditions at the cathode, the fourth can be determined. In order to obtain uniform current density at the cathode, it is convenient to specify that the curvature of the central axis at the cathode be zero. Otherwise,with a finite curvature, it follows from the work in Section 5 of Chap. II that the current density at the cathode would be nonuniform. Again, in order to allow for the effect of the hole in the anode, it is often convenient to specify that the potential gradient along the central trajectory is either zero or very small where the beam leaves the gun. This means that either the last anode does not intercept the beam or it intercepts the beam at some distance along it. In the second case the beam should be terminated before the point of interception, or the potential made uniform beyond the final anode; i.e., the beam should emerge into a unipotential drift region.

As has been pointed out earlier, the accuracy of paraxial techniques of this kind is not always easy to judge. The method does at least provide a good initial guess at a gun design which can produce a beam of a given type. Electrodes for this beam can be determined by the usual Pierce-type analytical procedures described in Chaps. VII and VIII. Often these electrodes turn out to be physically impractical. A useful procedure in this situation is to change the electrodes to more practical shapes, and use numerical methods of the kind described in Chaps. VIII and IX to determine how much the nature of the beam has been affected. Cut-and-try procedures of this type have been used to design ion-propulsion guns.

It should also be noted that the paraxial theory given here can be extended to yield higher-order approximations. Such techniques are familiar in optics, where they are used to describe the aberrations of lenses. In gun design, techniques of this kind have been used to arrive at estimates of the order of accuracy of the paraxial method and, more important still, to design thick beam guns which have certain prescribed properties along the central trajectory. This subject is discussed further in Refs. 7 to 9.

10. SPREADING OF A DRIFTING BEAM

In the absence of focusing forces, space-charge repulsion forces in drifting electron beams cause a gradual increase in the diameter (or thickness). It is possible to obtain quantitative information concerning this effect by solving the appropriate paraxial equations. As we are concerned with beams in which no focusing action whatever occurs, there can be no magnetic fields; in the case of a sheet beam, the curvature of the ray axis must vanish identically; i.e., the ray axis must be straight.

The asserted absence of electric-lens action implies that Φ'' must vanish identically; at most the potential may vary linearly with axial position. However, the development of this section will be concerned only with beams drifting in a uniform potential ϕ_0.

Subject to the foregoing restrictions, the appropriate paraxial-ray equations are, from Eqs. (2.25) and (3.7),

$$r'' = \frac{P}{4\pi\epsilon_0(2\eta)^{1/2}\,r} \tag{10.1}$$

for the round beam and

$$r'' = \frac{P}{4\epsilon_0(2\eta)^{1/2}\,\ell} \tag{10.2}$$

for a sheet beam. In these equations P is the beam perveance, that is, $P = I/\phi_0^{3/2}$. Without loss of generality, Eqs. (10.1) and (10.2) may be solved subject to zero initial slope; the proof of this fact is left to the reader. Also, in each equation the initial off-axis position is r_0, and we shall derive expressions for the variation of r/r_0 with axial position.

Equation (10.1) may be integrated a first time upon multiplication through by $2r'$. It is assumed that $r = r_0$, where $r' = 0$. A second integral is possible, in terms of a tabulated function, if the substitution $r = r_0 \exp u^2$ is made. In order to evaluate the constant of integration, r is set equal to r_0 at $z = 0$. The second integral is therefore in the form

$$k_1 \frac{z}{r_0} = \int_0^R \exp(u^2)\,du \tag{10.3}$$

where

$$k_1^2 = \frac{P}{8\pi\epsilon_0(2\eta)^{1/2}} = 7.6 \times 10^{-3}\,P, \qquad R^2 = \log\frac{r}{r_0} \tag{10.4}$$

and P is measured in micropervs.

As the exponential integral is a known tabulated function, Eqs. (10.3) and (10.4) permit a single universal beam-spread curve to be drawn, covering all possible cases. This curve, shown in Fig. 3.19, has for its ordinate the ratio r/r_0 and for its abscissa the normalized axial distance, i.e., the left side of Eq. (10.3).

For values of r/r_0 close to unity, Eqs. (10.3) and (10.4) very nearly represent a parabola; this may be shown upon expanding the pair of equations in a power series and retaining only the first two terms. Figure 3.19 shows the universal beam-spread curve for both round beams and sheet beams. The parabolic curve which applies to sheet beams also applies to round beams, subject to the above approximation.

From Fig. 3.19 it may be concluded that the diameter of a round beam will have doubled when the beam has drifted a distance z_2 given by

$$z_2 = \frac{1.07}{k_1} r_0 \tag{10.5}$$

Comparison of this distance with the corresponding distance for a sheet beam [Eqs. (10.6) and (10.9) below] reveals that, if the total perveance of the round beam equals the perveance per square of the sheet beam, the round beam will drift 30 per cent farther before its diameter has doubled. Thus, when the perveance of the two beams is equal, in the sense described, the space-charge spreading of sheet beams is slightly the faster. On the other hand, if there are many squares in the sheet beam ($\ell \gg 2r_0$) and the total perveances of the two types of beams are equal, the round beam will spread at a more rapid rate.

For a sheet beam the problem is simpler, as Eq. (10.2) may be twice integrated directly. The appropriate second integral has the form

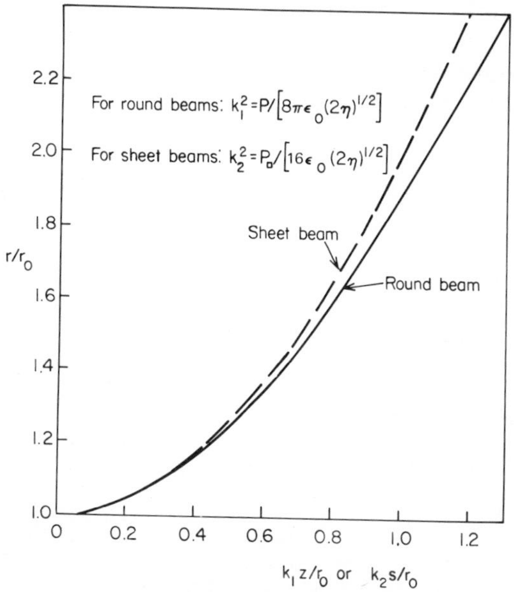

Fig. 3.19. Universal beam-spread curves for round and sheet beams.

$$\frac{r}{r_0} - 1 = k_2^2\left(\frac{s}{r_0}\right)^2 \tag{10.6}$$

$$\text{where} \quad k_2^2 = \frac{P\ r_0}{8\epsilon_0(2\eta)^{1/2}\ \ell} \tag{10.7}$$

from which it is evident that a drifting sheet beam spreads parabolically with distance.

From Eq. (10.6) it follows that the sheet beam spreads, under the influence of its own space charge, to twice its original thickness in the distance given by

$$s_2 = \frac{r_0}{k_2} \tag{10.8}$$

In the theory of sheet beams, in which the width ℓ is arbitrary, it is convenient to imagine that the beam is composed of a series of subbeams laid side by side; the individual subbeams are taken to have the width $2r_0$, as depicted in Fig. 3.20. The number N of such subbeams is therefore $N = \ell/2r_0$. The quantity perveance per square, designated by the symbol $P_\square$, is then the perveance contained within the bounds of a given subbeam, that is, $P_\square = P/N$. In terms of the perveance per square, Eq. (10.7) may be written in the universal form

$$k_2^2 = \frac{P_\square}{16\epsilon_0(2\eta)^{1/2}} = 1.20 \times 10^{-2}\, P_\square \tag{10.9}$$

where $P_\square$ is in micropervs. The relation between s/r_0 and r/r_0 is also depicted in Fig. 3.19.

Thus, in the theory of the space-charge spreading of sheet beams, the perveance per square plays the same role as the total perveance

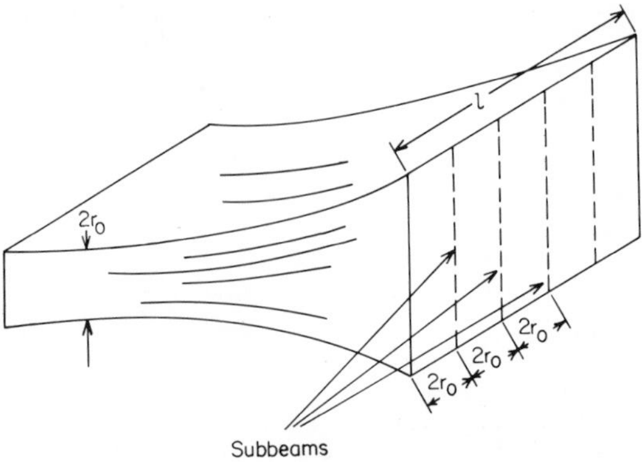

Fig. 3.20. A sheet beam may be thought of as divided into subbeams having a constant width $2r_0$, equal to the thickness of the beam at the plane where the beam slope vanishes.

of a round solid beam; of course, it was for this reason that the perveance per square was introduced.

It is evident from the foregoing analysis that the rate of spreading of drifting beams is governed by the square root of the beam perveance P (or $P_\square$); beams having a high perveance spread "faster" than beams having a low perveance. It is not surprising, therefore, that beam perveance also turns out to be an extremely important parameter in the theory of focused beams; this fact will be demonstrated in Chaps. IV and V.

The maximum current which can be transmitted through a drift tube by an unfocused beam is an important parameter. Equation (10.3) can be written in the form

$$k_1 \frac{z}{r} = \frac{r_0}{r} \int_0^R \exp(u^2)\, du = \exp(-R^2) \int_0^R \exp(u^2)\, du \tag{10.10}$$

where k_1 and R are given by Eq. (10.4). Because the universal beam-spread curve is symmetrical about the plane z = 0, the maximum beam current is transmitted through a drift tube when the slope of the edge electron trajectory at the center of the drift tube is zero as shown in Fig. 3.21. This corresponds to the minimum radius of the beam r_0, being at the center of the drift tube. In this case the maximum beam current is obtained for a length of drift tube L corresponding to the left-hand side of Eq. (10.10) being a maximum with z = L/2. This condition is reached at a value where

$$2R \exp(-R^2) \int_0^R \exp(u^2)\, du = 1 \tag{10.11}$$

Under these conditions, R = 0.924, and therefore $r/r_0 = 2.35$, and Eq. (10.10) becomes

$$k_1 \frac{L}{r} = 1.08 \tag{10.12}$$

The maximum current can be transmitted with the entering beam just grazing the opening of the drift tube; this corresponds to r = a, the radius of the drift tube. Using the definition of k_1 of Eq. (10.4), the perveance is

$$P = 155\left(\frac{a}{L}\right)^2 \quad \text{micropervs} \tag{10.13}$$

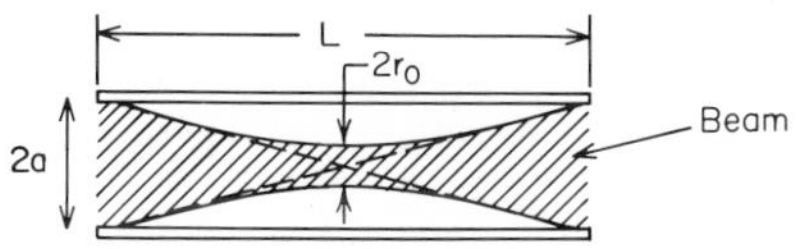

Fig. 3.21. Schematic of the maximum beam passing through a drift tube.

For the maximum perveance to be obtained, the beam must enter the drift tube at a specific angle, which may be obtained by integrating Eq. (10.1). This yields the result

$$r' = 2k_1R$$
$$\simeq \frac{2a}{L} \tag{10.14}$$

To obtain Eq. (10.14), the values of k_1, R, and P of Eqs. (10.4), (10.12), and (10.13) have been used. Thus, for maximum current transmission through the drift tube, the beam must be aimed at the center of the drift tube, as shown in Fig. 3.21. This angle of entry is not very critical, however. The minimum beam radius may be varied from 0.25 to 0.6 of the drift-tube radius with a loss of only 10 per cent of the maximum current.

A similar derivation can be carried out for a strip beam. In this case, the beam is considered to be transmitted through two plates, distance 2a apart of length L. It is then found, following the same procedures, that the value of r/r_0 for maximum perveance density is $r/r_0 = 2.0$, with the maximum value of perveance density

$$P_{\square} = 2\pi\left(\frac{a}{L}\right)^2 = 21\left(\frac{a}{L}\right)^2 \quad \text{micropervs per square} \tag{10.15}$$

This corresponds to the initial slope of the beam being

$$r' = \frac{2a}{L} \tag{10.16}$$

Thus, for the strip beam also, transmission is obtained when the beam is aimed at the center of the drift region.

REFERENCES FOR CHAPTER III

1. Morse, P. M., and H. Feshbach: "Methods of Theoretical Physics," McGraw-Hill Book Company, New York, 1953.
2. Sturrock, P. A.: "Static and Dynamic Electron Optics," Cambridge University Press, London, 1955.
3. Cosslet, V. E.: "Introduction to Electron Optics," chap. 4, Oxford University Press, Fairlawn, N. J., 1950.
4. Klemperer, O.: "Electron Optics," chap. 2, Cambridge University Press, London, 1953.
5. Salzberg, B., and A. V. Haeff: Effects of Space-charge Anode Region of Vacuum Tubes, *RCA Rev.*, vol. 2, p. 336, 1938.
6. Fay, C. E., A. L. Samuel, and W. Shockley: On the Theory of Space-charge between Parallel Plane Electrodes, *Bell System Tech. J.*, vol. 17, p. 49, 1938.
7. Harker, K. J.: A Higher Order Paraxial Theory, *Intern. J. Electronics*, vol. 18, p. 43, 1965.
8. Colburn, D. S., K. J. Harker, and G. S. Kino: A Synthesis Method of Electrostatic Gun Design, *AIAA J.*, vol. 2, p. 322, 1964.

9. Colburn, D. S., K. J. Harker, and G. S. Kino: New Rf Design of High Perveance Guns, *Proc. 4th Intern. Cong. on Microwave Tubes*, The Hague, p. 572, Holland Publishing Co., Eindhoven, 1963.

PROBLEMS

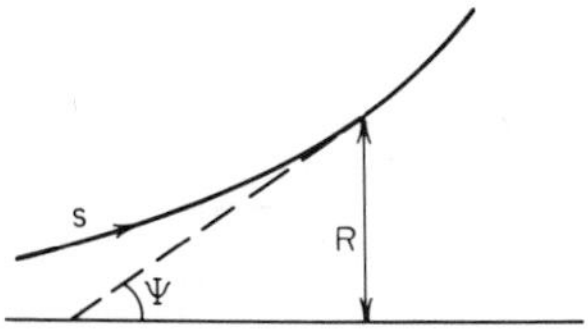

1a. Determine a paraxial equation for a thin hollow cylindrical beam without magnetic field. Use as coordinates the distance s along the curved hollow axis and r the distance normal to it. The equation will have to be stated in terms of r, s, κ, the curvature of the central axis, the distance from the axis of symmetry of the curved central axis R, and the angle Ψ the curved axis makes with a cylinder described about the central axis.

1b. Using the equations found in Prob 1a, consider the potential variation near a hollow cathode of radius a when the central axis of the beam is at an

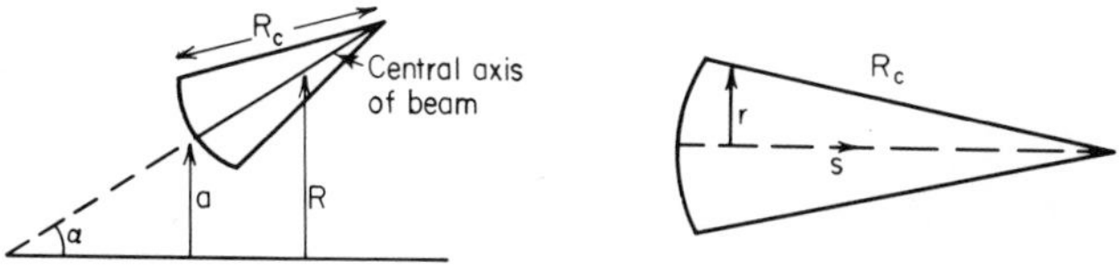

angle α to the axis. Take the cathode to have a radius of curvature R_c. Then the initial value of dr/ds for the beam is $(dr/ds)_c \approx r/R_c$. Taking the curvature of the central axis to be zero, show that near the cathode the potential variation has the form $\phi = as^{4/3}(1 + bs + \cdots)$. Find a and b in terms of the total current in the beam, the width of the cathode, R_c, α, and a. The cathode is taken to be at s = 0.

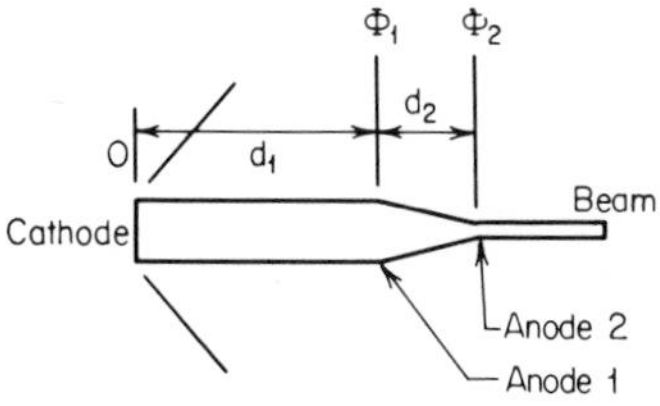

2. A two-anode electron gun is designed to yield a parallel cylindrical beam. The region between the flat cathode and first anode is designed to yield a parallel beam. The second anode is placed at a sufficiently high potential so that the field between the two anodes is such that the lens effect at the first anode is convergent ($\Phi_2 > \Phi_1$). The lens effect at the second anode is diverg-

ent. Find the relation between d_1, d_2, Φ_1, and Φ_2 to yield a parallel beam. Ignore space-charge effects in the region between the two anodes.

3. Determine the focal length of a lens formed by a slit in a metal plate where the potential gradients on each side of the plate are Φ_1' and Φ_2', respectively.

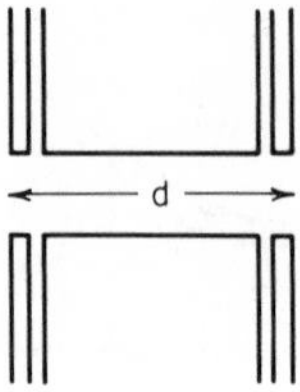

4. Work out the focal length of a lens consisting of a short solenoid with pole pieces, distance d long, the field being uniform of value B between the pole pieces and zero outside.

IV

Uniform Focusing

1. INTRODUCTION

This chapter is concerned with the properties of high-perveance focusing systems which are uniform with respect to a single rectilinear spatial coordinate. A variety of focusing systems for solid and annular round beams and for sheet beams are discussed. Purely magnetic focusing, purely electrostatic focusing, and a mixture of the two known as crossed-field focusing are included. Uniform focusing of high-perveance electron beams, in which the length is large compared with the transverse dimensions, is used in a wide variety of electron-tube devices, notably microwave tubes.

Uniform focusing systems have many common properties; for example, a maximum perveance and a maximum electron density can be confined in the focusing system. In uniform focusing systems, particles with the correct initial conditions will keep a constant distance from the axis; particles which are injected with incorrect initial conditions will perform periodic transverse oscillations. Associated with these oscillations, or ripples, in a focusing system are certain characteristic parameters; these are the characteristic wavelength and frequency, at which a given electron executes a single rippling cycle, and a particular ratio of the rippling amplitude to the slope of the outer boundary of the beam at the equilibrium radius (or thickness); the reciprocal of this last ratio is known as the beam stiffness.

In Section 2 some general properties of round beams of constant diameter are derived, assuming the flow is laminar (Sec. 5.1 of Chap. I). The properties of all specific uniform axially symmetric round beams may be obtained as special cases of the analysis presented in this section.

Section 3 is devoted to the detailed calculation of the properties of uniform round beams in which the axial velocity of the electrons is constant throughout the beam. Two special cases of uniform magnetic focusing, known as Brillouin flow, and one special case of uniform electrostatic focusing, known as Harris flow, are included. In addition to the derivation of explicit formulas for various properties of the flows, it is shown that for each type of flow there is a maximum permissible beam perveance; the beam perveance was defined, in Sec. 7.2 of Chap. I, as the ratio of the total current to the three-halves power of the highest potential occurring within the beam.

A paraxial analysis of the beams of Section 3 is presented in Section 4; explicit formulas for rippling wavelength, rippling frequency, and the beam stiffness are derived. Section 5 is concerned with unrippled theory, and Section 6 with perturbations in round beams for which the angular velocity of the electrons is constant throughout the beam (so-called isorotational beams). Included in Section 6 is a brief treatment of the stability of annular beams in the presence of a nonconservative perturbing force, and it is shown that a certain class of annular-beam focusing systems is unstable against such perturbations.

Rectilinear sheet beams are dealt with in Section 7 (properties of unrippled beams) and in Section 8 (paraxial treatment of rippled sheet beams). It is shown that, for a given magnetic field, the equilibrium electron plasma frequency in a sheet beam is higher than in the corresponding round beam. It is also shown that certain types of sheet beams are characterized by so severe a shearing phenomenon that only very thin beams can be used in practical devices.

Section 9 is concerned with three types of magnetic field perturbations, which can occur in otherwise uniform magnetic focusing systems:

1. Magnetic field reversals
2. Slowly tapered magnetic fields
3. Transverse magnetic fields

2. GENERAL TREATMENT OF UNRIPPLED ROUND BEAMS

2.1. Some Relations Pertaining to the Beam Remote from the Cathode. This section is concerned with certain general relations pertaining to a round beam in which:

1. All properties of the flow are uniform in both the axial and azimuthal directions.

2. Each electron in the beam moves at a constant radius from the axis of symmetry, with a constant angular velocity ω and a constant axial velocity v_z.

3. The beam is immersed in a uniform axial magnetic field; a d-c radial electric field is permitted throughout the system.

4. The beam was emitted from a unipotential cathode, with zero emission velocity; thus thermal velocities are ignored. Such a beam is depicted in Fig. 4.1.

The angular and axial velocities ω and v_z are constants for all electrons moving at a specified position, but both ω and v_z are as-

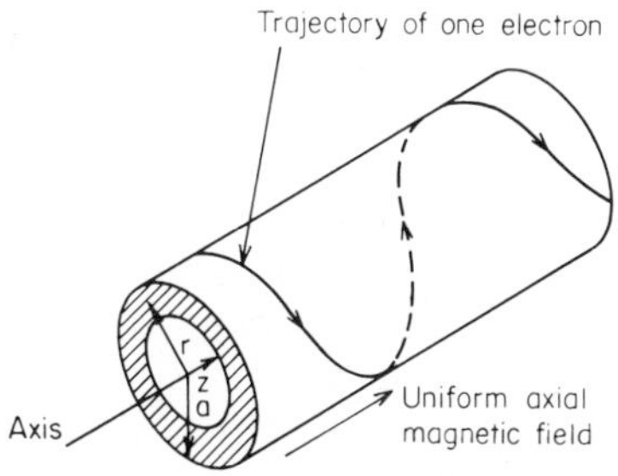

Fig. 4.1. General schematic representation of an axially symmetric round beam. The trajectories of an individual electron is a helix centered on the axis of symmetry.

sumed to be functions of radius throughout the beam. Vanishing of both the radial acceleration and radial velocity for any electron leads to the following radial-force balance equation, valid throughout the flow:

$$r\omega^2 - \eta r\omega B - \eta E_r = 0 \qquad (2.1)$$

This equation [Eq. (2.15) of Chap. I] merely states that the sum of the centrifugal force, the Lorentz magnetic force, and the Lorentz electric force, acting in the radial direction, vanishes.

The energy equation may be written in the form [Eq. (2.27) of Chap. I]

$$2\eta\phi(r) = v_z^2 + (r\omega)^2 \qquad (2.2)$$

Differentiation of Eq. (2.2) with respect to r, remembering that both v_z and ω are functions of r, and substitution for E_r from Eq. (2.1) yields the result

$$v_z v_z' + \omega\left[r^2\left(\omega - \frac{\omega_H}{2}\right)\right]' = 0 \qquad (2.3)$$

where ω_H is the cyclotron frequency ηB, and in this section a prime (′) denotes d/dr. Equation (2.1) may also be substituted into Poisson's equation to yield an expression for the electron charge density ρ, or the electron plasma frequency ω_p; one obtains the expression

$$-\frac{\eta\rho}{\epsilon_0} = \omega_p^2 = [2\omega(\omega_H - \omega) + r\omega'(\omega_H - 2\omega)] \qquad (2.4)$$

In the flow pattern being considered, the current-density vector will, in general, possess both axial and azimuthal components; the radial component $\dot{r}$ vanishes by hypothesis. Because it is assumed that the beam is uniform in both the axial and azimuthal directions, it follows that $\nabla \cdot \mathbf{i} = 0$ throughout the flow. Equation (2.3) is a first-order differential equation relating v_z and ω; therefore any solution of that equation represents a physically realizable beam (provided, of course, that v_z and ω remain finite and that the derivatives v_z' and ω' exist).

There are a large number of possible round-beam configurations satisfying the assumptions of this section. One may take an almost arbitrary radial behavior of either v_z or ω between two specified radial limits. Equation (2.3) must then be solved for the unstated variable. The results of the integration may then be substituted into Eq. (2.2) to obtain the potential, and into Eq. (2.4) to obtain the charge density. Next the charge density may be multiplied by v_z and $r\omega$, respectively, to yield the current-density components. Finally, the total current carried by the beam may be obtained upon integrating the current density i_z between the specified radial limits (with the weighting factor $2\pi r$ included).

The permissible choice of radial variation of v_z or ω is not quite arbitrary. It is necessary to ensure that ω_p^2, as obtained from Eq. (2.4), is everywhere positive or zero. Hence some assumed radial variations for either v_z or ω are precluded, whereas for others the condition that $\omega_p^2 > 0$ will be satisfied only in certain ranges of the radius. An example of this latter type of behavior will be given later.

2.2. Relation of the Beam to the Cathode. For each of the axially symmetric round beams which may be derived by the theory of Sec. 2.1, it is possible to deduce certain properties of the flow at the cathode surface. In particular, a differential equation may be derived, solutions of which yield relations between the shape of the (axially symmetric) cathode and the variation of the emission density over the cathode surface.

The space-charge flow is assumed to be laminar; i.e., no two trajectories intersect. This assumption permits the establishment of a one-to-one relation between a particular radially thin shell of the beam remote from the cathode and the section of the cathode surface from which it was emitted. The magnetic flux density is assumed to possess the constant value B_c over the entire cathode surface, but B_c is not necessarily restricted to the constant value B existing throughout the beam remote from the cathode. Figure 4.2 is a schematic representation of the system to be analyzed.

Let us now focus attention on a thin "layer" of the remote beam, the layer having inner radius r_b and radial thickness dr_b. Let $i_b(r_b)$ represent the longitudinal current density in the remote beam. The current in this layer is presumed to have been emitted from a corresponding region on the cathode having radius r_c, local slope angle θ_c, and emission density i_c. In this book the subscript c always refers to values at the cathode; in the rest of this section the subscript b refers to the remote beam.

Because of the assumption of laminar flow, the total current contained in the beam layer under discussion is constant; i.e.,

$$dI = 2\pi\ r_c i_c(r_c)\ d\ell = 2\pi\ r_b i_b(r_b)\ dr_b$$

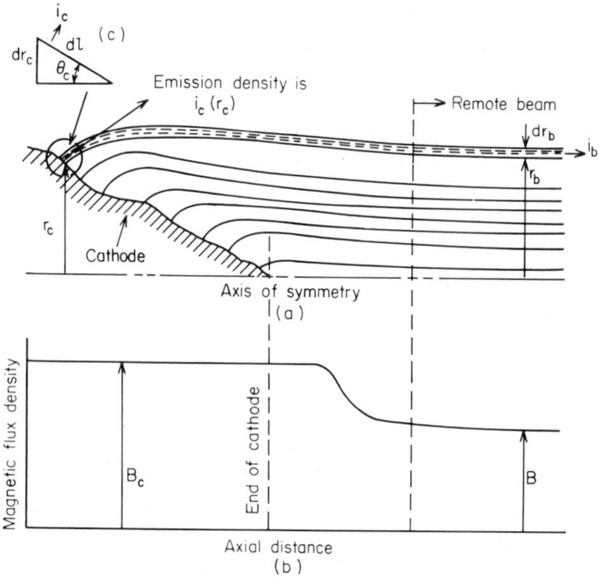

Fig. 4.2. Schematic of a laminar-flow axially symmetric beam. (a) General schematic of the beam, showing how each layer in the remote beam can be traced back to a corresponding region of the cathode surface; (b) axial variation of the axial magnetic field with distance; (c) schematic of the notation used near the cathode.

or
$$\frac{d\ell}{dr_b} = \frac{i_b(r_b)\, r_b}{i_c(r_c)\, r_c} \tag{2.5}$$

By inspection of Fig. 4.2 it is evident that

$$\sin\theta_c = \frac{dr_c}{d\ell}$$

or
$$\sin\theta_c = \frac{dr_c}{dr_b}\Bigg/\frac{d\ell}{dr_b} \tag{2.6}$$

Now Busch's theorem [Eq. (3.8) of Chap. I] may be written in the following form when the fields are uniform:

$$r_c = r_b\left(\frac{\omega_H}{\omega_{Hc}} - \frac{2\omega}{\omega_{Hc}}\right)^{1/2} \tag{2.7}$$

where $\omega_H = \eta B$, $\omega_{Hc} = \eta B_c$, and ω is the angular velocity in the remote beam at the radius r_b. Substituting dr_c/dr_b obtained from differentiating Eq. (2.7) (remembering that ω is a function of r), and Eq. (2.5) into Eq. (2.6), we obtain

$$\frac{\omega_{Hc}}{i_c}\sin\theta_c = -\frac{\omega_H(1 - 2\gamma - r_b\gamma')}{v_{zb}\rho_b} \tag{2.8}$$

where ρ_b and v_{zb} are the charge density and axial velocity in the remote beam at r_b, and γ and γ' are defined by

$$\gamma = \frac{\omega}{\omega_H} \qquad \text{and} \qquad \gamma' = \frac{d\gamma}{dr_b} \tag{2.9}$$

Equation (2.8) relates a local region on the cathode surface to its corresponding layer in the remote beam. Substitution for ρ_b from Eq. (2.4), which may be written in the form

$$-\eta\rho_b = \epsilon_0 \cdot \omega_H^2[2\gamma(1-\gamma) + r_b\,\gamma'(1-2\gamma)] \tag{2.10}$$

leads to the final expression

$$\frac{\epsilon_0}{\eta}\,\frac{\omega_{Hc}}{i_c}\sin\theta_c = \frac{1}{v_{zb}\omega_H}\,\frac{1-2\gamma-r_b\,\gamma'}{2\gamma(1-\gamma)+r_b\,\gamma'(1-2\gamma)} \tag{2.11}$$

The theory of the cathode problem is now formally complete. In order to make use of Eq. (2.11), the following steps are required:

1. A functional relation between either v_z or ω and the remote beam radius is assumed.
2. Equation (2.3) is then to be integrated, and the integration constant appropriately evaluated. The angular velocity ω is expressed in the normalized form $\omega = \gamma\omega_H$.
3. The substitution of the expressions for γ and v_z into the right side of Eq. (2.11) makes it an explicit function of r (that is, r_b); as a result, $(\sin\theta_c)/i_c$ is a known function of r_b.
4. By the use of Busch's theorem [Eq. (2.7)], each value of r_b corresponds to a particular value of r_c, as ω is now a known function of r_b. Thus the left side of Eq. (2.11) becomes an explicit function of r_c.

By the steps outlined above, we have shown how an explicit relation between $(\sin\theta_c)/i_c$ and r_c may be obtained, once the properties of the remote beam have been stated. It is important to note that expressions for $\sin\theta_c$ and i_c as separate functions of r_c have not been obtained, but only their ratio. The designer at this point has the further choice of stating either the shape of the cathode (which will yield θ_c as a function of r_c) or the manner in which the emission density i_c shall vary over the cathode surface, or both.

A special case of practical importance is that for which $\theta_c = 0$; i.e., the cathode is cylindrical. For this case the left side of Eq. (2.11) vanishes, and the preceding theory gives no information about the variation of the emission current density over the cathode surface. Alternatively, if the cathode is magnetically shielded, so that $\omega_{Hc} = 0$, again no information about the variation of emission density is obtained.

The treatment which led to Eq. (2.11) may also be used to calculate the detailed properties of the remote beam if one takes as ab initio information the shape of the cathode and the dependence of i_c

upon r_c. In this case the left side of Eq. (2.11) is a known function of r_c. Hence, from Busch's theorem [Eq. (2.7)], a relation between r_b and ω, with r_c as a connecting parameter, is established. Equation (2.11) may then be considered a first-order differential equation relating v_z and ω. A second such relation is given by Eq. (2.3). Simultaneous solutions of Eqs. (2.3) and (2.11) will then yield v_z and ω as explicit functions of radius in the remote beam.

A simple, yet extremely important example of the second method of using the theory relates to the type of electron gun often utilized in low-noise traveling-wave amplifier tubes. In such guns the cathode is a flat button, so that $\theta_c = 90°$, and the emission density is presumed to be constant over the cathode surface. For this case the left side of Eq. (2.11) is simply a constant.

A further example of the theory is the space-charge-limited emission from a conical cathode immersed in a uniform axial magnetic field. Electron guns based upon this flow pattern are known as magnetron injection guns. The principles of design were described in Chap. II, Secs. 2.4 and 5, and have been treated in detail in the literature.[1,2] For such guns the cathode angle has a constant value, say, θ_0, and the emission density is known to be proportional to cathode radius; that is, $i_c = i_0 r_c / r_0$, where i_0 is the emission density* at a reference radius r_0. Upon using Eq. (2.7) to eliminate r_c and assuming $\omega_{Hc} = \omega_H$, Eqs. (2.3) and (2.11) take the form

$$\frac{\epsilon_0}{\eta} \omega_H^3 \frac{r_0}{i_0} \sin \theta_c = \frac{r_b}{s} (1 - 2\gamma)^{1/2} \frac{1 - 2\gamma - r_b \gamma'}{2\gamma(1-\gamma) + r_b \gamma' (1 - 2\gamma)} \tag{2.12}$$

$$s s' + \gamma[r_b^2(\gamma - \tfrac{1}{2})]' = 0 \tag{2.13}$$

where the prime denotes, as before, d/dr_b, and s is given by

$$s = \frac{v_z}{\omega_H} \tag{2.14}$$

Simultaneous solution of Eqs. (2.12) and (2.13) yields the detailed radial dependence of γ and s; these in turn may be used to obtain the charge density, the two components of current density, and the potential, as explicit functions of radius in the remote beam.

3. UNRIPPLED ISOAXIAL-VELOCITY ROUND BEAMS

3.1. Classification of Beams. Although it is possible to synthesize a large variety of axially symmetric beams from the theoretical treatment presented in Section 2, most practical applications dictate the properties of the beam within narrow limits. Two special cases are of particular importance:

*For ion emission, i_c is numerically negative.

1. Isovelocity beams, in which the longitudinal velocity is a constant, independent of beam radius

2. Isorotational beams, in which the azimuthal angular velocity is a constant

In this section we present the theory of unrippled isovelocity beams, to be followed in Section 4 by the paraxial theory of the same beams. Isorotational beams are discussed in Section 5.

If the axial velocity is a constant, say, $v_z = v_0$, then v_z' vanishes in Eq. (2.3), and the solutions of that equation are either

$$\omega = 0 \qquad \text{or} \qquad \omega = \frac{\omega_H}{2} + \frac{k}{r^2} \tag{3.1}$$

where k is a constant to be determined. The case $\omega = 0$ simply represents a drifting beam in an equipotential region, in the absence of magnetic fields, which, as may be seen from Eq. (2.10), is a beam carrying negligible space charge. The space-charge expansion of drifting beams was discussed in Section 10 of Chap. III.

Two special cases of Eq. (3.1) are of interest; for these two cases the angular velocity ω either vanishes or takes on the specific value ω_0 at some reference radius r_0. For the first case, $\omega = 0$ at $r = r_0$, so that $k = -\omega_H r_0^2/2$ and

$$\omega = \frac{\omega_H}{2}\left(1 - \frac{r_0^2}{r^2}\right) \tag{3.2}$$

Comparison of Eq. (3.2) with Busch's theorem, [Eq. (2.7)] shows that the entire beam could have arisen from a cylindrical cathode of radius r_0, provided that $\omega_{Hc} = \omega_H$. This proviso means that the magnetic flux density is uniform throughout the entire system, including both the cathode region and the remote-beam region. Further properties of this space-charge-flow pattern, often referred to as a Brillouin hollow beam, will be presented shortly.

The second special case is that for which $\omega = \omega_0$ at $r = r_0$, so that $k = -r_0^2(\omega_H/2 - \omega_0)$, and

$$\omega = \frac{\omega_H}{2} - \left(\frac{\omega_H}{2} - \omega_0\right)\frac{r_0^2}{r^2} \tag{3.3}$$

Equation (3.3) is consistent with Busch's theorem if $r_0 = r_c$ and $\omega_0 = (\omega_H - \omega_{Hc})/2$.

Two particular values of ω_H in Eq. (3.3) are of special interest. First, if $\omega_0 = \omega_H/2$, then $\omega = \omega_H/2$ throughout the flow; i.e., not only is the longitudinal velocity a constant, but so is the angular velocity. This type of beam is known as a Brillouin solid beam; its properties will be developed extensively in succeeding sections.

Second, if $\omega_H = 0$, then $\omega = \omega_0 r_0^2/r^2$. The beam represented by this condition is electrostatically focused, and is known as a Harris-flow beam; the corresponding focusing system is referred to as centrifugal electrostatic focusing.

For any of the cases referred to above, a substitution of the second equation of Eq. (3.1) into the plasma-frequency formula [Eq. (2.4)] yields the expression

$$\omega_p^2 = \frac{\omega_H^2}{2} + \frac{2k^2}{r^4} \tag{3.4}$$

This relation shows that either the plasma frequency is a constant (k = 0), equal to 0.707 times the cyclotron frequency ω_H, or the plasma frequency is a rapidly decreasing function of increasing radius, and for large r, ω_p asymptotically approaches the value $0.707\omega_H$.

The properties of the two Brillouin beams and the Harris-flow beam are now developed in detail.

3.2. The Brillouin Solid Beam. The Brillouin solid beam, or simply the Brillouin beam,* is a special case of uniform focusing, which is important both theoretically and from an applications point of view. Because of the low magnetic field required, and the uniform current density and velocity within it, this type of beam has been used extensively in traveling-wave tubes.

It was shown after Eq. (3.3) that, if $\omega_0 = \omega_H/2$, the entire beam rotates at half the cyclotron frequency, i.e., at the Larmor frequency (Section 4 of Chap. I). For this fact to be consistent with Busch's theorem [Eq. (2.7)], either the cathode radius or the cathode flux density B_c must vanish. The former condition has no practical interest, for it implies that the cathode area would vanish. Hence we may conclude that a Brillouin beam arises from a cathode completely shielded from magnetic flux. For this reason, a Brillouin beam is often referred to as a shielded-flow beam.

The potential in the beam may be obtained directly from Eq. (2.2), letting $v_z = v_0$ and $\omega = \omega_H/2$; one thus obtains the relation

$$\phi = \phi_0 + \frac{r^2\,\omega_H^2}{8\eta} \tag{3.5}$$

where $\phi_0 = v_0^2/2\eta$ is the potential on the axis. The constant k in Eq. (3.1) vanishes, so that, from Eq. (3.4) and the definition of ω_p of Eq. (2.4), it may be deduced that the constant charge density ρ_0 is given by

$$\rho_0 = -\frac{\eta\epsilon_0 B^2}{2} \tag{3.6}$$

and the longitudinal current density is given by

$$i_z = \frac{v_0\eta\epsilon_0 B^2}{2} = \frac{v_0\epsilon_0\omega_H^2}{2\eta} \tag{3.7}$$

*The word hollow will always be used when a Brillouin hollow beam is being discussed.

If the beam has an outer radius a, the total current I carried by the beam will be simply $\pi a^2 i_z$. An important formula for the current is stated in terms of the potential ϕ_a at the outer beam radius; ϕ_a is readily obtained from Eq. (3.5), with r = a. The resulting expression may be solved for ϕ_0, and this potential in turn may be used to replace v_0 wherever it appears. By this process the following expression for the total current is obtained:

$$I = \frac{\pi}{\sqrt{2}} \frac{\epsilon_0}{\eta} a^2 \omega_H^2 \left(\eta\phi_a - \frac{\omega_H^2 a^2}{8}\right)^{1/2} \tag{3.8}$$

For a fixed value of ϕ_a the current is maximized for a particular value of $\omega_H a$, namely, $(\omega_H a)^2 = {}^{16}/_3\, \eta\phi_a$. Upon substituting this value of $\omega_H a$ back into Eq. (3.8), the maximum beam perveance P_M is found to be

$$P_M = \frac{I_M}{\phi_a^{3/2}} = \frac{16}{3} \pi \epsilon_0 \left(\frac{\eta}{6}\right)^{1/2} = 25.4 \text{ micropervs} \tag{3.9}$$

A Brillouin beam with perveance less than 25.4 theoretically can be focused by a uniform magnetic field. If an attempt is made to raise the perveance, an unstable condition is reached; the additional current lowers the axial potential, thereby raising the perveance. The axial potential is then lowered still further, and the fraction of the injected current which will pass through the system is abruptly reduced. An experimental test of this phenomenon is extremely difficult, partly because of ion-trapping effects and partly because of the extreme difficulty of creating a well-defined solid round beam the perveance of which is as high as 25.4 micropervs.

One measure of the efficiency of the magnetic field in any magnetic focusing system is the value of the focused plasma frequency, relative to the cyclotron frequency of the magnetic field. In this respect a Brillouin solid beam is realtively efficient, compared with other types of magnetic focusing, in that ω_p is 71 per cent of ω_H.

Because the cathode must be completely shielded from magnetic flux, the formation and injection of a beam into a uniform magnetic field, in order to produce a Brillouin beam, present a serious design problem. One solution to this problem is depicted in Fig. 4.3a. The electron gun is the Pierce gun, based upon the radially inward space-charge flow between concentric spheres; this flow is discussed in Appendix E. A pole piece made from a magnetic material is used to introduce the magnetic flux into the system. The pole piece is approximately coincident with the plane at which the beam would reach its minimum diameter in the absence of the magnetic field; the hole diameter in the pole piece is made as small as possible without interfering with the beam or, in many cases, with the anode itself.

Figure 4.3b is a representation of the axial magnetic field. In practice the transition region, in which the field rises from zero to

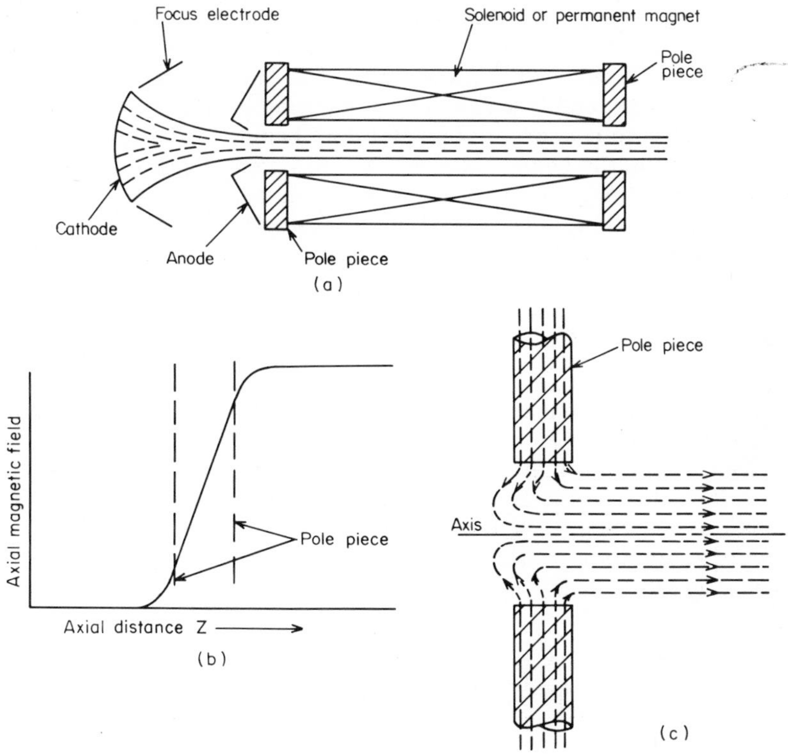

Fig. 4.3. Schematic of an electrode and magnetic field configuration used for producing a Brillouin beam. (a) General schematic of the configuration; (b) axial variation of the axial magnetic field; (c) behavior of flux lines in the vicinity of the pole-piece hole.

its maximum value, is kept as small as possible. Figure 4.3c represents the approximate behavior of the magnetic flux lines in the vicinity of the pole-piece hole; it is clear that in this region the magnetic field possesses strong radial components.

In order to pass from the gun, where the magnetic flux density is essentially zero, into the uniform magnetic field region, an electron is forced to pass through the pole-piece hole. In so doing the electron must move across the radially directed flux lines. From the Lorentz force equation, it follows that a radial component of flux density, together with an *axial* component of electron velocity, will give rise to an *azimuthal* force (or, in this axially symmetric case, a *torque*). It is this force which sets the beam to rotating around the axis of symmetry. An electron located at any radius in the focused beam must have cut across all the flux located between the axis and that radius; the reader may demonstrate that this is the condition which will cause any electron in the beam to rotate with the Larmor frequency.

In practice, it is found that the finite hole diameter required in the pole piece invariably gives rise to rippling of the beam diameter.

As a final note concerning the Brillouin beam we shall derive a formula relating the beam current, radius, potential, and the axial magnetic field which is equivalent to the condition $\omega_p = \omega_H/\sqrt{2}$. In Eq. (3.7) the current density is simply $I/\pi a^2$, where a is the outer beam radius, I is the magnitude of the current, and the axial velocity v_0 is simply $(2\eta\phi_0)^{1/2}$. Use of these relations in Eq. (3.7) then yields

$$I = \frac{\pi}{\sqrt{2}} \epsilon_0(\eta)^{3/2} B^2\phi_0^{1/2} a^2 = 1.46 \times 10^6 (Ba)^2 \phi_0^{1/2} \qquad \text{mks units} \tag{3.10}$$

Figure 4.4 is a nomograph which may be used to solve Eq. (3.10). If the beam current, beam voltage, and the magnetic field strength are given, Eq. (3.10) may be used to calculate a particular radius, often referred to as the Brillouin radius, for which unrippled flow of the beam is possible. It will be seen in later sections that the Brillouin radius is a particularly useful reference length in the theory of rippling beams.

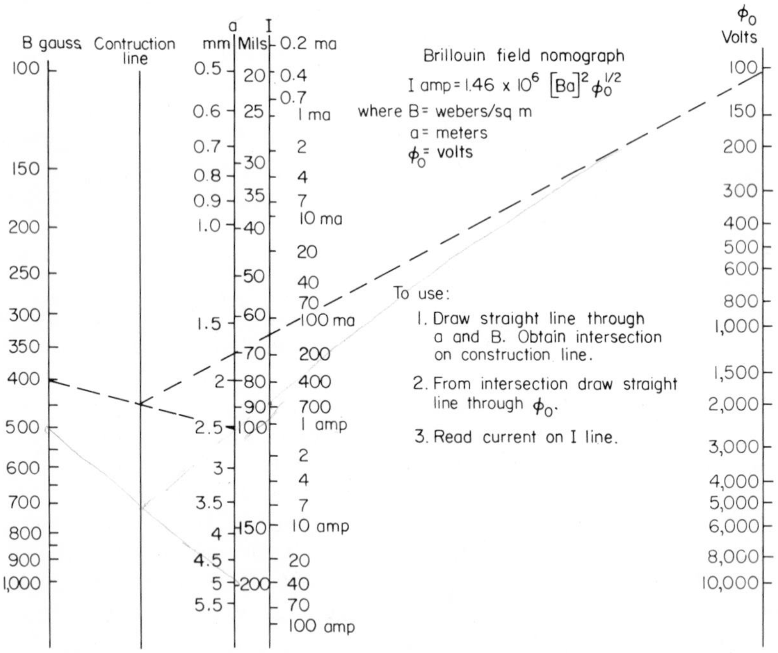

Fig. 4.4. Nomograph for the relation $\omega_p^2 = \omega_H/2$. In the example shown with dotted lines, the current is computed for B = 400 gauss, a = 100 mils, and ϕ_0 = 100 volts.

3.3. The Brillouin Hollow Beam. In many electron-beam devices, such as traveling-wave tubes and multicavity klystrons, it is desirable to employ an electron beam which is axially symmetric and has a uniform axial velocity through the beam and in which the current is confined between two finite radial limits. A Brillouin hollow beam may be designed to possess these properties.

Figure 4.5 depicts an electrode and magnetic field system often used to create a hollow beam. The cathode is a cylinder, and the entire system is immersed in a uniform magnetic field parallel to the axis of the cathode. Because of the magnetic flux at the cathode, the system is one of the class of immersed-flow, or confined-flow, beams. The cathode radius is r_c, and at the cathode the angular velocity of every electron vanishes. Therefore Eq. (3.2) is applicable, with r_0 replaced by r_c.

In a Brillouin hollow beam the inner radius of the focused beam is equal to the cathode radius r_c. Thus the innermost electrons of the beam do not rotate. Electrons located at radii greater than r_c rotate just sufficiently to give rise to a radial Lorentz magnetic force, which will overcome the centrifugal force due to the rotation and the space-charge repulsion force; Eq. (3.2) is merely a mathematical statement of the relation between the angular velocity and radius.

As the integration constant $k = -\omega_H r_c^2/2$ for a Brillouin beam, from Eq. (3.4) the plasma frequency is readily found to be given by the expression

$$\omega_p^2 = \tfrac{1}{2}\omega_H^2\left(1 + \frac{r_c^4}{r^4}\right) \tag{3.11}$$

Thus, at the inner radius of the beam, the plasma frequency equals the cyclotron frequency. For increasing radii the plasma frequency

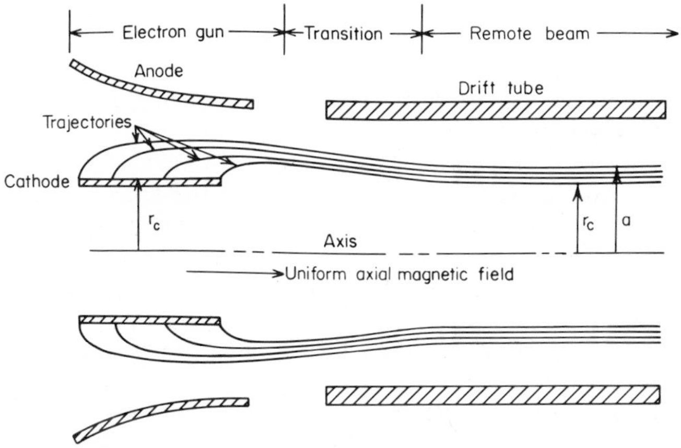

Fig. 4.5. Schematic of an electrode system used to form a hollow Brillouin beam. The system is immersed in a uniform axial magnetic field.

falls rather rapidly to the asympotic value of 71 per cent of the cyclotron frequency. One extremely useful property of the beam is the relatively high value of the focused plasma frequency.

Repeating the process which led to Eq. (3.8), the total current carried by a Brillouin hollow beam of inner radius r_c and outer radius a is found to be

$$I = \frac{\pi}{\sqrt{2}} \frac{\epsilon_0}{\eta} \omega_H^2 a^2 \left(1 - \frac{r_c^4}{a^4}\right)\left[\eta\phi_a - \frac{\omega_H^2 a^2}{8}\left(1 - \frac{r_c^2}{a^2}\right)^2\right]^{1/2} \tag{3.12}$$

where ϕ_a is the potential at the outer radius of the beam. For fixed values of ϕ_a and of the ratio of inner to outer radius, the current will be maximized for a particular value of $\omega_H a$; this value is given by the relation $(\omega_H a)^2 (1 - r_c^2/a^2)^2 = {}^{16}/_3\, \eta\phi_a$. Substitution of this expression back into Eq. (3.12) yields the maximum current and the maximum perveance. In place of Eq. (3.9), one finds that, for the hollow beam,

$$P_M = 25.4 \left(1 - \frac{r_c^4}{a^4}\right) \quad \text{micropervs} \tag{3.13}$$

Thus the maximum perveance of a Brillouin hollow beam is lower than that of the Brillouin solid beam; for a hollow beam in which $a = 2\, r_c$, the difference is less than 7 per cent.

It is possible to select design parameters so that the radial thickness Δr of the hollow beam is much smaller than the inner beam radius. Since the cross-sectional area of the focused beam may be very much smaller than the area of the cathode from which the beam was emitted, the longitudinal current density may be two or more orders of magnitude larger than the emission current density. For such beams Eq. (3.12) reduces to the approximate expression

$$I = \frac{4\pi}{\sqrt{2}} \epsilon_0(\eta)^{3/2} B^2 \phi_0^{1/2} r_c^2 \left(\frac{\Delta r}{r_c}\right) \tag{3.14}$$

where ϕ_0 is defined as in Eq. (3.10). This expression for current is smaller than the corresponding expression for a Brillouin solid beam of radius r_c [Eq. (3.10)] by the factor $4\Delta r/r_c$. If the beam current and voltage, the magnetic field, and the cathode radius are given, Eq. (3.14) may be used to calculate the approximate value of the radial thickness Δr. Note that, for a very thin beam, the plasma frequency is very nearly equal to the cyclotron frequency over the entire radial crosssection.

Figure 4.6 depicts several functions of r_c/a which are relevant to a Brillouin hollow beam.

No known solution exists to the space-charge-flow equations which will permit a detailed design of the electron gun depicted in Fig. 4.5. However, many different gun designs have been obtained by more or less empirical methods. The flow is of the skew-congruent variety, so that in principle the velocity should be expressible as the gradient of a velocity potential; unfortunately, this fact has not helped solve the problem.

In order that the emitted electrons may be ejected from the gun, it is necessary that an axial electric field E_z exist in the vicinity of the cathode (though not right on the cathode surface). Such a field is created in practice by making the anode a curvilinear surface of revolution, as depicted in Fig. 4.5. It is desirable, of course, to shape the anode so that the flow is laminar and the emission density approximately uniform over the entire cathode surface. The lack of an exact solution to the space-charge-flow equations make these aims difficult to achieve in practice.

There is strong, although not decisive, experimental evidence to support the view that the noisiness of a Brillouin hollow beam is related directly to the transit time of the electrons through the gun; long transit times invariably seem to produce noisy beams. It is beyond the scope of this book to consider beam noise phenomena in detail, but it is worth noting two possible qualitative explanations for the tendency of guns having large transit times to produce noisy beams.

If the longitudinal electric field created by the anode is much less than the radial field, the electrons will rotate many times around

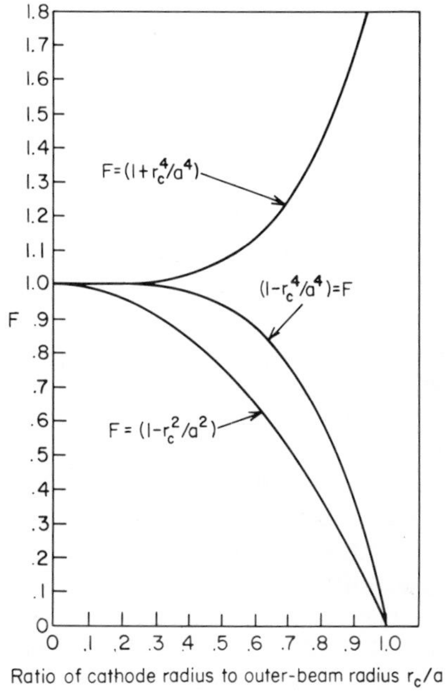

Fig. 4.6. Some functions of r_c/a pertinent to a Brillouin hollow beam.

the cathode while moving through the gun proper. It is possible to show that unstable space-charge waves may be generated by the inevitable small initial inhomogeneities in the beam; such irregularities then have an opportunity to grow to substantial size if the electron transit times are long. A by-product of growing noise waves in the gun is the phenomenon of cathode back bombardment; here a small percentage of the emitted electrons gain a-c energy from the growing space-charge waves, then return to and strike the cathode with this excess energy. Back bombardment of the cathode probably makes the beam noisier still, and the overall result is an exceedingly noisy beam.

The cure for such beam noisiness is to design the gun for the smallest possible electron transit times. This can be accomplished by reducing the length-to-diameter ratio of the cathode and by increasing the local slopes of the anode; the first reduces the cathode area, and the second may increase the variation of emission current density over the cathode surface, and possibly introduce substantial nonlaminarity into the flow.

3.4. Harris Flow. An important form of electrostatic focusing which has found application in both forward-wave and backward-wave traveling-wave tubes is known as Harris flow. As $\omega_H = 0$ in this type of beam, the constant k in Eq. (3.1) is simply $\omega_0 r_0^2$. Hence the angular velocity is given by

$$\omega = \frac{\omega_0 r_0^2}{r^2} \tag{3.15}$$

and the plasma frequency is given by

$$\omega_p^2 = 2\,\omega_0^2 \frac{r_0^4}{r^4} \tag{3.16}$$

Comparison of Eqs. (3.15) and (3.16) shows that, in Harris flow, the plasma frequency at every radius is $\sqrt{2}$ times the local angular velocity.

Harris flow is created by injecting a rotating annular beam between two concentric conducting cylinders, as shown in Fig. 4.7a, the inner of which is maintained at the higher d-c potential. The radial electric field is adjusted to a value which will just balance the centrifugal force acting on the electrons. Provided that the electron charge density of the injected beam varies as the inverse fourth power of the radius, as in Eq. (3.16), a force balance is possible at every radius in a beam of finite radial thickness.

Suppose the beam just fills the annular gap between the two cylinders, as depicted in Fig. 4.7b. Let the cylinder radius and potentials be a, ϕ_a and b, ϕ_b, respectively, with $a < b$ and $\phi_a > \phi_b$. The potential in the beam is given by Eq. (2.2):

$$2\eta\ \phi(r) = v_0^2 + \frac{\omega_0^2 r_0^4}{r^2} \tag{3.17}$$

from which it follows that

$$2\eta\ (\phi_a - \phi_b) = \left(\frac{\omega_0 r_0^2}{ab}\right)^2 (b^2 - a^2) \tag{3.18}$$

The factor $\omega_0 r_0^2$ may be eliminated by using Eq. (3.17), again at radius a, to obtain the relation

$$\phi_a - \phi_b = \left(\phi_a - \frac{v_0^2}{2\eta}\right)\left(1 - \frac{a^2}{b^2}\right) \tag{3.19}$$

Equation (3.19) gives the required potential difference in terms of the inner cylinder potential, the axial velocity, and the ratio of the cylinder radii.

From Eq. (3.16) the longitudinal current density of the Harris-flow beam is found to be

$$i_z = 2\epsilon_0\ \omega_0^2\ r_0^4\ \frac{v_0}{r^4\eta} \tag{3.20}$$

from which the magnitude of the total current I, confined between the cylinders of radii a and b, can be expressed in the form

$$I = \frac{2\pi\epsilon_0}{\eta}\ \omega_0^2 r_0^4 \left(2\eta\phi_a - \frac{\omega_0^2 r_0^4}{a^2}\right)^{1/2} \left(\frac{1}{a^2} - \frac{1}{b^2}\right) \tag{3.21}$$

In Eq. (3.21) the longitudinal velocity has been replaced by the expression obtained from Eq. (3.17) at radius a.

For a fixed value of ϕ_a, the current is at a maximum value if $\omega_0^2 r_0^4 = \frac{4}{3}\eta\phi_a a^2$. Substitution of this value into Eq. (3.21) then yields the maximum perveance expression, namely,

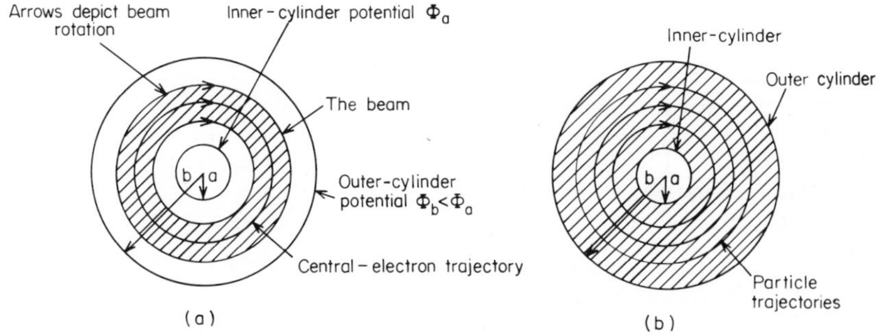

Fig. 4.7. Cross section of a Harris-flow beam. (a) With beam not filling annular gap between focusing cylinders; (b) with beam filling annular gap between focusing cylinders.

$$\frac{I_M}{\phi_a^{3/2}} = P_M = {}^{16}\!/_{3}\pi\epsilon_0\left(\frac{\eta}{6}\right)^{1/2}\left(1 - \frac{a^2}{b^2}\right) = 25.4\left(1 - \frac{a^2}{b^2}\right) \text{ micropervs} \quad (3.22)$$

Equation (3.22) indicates that, for a fairly thick Harris-flow beam that is, $a/b \ll 1$), the maximum perveance is high.

Substitution of the initial value for $\omega_0^2 r_0^4$ back into Eq. (3.17) indicates that, at the inner radius a, one-third of the total beam energy is associated with longitudinal motion and two-thirds of the energy is associated with rotation. At larger radii, ω decreases sufficiently fast so that the fraction of total energy associated with rotation decreases; in fact, that fraction at any radius is easily found to be $(2\,a^2/r^2)/[1 + (2\,a^2/r^2)]$.

The requirements that, in Harris flow, the entire beam must rotate and that the charge density ideally should vary as the inverse fourth power of radius are difficult to satisfy simultaneously. The focusing system itself is both electrostatic and axially symmetric. Any attempt to design an electron gun possessing the same two properties is doomed to failure; the axial symmetry precludes the existence of an azimuthal electric field, which might otherwise produce the torque needed to set the beam rotating. One solution of this problem, which has been found usable for relatively low perveance beams, is illustrated in Fig. 4.8a. Here the gun per se is electrostatic and axially symmetric. Just beyond the anode a radial magnetic field is introduced, and the beam is forced to cut across the radial flux. With proper adjustment of the radial-flux density, the correct angular velocity may be imparted to the beam.

The simple electron gun depicted in Fig. 4.8a is not capable of producing the required $1/r^4$ variation of charge density. A more elaborate gun, based upon the electrostatic flow from a conical cathode, is depicted in Fig. 4.8b; this gun produces the required charge-density variation.[3] Again, a radial magnetic field is employed to create the beam rotation.

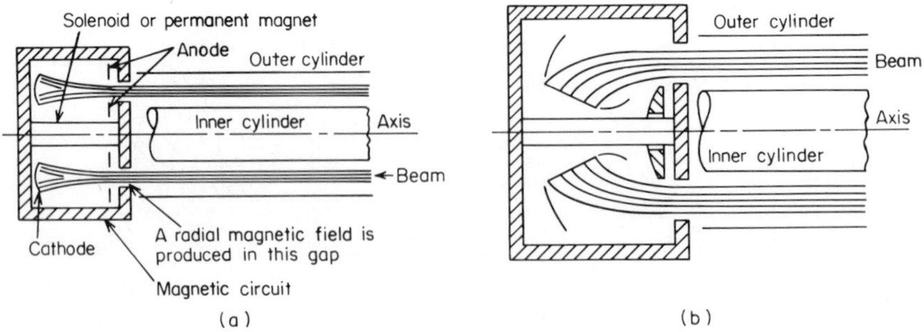

Fig. 4.8. Electrode systems for producing Harris-flow beams. (a) Simple electrode system for producing approximate Harris flow; (b) more complex electrode system for producing $\rho \propto r^{-4}$.

4. PARAXIAL ANALYSIS OF ROUND BEAMS

4.1. Uniform Magnetic Focusing; Equilibrium Radii. This section is concerned with the paraxial theory of round beams immersed in a uniform axial magnetic field and possessing a uniform axial potential ϕ_0. Two important special cases of the theory of this section are:

1. The Brillouin solid beam, discussed in Sec. 3.2 and illustrated in Fig. 4.3a
2. The Brillouin hollow beam, discussed in Sec. 3.3 and illustrated in Fig. 4.5

The discussion of this section is not restricted to any particular value of magnetic flux density at the cathode; thus B_c is not required to vanish, as in the case of the Brillouin solid beam, and the flux density is not assumed to be uniform throughout the entire system, as in the case of the Brillouin hollow beam.

The paraxial-ray equation, [Eq. (2.25) of Chap. III] is applicable for the present problem. As the axial potential is constant, $\mathcal{B} = B$, $\mathcal{B}_0 = B_c$, and the paraxial-ray equation assumes the form

$$r'' + \frac{\eta}{8\phi_0}\left(rB^2 - \frac{B_c^2 r_c^4}{r^3}\right) - \frac{P}{4\pi\epsilon_0(2\eta)^{1/2}\, r} = 0 \tag{4.1}$$

where P is the beam perveance $I/\phi_0^{3/2}$. It is evident that Eq. (4.1) is the equation of an undamped nonlinear harmonic oscillator; in this section, several important properties of this oscillatory system are deduced.

One particular solution of Eq. (4.1) has the form $r = r_e$ = constant; here r_e is the equilibrium radius, corresponding to a force-balance condition for which the outer radius of the beam is constant. Substitution into Eq. (4.1) yields the relation

$$r_e^4 - \frac{\sqrt{2}\,P\,\phi_0}{\pi\epsilon_0(\eta)^{3/2}\,B^2}\, r_e^2 - \left(\frac{B_c}{B}\right)^2 r_c^4 = 0 \tag{4.2}$$

There are two special cases of Eq. (4.2), namely,

1. $P = 0$; i.e., the current carried by the beam produces a negligible space-charge force. The value of r_e is defined as r_a, where*

$$r_e = r_a = r_c\left(\frac{B_c}{B}\right)^{1/2} \tag{4.3}$$

2. $B_c = 0$; i.e., the cathode is completely shielded from magnetic flux. For this case, the value r_e is defined as r_b, where

$$r_e^2 = r_b^2 = \frac{\sqrt{2}\,I}{\pi\epsilon_0(\eta)^{3/2}\,B^2\phi_0^{1/2}} \tag{4.4}$$

*Since the paraxial equation involves only the square of B and B_c, without loss of generality these fields may be considered positive.

Comparison of Eqs. (4.4) and (3.10) shows that r_b is simply the Brillouin radius of the (shielded-cathode) beam. In this case paraxial theory agrees perfectly with the exact theory of Sec. 3.2.

In terms of the radii r_a and r_b, Eq. (4.2) may conveniently be expressed in the form

$$r_e^4 - r_e^2 r_b^2 - r_a^4 = 0 \tag{4.5}$$

This equation may be solved for the equilibrium radius r_e in either of the equivalent forms

$$r_e = r_b\left[\frac{1 + (1 + 4\, r_a^4/r_b^4)^{1/2}}{2}\right]^{1/2} \tag{4.6a}$$

$$r_e = r_a\left[\left(1 + \frac{r_b^4}{4r_a^4}\right)^{1/2} + \frac{r_b^2}{2r_a^2}\right]^{1/2} \tag{4.6b}$$

Equation (4.6a) is particularly useful if $r_a < r_b$, that is, if the cathode flux is sufficiently small to produce only a beam-diameter perturbation in a system with an otherwise completely shielded cathode. Similarly, Eq. (4.6b) is useful if $r_b < r_a$; that is, if the space-charge force is small enough to produce only a beam-diameter perturbation in a system with the cathode immersed in a finite flux density. A common example of a beam of the first type is the Brillouin beam illustrated in Fig. 4.3a; in this system, a small but finite magnetic field often threads through the cathode. Beams of the second type are often used in low-noise traveling-wave amplifiers; in these beams the current is usually so small that the Brillouin radius is only a very small fraction of the equilibrium radius of the focused beam. In both cases the equilibrium radius r_e is larger than

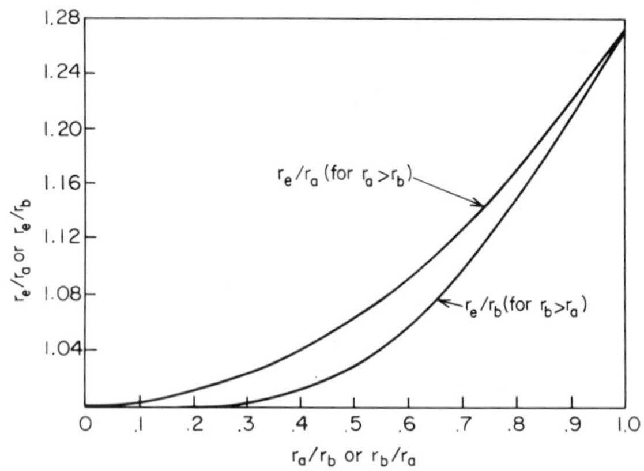

Fig. 4.9. The variation of r_e versus r_a/r_b deduced from Eq. (4.6). For $r_a > r_b$, the abscissa is r_b/r_a and the ordinate r_e/r_a; for $r_b > r_a$, the abscissa is r_a/r_b and the ordinate r_e/r_b.

either r_a or r_b; curves of r_e/r_b, for the first case, and of r_e/r_a, for the second case, are given in Fig. 4.9.

Equation (4.3) shows that, if $I \approx 0$, the equilibrium radius r_a is greater or less than the cathode radius r_c, as the cathode flux density B_c is greater or less than the uniform magnetic field B. Thus the focused beam is magnetically expanded or magnetically compressed as B_c is greater or less than B. Such behavior of the focusing system is illustrated in Fig. 4.10. The phenomena of magnetic expansion and compression can be of material assistance to the electron-gun designer. It is left as an exercise for the reader to show that magnetic expansion or compression is also possible even if the beam current is not vanishingly small. This is discussed further in Section 9.

As pointed out above, if $B_c \neq 0$, the equilibrium radius of the focused beam will exceed the Brillouin radius. The reader will recall, from Sec. 3.2, that in a Brillouin solid beam $\omega_p = \omega_H/\sqrt{2}$. Therefore, if magnetic flux threads through the cathode, the electron plasma frequency must be less than 71 per cent of the cyclotron frequency (in later sections it is shown that this statement is not true if a radial variation of axial velocity is permitted).

4.2. First Integral of the Paraxial Equation; Beam Stiffness. If rippling occurs, Eq. (4.1) may be used to deduce the beam properties; Fig. 4.11 depicts the radial behavior of a rippled Brillouin beam. A first integral of the equation may be used to obtain the turning points of the motion (maximum and minimum radii), but information concerning the rippling frequency and wavelength requires a second integration. The first integral can always be made, but the second integral is possible, in closed form, only if the current vanishes. In the presence of finite current, the most useful information is obtained by perturbing the unrippled solution, assuming that the maximum change in radius due to rippling is small compared with the mean radius; it is thereby possible to obtain approximate information concerning rippling frequency and wavelength. Fortunately, this latter information, which is the most difficult to obtain, is often the least necessary in practical applications.

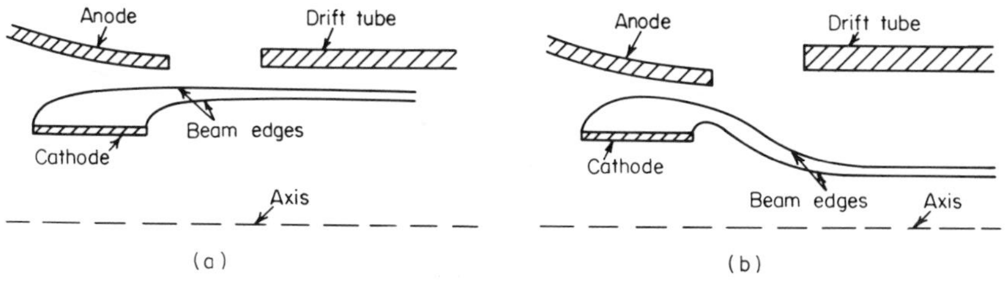

Fig. 4.10. Schematic of electron trajectories in a Brillouin beam. (*a*) $B_c > B$; (*b*) $B > B_c$.

It is convenient to make the substitutions

$$\begin{aligned} \beta_H^2 &= \frac{\eta B^2}{2\phi_0} \\ \beta_{Hc}^2 &= \frac{\eta\, B_c^2}{2\phi_0} \\ p &= \frac{P}{4\pi\epsilon_0(2\eta)^{1/2}} \\ \sigma &= \frac{r}{r_e} \end{aligned} \tag{4.7}$$

The parameter β_H may be written as ω_H/v_0, and has dimensions of inverse length. Equation (4.1) may be integrated after multiplying through by $2r'$, and the constant of integration is determined by letting $r' = r'(0)$ at the equilibrium radius r_e of Eq. (4.5). By this means the following first integral is obtained:

$$(\sigma')^2 = [\sigma'(0)]^2 + \frac{\beta_H^2}{4}(2 - \sigma^2 - \sigma^{-2}) + \frac{p}{r_e^2}(\sigma^{-2} + \ln \sigma^2 - 1) \tag{4.8}$$

The turning points are found upon setting σ' to zero, then solving a transcendental relation for σ as a function of $\sigma'(0)$, p, and $\beta_H^2 r_e^2$. Over a large range of initial slope, it is found that a nearly linear relation exists between $\sigma'(0)$ and the maximum excursion of the beam radius from the equilibrium radius r_e. For small slopes it is found that the maximum outward excursion is nearly equal to the maximum inward excursion, the equality being approached as the initial slope is reduced. This result is easily seen by expressing σ in the form $\sigma \approx 1 + \epsilon$ and expanding Eq. (4.8) in powers of ϵ; keeping terms up to ϵ^2, Eq. (4.8) becomes

$$(\sigma')^2 = [\sigma'(0)]^2 - \epsilon^2\left(\frac{\beta_H^2}{2} - 2\frac{p}{r_e^2}\right) \tag{4.9}$$

The turning points are obtained when the right-hand side of Eq. (4.9) is zero.

An extremely useful property of the beam is the ratio of the initial slope $r'(0)$ to the maximum radial excursion from equilibrium produced by that slope, in the limit of small initial slope. This ratio is known as the <u>beam stiffness</u>, and is represented by the symbol $\mathcal{S}$. Mathematically, $\mathcal{S}$ is therefore given by

$$\mathcal{S} = \frac{r'(0)}{r_M - r_e} = \frac{\sigma'(0)}{\sigma_M - 1} \approx \frac{r'(0)}{r_e - r_m} = \frac{\sigma'(0)}{1 - \sigma_m} \tag{4.10}$$

where $r'(0)$, $\sigma'(0)$ are small, and as usual the subscripts M and m denote the maximum and minimum values of r and σ. The equality of the four expressions in Eq. (4.10) follows from the lack of a coefficient of ϵ in Eq. (4.9).

One purpose of a focusing system is to keep the beam closely bound to its equilibrium diameter, even in the presence of an initial transverse velocity. Beam stiffness is a quantitative measure of the ability of the focusing system to achieve this end. As the stiffness is increased, a larger initial beam slope is required to produce a given radial-oscillation amplitude; alternatively, for a given initial slope, the oscillation amplitude will decrease with increasing stiffness. The stiffness is a measure of the ability of the focusing system to tolerate improper beam-injection conditions while keeping the beam bound between prescribed radial limits.

An approximate relation for the stiffness, valid if the maximum radial excursions are small compared with the equilibrium radius, may be obtained by setting $\sigma' = 0$ in Eq. (4.9) to find ϵ_M and then substituting in Eq. (4.10) to give

$$\mathcal{S} = \frac{\sigma'(0)}{\epsilon_M} = \beta_H \left(1 - \frac{r_b^2}{2r_e^2}\right)^{1/2} \tag{4.11}$$

In Eq. (4.11), ϵ_M is the maximum value of ϵ, and p has been replaced, using Eqs. (4.4) and (4.7), by $\beta_H^2 r_b^2/4$.

If the cathode is magnetically shielded, $r_e = r_b$, and the stiffness is just $0.707\,\beta_H$. On the other hand, if magnetic flux threads the cathode, $r_e > r_b$, and the stiffness is increased, tending toward β_H as $r_b/r_e \to 0$. Thus the presence of cathode flux increases the stiffness, but only at the expense of an increase in beam radius.

4.3. Second Integral of the Paraxial Equation; Resonant Frequency and Wavelength. If the current vanishes, p = 0 in Eq. (4.1), and a second integral of that equation may be obtained by elementary methods. The second integral may be expressed in the form

$$r = \frac{\sqrt{2}}{\beta_H}\left\{k - \left(k^2 - \frac{\beta^4}{4} r_e^4\right)^{1/2} \sin\left[\beta_H (z + z_0)\right]\right\}^{1/2} \tag{4.12}$$

where $$k = [r'(0)]^2 + \frac{\beta_H^2}{2} r_e^2 \tag{4.13}$$

and

$$z_0 = -\beta_H^{-1} \sin^{-1} \frac{k - \frac{1}{2}\beta_H^2 r_e^2}{(k^2 - \frac{1}{4}\beta_H^4 r_e^4)^{1/2}} \tag{4.14}$$

The initial conditions of the motion are that $r = r_e$ and $r' = r'(0)$, where $z = 0$.

From Eq. (4.12), it is evident that the radial motion is periodic, although not sinusoidal, in z. The axial period of the motion is known as the rippling wavelength, and is designated by the symbol λ_n; it follows from Eq. (4.12) that

$$\lambda_n = \frac{2\pi}{\beta_H} = \frac{2\pi\, v_0}{\omega_H} \tag{4.15}$$

where v_0 is the constant axial velocity, and we have used Eq. (4.7).

If, in Eq. (4.12), we replace z in terms of time, letting $z = v_0 t$, then it follows that the motion is periodic in time. A radian frequency ω_n, known as the transverse resonant frequency, or the rippling frequency, may be defined; it is easily verified that ω_n is given by the relation

$$\omega_n = \omega_H \tag{4.16}$$

where we have again used Eq. (4.7). Thus, in a magnetically focused round beam carrying negligible current, the radian frequency of the radial oscillation is equal to the cyclotron frequency of the focusing magnetic field. It is important to note that both λ_n and ω_n are independent of the cathode-flux density B_c.

All uniform and periodic focusing systems are characterized by a certain beam stiffness, rippling wavelength, and rippling frequency; these quantities may be used to compare one focusing system with another. In purely electrostatic focusing systems the terms rippling wavelength and rippling frequency of the beam oscillations are used also for the terms λ_n and ω_n.

Further study of Eq. (4.12) shows that the motion is not symmetrical about the equilibrium radius. In fact, the outward excursion exceeds the inward excursion, as depicted in Fig. 4.11. It is also possible to show that the average value of r, obtained by averaging Eq. (4.12) over a cycle, exceeds the equilibrium radius. As a final remark we may note that Eq. (4.12) may be expanded in terms of $r'(0)$ as that slope tends toward zero. If the resulting expression is used to calculate the stiffness, it is found that $\mathcal{S} \approx \beta_H$, in agreement with Eq. (4.11), if $r_b = 0$ (i.e., if $I = 0$).

If the current is not negligibly small, an approximate solution of Eq. (4.1) may be obtained, assuming that the rippling is small compared with the equilibrium radius. Let us express r in the form $r = r_e + r_1$, with $|r_1| \ll r_e$. This form may be inserted into Eq. (4.1), which may then be expanded. If only first-order terms in r_1 are retained, the following linear harmonic oscillator equation ensues:

$$r_1'' + r_1 \beta_H^2 \left(1 - \frac{r_b^2}{2r_e^2}\right) = 0 \tag{4.17}$$

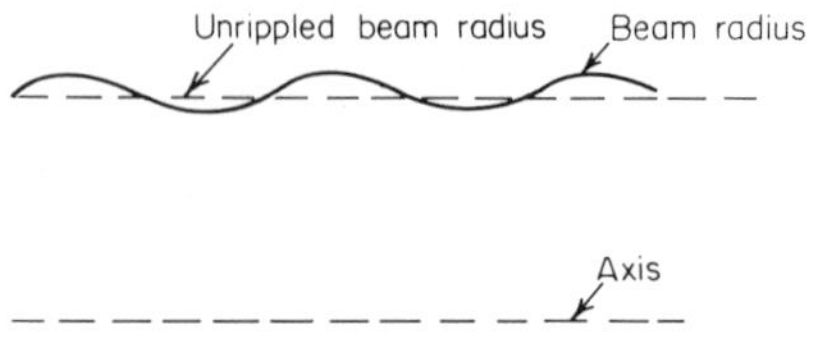

Fig. 4.11. Schematic of rippled Brillouin beam showing unsymmetric ripple.

The complete solution of this equation is sinusoidal; the rippling frequency of the motion is given by $\omega_n = (1 - r_b^2/2r_e^2)^{1/2}$, and the rippling wavelength is given by $\lambda_n = 2\pi/[\beta_H(1 - r_b^2/2r_e^2)^{1/2}]$.

Equation (4.17) can be written, from Eq. (4.11),

$$r_1'' + r_1 \mathcal{S}^2 = 0 \tag{4.18}$$

This is a general result. If the excursions are small, so that the rippling equation can be linearized, then the definition of $\mathcal{S}$ of Eq. (4.10) is equivalent to

$$\mathcal{S} = \frac{2\pi}{\lambda_n} = \beta_n \tag{4.19}$$

This form of the definition of $\mathcal{S}$ is used in the subsequent analysis.

The presence of space charge reduces the stiffness and the rippling frequency and increases the rippling wavelength of the radial motion, as compared with a magnetically focused round beam carrying negligible current. It is easily verified that, in a Brillouin beam for which $B_c = 0$ and $r_b = r_e$,

$$\lambda_n = 2\pi\sqrt{2}/\beta_H \qquad \text{and} \qquad \omega_n = \omega_H/\sqrt{2}$$

Although space charge decreases the stiffness, it also decreases the percentage ripple caused by a given absolute error in entrance conditions. For small r_1, caused by a slope error r_0', the solution of Eq. (4.17) is

$$r = r_e + \frac{r_0'}{\mathcal{S}} \sin \mathcal{S} z \tag{4.20}$$

Thus the fractional ripple is Δ_M, where

$$\Delta_M = \frac{r_0'}{r_e \mathcal{S}} \tag{4.21}$$

Using the r_e and $\mathcal{S}$ of Eqs. (4.6) and (4.11),

$$\Delta_M = \frac{r_0'}{(1 + r_b^4/4r_a^4)^{1/2}} = \frac{r_0'}{\beta_H^2(r_b^4 + 4r_a^4)^{1/2}} \tag{4.22}$$

As space charge is increased for the same magnetic fields, r_b/r_a increases; therefore Δ_M decreases.

The foregoing argument applies generally. In sheet-beam geometries $\mathcal{S}$ is independent of space charge but Δ_M still decreases with increasing space charge.

4.4. Application to a Brillouin Hollow Beam. Paraxial theory of hollow beams was discussed in Section 7 of Chap. III. It was shown that beam rippling could be analyzed approximately under certain conditions; i.e., for the inner surface of the beam the paraxial equation is written with I = 0, and for the outer surface of the beam the equation is taken to include the total beam current. The development presented in Sec. 4.3 is therefore applicable to the Brillouin hollow beam depicted in Fig. 4.5 under the following conditions: For the inner surface of the beam, r_b and r_e are defined by $r_b = 0$ and $r_e = r_c$; for the outer surface of the beam, r_b is the value calculated from Eq. (4.4), and r_e is the value of a calculated from Eq. (3.12). Therefore, for the inner beam surface Eq. (4.2) is applicable, r_e being replaced by r_c in that equation. From the general relation between r_b, r_a, and r_e of Eq. (4.5), the expression $(1 - r_b^2/2r_e^2)$ can be written $(r_e^4 + r_a^4)/2r_e^4$. If the outer edge of the beam is written $r_e = r_c(1 + \alpha)$, Eq. (4.17) for this outer edge becomes

$$r_1'' + \tfrac{1}{2} r_1 \beta_H^2 \left[1 + \frac{1}{(1+\alpha)^4} \right] = 0 \qquad (4.23)$$

This equation is applicable if the rippling is small. It is frequently the case that a Brillouin hollow beam is designed to be radially thin, so that the approximate relation (3.14) may be used in place of the exact relation (3.12). In this case an approximate form of Eq. (4.23) may be used, since α is small.

$$r_1'' + r_1 \beta^2 (1 - 2\alpha) = 0 \qquad (4.24)$$

For the inner beam radius, Eq. (4.24) is valid with $\alpha = 0$, which predicts a rippling frequency $\omega_n = \omega_H$. Equations (4.23) and (4.24) show that the rippling wavelength λ_n is greater for the outer beam radius than for the inner beam radius of a Brillouin hollow beam. A given perturbation at both inner and outer radii will therefore result in a rather confused beam outline; the amplitude of radial oscillations for the inner surface will exceed that of the outer surface, and the wavelength for the inner surface will be smaller. If laminar flow is assumed, the discussion of Section 7 of Chap. III leads to the conclusion that the rippling amplitude and wavelength vary smoothly between the inner and outer bounding surfaces of the beam. Figure 4.12 is intended to depict the behavior of the rippled beam.

4.5. Harris Flow. The electrostatic focusing system depicted in Fig. 4.8, known as Harris flow, is a uniform system which is readily analyzed by paraxial methods, provided it is assumed the radial

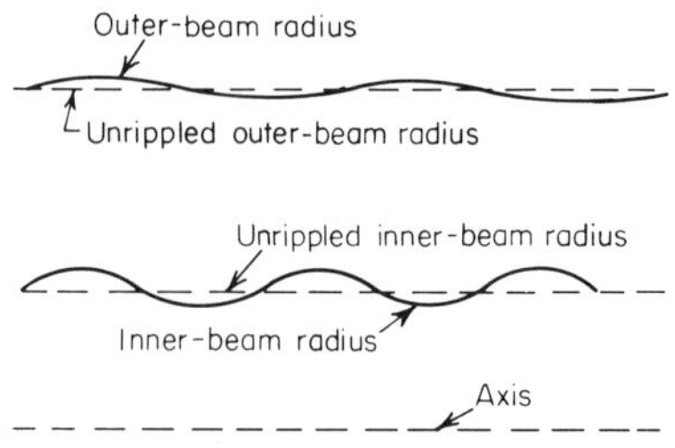

Fig. 4.12. Schematic of rippled hollow Brillouin beam showing the different rippling wavelengths of the inner and outer edges.

thickness of the beam is small compared with the mean radius. The beam may be considered to be a curvilinear sheet beam; since there is no axial acceleration and the axial motion is uncoupled to the (r,θ) motion, without loss of generality the axial motion may be ignored.

In the paraxial theory of Harris flow the ray axis is considered to be an equipotential circle; this circle is the central electron trajectory shown in Fig. 4.8a. The paraxial-ray equation for a curvilinear sheet beam [Eq. (6.19) of Chap. III] is applicable with κ = constant, $\phi = \phi_0$ = constant, and $\mathcal{A} = \mathcal{A}_1 = B_z = 0$. (Note that ϕ_0 is the potential which accounts for only the azimuthal velocity; it is the full beam potential only if the axial velocity vanishes.) Under these restrictions the paraxial equation is simply

$$r'' + 2\,\kappa^2\,r = \frac{P}{4\,\epsilon_0 \ell (2\eta)^{1/2}} \tag{4.25}$$

It is assumed that $r > 0$ to avoid the used of the $\pm$ sign in the right side of Eq. (4.25). (Refer to last paragraph of Section 3, Chap. III.)

It is evident that the particular solution of Eq. (4.25) has the form

$$r = r_e = \frac{P}{8\,\kappa^2\,\ell\epsilon_0(2\eta)^{1/2}} \tag{4.26}$$

which is the unrippled, or equilibrium, half thickness. Equation (4.25) may then be written in the form

$$r'' + 2\,\kappa^2\,r = 2\,\kappa^2\,r_e \tag{4.27}$$

which has the general solution

$$r = r_e + (r_0 - r_e)\cos(\sqrt{2}\,\kappa z) + \frac{r_0'}{2\kappa}\sin(\sqrt{2}\,\kappa z) \tag{4.28}$$

where the initial conditions are $r = r_0$ and $r' = r_0'$ at $= 0$.

In a thin Harris-flow beam the equilibrium perveance is given by Eq. (4.26); if the initial half-thickness r_0 does not equal the equilibrium half-thickness r_e, or if the initial slope is finite, the beam will oscillate with rippling wavelength $\lambda_n = \sqrt{2}\,\pi/\kappa$ and with rippling frequency $\omega_n = \sqrt{2}\,\kappa\,v_0$, where v_0 is the linear velocity of the central (ray axis) electron around the axis. The angular velocity ω_0 of this electron is simply $\omega_0 = \kappa\,v_0$; so the cyclotron frequency of the rippling is $\sqrt{2}$ times the angular velocity ω_0. The angular distance covered by an electron during one complete oscillation cycle is $\sqrt{2}\pi$ radians $\approx 254^\circ$; this is a well-known result for the cylindrical condenser lens,[4] which is an early form of Harris focusing.

The equilibrium condition represented by Eq. (4.26) may be written in terms of the perveance per square $P_\square$ (Section 10 of Chap. III), given by $P_\square = 2r_eP/\ell$. Equation (4.26) then assumes the form $P_\square = 16\epsilon_0(2\eta)^{1/2}(r_e\kappa)^2$. Upon letting $w = r_e$ = equilibrium beam half-thickness, and letting $R = 1/\kappa$ = mean beam radius, the formula for $P_\square$ becomes

$$P_\square = 16\,\epsilon_0(2\eta)^{1/2}\left(\frac{w}{R}\right)^2 = 84.0\left(\frac{w}{R}\right)^2 \text{ micropervs} \qquad (4.29)$$

In Chap. V it will be shown that Eq. (4.29) is a special case of a general result pertaining to curvilinear sheet beams.

The stiffness, derived from Eq. (4.28), is $\mathcal{S} = \sqrt{2}\,\kappa$, so that the stiffness increases as the radius of the ray axis decreases. This is a serious disadvantage for Harris flow, for in many applications the stiffness may be raised to practical values only by reducing the beam diameter, and therefore the inner cylinder diameter, to a value which is impractically small. This fact, plus the fundamental difficulty of launching a Harris-flow beam, discussed in Sec. 3.4, has restricted Harris flow to applications in which the power level of the beam is low and in which substantial interception of the beam on the focusing cylinders is tolerable. A detailed analysis of the rippling inside a Harris-flow beam has been given by Crumly;[5] the analysis includes the case for which the charge density ρ is independent of radius, rather than varying as r^{-4} as in Eq. (3.19). Crumly's paper also includes the effects of the constant longitudinal velocity.

5. ISOROTATIONAL BEAMS; UNRIPPLED THEORY

In an isorotational beam the angular velocity ω is independent of radius. Beams of this type have been utilized in a variety of crossed-field microwave tubes, such as the voltage-tuned magnetron, in which it is required that the electrons of the beam rotate synchronously with rotating high-frequency waves. This section is confined to the theory of unrippled isorotational beams; the paraxial theory of thin beams of the same type is treated in Section 6.

If the angular velocity is constant, say, $\omega = \omega_0$, Eq. (2.3) assumes the form

$$(v_z^2)' + 4r\omega_0(\omega_0 - \omega_L) = 0 \qquad (5.1)$$

It is possible to develop the theory of isorotational beams with the general boundary condition that v_z possesses some finite value v_{z0} on some finite reference radius r_0. The theory to be presented here, however, is confined to the special case for which the axial velocity vanishes on the axis; this is the most useful case.

If $v_z = 0$ on the axis, the solution of Eq. (5.1) is

$$v_z = r[2\,\omega_0(\omega_L - \omega_0)]^{1/2} \qquad (5.2)$$

This expression may be substituted into Eq. (2.2) to yield the expression for the beam potential:

$$2\eta\,\phi = r^2\,\omega_0(\omega_H - \omega_0) \tag{5.3}$$

From Eq. (2.4) it is found that the charge density and plasma frequency are constants; namely,

$$\omega_p^2 = -\frac{\eta\rho_0}{\epsilon_0} = 2\,\omega_0(\omega_H - \omega_0) \tag{5.4}$$

Solution of Eq. (5.4) for ρ_0 and the use of Eq. (5.2) will yield the longitudinal current density i_z. The current density may then be integrated (with the weighting factor $2\pi r$) between the radial limits a and b, $b > a$, to obtain the expression for the total beam current

$$I = \frac{4\pi}{3}\frac{\epsilon_0}{\eta}\,\omega_0^{3/2}\,(\omega_H - \omega_0)(\omega_H - 2\omega_0)^{1/2}\,(b^3 - a^3) \tag{5.5}$$

The perveance of an isorotational beam is defined in terms of the current I and the highest potential occurring in the beam. From Eq. (5.3) it is evident that $\phi > 0$, and the beam kinetic energy is real, only if $0 < \omega_0 < \omega_H$; it follows that the potential increases with increasing radius, and hence the highest potential occurs at radius b. The perveance is therefore

$$P = \frac{I}{\phi_b^{3/2}} = {}^8\!/_3\,\pi\epsilon_0\,(2\eta)^{1/2}\left(\frac{1-2\gamma}{1-\gamma}\right)^{1/2}\left[1 - \left(\frac{a}{b}\right)^3\right] \tag{5.6}$$

or

$$P = 44.4\left(\frac{1-2\gamma}{1-\gamma}\right)^{1/2}\left[1 - \left(\frac{a}{b}\right)^3\right] \quad \text{micropervs} \tag{5.7}$$

In these expressions $\gamma = \omega_0/\omega_H$.

The isorotational beam under discussion may be generated by a magnetron injection gun with a conical cathode, the entire system being immersed in a uniform axial magnetic field. Such a system is depicted in Fig 1.4 of Chap. I; an alternative version of this system is shown in Fig. 4.13, with a = 0, so that the conical cathode is extended to its apex. Detailed descriptions of magnetron injection guns of the type depicted have been given by Dryden[1] and Waters.[2]

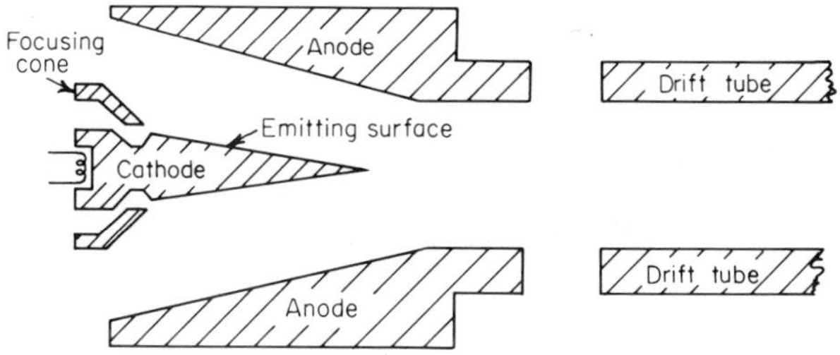

Fig. 4.13. Schematic of electrode system for a magnetron injection gun from a conical cathode without a central focusing electrode.

The example discussed at the end of Section 2 is relevant to this isorotational beam. By hypothesis ω is constant and v_z is proportional to r, as shown in Eq. (5.2); it follows that γ, r_b/s, and therefore the whole right side of Eq. (2.12) are a constant, equal to the (also constant) left side. Equation (2.12) may therefore be used to calculate γ from a knowledge of B, r_0, θ_c, and i_0. In fact, if a quantity $\mathcal{K}$ is defined by the relation

$$\mathcal{K} = \frac{\eta i_0 \sin^2 \theta_c}{\epsilon_0 r_0 \omega_H^3} \tag{5.8}$$

the following relation may be derived from Eq. (2.12):

$$\frac{\mathcal{K}}{\sin^3 \theta_c} = 2\gamma^{3/2} \frac{1-\gamma}{1-2\gamma} \tag{5.9}$$

It is easily verified from Eq. (5.9) that as $\mathcal{K}$ varies from zero to infinity, γ varies monotonically from 0 to $\frac{1}{2}$. From Eq. (5.7) it follows that the maximum perveance of an isorotational beam is 44.4 micropervs, and the realization of this perveance requires that $a = 0$ and $\gamma = 0$.

The quantity γ has been defined as ω_0/ω_H. Busch's theorem [Eq. (3.8) of Chap. I] may be written in the form

$$\frac{\omega}{\omega_H} = \gamma = \tfrac{1}{2}\left(1 - \frac{r_c^2}{r^2}\right) \tag{5.10}$$

Since γ must lie between 0 and $\frac{1}{2}$, Eq. (5.10) implies that $r_c < r$, that is, the radius of an electron trajectory in the isorotational beam must exceed the cathode radius of that trajectory, so that beam expansion must have occurred. The expansion ratio r/r_0 may be calculated from Eq. (5.10) if $\mathcal{K}$ and θ_c are known in Eq. (5.9).

If the cathode of the magnetron injection gun does not extend all the way to its apex, an annular beam is produced. From Eq. (5.3) it follows that at any finite radius a radial electric field must exist. Therefore, if a truncated cathode is used to produce an annular isorotational beam, a center electrode must be employed inside the

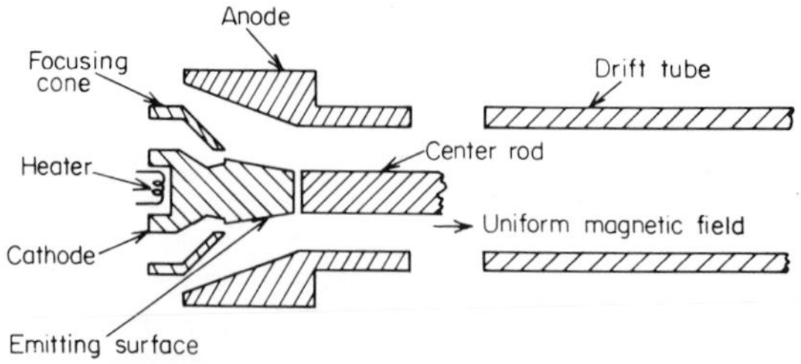

Fig. 4.14. Schematic of electrode system for a magnetron injection gun with truncated conical cathode. (Based on Ref. 2, courtesy of the Institute of Electrical and Electronic Engineers.)

beam, as shown in Fig. 4.14. In fact, it is this electron-optical system which is commonly employed in a voltage-tuned magnetron.

The center rod may be discarded, thus giving rise to a hollow beam, as shown in Fig. 1.4 of Chap I. We have shown that the radial electric field at the inner radius of a hollow beam must vanish; this condition violates the electric field relation obtained from Eq. (5.3). It may therefore be concluded that elimination of the center rod prevents the creation of the isorotational beam being discussed in this section. In order to calculate the properties of the hollow beam, it is necessary to solve Eqs. (2.12) and (2.13) with the boundary conditions $v_z = v_{z0}$ and $\gamma = 0$ at the inner radius of the beam.

6. PERTURBATIONS IN THIN CROSSED-FIELD ANNULAR BEAMS

6.1. Paraxial Theory. It was explained in Sec. 4.5 that the paraxial equation for a curvilinear sheet beam may be applied to the analysis of a radially thin Harris-flow beam and that the axial velocity may be ignored. The same type of analysis is applicable to a much more general type of focusing, i.e., a focusing system for annular beams in a uniform axial magnetic field and a radial d-c electric field, established by a potential difference between concentric cylinders. Harris flow is the special case of this more general system for which B = 0.

The system to be analyzed is depicted in Fig. 4.15. In this focusing system, the circle of radius r_0, concentric with the focusing cylinders, is defined as the ray axis; the sheet-beam paraxial equation [Eq. (6.19) of Chap. III] is used to obtain the rippling, stiffness, etc. The beam is assumed to be radially thin, that is, $r \ll r_0$, and the axial length of the beam is ℓ.

Because the ray axis is assumed to be a circle, and because the potential is a function of radius only, the paraxial-ray equation [Eq. (6.19) of Chap. III], with $\mathfrak{a} = \mathfrak{a}_1 = 0$, may be written in the form

$$r'' + r\,\frac{(4\kappa^2\phi_0 - 2\,B\omega_0\,\kappa r_0 + \eta B^2)}{2\phi_0} = \frac{P}{4\epsilon_0(2\eta)^{1/2}\,\ell} \tag{6.1}$$

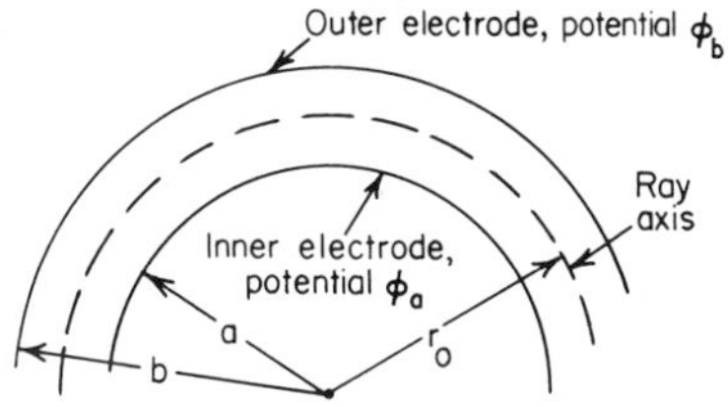

Fig. 4.15. Schematic of a paraxial beam with a circular ray axis. Depending on the magnetic field, ϕ_a may be greater or less than ϕ_b.

For the ray-axis electron, $2\eta\phi_0 = r_0\omega_0 = v_0$ and $\kappa = 1/r_0$, so that Eq. (6.1) may be written

$$r'' + r\left(\frac{\overline{\omega}}{v_0}\right)^2 = \frac{P}{4\epsilon_0(2\eta)^{1/2}\,\ell} \tag{6.2}$$

where $$\overline{\omega}^2 = \omega_H^2 - 2\omega_0\,\omega_H + 2\,\omega_0^2 \tag{6.3}$$

Equation (6.2) is formally identical with Eq. (4.25), the paraxial-ray equation for Harris flow, if we note that $\overline{\omega}/v_0$ has the dimensions of reciprocal length (i.e., curvature). Therefore, if we define an equivalent curvature $\overline{\kappa}$ by the relation

$$\frac{\overline{\omega}}{v_0} = \sqrt{2}\,\overline{\kappa} \tag{6.4}$$

the theory developed in Sec. 4.5 is directly applicable, provided we substitute $\overline{\kappa}$ wherever κ appears in Sec. 4.5. In this manner we may conclude that, in the general crossed-field beam, the rippling frequency, rippling wavelength, and the stiffness are given by the relations

$$\omega_n = \overline{\omega}, \qquad \lambda_n = 2\pi\frac{v_0}{\overline{\omega}}, \qquad \mathcal{S} = \frac{\overline{\omega}}{v_0} \tag{6.5}$$

It is readily found that during one complete oscillation cycle, the beam has rotated through an angle $\theta = \lambda_n/r_0$ radians. Finally, if Eq. (6.3) is differentiated with respect to ω_H for a fixed value of ω_0, it will be found that a minimum value of $\overline{\omega}$ is obtained if $\omega_H = \omega_0$, and at this minimum, $\overline{\omega} = \omega_H$. Inserting this condition into Eq. (2.1), it is found that $E_r = 0$. The corresponding type of focusing is known as cyclotron focusing, and was mentioned in Section 6 of Chap. III. Of all possible combinations of focusing relying upon a crossed radial electric field and an axial magnetic field, cyclotron focusing possesses the lowest stiffness and greatest rippling wavelength (for a fixed value of ω_0).

6.2. Stability. The paraxial theory of perturbed beams so far presented has been a theory of conservative perturbations; the total energy of the paraxial electron is equal to the total energy of the ray-axis electron, i.e., zero. It is easily shown that the rippling frequency $\overline{\omega}$ and the stiffness $\mathcal{S}$, as given by Eq. (6.3), are always real quantities. Equation (6.5) appears to imply, therefore, that the oscillations in a crossed-field annular beam are at worst undamped; hence all annular-beam crossed-field focusing systems seem stable.

The question of stability in the presence of nonconservative perturbations, in which the total energy of a paraxial electron is also perturbed, has not been examined. This problem is treated in this section, and it is shown that only certain types of crossed-field focusing of annular beams yield stability in the presence of nonconservative force perturbations. A comprehensive treatment of the subject is outside the scope of this book; the subject is but poorly understood in detail, and the reader is referred to more complete papers by Pierce[6] and by Kyle and Webster.[7]

In the analysis of the motion of a single electron moving in the coaxial crossed-field systems depicted in Fig. 4.15, the presence of a perturbing force $\mathfrak{F}_\theta$, acting entirely in the azimuthal direction, is included. The appropriate radial and azimuthal equations of motion are

$$\ddot{r} - r\,\dot{\theta}^2 + r\,\dot{\theta}\,\omega_H + \frac{\eta k}{r} = 0 \tag{6.6}$$

$$2\,\dot{r}\,\dot{\theta} + r\,\ddot{\theta} - \dot{r}\,\omega_H = \frac{\mathfrak{F}_\theta}{m} \tag{6.7}$$

In these relations k is a constant dependent upon the potential difference between, and the diameter ratio of, the concentric focusing cylinders; for the moment it suffices to note that k may be of either sign.

Only perturbations relative to an unperturbed circular orbit are of interest. If $\mathfrak{F}_\theta$ vanishes, the unperturbed orbit has radius r_0 and the angular velocity is ω_0. It is easily found from Eq. (6.6) that

$$\frac{\eta k}{r_0^2} = \omega_0^2 - \omega_0\,\omega_H \tag{6.8}$$

which is an alternative way of writing the radial-force-balance equation (2.1).

In the presence of the perturbing force both r and $\dot{\theta}$ will be perturbed. If the perturbing force $\mathfrak{F}_\theta$ is small compared with the centrifugal force, or the Lorentz magnetic force, first-order perturbation equations may be obtained from Eqs. (6.6) and (6.7), and these give an accurate account of the effects produced by $\mathfrak{F}_\theta$. Thus r and $\dot{\theta}$ may be written as

$$r = r_0 + r_1(t), \qquad \dot{\theta} = \omega_0 + \omega_1(t) \tag{6.9}$$

These forms may be inserted into Eqs. (6.6) and (6.7), the equations expanded, and only zero- and first-order terms retained. By this process the following pair of perturbation equations is obtained:

$$\ddot{r}_1 - 2\,r_1(\omega_0^2 - \omega_0\,\omega_H) = \omega_1\,r_0(2\,\omega_0 - \omega_H) \tag{6.10a}$$

$$r_0\,\dot{\omega}_1 = \frac{\mathfrak{F}_\theta}{m} + \dot{r}_1(\omega_H - 2\,\omega_0) \tag{6.10b}$$

Here a dot denotes, as usual, d/dt.

An equation in r_1 only may be obtained by differentiating Eq. (6.10a) with respect to t, and then substituting for $r_0\omega_1$ from Eq. (6.10b), resulting in the equation

$$\frac{d^2\,\dot{r}_1}{dt^2} + \overline{\omega}^2\,\dot{r}_1 = \frac{\mathfrak{F}_\theta}{m}\,(2\omega_0 - \omega_H) \tag{6.11}$$

where $\overline{\omega}$ is obtained from Eq. (6.3).

Equation (6.11) may be solved subject to the initial conditions that $r_1(0) = \dot{r}_1(0) = \ddot{r}_1(0) = 0$; these conditions merely state that, at $t = 0$, the electron is not radially perturbed, is not moving radially, and is not experiencing a net radial acceleration. The appropriate solution of Eq. (6.11) is therefore

$$r_1 = \frac{\mathfrak{F}_\theta(2\omega_0 - \omega_H)}{m\overline{\omega}^3}(\overline{\omega}t - \sin\overline{\omega}t) \tag{6.12}$$

Equation (6.12) may now be used to find $\dot{r}_1$, which may be substituted into Eq. (6.10b) to yield $r_0\dot{\omega}_1$ in the form

$$r_0\dot{\omega}_1 = \frac{\mathfrak{F}_\theta}{m\overline{\omega}^2}\left[-\frac{2\eta k}{r_0^2} + (2\omega_0 - \omega_H)^2 \cos\overline{\omega}t\right] \tag{6.13}$$

The presence of the constant term involving k in Eq. (6.13) is the key to the presence or absence of beam instabilities. Over many periods of the oscillation at frequency $\overline{\omega}$, the constant term in Eq. (6.13) will dominate the angular perturbation ω_1; to this degree of approximation the term in $\cos\overline{\omega}t$ may be dropped, yielding

$$r_0\,\dot{\omega}_1 \simeq -\frac{2\eta k}{mr_0^2\,\overline{\omega}^2}\,\mathfrak{F}_\theta \tag{6.14}$$

It was stated earlier that k may be of either sign; in fact, it is easily shown that

$$k = \frac{\phi_a - \phi_b}{\log(b/a)} \tag{6.15}$$

where a refers to the inner, and b to the outer, focusing cylinder. If $\phi_b > \phi_a$, $k < 0$, and conversely. The sign of the azimuthal angular acceleration $\dot{\omega}_1$ is therefore the same as the sign of $\mathfrak{F}_\theta$, if k is negative, and hence $\phi_b > \phi_a$; if $\phi_b < \phi_a$, k is positive, and the sign of $F_\theta/\dot{\omega}_1$ is negative.

In problems ordinarily treated by Newtonian mechanics, the vector acceleration of a particle has the same direction as the applied force which produces the acceleration. Here, however, we are faced with a situation in which the angular acceleration $\dot{\omega}_1$ may be in a direction opposite to that of the applied force $\mathfrak{F}_\theta$, if $\phi_a > \phi_b$. The situation may be described by the statement that the electron behaves, insofar as its azimuthal motion is concerned, as if its mass were negative. It is the negative-mass phenomenon which is responsible for a beam instability, as the following explanation shows.

Consider two electrons moving on the ray axis of an annular-beam crossed-field system, the angular separation of the two initially being small, as depicted in Fig. 4.16. The outer cylinder is at the lower potential, so that the negative-mass condition exists. Each electron produces a Coulomb repulsion force on the other electron,

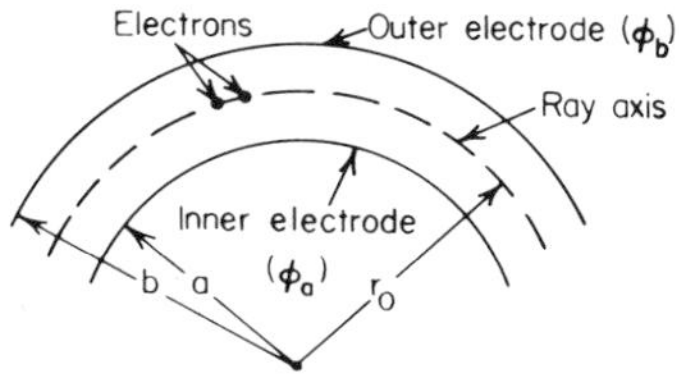

Fig. 4.16. Schematic of two electrons on the ray axis of a hollow beam; either electrode may be the more positive.

and these forces are almost entirely azimuthal (it may be verified that the presence of a small radial perturbation force does not remove the negative-mass condition). According to Eq. (6.13), the electrons initially will accelerate away from one another, but eventually the long-time trend will dominate, and the electrons will begin to accelerate toward one another.

As the two electrons move closer together, the repulsion force increases, resulting in an even higher acceleration, a still larger repulsion force, etc.; it is clear that such a physical situation is unstable.

The subject of space-charge-wave properties in dense electron beams is outside the scope of this book. Suffice it to say that the presence of a beam instability of the type discussed above gives rise to space-charge waves having real, rather than imaginary, propagation constants. The exponential growth of such waves may be used to describe the consequences of the instability.[6, 7]

The foregoing treatment shows that all coaxial crossed-field focusing systems in which the potential is a decreasing function of radius are inherently unstable, and conversely, a radially increasing potential results in stability. Thus Harris flow must be considered unstable, and an analysis of the space-charge waves in this system predicts a high growth constant for the exponentially increasing wave. Cyclotron focusing, on the other hand, is a borderline case for which the radial electric field vanishes. In this system an azimuthally applied perturbing force results in oscillation of the sign of the azimuthal acceleration.

A more thorough analysis shows that the energy source for the instability is the stored energy of the radial electric field. This energy is made available to electrons in the beam through the changes occurring in their radial positions, as a result of the perturbing forces. This phenomenon is called the negative mass instability, and has been widely studied in the theory of accelerators.[8]

Another well-known physical system which is characterized by this type of instability is the motion of a satellite around its parent planet. If the unperturbed motion is circular, the presence of a weak perturbing force acting in the direction of motion of the satellite will result in an angular acceleration in the opposite direction. For earth satellites a common source of such a force is atmospheric drag; it is well known that the effect of the drag on a circular, or nearly circular, orbit is to decrease the period of the satellite as it moves closer to the earth, thereby increasing the angular velocity.

An important limiting case of the foregoing theory is obtained if the radii of the focusing cylinders are permitted to increase without limit, while the separation of the cylinders, b − a, remains constant. In addition, the linear velocity $r_0\omega_0$ in the azimuthal direction is also assumed to remain constant. In the limit the annular beam tends toward the crossed-field sheet beam to be discussed in Sections 7 and 8. Under these assumptions it can be verified that the quantity k/r_0^2 appearing in Eq. (6.13) tends to the following limit:

$$\frac{k}{r_0^2} \rightarrow \frac{\phi_a - \phi_b}{a/(b-a)} \rightarrow 0 \qquad \text{as } a \rightarrow \infty \tag{6.16}$$

The term in Eq. (6.13) to which the instability was attributed is lost as the beam becomes a crossed-field sheet beam; it may be concluded that this type of sheet beam is stable in the presence of a nonconservative force perturbation.

A different type of instability may occur in either annular beams or sheet beams having a finite thickness. The source of the instability may be described in terms of the interaction between space-charge waves propagating in different layers of the beam. The name Diocotron effect has been given to this phenomenon; a detailed discussion is outside the scope of this book.[9]

7. UNRIPPLED RECTILINEAR SHEET BEAMS

7.1. General Development. Two particularly important cases of uniform magnetic focusing of sheet beams result in unrippled rectilinear flow. The first is the sheet-beam counterpart of a Brillouin solid beam; the second is a form of crossed-field focusing. In this section certain relations pertaining to these flow patterns are derived.

The flow is assumed to be rectilinear, as shown in Fig. 4.17, and it is convenient to develop the theory in a cartesian coordinate system. All properties of the flow are assumed functions of only one coordinate, which will be designated as the y coordinate. The magnetic field is assumed to be uniform, but both it and the velocity vector for any particle possess x and z components. It follows that the stream potential ϕ is a function only of y, and therefore the electric field vector possesses only a y component, which may also be a function of y. Thus **B**, **E**, and **v** have the form

$$\mathbf{B} = (B_x, 0, B_z) \qquad \mathbf{E} = [0,\ E_y(y),\ 0] \qquad \mathbf{v} = [\dot{x}\,(y),\ 0,\ \dot{z}(y)] \tag{7.1}$$

The Lorentz equation of motion [Eq. (2.15) of Chap. I] may be written

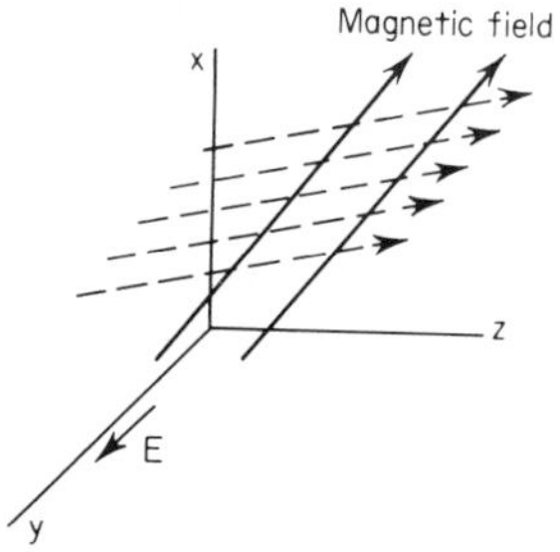

Fig. 4.17. Schematic of rectilinear flow in the xz plane with a normal electric field.

$$\ddot{x} = 0, \quad \dot{x} = v_x(y) \tag{7.2a}$$

$$\ddot{z} = 0, \quad \dot{z} = v_z(y) \tag{7.2b}$$

and because $\dot{y}$ and $\ddot{y}$ are both assumed zero,

$$\dot{y} = \ddot{y} = 0, \quad E_y(y) + B_x\dot{z} - B_z\dot{x} = 0 \tag{7.2c}$$

Using Eq. (7.2), the energy equation [Eq. (2.27) of Chap. I] and Poisson's equation [Eq. (2.1) of Chap. I] may be written

$$2\eta\,\phi = \dot{x}^2 + \dot{z}^2 \tag{7.3}$$

and
$$\frac{\partial}{\partial y}(\dot{x}\,B_z - \dot{z}\,B_x) = \frac{\rho}{\epsilon_0} \tag{7.4}$$

which becomes

$$B_z\frac{\partial \dot{x}}{\partial y} - B_x\frac{\partial \dot{z}}{\partial y} = \frac{\rho}{\epsilon_0} \tag{7.5}$$

since both B_x and B_z are assumed to be constant parameters.

Although an infinite number of flow patterns may be derived from Eq. (7.5), depending upon how $\dot{x}$ and $\dot{z}$ are assumed to vary with y, the remarks of this section are confined to two special cases. It should be noted that Eq. (7.5) is analogous to Eq. (2.4), the corresponding equation for a round beam.

7.2. Brillouin Flow. For the first special case it is assumed that $B_z = 0$ and $\dot{x} = v_0$, where v_0 is a constant. The resulting flow pattern is the direct counterpart of the round Brillouin beam discussed in Sec. 3.2.

Under the assumption $B_z = 0$, Eq. (7.2c) yields $\dot{z} = (1/B_x)(d\phi/dy)$, which may be substituted into Eq. (7.3) to yield a differential equation for the potential, namely,

$$2\eta\,\phi\,(y) = v_0^2 + \frac{1}{B_x^2}\left(\frac{d\phi}{dy}\right)^2 \tag{7.6}$$

which is integrable by elementary methods. The constant of integration is evaluated on the assumption that, on the plane y = 0, $2\eta\phi = v_0^2$. The appropriate solution of Eq. (7.6) is, therefore

$$2\eta\, \phi(y) = v_0^2 + y^2\, \omega_{Hx}^2 \tag{7.7}$$

where $\omega_{Hx} = \eta\, B_x$. This potential is a quadratic function of y, increasing indefinitely on either side of the plane of symmetry, y = 0.

Equation (7.7) and Poisson's equation may be combined to obtain expressions for the electron charge density, and eventually the plasma frequency. These quantities are given by the expressions

$$\rho = -\frac{\epsilon_0\, \omega_{Hx}^2}{\eta} = -\epsilon_0\, \eta B_x^2 \tag{7.8}$$

and $$\omega_p^2 = \omega_{Hx}^2 \tag{7.9}$$

Comparison of Eqs. (3.6) and (7.8) revals that, for a given magnetic field strength, the charge density and the plasma frequency are larger by the factor 1.41 in the case of a sheet beam.

Equations (7.2c) and (7.7) may also be combined to give

$$\dot{z} = y\, \omega_{Hx} \tag{7.10}$$

and $$\frac{\dot{z}}{v} = \frac{\alpha}{(1 + \alpha^2)^{1/2}} \tag{7.11}$$

where v is the total velocity and $\alpha = y\omega_{Hx}/v_0$.

Equation (7.10) shows the presence of shear in a Brillouin sheet beam. Although various layers of the beam possess the same velocity v_0 in the direction of the magnetic field, the z velocity component, perpendicular to the field, increases in proportion to the displacement y from the plane of symmetry. Such shearing is directly analogous to the rotation of a round Brillouin beam. Unless the sheet beam is very thin (that is, $\alpha \ll 1$), shearing will cause a relatively rapid increase in the width of the sheet beam. Equation (7.11) shows that, in a thick beam ($\alpha \gg 1$), shearing causes the electrons at the outer beam boundaries to move at an angle approaching 90° relative to the x direction; for $\alpha = 1$ this angle is 45°.

Expressions for the beam current and perveance are derivable for a beam having a thickness 2w and a width ℓ by the methods used for the Brillouin round beam. In the case of the sheet beam it is more convenient to deal with the current per square $I_\square$ and the perveance per square $P_\square$ (Section 10 of Chap. III). It is found that the total current in the x direction is given by

$$I = 2\epsilon_0\eta\, v_0 B_x^2 w\ell \tag{7.12}$$

and the current per square is given by

$$I_\square = \frac{\epsilon_0}{\eta}\, v_0^3\, \xi^2 \tag{7.13}$$

The perveance per square $P_\square$ can be defined either in terms of the potential ϕ_0 on the mid-plane of the beam or in terms of the potential ϕ_W on the outer surfaces of the (symmetrical) beam; the former definition leads to the expression

$$P_{\square 0} = 2\epsilon_0(2\eta)^{1/2}\,\xi^2$$
$$= 10.5\,\xi^2 \quad \text{micropervs} \tag{7.14}$$

and the latter definition yields

$$P_{\square W} = 2\epsilon_0(2\eta)^{1/2}\frac{\xi^2}{(1+\xi^2/4)^{3/2}} \tag{7.15}$$

where ξ is given by

$$\xi = \frac{2w\,\omega_{Hx}}{v_0} \tag{7.16}$$

As ξ increases from zero (infinitely thin beam), both $I_\square$ and $P_\square$, defined in terms of the centerplane potential ϕ_0, increase parabolically with ξ. However, $P_\square$, defined in terms of the maximum beam potential ϕ_W, passes through a maximum of 16 micropervs when $\xi = 2\sqrt{2}$.

7.3. Rectilinear Crossed-field Flow. For the second special case of unrippled rectilinear flow it is assumed that $B_x = 0$, B_z = constant, and that the velocity of every electron is entirely in the x direction. The flow is depicted in Fig. 4.18. The combination of the x = directed velocity and the z-directed magnetic field gives rise to a y-directed Lorentz force; if the motion is entirely in the x direction, the Lorentz force must be balanced by an electric field force, thus demanding the existence of a y component of electric field, E_y. Again it is assumed that E_y is the only electric field component.

With $B_x = 0$, Eq. (7.2c) may be solved for $\dot{x}$ and the result substituted into the energy equation (7.3) to yield the following differential equation for the potential:

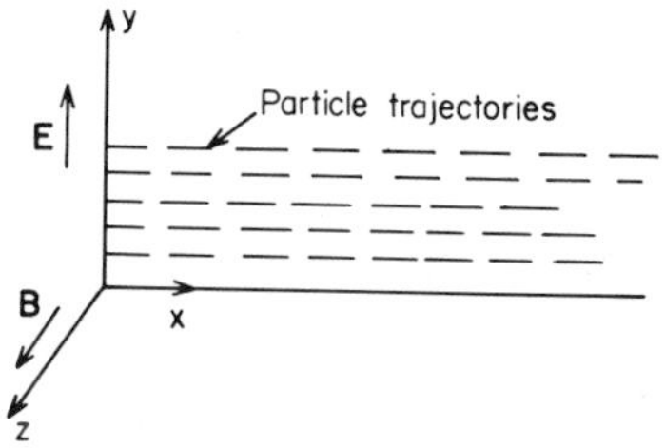

Fig. 4.18. Schematic of rectilinear flow along the x direction in normal electric and magnetic fields.

$$2\eta\, B_Z^2\, \phi = \left(\frac{d\,\phi}{dy}\right)^2 \tag{7.17}$$

This equation may be integrated directly; it is assumed that, on the plane y = 0, the potential has some specified value ϕ_0. The appropriate solution of Eq. (7.17) is therefore

$$\phi = \phi_0\left(1 + \frac{\omega_{Hz}\, y}{v_0}\right)^2 \tag{7.18}$$

where $\omega_{Hz} = \eta B_Z$ and $v_0^2 = 2\eta\, \phi_0$. Equation (7.18) may be substituted into Poisson's equation to yield the charge density ρ and the plasma frequency. The expressions for these quantities will be found to be given by Eqs. (7.8) and (7.9) if ω_{Hz} is substituted for ω_{Hx}. Thus, in the case of the unrippled crossed-field sheet beam, the electron plasma frequency equals the cyclotron frequency ω_{Hz}, exactly as in the case of the Brillouin-flow sheet beam discussed in Sec. 7.2.

The current density i_X may be found upon multiplying the velocity $\dot{x}$, found from Eq. (7.18), by the charge density $\rho = -\epsilon_0\, \omega_{Hz}^2/\eta$; the total current and the current per square are then obtained upon integrating i_X over the cross section of a beam of width ℓ and thickness 2w, as depicted in Fig. 4.18. It is convenient to define the perveance per square in terms of the potential occurring on the high-potential side of the beam. These considerations lead to the relation

$$P_\square = 2\epsilon_0 (2\eta)^{1/2}\, \frac{\xi^2(1 + \frac{1}{2}\xi)}{(1 + \xi)^3} \tag{7.19}$$

$$\text{where} \quad \xi = \frac{\omega_{Hz}\, w}{v_0} \tag{7.20}$$

The exact determination of electrodes which will establish either the Brillouin sheet beam or the crossed-field sheet beam is straightforward. At the surfaces of the beam, the potential and the (y-component) electric field may be obtained from Eq. (7.7) or (7.18); these quantities constitute the boundary conditions on the Laplacian potential function between the beam boundaries and the electrodes. Details are left as an exercise for the reader, but the method of solution is outlined in Section 3 of Chap. VII.

8. RIPPLING IN SHEET BEAMS

8.1. Introduction. This section is concerned with a paraxial analysis of the sheet-beam flows discussed in Section 7. From a mathematical point of view the analysis of sheet beams is somewhat simpler than the analysis of round beams (Section 4), in that the appropriate paraxial-ray equation can always be integrated twice in terms of elementary functions. However, there is little fundamental difference between a sheet beam and a round beam. In this section, solutions to the paraxial equations and explicit formulas for such quantities as beam stiffness, rippling wavelength, etc., are stated without proof; the major differences between a magnetically focused sheet beam and its round-beam counterpart are discussed. The derivation of the equations of this section by the methods of Secs. 4.1 and 4.4 is left as an exercise for the reader.

8.2. Rippling in a Brillouin Sheet Beam. The paraxial-ray equation for a sheet beam in an axially directed magnetic field was given in Eq. (3.7) of Chap. III. This equation is applicable to a Brillouin sheet beam provided the potential is assumed to possess a constant value ϕ_0. With this restriction the paraxial-ray equation is

$$r'' + \beta_H^2 r = r_0 \beta_H^2 \alpha + \frac{P}{4 \epsilon_0 (2\eta)^{1/2} \ell} \tag{8.1}$$

where β_H is given by Eq. (4.7), $\alpha = B_0/B$, and P is the total perveance.

The solution of Eq. (8.1) may be expressed in terms of the Brillouin half-thickness r_b, which is the unrippled solution of Eq. (8.1) when $\alpha = 0$ (shielded cathode), and the confined-flow half-thickness r_a, which is the unrippled solution of Eq. (8.1) when $P = 0$ (vanishing current). It is easily found that

$$r_a = \alpha r_0 \tag{8.2a}$$

and
$$r_b = \frac{P}{4 \epsilon_0 (2\eta)^{1/2} \beta_H^2 \ell} \tag{8.2b}$$

Equation (8.1) then may be written in the form

$$r'' + \beta_H^2 (r - r_a - r_b) = 0 \tag{8.3}$$

Equation (8.3) possesses an unrippled solution $r_e = r_a + r_b$; this is merely the equilibrium solution. The linear nature of Eq. (8.3)* enables r to be expressed in the form $r = r_e + r_1$, where r_1 is a function of axial position, thus obtaining the equation

$$r_1'' + \beta_H^2 r_1 = 0 \tag{8.4}$$

The solutions of Eq. (8.4) are sinusoidal. In terms of the initial displacement from equilibrium r_{10}, the initial slope r'_{10}, and the stiffness $\mathcal{S}$, the complete solution of Eq. (8.3) is

$$r = r_e + r_{10} \cos(\beta_H z) + \frac{r'_{10}}{\mathcal{S}} \sin(\beta_H z) \tag{8.5}$$

which is analogous to Eq. (4.12). The stiffness $\mathcal{S}$ is equal to β_H, irrespective of either beam current or magnetic flux at the cathode; in this respect the stiffness of a magnetically focused sheet beam differs from its round-beam counterpart, as may be seen from Eq.

*See paragraph following Eq. (3.7) of Chap. III.

(4.11). The rippling wavelength λ_n and frequency ω_n are given by $\lambda_n = 2\pi/\beta_H$ and $\omega_n = \eta B$.

8.3. Rippling in a Crossed-field Sheet Beam. The paraxial-ray equation for crossed-field sheet beams was derived in Section 6 of Chap. III. On setting the ray-axis potential equal to a constant, ϕ_0, the s and r components of **B** ($\mathcal{a} = \mathcal{a}_1 = 0$), and the ray-axis curvature κ identically equal to zero, the appropriate paraxial-ray equation [Eq. (6.19) of Chap. III] is written in the form

$$r'' + \beta_H^2 r = \frac{P}{4\,\epsilon_0(2\pi)^{1/2}\,\ell} \tag{8.6}$$

Equation (8.6) is identical with Eq. (8.1) provided that, in the latter equation, $\alpha = 0$. Therefore the analysis presented in Sec. 8.2, subject to the restriction of a shielded cathode, is directly applicable to the crossed-field sheet beam. A more general analysis, valid when the curvature κ possesses a finite constant value, was given in Section 6 of this chapter.

9. MAGNETIC FIELD PERTURBATIONS

9.1. General Discussion. Up to this point the analyses of magnetic focusing presented in this chapter have been confined to systems in which the magnetic field is uniform, except for the possibility of a different magnetic field at the cathode. Two types of magnetic field perturbations have considerable practical application:

1. Sudden magnetic field reversals
2. Slowly tapered magnetic fields

Elementary treatments of these perturbations are presented in this section.

In many applications, particularly in microwave tubes such as low-noise traveling-wave amplifiers and backward-wave oscillators, it is desirable to focus the electron beam with an approximately uniform axial magnetic field. Although such fields are perfectly straightforward to generate with a carefully constructed solenoid, in many applications the weight of the solenoid and the need for a solenoid power supply constitute such severe practical obstacles that the designer must use a permanent magnet. An excellent paper on the subject of the design of minimum-weight permanent magnets for generating a uniform axial magnetic field has been published by Glass.[10]

A typical magnet designed by Glass' procedure is depicted in Fig. 4.19a. Except near the ends of the magnet, the axial field inside the hole is essentially uniform, as shown in Fig. 4.19b. A large amount of magnetic energy exists in the space surrounding the magnet; the source of this energy, which is completely useless for focusing an electron beam, is the large dipole moment associated with the magnet. The large amount of external magnetic energy necessitates

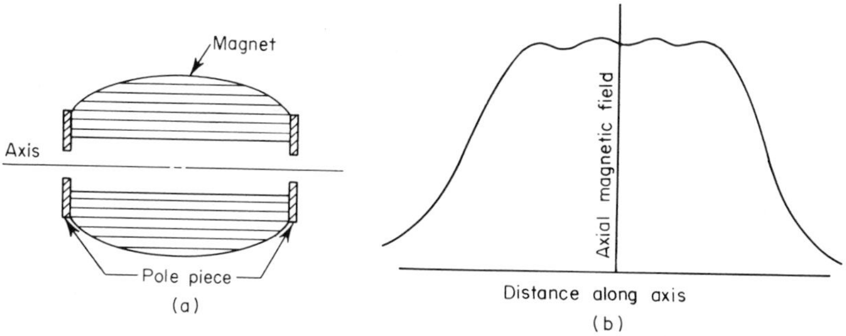

Fig. 4.19. Magnet design for uniform axial magnetic field. (a) Configuration from the side; (b) axial magnetic field on the axis.

the use of a much heavier magnet than would otherwise be the case; it is also possible to show, both theoretically and experimentally, that the detailed shape of the field configuration inside the magnet hole is a sensitive function of the magnetic environment in the vicinity of the magnet.

Figure 4.20 depicts a magnetic system consisting of two colinear magnets with opposite excitation. The axial magnetic field is depicted in Fig. 4.20b. Now the external magnetic energy of the pair is roughly that of two magnetic dipoles displaced axially and having opposite directions of magnetization. It is intuitively evident that the external magnetic energy of such a system is far less than that of a single magnet, particularly if the axial length of the single magnet is equal to the combined lengths of the colinear pair. The primary purpose of field-reversal, often called alternative-gradient, focusing is to reduce magnet weight and the sensitivity of the system to the external magnetic environment.

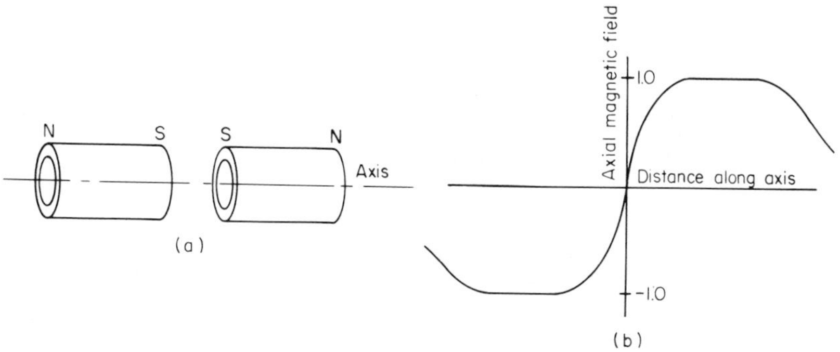

Fig. 4.20. Magnet design for a reversing axial magnetic field. (a) Pole-piece configuration; (b) axial magnetic field on the axis.

In the paraxial-ray equation for a round beam [Eq. (2.25) of Chap. III] the magnetic field quantities $\mathcal{B}$ and $\mathcal{B}_0$ appear only quadratically, so that the equation is independent of the algebraic signs of $\mathcal{B}$ or $\mathcal{B}_0$; it is this fact which makes field-reversal focusing possible for round beams. Therefore one or more sudden changes in the direction of the axial magnetic field would not appreciably affect the radial behavior of the beam. From Fig. 4.20b it is seen that the reversal of the axial magnetic field does not occur instantaneously, but over a finite axial distance. In practice, a magnetically conducting pole piece with a hole for the beam to pass through is usually inserted between the two magnets. It is possible to show that the axial length of the magnetic field transition is about 1.5 times the hole diameter.

A study of field-reversal focusing is largely a study of the effects produced by the finite axial length of the transition region. With the assumption of a uniform beam potential, it is convenient to measure the axial length L of the transition in units of the rippling wavelength λ_n, where λ_n is determined in a uniform region of the magnetic field. In Sec. 9.2, the effect of the transition region is estimated analytically; the theory presented is then compared with paraxial-ray calculations obtained with a digital computer, for a selected range of L/λ_n and for selected field variations in the transition region. It is intuitively evident, and it is verified by the computer calculations, that the finite length of the transition will in general cause an otherwise unrippled beam to experience rippling; the extent of the rippling will decrease smoothly toward zero with a corresponding decrease in L/λ_n.

In a second type of magnetic field perturbation, the axial field strength changes so gradually that the percentage change in the field is small over the axial length of a single rippling wavelength. Field tapering of this type, often called adiabatic tapering, is useful for gradually increasing or decreasing the diameter of a round beam. With careful tapering it is possible to obtain substantial changes in beam diameter without the introduction of excessive rippling. An elementary analytical treatment of adiabatic tapering is presented in Sec. 9.4.

9.2. Rippling Caused by a Field Reversal. The paraxial-ray equation [Eq. (2.25) of Chap. III] may be used to study the effects produced by the transition region associated with a field reversal; in that equation it is necessary to put $\phi = \phi_0 =$ constant. Two assumptions are made:

1. As the beam approaches a field reversal, small-amplitude rippling about the equilibrium radius is occurring, so that a finite slope at the onset of the reversal is admissible.

2. The transition region is so short, measured in terms of the uniform-field rippling wavelength, that the primary effect of the reversal is to create a radial impulse, so that only the slope of the

trajectory is altered in passing through the transition.

The rippling amplitude resulting from the impulse may then be calculated, as a fraction of the equilibrium radius, and this fraction expressed as a function of L/λ_n for various shapes of the transition region.

By the use of the relations derived in Sec. 4.1 it is possible to express the paraxial-ray equation [Eq. (2.25) of Chap. III] in the form

$$r'' + \frac{\eta B_0^2}{8\phi_0}\left(r\,\alpha^2 - \frac{r_e^4}{r^3}\right) + \frac{P}{4\pi\epsilon_0(2\eta)^{1/2}}\left(\frac{1}{r_e} - \frac{1}{r}\right) = 0 \tag{9.1}$$

where B_0 = magnitude of the field in uniform-field region

P = perveance $I/\phi_0^{3/2}$

α = field shape factor $\mathcal{B}/B_0$

r_e = equilibrium radius in uniform-field region, obtained by putting $r = r_e$, $r'' = 0$, $\alpha = 1$ in Eq. (2.25).

It is assumed that $\mathcal{B}$, and hence α, is a function of axial distance z, and $\Phi = \phi_0$, where ϕ_0 is a constant.

The change in slope caused by the magnetic field transition is easily found from Eq. (9.1) if it is assumed that the radius of an electron is unaltered within the transition region. The error due to this assumption decreases with the length L of the transition. On the assumption that $r = r_e$, Eq. (9.1) approximates the form

$$r'' + \left(\frac{\pi}{\lambda_n}\right)^2 r_e\,(\alpha^2 - 1) = 0 \tag{9.2}$$

where λ_n is the rippling wavelength of Eq. (4.15) associated with the field B_0 and the potential ϕ_0. Upon integrating Eq. (9.2) through the transition, an expression for the change in slope $\Delta r'$ is obtained:

$$\Delta r' = \left(\frac{\pi}{\lambda_n}\right)^2 r_e \int_L (1 - \alpha^2)\,dz \tag{9.3}$$

In the uniform-field region beyond the transition, the rippling amplitude Δr may be calculated from a knowledge of the stiffness $\mathcal{S}$ and from Eq. (9.3). Now $\mathcal{S} = 2\pi/\lambda_n$ [see paragraph following Eq. (4.16)], so that

$$\frac{\Delta r}{r_e} = \frac{\pi}{2\lambda_n} \int_L (1 - \alpha^2)\,dz \tag{9.4}$$

Equation (9.4) represents the fractional ripple for any shape of transition, for either magnetically shielded or magnetically immersed flow, provided only that $L/\lambda_n \ll 1$. This equation will now be applied to two shapes of magnetic transitions which are close approximations to experimentally measured transitions. The results will be compared with digital-computer solutions of the paraxial-ray equation; the computer computations do not require that $L/\lambda_n \ll 1$.

For the sinusoidal transition of magnetic field, it is assumed that, for $-L/2 \le z \le L/2$, the axial field has the form $\mathcal{B} = B_0 \sin(\pi z/L)$, so that

$$\alpha(s) = \sin \frac{\pi z}{L} \tag{9.5}$$

Inserting Eq. (9.5), Eq. (9.4) becomes

$$\frac{\Delta r}{r_e} = \frac{\pi L}{4\lambda_n} \tag{9.6}$$

that is, $\Delta r/r_e$ is proportional to L/λ_n.

For a hyperbolic-tangent transition of magnetic field, it is assumed that the axial field has the form $\mathcal{B} = B_0 \tanh \gamma z$, so that

$$\alpha(z) = \tanh \gamma z \tag{9.7}$$

In this expression γ is a scale factor proportional to the slope of the field at $z = 0$, so that

$$\gamma = \frac{\mathcal{B}'(0)}{B_0} \tag{9.8}$$

For this case it is necessary to set the limits of integration of Eq. (9.3) equal to $\pm\infty$; so Eq. (9.4) may be expressed in the form

$$\frac{\Delta r}{r_e} = \frac{\pi B_0}{\lambda_n \mathcal{B}'(0)} \tag{9.9}$$

showing that, as the field slope increases at $z = 0$ (where the field vanishes), the fractional ripple decreases. Equation (9.9) is identical with Eq. (9.6), if an equivalent transition length is defined by the relation $L = 4\, B_0/\mathcal{B}'(0)$.

In Fig. 4.21 the fractional ripple is plotted for both sinusoidal and hyperbolic-tangent transitions. The theoretical curves are shown dashed, whereas the solid lines have been taken from digital-computer calculations. As expected, the agreement is very good for short transitions. For longer transitions the computer calculations predict that the rippling increases more slowly than L. It should be pointed out, however, that the stiffness of a uniform system increases slowly with increasing slope of a trajectory. Had this fact been used to correct the theoretical formulas, the agreement between the theory and the computer data would be better for the longer transitions.

Figure 4.21 shows that the theory presented above is a good approximation for values of L/λ_n not exceeding about 1.5 to 2; in order to avoid a substantial fractional ripple, the transition region is permitted to be only a small fraction of the rippling wavelength. Since this requirement may be difficult to achieve in practice, a more elaborate form of transition is often used; it is beyond the scope of the book to pursue this interesting matter further.

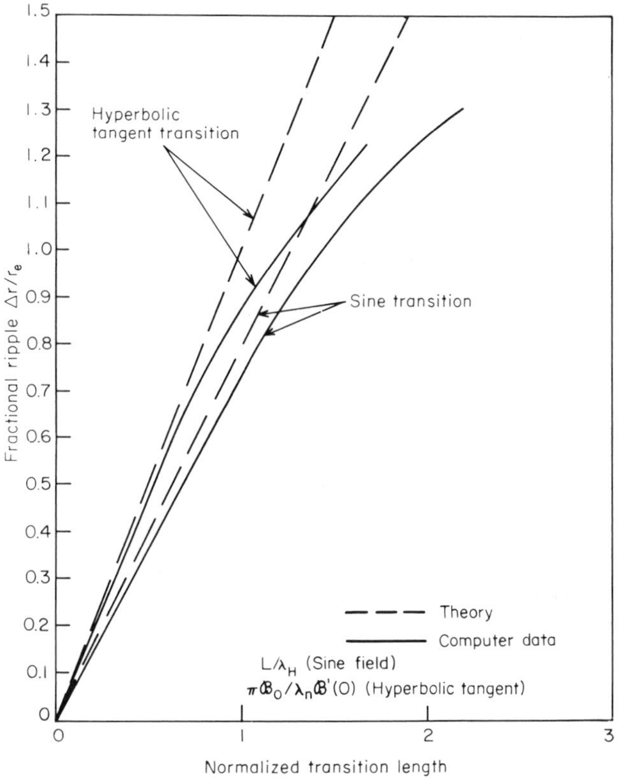

Fig. 4.21. Plot of fractional beam ripple as a function of the length of the transition region in a reversing magnetic field.

A second source of rippling may be caused by even an extremely short field reversal, if the magnitudes of the magnetic field on opposite sides of the reversal are not exactly equal. In this event the actual radius of the beam upon passing the transition region will not equal the equilibrium radius; the amplitude of the resulting ripple is the difference between the equilibrium radii on the two sides of the reversal.

As an example, consider a confined flow beam with $I = 0$; let the magnetic field have a uniform value B_0 prior to the reversal and a second uniform value $-(B_0 + \Delta B)$ following the reversal. Then, from Eq. (4.3), the equilibrium radius is r_0 before the reversal and $r_0(1 + \Delta B/B_0)^{-1/2} \approx r_0(1 - \Delta B/2\, B_0)$ after the reversal, if $|\Delta B| \ll |B_0|$. It is assumed that the transition region is so short that neither the radius nor the slope of the beam changes through the transition region. Hence the actual radius of the beam beyond the transition is also r_0, which differs from the equilibrium radius by an amount $\Delta r = -r_0 \, \Delta B/2\, B_0$; it is with this amplitude that rippling occurs beyond the transition.

According to the approximation leading to Eq. (9.3), the rippling caused by a field reversal vanishes if the integral in that equation vanishes; the integral, of course, does vanish in the trivial case $\alpha = 1$. A more interesting case occurs if α rises above unity through a portion of the interval L, while falling below unity elsewhere in the interval, as depicted in Fig. 4.22. In practice, the detailed shape and axial extent of the peaked transition region are best found empirically, especially when the magnetic field is established by permanent magnets. This subject is treated further in Section 2 of Chap. V.

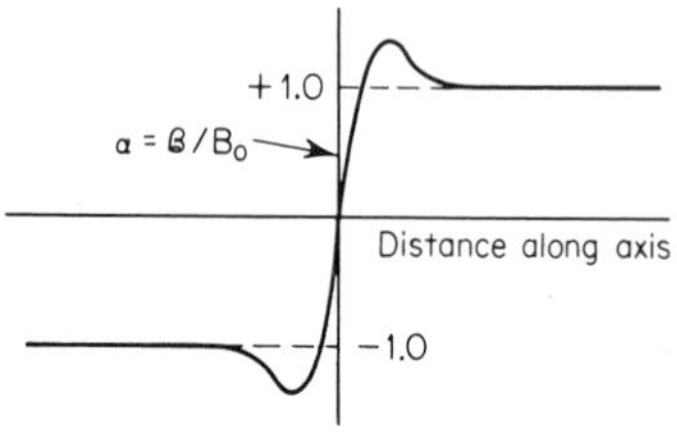

Fig. 4.22. Possible variation of α, that is, $\mathcal{B}(z)/B_0$ through a reversal of the magnetic field such that, to first order, the ripple is zero.

To the approximation inherent in Eq. (9.3), if a peaked magnetic reversal can be found such that the integral in the equation vanishes, a condition of zero ripple will have been established, independent of the beam voltage. Although this is an extremely important practical consideration, Eq. (9.3) is reliable only if L/λ_n is relatively small, so that the beam voltage may not be lowered indefinitely. The actual behavior of a beam in a peaked reversal of the type under discussion, in the event the integral can be made to vanish, may be obtained by study of higher-order approximations of the preceding theory or by direct computer computation of trajectories.

9.3. Beam Rotation Caused by a Field Reversal; Magnetic Mirrors. In Sec. 9.2 we showed that, under suitable conditions, a magnetic field reversal causes only a small fractional ripple in a beam. However, the field reversal may create a large and serious perturbation in the angular motion of the beam. Certain devices, such as microwave backward-wave oscillators employing a helical delay line, are extremely sensitive to beam rotation; in such devices a magnetic field reversal must be used only with extreme caution, since the perturbations of the angular motion may preclude successful operation of the device. In certain other types of devices, such as injected-beam magnetron oscillators, a field reversal is advantageous; a much higher angular velocity may be obtained with a given magnetic field strength when a reversal is employed than when the field is uniform. This last result is demonstrated in this section.

In the last paragraph of Sec. 2.3 of Chap. III it was shown that the resultant of the Lorentz radial force and the centrifugal force is always directed toward a particular radius, $r = r_0 (|B_0/\mathcal{B}|)^{1/2}$, independent of the algebraic signs of either $\mathcal{B}$ or B_0. However, it is apparent, from Eq. (2.20) of Chap. III, that the angular velocity is sensitive to a change in the signs of either $\mathcal{B}$ or B_0

We now consider an unrippled beam moving at constant radius and carrying negligible current in a magnetic field uniform from the cathode out to some point P, at which the field suddenly reverses direction. Prior to the reversal, $\mathcal{B} = B_0$ and there is no rotation of the beam, so that $r = r_0$ and $\theta = 0$ in Eq. (2.20) of Chap. III. If the reversal occurs very suddenly ($L/\lambda_n \ll 1$), the radial ripple following the reversal is negligible, and again $r = r_0$. However, the sign of $\mathcal{B}$ is changed, and following the reversal, the angular velocity is given by the relation

$$\dot{\theta} = \tfrac{1}{2}\,\eta\left(-B_0 - B_0\,\frac{r_0^2}{r^2}\right) = -\,\eta\,B_0 \tag{9.10}$$

This means that the magnitude of the angular velocity is exactly the cyclotron frequency associated with B_0. Thus the reversal creates a drastic change in the angular velocity, from a value of zero preceding the reversal to the full cyclotron frequency following the reversal. It is important to note that the direction of rotation is opposite to the vector direction of the magnetic field preceding the reversal, or in the vector direction of the magnetic field following the reversal; the same is true even if the two fields are of unequal magnitude.

A study of Busch's theorem shows that if, in a uniform magnetic field, a beam expands to a radius larger than the cathode radius, the angular velocity of the beam cannot exceed the Larmor frequency of the magnetic field. Equation (9.10) indicates, on the other hand, that a field reversal results in twice the Larmor frequency, even in a beam which has experienced no radial expansion. For beams in which only a moderate amount of expansion is desirable, as in injected-beam magnetron devices, a field reversal is often advantageous to reduce magnet weight and, incidentally, the external fields associated with the magnets.

The energy associated with beam rotation must be explained. Since the beam under consideration is drifting in a constant-potential drift tube, it is obvious that if any kinetic energy is converted into beam rotation, that energy must result in a reduction in the longitudinal beam velocity. From Eq. (9.10) the equivalent potential ϕ_θ associated with beam rotation following the reversal is found to be

$$2\eta\,\phi_\theta = v_\theta^2 = (r\dot{\theta})^2 = (\eta B_0 r_0)^2$$

or $$\phi_\theta = \frac{\eta}{2}(B_0 r_0)^2 \tag{9.11}$$

If the potential of the drift tube, and hence of the beam, were less than ϕ_θ, a negative longitudinal kinetic energy would be required following the rotation. Since a negative kinetic energy is impossible, the beam would not pass through the field-reversal transition region, but would be reflected. This effect, known as magnetic mirroring, has been used both to contain a high-temperature plasma and in certain types of microwave reflex oscillators. If the condition for magnetic mirroring is approached, the drastic perturbation in the longitudinal velocity will invalidate the paraxial theory; in this event a more rigorous analysis of the trajectories is required.

As an illustration of the magnitude of both the angular velocity and the angular energy which may occur in a typical device, let us consider a backward-wave oscillator operating at a frequency of 10 kMc. Representative values for the beam radius, magnetic field, and overall length of the r-f interaction region are 1 mm, 1000 gauss, and 12 cm, respectively. From Eq. (9.11) it is calculated that $\phi_\theta = 880$ volts; hence the beam will be reflected if the r-f circuit voltage has any lower value.

From Eq. (9.10) it is seen that $\dot{\theta} = 1.76 \times 10^{10}$ radians/sec following the reversal. If, for example, a potential of 1280 volts is applied to the r-f circuit, then, following the reversal, 880 volts will be associated with the rotational energy, and only 400 volts with the longitudinal motion. It may then be calculated that the transit time of the beam through the r-f circuit will be 10^{-8} sec, and the beam will rotate through 17.6 radians, or 2.8 full revolutions in passing through the r-f circuit.

The force which alters the longitudinal velocity in the transition region arises from the product of the angular velocity of the beam and the radial component of the magnetic field.

9.4. Adiabatic Tapering of the Magnetic Field. Electrons drifting in a constant-potential drift tube tend to follow along magnetic flux lines. This tendency suggests that a gradual change in the axial magnetic field strength may be used either to compress or to expand the diameter of a round beam. Such a procedure might, however, introduce rippling into the beam. Paraxial theory may be used to estimate the magnitude of the rippling created by field tapering. The ripples can be estimated accurately if the magnetic field tapering is adiabatic, so that the quasi-static approximation can be used. By the term adiabatic in this context is meant that the rate of change of magnetic field is sufficiently small, at every axial position, so that the equilibrium beam radius calculated from the local magnetic field with the help of Eq. (4.6a) or (4.6b) can be used to approximate the actual beam radius. This is equivalent to the assumption that the acceleration term r'' may be omitted from the paraxial-ray equation

(4.1). To this order of approximation, field tapering causes no rippling.

Two extreme cases will now be treated:

1. The cathode is completely shielded ($B_c = 0$).
2. The beam carries negligible current ($I = 0$).

For these two cases approximate formulas will be derived for the rippling introduced by the field tapering. Let $\beta_H = \eta \mathcal{B}/v_{z0}$, where $\mathcal{B}$ is a function of axial position z.

In the first limiting case of shielded cathode ($B_c = 0$), the paraxial equation (4.1) assumes the form

$$r'' + \frac{r\,\beta_H^2}{4} = \frac{P}{4\pi\epsilon_0(2\eta)^{1/2}\,r} \tag{9.12}$$

If $\mathcal{B}$ varies so slowly that $r'' \ll r\,\beta_H^2/4$, the radius r at any axial position is simply the Brillouin radius r_b calculated from Eq. (3.10), using the local value for $\mathcal{B}$, that is,

$$r_b^2 = \frac{P}{\pi\epsilon_0\beta_H^2(2\eta)^{1/2}} \tag{9.13}$$

It is now assumed that the tapering creates a ripple of amplitude δ around the Brillouin radius; that is, $r = r_b + \delta$; it is also assumed that $\delta \ll r_b$ everywhere. Substituting this expression for r using Eq. (9.13) and keeping only zero- and first-order terms in δ, Eq. (9.12) becomes

$$\delta'' + \frac{\delta\beta_H^2}{2} = -r_b'' \tag{9.14}$$

It must be remembered that β is a function of z.

The complementary solution of Eq. (9.14) represents any initial ripple in the beam which existed prior to the onset of the tapering. Provided the magnetic field is changed so slowly that $\beta_H' \ll \beta_H^2$, an approximate complementary solution is

$$\delta \cong \beta_H^{-1/2}\left[a\cos\left(\frac{1}{\sqrt{2}}\int\beta_H\,dz\right) + b\sin\left(\frac{1}{\sqrt{2}}\int\beta_H\,dz\right)\right] \tag{9.15}$$

where a and b are constants, which may be written in terms of the ripple amplitude and slope at the onset of the tapering.

The important feature of Eq. (9.15) is that any initial ripple in the beam varies in magnitude approximately as $\beta_H^{-1/2}$; this implies that a substantial degree of beam compression (β_H increasing) tends to reduce any initial ripple. From Eq. (9.13), it follows that r_b varies $1/\beta_H$; therefore, in a beam which has been magnetically compressed, the absolute magnitude of any initial ripple will be reduced by the compression, but the fractional ripple will be increased. The converse holds for a magnetic expansion.

The particular solution of Eq. (9.14) represents ripple introduced by the process of field tapering. To a first approximation, if the tapering is slow, the particular solution is simply

$$\delta_p \approx -\frac{2\, r_b''}{\beta_H^2} \tag{9.16}$$

if we neglect δ'' compared with $\delta\beta_H^2/2$. In view of Eq. (9.13) the particular solution may be written

$$\delta_p = \frac{2r_b}{\beta_H^2}\left[\frac{\beta_H''}{\beta_H} - 2\left(\frac{\beta_H'}{\beta_H}\right)^2\right] \tag{9.17}$$

If it is assumed that the field is tapered slowly from some uniform value B_1 to a different value B_2, then, in the region beyond the taper, $\mathcal{B}'$ and $\mathcal{B}''$ vanish. Equation (9.17) then predicts that, to the order of approximation employed to obtain the equation, the taper itself introduces no rippling; higher-order approximations must be used to account for such rippling. It is largely for this reason that magnetic tapering can be successfully employed in practice, without the need for critically shaped magnetic fields or for critical adjustments of the beam entrance conditions as the taper is approached.

In the second limiting case of zero current ($I = 0$), the analysis for field tapering of a confined-flow beam proceeds exactly as in the case of a Brillouin beam. In place of Eq. (9.12), however, the paraxial-ray equation (4.1) assumes the form

$$r'' + \frac{r\,\beta_H^2}{4} = \frac{r_c^4\,\beta_{Hc}^2}{4r^3} \tag{9.18}$$

where $\beta_{Hc} = \eta\, B_c/v_0$.

The equilibrium radius in this case is given by Eq. (4.3). We are again led to the conclusion that the complementary solution varies as $\beta_H^{-1/2}$ and that the fractional ripple varies as $\beta_H^{1/2}$. In place of Eq. (9.17) it is found that the expression for the taper-induced ripple is

$$\delta_p = \frac{1}{2}\frac{r_a}{\beta_H^2}\left[\frac{\beta_H''}{\beta_H} - \frac{3}{2}\left(\frac{\beta_H'}{\beta_H}\right)^2\right] \tag{9.19}$$

so that the conclusion following Eq. (9.17) is also valid for confined flow.

9.5. Transverse Fields. It is inevitable that, in both solenoids and in permanent magnets designed to produce a uniform longitudinal magnetic field, there are inhomogeneities in the materials, or mechanical construction errors. These inhomogeneities or errors cause the appearance of a small magnetic field component perpendicular to the axis of the system. Such fields are known as transverse fields. The effect of a transverse field is to cause the bending of an otherwise rectilinear beam.

In beams having a high length-to-diameter ratio, usually encountered in traveling-wave amplifiers, for example, the presence of transverse fields may make satisfactory operation of the focusing system difficult, critical of adjustment, or altogether impossible. Fortunately, the magnitude of transverse field which is encountered in carefully constructed solenoids and axially symmetric permanent magnets is a small fraction of the longitudinal field; this fraction may readily be kept below 2 per cent, but it is only by taking the most elaborate precautions that it can be reduced below about 0.1 per cent.

Because the transverse field is usually a very small fraction of the longitudinal field, and because in most applications only a small amount of bending due to the transverse field is tolerable, a comprehensive analysis of the beam behavior is not warranted. It is sufficient to approximate the effect by assuming that the transverse field causes the entire beam to bend in a direction perpendicular to both the axial field and transverse field directions. The radius of curvature of the bent beam is simply the cyclotron radius given by Eq. (4.6) of Chap. I. This radius may be written

$$R = \frac{v_0}{\omega_{Hn}} \tag{9.20}$$

where $\omega_{Hn} = \eta B_n$, and B_n is the transverse field strength.

Now consider a hollow drift tube of length L and internal diameter D. For $L \gg D$, the radius of a circle, tangent to one side of the cylinder at its mid-plane and just touching the opposite sides of the cylinder at each end (Fig. 4.23), is $R = L^2/8D$. For a beam of zero thickness, bent by a transverse field to pass through the cylinder, the cyclotron radius of the transverse field must exceed the radius of the tangent circle; this is equivalent to the inequality

$$B_n < \frac{8Dv_0}{\eta L^2} \tag{9.21}$$

Any higher transverse field (acting along the entire beam length) will prevent the beam from passing through the drift tube.

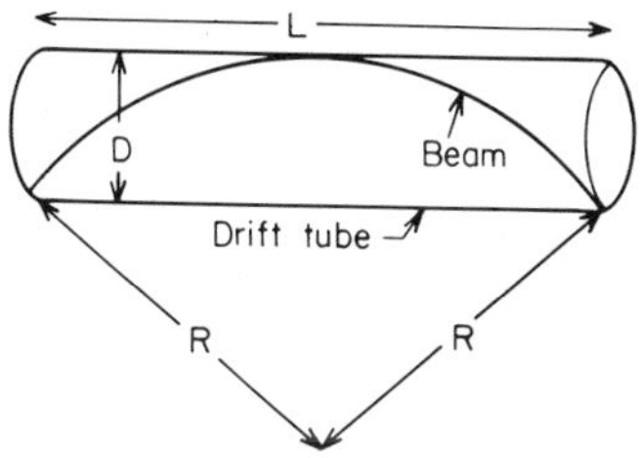

Fig. 4.23. Schematic of a thin beam passing through a drift tube grazing both ends and center of the tube.

As an example, consider a 900-volt low-power traveling-wave amplifier operating at about 9 kMc. Typical dimensions for a helical delay line for such a tube would be D = 2 mm, L = 10 cm. Then, from Eq. (9.21), it may be calculated that $B_n < 1.64$ gauss, which is only about two to three times typical values of the earth's magnetic field. Thus the need for careful magnetic shielding of the device becomes clear.

From a practical point of view, it is far more difficult to obtain a low transverse field with permanent magnets than with a solenoid designed to produce the same axial field strength over the same axial length. Transverse fields can be greatly reduced in magnitude on and close to the axis, both in solenoids and permanent magnets, by the use of devices known as flux straighteners. The design of flux straighteners is largely an art, and is outside the scope of this book.

PROBLEM

1.

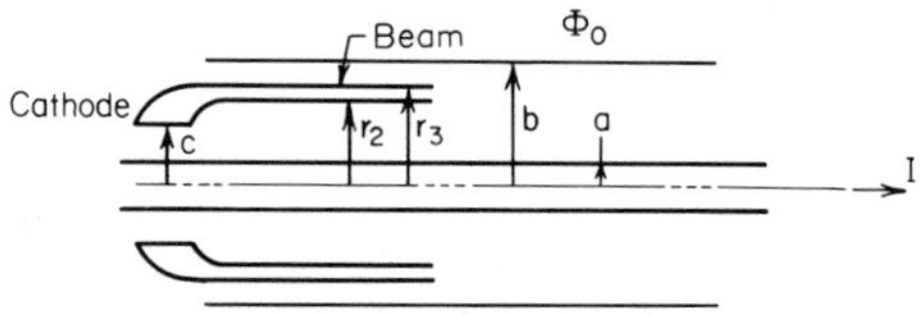

A hollow beam is focused by an azimuthal magnetic field produced by a current I flowing down a central rod of radius a. The beam is emitted from a hollow cathode of radius r_1 and finally flows in a rectilinear path into the drift tube of radius b. The rod is operated at zero potential with respect to the cathode, and the drift tube at potential Φ_0. Find the charge-density variation in the beam and the way the longitudinal velocity component varies with radius. For a thin beam in which the longitudinal velocity can be regarded as being approximately constant, find, for a total beam current I, the relation yielding the inner and outer radii of the beam and the beam potential. This is a wrapped-around hollow-beam version of a crossed-field focusing system.

2. DIAGRAM

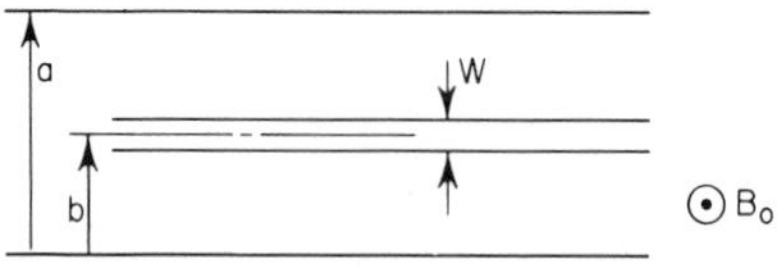

A thin crossed-field Brillouin sheet beam of height $W \ll a$ and width l flows between two plates distance a apart. The bottom plate is at zero potential, the top one at potential ϕ_0. The center of the beam is distance b from the lower plate. Assuming that the magnetic field is B_0, and the current in the beam I_0, find a relation between I_0, B_0, and ϕ_0. Find the potential at the center of the beam. Suppose, for simplicity, that W is small enough so that the beam velocity may be assumed to be uniform.

REFERENCES FOR CHAPTER IV

1. Dryden, V. W.: Exact Solutions to Space-charge Flow in Spherical Coordinates with Application to Magnetron Guns, *J. Appl. Phys.*, vol. 33, p. 3118, 1962.
2. Waters, W. E.: Theory of Magnetron Injection Guns, *Trans. IRE*, vol. ED-10, p. 226, 1963.
3. Waters, W. E.: Azimuthal Electron Flow in a Spherical Diode, *J. Appl. Phys.*, vol. 30, p. 368, 1959.
4. Sturrock, P. A.: "Static and Dynamic Electron Optics," Cambridge University Press, London, 1955.
5. Crumly, C. B.: A Travelling Wave Amplifier Tube Employing an Electrostatically Focused Hollow Beam, *Trans. IRE*, vol. ED-3, p. 62, 1956.
6. Pierce, J. R.: Instability of Hollow Beams, *Trans. IRE*, vol. ED-3, p. 183, 1956.
7. Kyle, R. L., and H. F. Webster: Breakup of Hollow Cylindrical Electron Beams, *Trans. IRE.*, vol. ED-3, p. 172, 1956.
8. Nielsen, C. E., A. M. Sessler, and K. R. Symon: Longitudinal Instabilities in Intense Relativistic Beams, *Proc. 2nd Intern. Conf. on High Energy Accelerators and Instrumentation*, p. 239, CERN, Geneva, 1959.
9. Chodorow, M., and C. Susskind: "Fundamentals of Microwave Electronics," McGraw-Hill Book Company, New York, 1964.
10. Glass, M. S.: Straight Field Permanent Magnets of Minimum Weight for T.W.T. Focusing: Design and Graphic Aids in Design, *Proc. IRE.*, vol. 45, p. 1100, 1957.

V

Periodic Focusing

1. INTRODUCTION

Several different methods for uniform focusing of an electron beam were discussed in Chap. IV. The most commonly used of these employ a uniform magnetic field produced either by a solenoid or a permanent magnet. Most of the other types which can be used for focusing a cylindrical beam have practical disadvantages.

The disadvantages of a solenoid in producing a uniform magnetic field for focusing an electron beam are that it consumes electric power, in addition to being bulky and having some leakage field associated with it. It is possible to design permanent magnets which can produce a uniform magnetic field over the length of an electron beam.[1] Such focusing systems, however, have large external leakage fields associated with them and, because of the large magnet gap required, make inefficient use of the magnet materials. Consequently, permanent magnet systems are relatively heavy. In certain cases compensating magnets can be used to reduce these external leakage fields, but complete compensation is difficult, if not impossible. Nevertheless, permanent magnet systems of this kind are widely used.

An alternative approach is to use nonuniform electrostatic or magnetic fields for focusing. Certain features of this method have already been discussed in Chaps. III and IV. The focusing effect of a magnetic field depends only on the magnitude of the square of the field, not on its direction. Consequently, if the field were periodically reversed in direction, there would still be an inward focusing force on the beam with an average value which would depend only on the rms value of the field. Such a nonuniform system, known as periodic permanent magnet, or PPM focusing, is used widely in traveling-wave tubes, and is discussed in Section 2. The most important advantage is that the weight of the focusing system is radically reduced; the gap length, as shown schematically in Fig. 5.1b, is one half the periodic length of the system, whereas the gap length in a uniform focusing system using a permanent magnet is essentially the length of the beam (Fig. 5.1a). Typically, the length

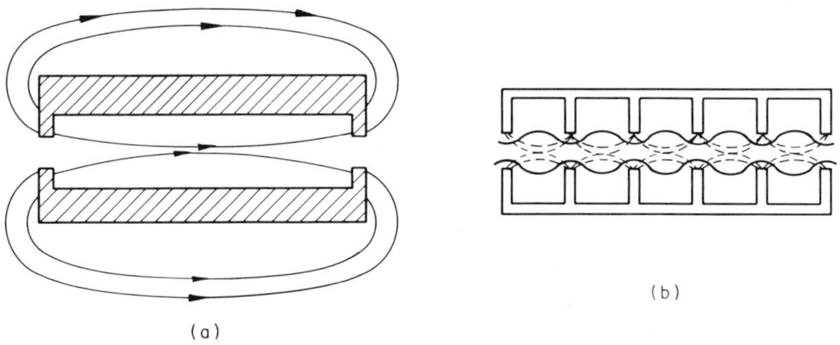

Fig. 5.1. Schematic of magnetic field configurations. (a) Uniform magnetic field; (b) periodic magnetic field. (Reproduced from Ref. 6, courtesy of the Institute of Electrical and Electronics Engineers.)

of one period of a periodic focusing system is a very small fraction of the total length of beam. Therefore the efficiency of a periodic focusing system is considerably greater than that of the equivalent uniform-field type; the weight of the system is reduced by a factor of the order of $(d/h)^2$, where d is the gap between pole pieces in a periodic system and h is the length of the equivalent uniform system. The gap length is small in a periodic system, and the leakage fields extend, at worst, only over regions comparable with the gap length. Moreover, shielding of the magnets is convenient, and the external leakage field can be eliminated almost entirely. For use with a traveling-wave tube, the internal diameter of a uniform focusing system tends to be at least the diameter of the gun, which is larger than that of the beam, whereas the periodic focusing system can have an internal diameter only a little larger than that of the circuit.

The interaction of a PPM focusing system with an electron beam is illustrated by reference to Fig. 5.2. As an electron, entering the system with zero angular velocity about the axis, passes through the first pole piece, its angular velocity increases because of the inter-

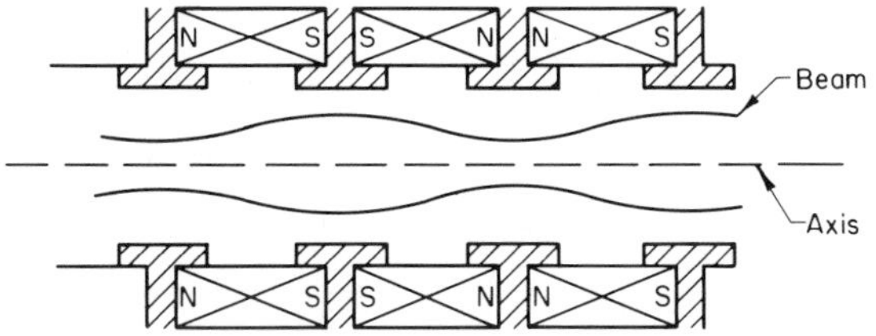

Fig. 5.2. Schematic of the magnetic fields and electron trajectories in a PPM focusing system.

action with the radial component of field. Because of the spin it receives, the centrifugal force pushes it outward. As the electron moves toward the mid-plane between the pole pieces, the interaction of this angular component of velocity with the longitudinal component of magnetic field gives rise to an inward force on the electron which pushes it toward the axis. In a similar way, as the electron passes through the next pole piece, its angular component of velcocity is reversed; in the next section the interaction of this velocity component with a longitudinal field of opposite sign gives rise once more to an inward force. The net impulse an electron receives in the outward direction is smaller than the net impulse it receives in the inward direction, because by conservation of energy, its velocity in the axial direction is least in the region between the pole pieces. More important still, the outward centrifugal force on an electron due to its angular velocity is smaller than the inward force due to its interaction with the longitudinal field. Consequently, there is an average inward focusing force acting on the electron, which can balance the outward force due to space charge.

An alternative to PPM focusing is periodic electrostatic focusing, which is treated in Section 3 and illustrated schematically in Fig. 5.3. This focusing system consists of a series of rings periodically spaced, every other ring being at potential Φ_a, alternate rings being at potentials Φ_b, where $\Phi_a < \Phi_b$. When an electron passes through an electrode at potential Φ_a, it experiences a force pushing it toward the axis. Similarly, when an electron passes through an electrode at potential Φ_b, it experiences a force pushing it away from the axis. Its trajectory tends, therefore, to have a periodic shape. However, since an electron is in the lower potential region longer, with a smaller velocity, the time-averaged force exerted on an electron as it passes through one period of the system is inward. On the other hand, the average force exerted by space charge is outward. With

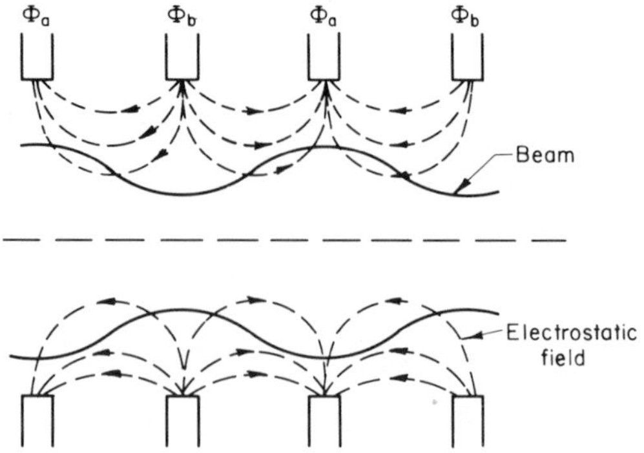

Fig. 5.3. A schematic of the electric fields and electron trajectories in a periodic electrostatic focusing system.

the correct choice of the parameters, these two forces are balanced, and so the electron beam can be confined by a periodic electrostatic focusing system.

A third type of periodic-focusing method, periodic deflection focusing, is discussed in Section 4. In this system the beam axis has a periodic variation of curvature with distance. It was shown in Section 6 of Chap. III that a strip beam with a curved beam axis, which is itself an equipotential, experiences an inward focusing force proportional to the square of the curvature of the axis. Consequently, even if the central axis is an equipotential but has a curvature which varies periodically with distance, there is still an inward focusing force on the beam. A variant of this type of focusing scheme is to use a periodic magnetic focusing field, with components of field both along and perpendicular to the beam axis. This causes the beam axis itself to be periodic in shape, which gives rise to a focusing action. Combinations of such deflection focusing schemes with the other types of focusing already described can be used.[2] A combination of a periodic variation of potential and of longitudinal magnetic field along the beam axis can also be employed.

The analysis of the behavior of periodic focusing systems is more difficult than that for uniform systems. Generally, it is necessary to use approximate methods based on the equations of paraxial flow, in which the velocity of an electron in the direction perpendicular to the beam axis is assumed to be much less than its velocity along the beam axis. Such an assumption is justified in most practical situations. In addition, the use of the paraxial equations assumes that the radial component of electric or magnetic field is proportional to the distance from the beam axis. In certain cases, some of which are treated in this chapter, the latter assumption can be relaxed.

The nature of the beam focused by a periodic focusing system differs in two important respects from that obtained in a uniform focusing system. First, because the focusing fields are themselves nonuniform, it is not possible to obtain a completely ripple-free beam; there is always some ripple in a periodic focusing system. Second, it is possible for the beam to be overfocused. Consider, for example, a beam passing through the periodic electrostatic focusing system shown in Fig. 5.4. The average force on an electron as it passes through one period of the focusing system is always toward the axis. If the fields are very strong, however, the inward force on an electron as it passes through a ring at the lower potential Φ_a may be sufficiently large to cause its trajectory to cross the axis. Again, as the electron passes through a ring at the higher potential Φ_b, it experiences a large force pulling it away from the axis. The net effect is to cause the maximum radius of the trajectory to <u>increase</u> as the electron moves through the system. A system operated in such a range of parameters is said to be <u>unstable</u>. This instability phenomenon has no counterpart in a uniform system. In this chapter a

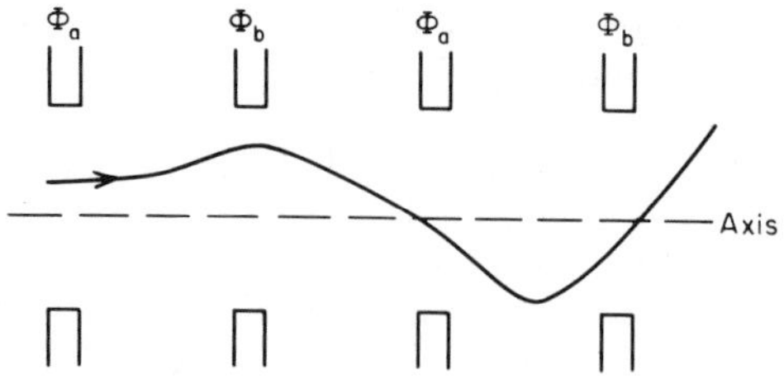

Fig. 5.4. Electron trajectories in an overfocused periodic electrostatic focusing system.

theory is presented which predicts where the instabilities occur. In many practical situations, however, the range of useful parameters required is such that the system is far from the instability region. Consequently, it is often possible to make simple approximations to the theory; an average focusing force proportional to the rms value of the focusing fields is determined, and the rippling associated with this value of field found. For certain cases near the limit of stability, it is not possible to carry out such analytic procedures. Consequently, it will be necessary to refer occasionally to numerical computations which have been made to elucidate the behavior further. Such numerical computations also serve as a useful check on the accuracy of the purely analytical procedures.

The mathematical analysis of periodic focusing systems is much more complicated than that of the uniform focusing systems of Chap. IV. In order to simplify the algebra as much as possible, we frequently resort to normalizations of physical quantities such as length, magnetic field, and space-charge density. One of the fundamental lengths used in the normalization is the length L of one period of the system. Many of the formulas are derived in terms of fairly general electromagnetic fields; these formulas can be used, if desired, for uniform focusing systems by putting the form factor describing the variation of the electric or magnetic fields equal to unity. Any convenient length, e.g., the total length of the focusing system, can be used in place of the periodic length L to apply the formulas of this chapter to a uniform focusing system.

2. PERIODIC PERMANENT MAGNET (PPM) FOCUSING OF ROUND UNIPOTENTIAL BEAMS

2.1. Introduction. The most commonly used type of the periodic focusing system is periodic permanent magnet (PPM) focusing of a round unipotential beam. This particular focusing system is applicable to a wide range of traveling-wave tubes and, to a more limited extent, to klystrons and other devices employing long unipotential round beams. The reasons why PPM focusing has had such wide application are largely practical; among the more important ones are the following:

1. A PPM system can be used to obtain a relatively high value of perveance and beam stiffness. The parameters obtained may be comparable with those for a focusing system which employs a uniform magnetic field of the same value as the rms average field of a PPM focusing system.

2. The PPM focusing system is relatively easy to manufacture.

3. The PPM focusing system can be designed to produce satisfactory focusing over a wide range of environmental conditions; it does not require external power supplies for its operation and, if properly designed, is not critical with respect to beam velocity.

4. The high-frequency circuit of a traveling-wave tube or other microwave device using PPM focusing can be designed and fabricated, in many cases, as an entity completely separate from the focusing system itself. Thus the high-frequency circuits and the focusing system can be designed and optimized independently to obtain the most efficient operation.

5. Compared with a uniform-field permanent magnet of the same length, capable of focusing the same perveance, a PPM system is lighter, has a much weaker stray magnetic field external to the magnetic system, and hence can be shielded completely with much less weight and bulk of shielding material.

A schematic of a typical cross section of a PPM focusing system used with a magnetically shielded convergent electron gun is shown in Fig. 5.5. In this system permanent magnet rings are held between steel or other suitable ferromagnetic pole pieces. The pole pieces themselves are shaped to give an optimum field, typically a sinusoidal variation of magnetic field in the neighborhood of the beam. When the gap d between two adjacent pole pieces is comparable with the half-period L/2 of the system, only the fundamental and third-harmonic space component of the field will have appreciable strength. With a gap spacing $d = L/3$, it can be shown that the third-harmonic amplitude is zero. Consequently, a design with this gap spacing, typical of that used in practice, gives an almost sinusoidal field variation.

It should be remarked that a periodic magnet system does not give a perfect periodic magnetic field near its ends because of the fringing of flux from the exposed end pole-piece face. This fringing of leakage flux reduces the field on the first, third, fifth, etc., magnets, the perturbation rapidly becoming smaller with distance from the end of the stack.

A paper by Palmer and Susskind[3] gives details of the effects of a particular magnetic field taper on the beam formation. The theory, which is carried out for a special case, is not dealt with here. It is common practice to adjust the first few magnets in the periodic system to arrive at the correct entrance conditions for the beam. This

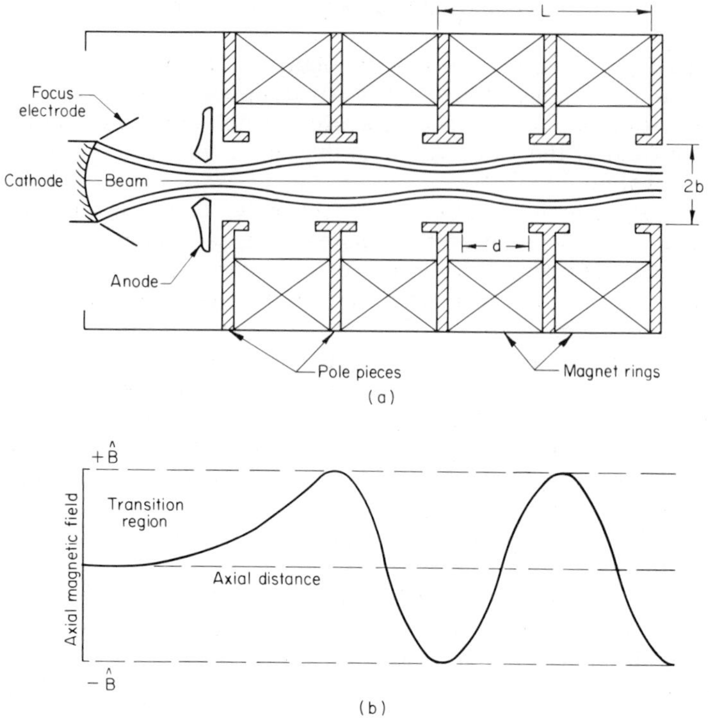

Fig. 5.5. Schematic of a periodic magnetic focusing system. (a) Cross section of focusing system; (b) variation of axial magnetic field along the axis.

is usually done entirely by cut-and-try experimental methods.

It is often found in practical PPM-focused wave tubes that substantial departures from true periodicity may be used to advantage in helping to achieve desired electrical characteristics. In such cases the theory of this section may be used as a starting point for designing the PPM stack, but the final version may well be determined only by empirical methods or detailed trajectory studies with a computer.

The design of the magnet system itself has been discussed in many papers, e.g., Ref. 4. Experience has shown that over a wide range of parameters, a magnet stack designed according to the procedures outlines in that paper possesses an axial magnetic field strength in close agreement with the design value, provided an accurate demagnetization curve for the permanent magnets employed is available.

Three different types of periodic magnetic focusing fields will be considered. The first shown in Fig. 5.6a has a square-wave variation of field with distance; i.e., the field is uniform in amplitude over

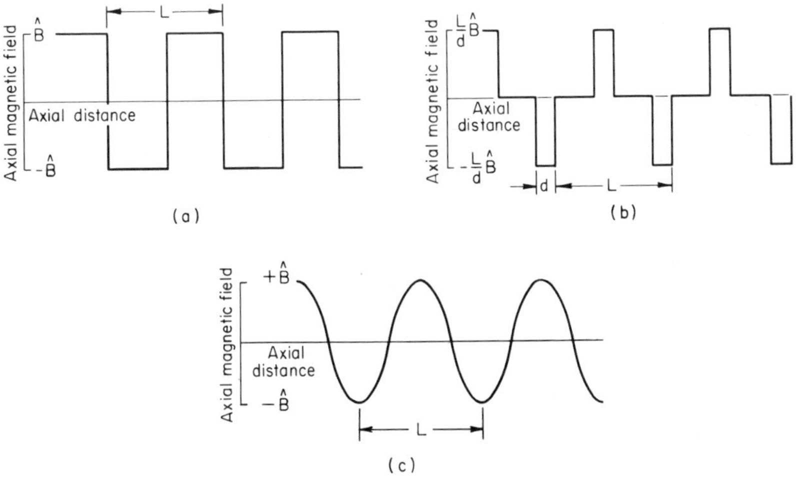

Fig. 5.6. The variation of axial magnetic field along the axis in several different configurations. (a) Alternate square-wave magnetic field variation; (b) a magnetic field with rectangular pulses of alternate sign separated by drift spaces; (c) a sine-wave variation of magnetic field.

a half-period of the system, then reverses in sign, and stays uniform over the next half-period. In the second case, illustrated in Fig. 5.6b, the field has a uniform amplitude over the first part of a half-period of the system; there is a step change to zero amplitude over the rest of this half-period, and the same form is repeated, with the sign reversed, over the next half-period. The third case, shown in Fig. 5.6c, and technically the most important, is that of a field with a sinusoidal variation in amplitude. In all cases the period of the system is taken to correspond to the distance between two points of equal field amplitude and sign.

We are interested in the focusing of a long uniform beam in which the electron velocity in the axial direction is large compared with its transverse velocity component. Consequently, it is possible to express the motion of an edge electron of the beam in terms of a paraxial equation of motion. For a periodic magnetic focusing system, the potential is assumed to be uniform along the length of the beam. The required paraxial equation for a cylindrical beam [Eq. (2.25) of Chap. III] with $\Phi' = \Phi'' = 0$ is

$$r'' + \frac{\eta r \mathcal{B}^2}{8\Phi} - \frac{\eta \mathcal{B}_c^2 r_c^4}{8 r^3 \Phi} = \frac{\eta I}{2\pi\epsilon_0 (2\eta\Phi)^{3/2}\, r} \tag{2.1}$$

It is convenient to normalize Eq. (2.1), and to express the independent variable in terms of the periodic length L of the system, and the radius r in terms of the initial radius r_0 of the beam when it enters the magnetic focusing system. Thus we put

$$X = \frac{2\pi z}{L} \qquad\qquad (2.2)$$
$$r = r_0\sigma$$

It is also convenient to express the current and magnetic field in terms of normalized quantities. We write

$$\mathcal{B} = \hat{B}\, f(X) \qquad\qquad (2.3)$$

where $\hat{B}$ is the rms value of the magnetic field, so that

$$\frac{1}{2\pi}\int_0^{2\pi} f^2(X)\, dX = 1 \qquad\qquad (2.4)$$

For the square-wave field variation of Fig. 6.6a, it follows that $f^2(X) = 1$ and $\hat{B}$ is also the peak value of the field. For a sinusoidal variation of field, $f^2(X) = 1 - \cos 2X = 2\sin^2 X$. The rms value of the field $\hat{B}$ is normalized in terms of a parameter α,

$$\alpha = \frac{\eta L^2 \hat{B}^2}{32\pi^2\Phi} = \frac{1}{4}\left(\frac{L}{\lambda_H}\right)^2 \qquad\qquad (2.5)$$

where $\lambda_H = 2\pi v/\omega_H$ is the cyclotron wavelength corresponding to the rms value of the magnetic field. Similarly, the current is normalized in terms of a parameter $\mathcal{P}$, where

$$\mathcal{P} = \frac{IL^2}{16\pi^3\epsilon_0(2\eta)^{1/2}\, r_0^2\Phi^{3/2}} = \frac{1}{2}\left(\frac{L}{\lambda_p}\right)^2 \qquad\qquad (2.6)$$

where $\lambda_p = 2\pi v/\omega_p$ is the plasma wavelength of the beam at the entrance plane into the magnetic field, at which plane the beam radius is r_0. Finally, the magnetic field at the cathode is normalized in terms of the rms value of the magnetic field in the beam by a parameter $\mathcal{K}$ defined as

$$\mathcal{K} = \frac{r_c^4\mathcal{B}_c^2}{2\hat{B}^2 r_0^4} \qquad\qquad (2.7)$$

The parameters α, $\mathcal{P}$, and $\mathcal{K}$ are often referred to as the lens-strength parameter, the space-charge parameter, and the cathode-shielding factor, respectively. In terms of these parameters the paraxial equation (2.1) reduces to the normalized form

$$\sigma'' + \alpha\,\sigma\, f^2 - \frac{2\mathcal{K}\alpha}{\sigma^3} - \frac{\mathcal{P}}{\sigma} = 0 \qquad\qquad (2.8)$$

where the prime denotes d/dX.

It would have been possible to express Eq. (4.1) of Chap. IV in this form, where the definition of α of Eq. (2.5) contains B instead of $\hat{B}$. Much of Section 4 of Chap. IV could then have been written more simply. This was not done for two reasons: First, the natural normalizing length L of periodic systems is absent in uniform systems. Second, the simple approach of Section 4 of Chap. IV shows rather clearly the role of the different parameters P, β_H/β_{Hc}, etc., in determining specific radii. The algebra of Chap. IV is comparatively simple, so that the normalization of this chapter is not essential. The algebra here is so complicated that without normalization the argument would be difficult to follow. At times the similarities in the equations of this chapter and of Chap. IV will be pointed out. Clearly, uniform focusing must always be a special case of periodic focusing.

For the types of fields illustrated in Fig. 5.6a and b, Eq. (2.8) is solved most easily by using matrix methods. However, it is more convenient to solve this equation directly when the field variation is sinusoidal. In this case the solution is very closely related to the solution of Mathieu's equation.

When there is a finite field at the cathode or when space-charge fields are not negligible, so that the parameters $\mathcal{P}$ and $\mathcal{K}$ are finite, the equation is nonlinear. Under these conditions it is necessary to make a further small-ripple approximation in order to reduce Eq. (2.8) to a soluble linear form. The ranges of stability of the nonlinear equation are far more difficult to establish by analytic methods.

2.2. Stability of a Beam with Negligible Space Charge. When the magnetic field is uniform and nonperiodic, the equation of motion governing the motion of the edge trajectory is Eq. (2.8) with f = 1. If the initial radius of the beam is given by $\sigma = 1$, the condition for focusing of a uniform-diameter beam becomes

$$\mathcal{P} = \alpha(1 - 2\mathcal{K}) \tag{2.9}$$

or

$$\omega_P^2 = \frac{\omega_H^2}{2}(1 - 2\mathcal{K}) \tag{2.10}$$

This is the condition already derived in Section 4 of Chap. IV.* In this case the inward forces due to the magnetic field cancel the sum of the outward forces due to space charge and the rotational motion of the beam.

Consider now the situation when the field is periodic and has a square-wave variation with distance, as illustrated in Fig. 5.6a. In this case $f^2 = 1$, as with the uniform magnetic field, and the focusing forces depend only on the magnitude of the field, not on its direction. It can be shown, by integrating Eq. (2.8) over the region where the field reverses in sign, that there is no lens effect associated with the sudden reversal of the field. Therefore all the conditions for correct focusing are the same as for a uniform field, and are given by Eq. (2.9) or (2.10). Thus, in this idealized case, a square-wave

*Equation (2.10) is another way of writing Eq. (4.2) of Chap. IV.

periodic magnetic focusing field focuses a beam in exactly the same way as a uniform magnetic field.

A real focusing field does not behave so conveniently. In general, the beam ripples and may even become unstable. As a simple illustration of this latter phenomenon, we consider the case when the cathode is magnetically shielded, so that $\mathcal{K} = 0$, and the current in the beam is negligible, so that $\mathcal{P} = 0$. When the field is uniform or has a square-wave variation, $f^2 = 1$. The solution of Eq. (2.8) is then

$$\sigma = \sigma_0 \cos(\alpha^{1/2} X) + \frac{\sigma_0'}{\alpha^{1/2}} \sin(\alpha^{1/2} X) \tag{2.11}$$

where σ_0 and σ_0' are the initial values of σ and σ', respectively, at the plane $X = 0$. Thus, in this case, whether the field is uniform or has a square-wave periodicity, the motion is bounded and the radius of an electron trajectory varies periodically with distance along the axis.

Consider now the motion of an electron through one period of the system shown in Fig. 5.6b, with $\mathcal{P} = \mathcal{K} = 0$. For this system, f is defined to have the value $f = (L/2d)^{1/2}$, when $\pi < X < 2\pi d/L$, $f = 0$ when $2\pi d/L < X < \pi$, $f = -(L/2d)^{1/2}$ when $2\pi d/L < X < \pi + 2\pi d/L$, and $f = 0$ when $\pi + 2\pi d/L < X < 2\pi$. Thus the rms value of f is unity, and d is such that $d < L/2$. An electron trajectory through the region $2\pi d/L < X < \pi$ can be found from Eq. (2.11) with α replaced by $\alpha L/2d$. The values of σ and σ' at $X_d = 2\pi d/L$, denoted by σ_d and σ_d', respectively, are given by the relation

$$\begin{bmatrix} \sigma_d \\ \sigma_d' \end{bmatrix} = \begin{bmatrix} \cos\mu & \dfrac{X_d}{\mu}\sin\mu \\ -\dfrac{\mu}{X_d}\sin\mu & \cos\mu \end{bmatrix} \begin{bmatrix} \sigma_0 \\ \sigma_0' \end{bmatrix} \tag{2.12}$$

where $\mu = \left(\dfrac{\alpha L}{2d}\right)^{1/2} X_d = 2\pi\left(\dfrac{\alpha d}{2L}\right)^{1/2}$

The values of σ and σ' at $X = \pi$, denoted by σ_π and σ_π', respectively, can be determined by integrating Eq. (2.8) with $f = 0$. This yields the result

$$\begin{bmatrix} \sigma_\pi \\ \sigma_\pi' \end{bmatrix} = \begin{bmatrix} 1 & \pi - X_d \\ 0 & 1 \end{bmatrix} \begin{bmatrix} \sigma_d \\ \sigma_d' \end{bmatrix} \tag{2.13}$$

Multiplying the two matrices together, the exit conditions from one period of the system are found in terms of the entrance conditions. The result is

$$\begin{bmatrix} \sigma_\pi \\ \\ \sigma'_\pi \end{bmatrix} = \begin{bmatrix} \cos\mu - \frac{\mu}{X_d}(\pi - X_d)\sin\mu & \frac{X_d}{\mu}\sin\mu + (\pi - X_d)\cos\mu \\ \\ -\frac{\mu}{X_d}\sin\mu & \cos\mu \end{bmatrix} \begin{bmatrix} \sigma_0 \\ \\ \sigma'_0 \end{bmatrix} \tag{2.14}$$

Actually, the matrix of Eq. (2.14) is the matrix for a half-period; since Eq. (2.8) depends only on f^2, the matrix for the whole period is the square of that of Eq. (2.14).

It is shown in Appendix C how this result may be used to determine the position and slope of an individual electron trajectory after an electron has passed through n periods of the system. The radius of the beam would increase indefinitely with n, and the beam become unstable, if the magnitude of the sum of the two diagonal terms of the matrix for one period defined in Eq. (2.14) were greater than 2. Thus the condition for instability is

$$\left|\left[\cos\mu - \frac{\mu}{2}\left(\frac{\pi}{X_d} - 1\right)\sin\mu\right]\right| \geq 1 \tag{2.15}$$

The solution of Eq. (2.15) implies that there is an instability region or beam-cutoff region beginning at a value of $\mu = \mu_A$, where $\mu_A < \pi$, and ending at a value $\mu = \pi$. There are also other instability regions in the neighborhood of $\mu = \pi n$. Thus the range of α for which the beam is cut off is given by

$$\alpha_A < \alpha < \frac{L}{2d} \tag{2.16}$$

where $\alpha_A = 2(\mu_A^2/4\pi^2)(L/d)$. It is shown in Fig. 5.7 that α_A is a monotonically increasing function of d/L. When d/L = 0.5, so that the field has a square-wave variation, $\alpha_A = 1$ and the range of α over which the beam is unstable becomes infinitesimally narrow. This is in agreement with the results of Appendix C, for in this case, when $\mu = \pi$ and $X_d = \pi$, the two diagonal terms of the matrix are such that A = D = −1, and the other two terms are given by B = C = 0. This is the condition for the system to be stable when A + D = 2. Figure 5.7 shows that when $d/L \to 0$, so that the field variation becomes a series of infinite spikes in the magnetic field, $\alpha_A \to 4/\pi^2 = 0.406$. The upper limit of the unstable region under the same condition is $\alpha = \infty$. Similarly, when d/L = 0.33, so that the third harmonic of the field is missing, $\alpha_A = 0.72$, and the upper limit of the cutoff region is at $\alpha = 1.5$. We infer that if the field is decomposed into its harmonics, the system becomes unstable most easily when all the harmonics are present in equal amplitude. It will be seen that when the field is a pure sinusoid, then the lower cutoff is at

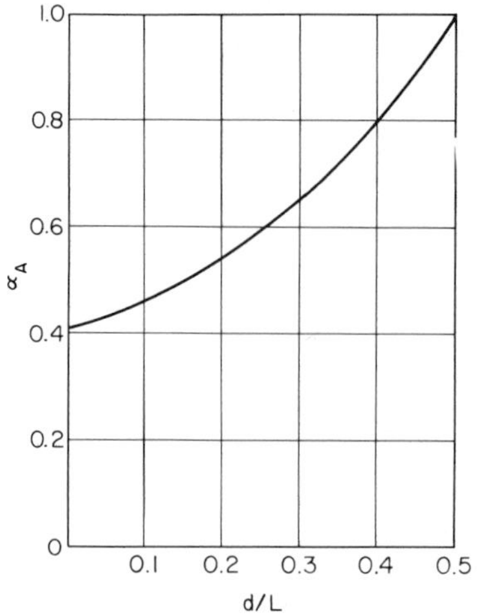

Fig. 5.7. Variation of α_A with d/L.

$\alpha_A = 0.66$ and the upper cutoff at $\alpha = 1.75$. The presence of strong higher-order harmonics in the field tends to make the system unstable. For this reason it is common practice to design magnetic focusing systems so that the field has almost a pure sinusoidal variation. In practice, the system is designed to eliminate completely the third-harmonic component of the field; the rest normally have small amplitude. A further discussion of this subject is given in Sec. 2.3.

The process which gives rise to the instability can be explained physically by considering the motion of a single electron when the condition $\mu = \pi$ is satisfied. This implies that an electron reaches the point $X = X_d$ with exactly its initial radius and transverse velocity; that is, $\sigma_d = -\sigma_0$ and $\sigma'_d = -\sigma'_0$. In the region where there is no magnetic field between $X_d < X < \pi$, no forces are applied to the electron, so that it drifts radially with its initial transverse velocity, reaching a new radial position corresponding to σ_π at $X = \pi$. The process is repeated through the next half-period of the system, and the electron drifts out still farther in the opposite direction. Consequently, after an indefinite number of periods, an electron will have drifted indefinitely far from the axis of the system, and there is no confinement. If now α is reduced so that $\mu < \pi$ at $X = X_d$, the change in transverse position is decreased, until eventually, with decreasing μ, a stable beam is obtained.

It is important to note that, even with a stable beam, the motion may not repeat itself exactly. Two periods enter into the motion: The first is the period of the focusing system itself; the second is the period over which the motion almost repeats itself. These periods are not integrally related except in special cases. One such case is, for instance, that for which $\mu = \pi$ and $X_d = \pi$. Under these conditions the motion repeats itself every period.

Consider now the situation with no space charge and no magnetic field at the cathode, but with a sinusoidal magnetic focusing field. In this case Eq. (2.8) assumes the form

$$\sigma'' + \alpha\sigma[1 + \cos(2X)] = 0 \tag{2.17}$$

This is Mathieu's equation; its solutions are discussed in Appendix D. There it is shown that, in this case, for which $a = \alpha$ and $q = \frac{1}{2}\alpha$, the first unstable region occurs where $a = \alpha_A = 0.66$, with its upper limit at $\alpha = 1.75$. This may be contrasted to the situation already discussed, for fields with a high harmonic content. The lower cutoff then lies between $0.40 < \alpha < 1.0$, depending on the value of L/d. In all cases except that of the purely square-wave field, the beam becomes unstable for sufficiently large values of α. These conclusions have been confirmed experimentally by Mendel et al.[6] An experimental curve, taken under conditions where space-charge forces are negligible, is shown in Fig. 5.8. The regions of instability, where the beam transmission is zero, are shown clearly.

Usually, it is not convenient to operate a beam-focusing system in a range of α near the instability condition. This is because the rippling amplitude, with or without space charge present, becomes quite large in this range. Consequently, it is preferable to work with small values of α, in which case it will be shown that the relevant equations simplify considerably. With small α, the average inward focusing force on the beam depends only on the rms value of the magnetic field; the fact that the field variation is periodic is relatively unimportant.

2.3. Focusing with Space Charge. It has already been pointed out that, when the space-charge forces or magnetic field at the cathode is not negligible, Eq. (2.8) becomes nonlinear, and a small-ripple

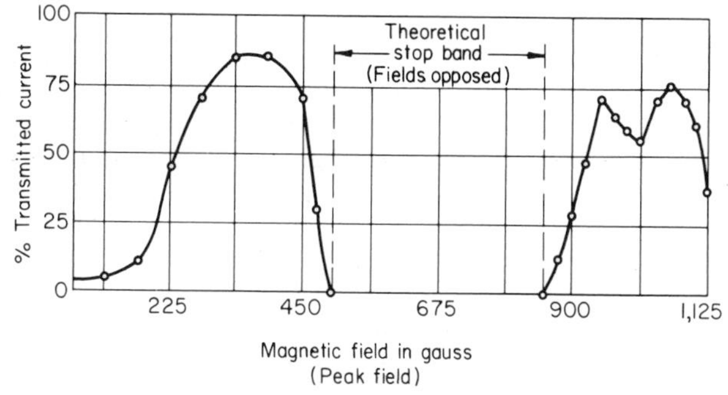

Fig. 5.8. An experimental curve showing the variation of beam transmission with magnetic field strength. (Reproduced from Ref. 6, courtesy of the Institute of Electrical and Electronics Engineers.)

assumption is required to solve the equation analytically. Since we are primarily interested in physical situations of this kind, σ is written

$$\sigma = 1 + \Delta \tag{2.18}$$

where it is assumed that $\Delta \ll 1$. In this case Eq. (2.8) can be written in the form

$$\Delta'' + \Delta[\alpha(1 + F) + 6\,\mathcal{K}\alpha + \mathcal{P}] = \mathcal{P} + 2\,\mathcal{K}\alpha - \alpha(1 + F) \tag{2.19}$$

where $f^2 = 1 + F$, and F is a periodic function.

To solve this equation, $\mathcal{P}$ and Δ are expanded in the power series

$$\begin{aligned} \mathcal{P} &= \alpha\mathcal{P}_1 + \alpha^2\mathcal{P}_2 + \cdots \\ \Delta &= \alpha\Delta_1 + \alpha^2\Delta_2 + \cdots \end{aligned} \tag{2.20}$$

and different orders in α are equated. It follows that, to first order,

$$\Delta_1'' = \mathcal{P}_1 + 2\mathcal{K} - (1 + F) \tag{2.21}$$

The right-hand side of Eq. (2.21) contains a constant term and a periodic one. For equilibrium, Δ must not increase with distance, but may be periodic. Thus the condition for equilibrium is that the constant term in the right-hand side of Eq. (2.21) be zero; i.e.,

$$\mathcal{P}_1 = 1 - 2\mathcal{K} \tag{2.22}$$

It follows that, to first order in α, the condition for equilibrium is

$$\mathcal{P} = \alpha(1 - 2\mathcal{K}) \tag{2.23}$$

This condition for equilibrium depends only on the rms strength of the magnetic focusing field, i.e., on the value of α. The condition for equilibrium [Eq. (2.23)] is precisely the same as that for focusing in a uniform magnetic field which has a magnitude equal to the rms value of the periodic magnetic focusing field. Equation (2.23) is identical with Eq. (2.9), and is a neater way of writing Eq. (4.2) of Chap. IV.

The beam itself does not remain uniform in radius, but has a small ripple determined by the form of the magnetic focusing field and the solution of Eq. (2.21). Consequently, in order to proceed further, it is necessary to assume a particular field shape, which we take to be the cosine variation F = cos 2X. Equation (2.8) can then be written in the form

$$\sigma'' + \alpha\sigma[1 + \cos(2X)] - \frac{2\mathcal{K}\alpha}{\sigma^3} - \frac{\mathcal{P}}{\sigma} = 0 \tag{2.24}$$

In this case Eqs. (2.21) and (2.22) yield the solution

$$\Delta_1 = -\frac{1}{4}[1 - \cos(2X)] \tag{2.25}$$

or $$\Delta = -\frac{\alpha}{4}[1 - \cos(2X)] \tag{2.26}$$

where it has been assumed that $\Delta = \Delta_1 = \Delta' = \Delta_1' = 0$ at $X = 0$, and the current is the correct value for equilibrium. Thus the equilibrium beam has an average radius slightly less than that of the equivalent beam focused by a uniform magnetic field. Its radius ripples around the average radius, the amplitude of the ripple being given by $\Delta_M = \alpha/4$.

By solving Eq. (2.24) with more care, in the manner discussed later in Secs. 3.3 and 3.9, it is possible to determine the stiffness of the beam and the effect of using an incorrect value of beam current. However, since we have already shown that the beam is equivalent to that focused by a uniform magnetic field of the same value, we may transfer the results obtained in Chap. IV for a uniform focusing field to the situation represented here. When α is small, the two fields are equivalent and the stiffness and criticality with respect to beam current are precisely that of a beam in the equivalent uniform magnetic focusing field. It should be noted, however, that this result pertains only to the ripple and stiffness of the electrons at the edge of the beam. The theory is valid only if the strength of the magnetic focusing field over the cross section of the beam is essentially uniform. If the strength of the magnetic field varies appreciably with radius, it is necessary to carry out the more detailed treatment given in Sec. 2.4.

To obtain the solution of Eq. (2.24) to second order in α, we equate second-order terms in Eq. (2.24) and obtain the following relation:

$$\Delta_2'' + \Delta_1[1 + \cos(2X) + 6\mathcal{K} + \mathcal{P}_1] = \mathcal{P}_2 \tag{2.27}$$

Neglecting terms in cos (4X) and writing $\cos^2(2X) = \frac{1}{2}[1 + \cos(4X)]$, the condition for Δ_2 to be periodic is

$$\mathcal{P}_2 = -\frac{6\mathcal{K} + \mathcal{P}_1 + \frac{1}{2}}{4} = -\frac{3 + 8\mathcal{K}}{8} \tag{2.28}$$

with $$\Delta_2 = -\tfrac{1}{16}(1 + 4\mathcal{K})[1 - \cos(2X)] \tag{2.29}$$

It follows that, to second order,

$$\mathcal{P} = \alpha(1 - 2\mathcal{K}) - \frac{\alpha^2}{8}(3 + 8\mathcal{K}) \tag{2.30}$$

and

$$\Delta = -\frac{\alpha}{4}[1 - \cos(2X)]\left[1 + \frac{\alpha}{4}(1 + 4\mathcal{K})\right] \tag{2.31}$$

The use of the higher-order approximation shows that the current which can be confined by a given periodic magnetic field is somewhat less than is predicted for the equivalent beam focused by a uniform magnetic field, though the differences are not normally very large. It also indicates that the beam ripples in the same way as for the first-order solution, but with a slightly greater amplitude. In both cases, as shown in Figs. 5.2 and 5.5, the radius of the beam is maximum at the point where the magnetic field has its maximum value, and conversely, the radius is minimum where the magnetic field is zero. The period of the ripple is half the period of the magnetic field.

A similar analysis may be carried out for a nonsinusoidal field by decomposing the square of the field into its Fourier components. From such an analysis it is clear that the rms value of the magnetic field controls the current which may be focused. However, the degree of rippling is related to the peak field. For this reason a d/L ratio of $\frac{1}{3}$ is often used in practice to eliminate the third harmonic of the field.

A detailed study of the solution of Eq. (2.24) has been made on an analog computer by Harker.[5] Curves relating α, $\mathcal{P}$, and $\mathcal{K}$ for minimum ripple are given in Fig. 5.9. The percentage ripple at the condition for minimum ripple is given in Fig. 5.10, as a function of α, with $\mathcal{K}$ as a parameter. The solutions of Eqs. (2.23), (2.26), (2.30),

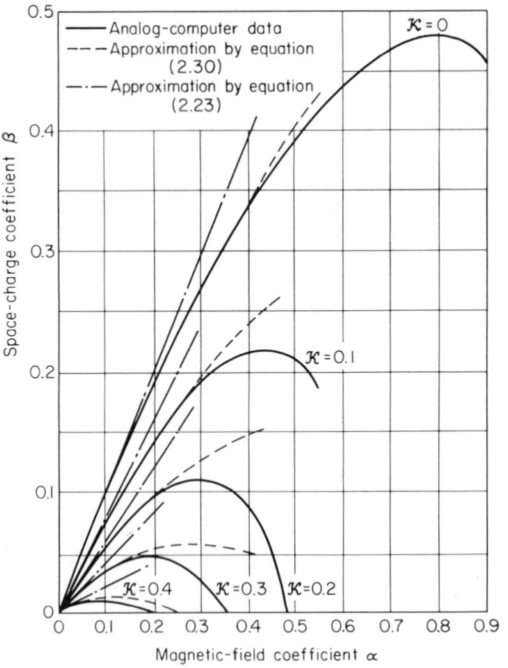

Fig. 5.9. Curves relating the lens-strength parameter α, the space-charge parameter , and the cathode-shielding parameter . (Reproduced from Ref. 5, courtesy of the Institute of Electrical and Electronics Engineers.)

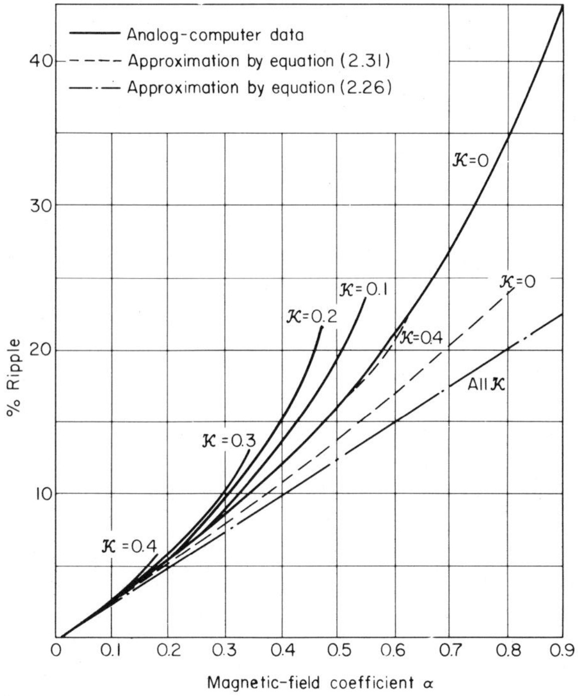

Fig. 5.10. Curves of the variation of the percentage ripple, under conditions of minimum ripple, with lens strength α. The cathode-shielding parameter $\mathcal{K}$ is a parameter. (Reproduced from Ref. 5, courtesy of the Institute of Electrical and Electronics Engineers.)

and (2.31) are plotted in the same graphs. For $\mathcal{K} = 0$, the differences are not large between the analog-computer solutions and the solutions given here when $\alpha < 0.3$.

When the substitution F = cos 2X is made in Eq. (2.19), it becomes

$$\Delta'' + \Delta\{\alpha[1 + \cos(2X)] + 6\mathcal{K}\alpha + \mathcal{P}\} = \mathcal{P} + 2\mathcal{K}\alpha - \alpha[1 + \cos(2X)] \tag{2.32}$$

This is a form of Mathieu's equation [Eq. (2) of Appendix D], with $a = \alpha(1 + 6\mathcal{K}) + \mathcal{P}$, $2q = \alpha$. The complementary solution to this equation is unstable where indicated by the solution of Mathieu's equation. Consequently, at least to the limits of the approximation used here, even a minor error in entrance conditions would give rise to an unstable beam. Assuming that the condition of Eq. (2.23) for $\mathcal{P}$ is valid, the first unstable region of the solution of Eq. (2.32) begins where $\alpha = 0.66(1 - \mathcal{P})/(1 + 4\mathcal{K})$; that is, $\alpha = 0.4/(1 + 1.6\mathcal{K})$. Harker's analog-computer solution indicates no instability in this range. This is because Eq. (2.32) pertains only to a small-ripple solution and is not necessarily valid when the ripples are large. In fact, the presence of magnetic flux through the cathode ($\mathcal{K} > 0$) or the inclusion of finite current ($\mathcal{P} > 0$) inhibits a paraxial electron from crossing the axis, a behavior which would be characteristic of an unstable solution of Mathieu's equation. It must be emphasized that the large component of azimuthal velocity in electrons from a shielded cathode may cause focusing difficulties. These effects are discussed in Sec. 2.4, and are not considered in the simple theory presented here.

When $\mathcal{K} = \mathcal{P} = 0$, the condition for instability to begin is $\alpha = 0.66$, as is discussed in Sec. 2.2. Harker's data indicate a ripple of approximately 25 per cent for a value of α slightly less than 0.66. Such a large ripple is seldom acceptable in practice, so that, although the instability is theoretically very important, and has been measured, it does not occur in a practical tube.

When the magnetic field at the cathode is zero ($\mathcal{K} = 0$), the unstable region covers the range $0.4 < \alpha < 0.66$. In PPM-focused traveling-wave amplifiers, a magnetically shielded convergent electron gun is often used. For such tubes the above theory is applicable. As already discussed, however, α is seldom allowed to exceed 0.3 in order to keep the beam rippling small, and so the question of focusing stability almost never occurs in practice.

In PPM-focused low-noise traveling-wave amplifiers, very low current beams are often used, for which it is a good approximation to neglect space-charge fields ($\mathcal{P} \simeq 0$). When the condition for focusing, at least to first order in α, is $\mathcal{K} = 0.5$, the unstable region of operation then lies in the range $0.22 < \alpha < 0.28$. A completely unstable beam in the range of α indicated is not observed; however, it is observed that this is a range of α for which the entrance conditions of the beam are critical.

From these considerations, it follows that the presence of cathode flux in a beam carrying negligible space charge can considerably reduce the maximum permissible value of α. The only solution to this problem is to design a magnet system of period L sufficiently short to reduce the value of α, or alternatively, to increase the beam voltage, which has the same effect. Also, the smaller the value of α, the less critical are the focusing conditions. Consequently, the least-critical focusing arrangement is one for which the period of the magnetic focusing system is as small as possible. Thus the conditions with small α are not distinguishable from the conditions for beam focusing in a uniform magnetic focusing field, provided that the magnetic field of the periodic system is uniform over the cross section of the beam. In some applications it is virtually impossible to design PPM systems for sufficiently small α, using available permanent-magnet materials.

2.4. Hollow Beams and Beams with a Radial Variation of Density. The radial variation of the magnetic field has not been discussed so far. If the magnetic field strength were uniform over the diameter

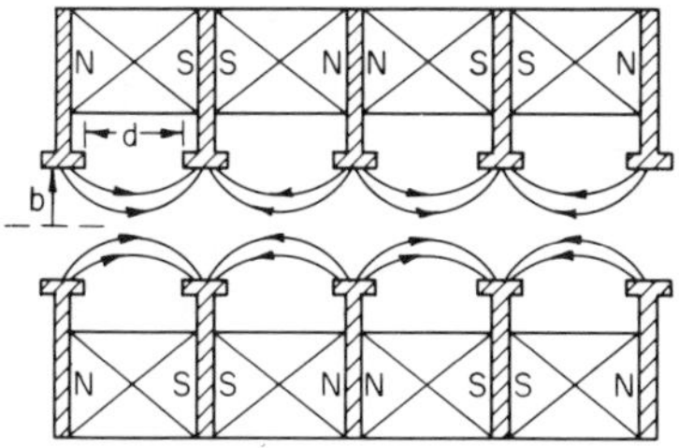

Fig. 5.11. The magnetic field variation of a typical PPM focusing system.

of the beam, it would be expected that the equilibrium beam from a shielded gun would have uniform density over its cross section. This condition could be achieved also with a beam entering from an unshielded cathode, provided $\mathcal{K}$ were uniform throughout the beam, that is, $\mathcal{K}$ were to be independent of r_1. Consider the field of a typical PPM system illustrated in Fig. 5.11. The field in the beam region can be written in the form

$$B_z = \sum_{n=1}^{\infty} b_n \sin \frac{2\pi nz}{L} I_0\left(\frac{2\pi nr}{L}\right)$$

$$B_r = \sum_{1}^{\infty} b_n \cos \frac{2\pi nz}{L} I_1\left(\frac{2\pi nr}{L}\right) \tag{2.33}$$

where I_0 and I_1 are modified Bessel functions of the first kind. If the magnetic field in one half-period is the reverse of that in the other, only the terms for odd n are nonzero. If the longitudinal field at the magnet pole pieces of inner radius b is taken to be $\mathcal{B}(z,b)$, it follows from Fourier analysis that

$$b_n = \frac{2}{L}\left[I_0\left(\frac{2\pi nb}{L}\right)\right]^{-1}\int_0^L \mathcal{B}(z,b) \sin \frac{2\pi nz}{L}\, dz \tag{2.34}$$

It is often a reasonable approximation to take $\mathcal{B}(z,b)$ to be uniform between the pole pieces and zero at the pole pieces. When the spacing is chosen so that $d/L = 1/3$, the third harmonic of the field amplitude vanishes. In the region of the beam, because of the rapid rate of radial fall-off of the higher-order components of field, only the fundamental component is significant. In this case the field is essentially uniform across the radius of the beam if the radius a of the beam is such that $I_0(2\pi a/L) \approx 1$, i.e., if $2\pi a/L < 0.5$. If this condition does not hold, it is necessary to take the radial variation of field into account. Thus the theory given in the preceding sections is strictly valid only when $2\pi a/L < 0.5$. When there is a large variation of magnetic field with radius over the cross section of the beam, it is not possible to work with the usual paraxial equations. In addition, the radial component of magnetic field can be comparable in magnitude with the longitudinal component, so it too exerts a focusing force on the beam. However, the assumption that the radial component of velocity of the beam is small compared with this longitudinal component of velocity is still a reasonable one. It is therefore possible to work with a modified form of the paraxial equation of motion, derived below.

The angular velocity of the electron beam is, from Busch's theorem [Eq. (3.8) of Chap. I],

$$\dot{\theta} = \frac{\eta}{2\pi r^2}(\Psi - \Psi_c) \tag{2.35}$$

If it is assumed that the magnetic field is uniform in the cathode region, and the total flux Ψ is written in terms of the magnetic vector potential A_θ, of the axially symmetric magnetic field, Eq. (2.35) then becomes

$$\dot{\theta} = -\frac{\eta B_c r_c^2}{2r^2} + \frac{\eta A_\theta}{r} \tag{2.36}$$

The axial and radial components of the magnetic B_z and B_r may be written in terms of the magnetic potential, from Eq. (3.4) of Appendix A, in the form

$$B_z = \frac{1}{r}\frac{\partial}{\partial r}(rA_\theta) \tag{2.37}$$

and

$$B_r = -\frac{\partial A_\theta}{\partial z} \tag{2.38}$$

The radial equation of motion for the electrons is

$$\ddot{r} = r\dot{\theta}^2 - \eta E_r - \eta r\dot{\theta} B_z \tag{2.39}$$

By substituting Eqs. (2.36) and (2.37) in Eq. (2.39) the following result is obtained:

$$\ddot{r} = \eta^2\left(\frac{B_c^2 r_c^4}{4r^3} - A_\theta\frac{\partial A_\theta}{\partial r}\right) + \frac{\eta^2 B_c r_c^2}{2}\frac{\partial}{\partial r}\left(\frac{A_\theta}{r}\right) - \eta E_r \tag{2.40}$$

This expression can be transformed into a form similar to that of Eq. (2.1) by expressing the velocity in the z direction in terms of the potential. For the purpose of arriving at an equilibrium condition, it is sufficient to assume that the magnetic field or the periodic length (the effective α) is sufficiently small so that the ripple is small. The condition for equilibrium in the periodic magnetic field is that the acceleration $\ddot{r}$ be periodic with time. We assume $A_\theta = \sqrt{2}\,\hat{A}(r)\sin(2\pi z/L)$, where $\hat{A}(r)$ is the rms value of the magnetic vector potential A_θ at radius r. It follows that the equilibrium condition for the flow is

$$E_r = \eta \frac{B_c^2 r_c^4}{4r^3} - \eta\hat{A}\left(\frac{\partial \hat{A}}{\partial r}\right)$$
$$= \eta \frac{B_c^2 r_c^4}{4r^3} - \frac{\eta}{2}\frac{\partial}{\partial r}(\hat{A}^2) \tag{2.41}$$

The radial electric field E_r is due entirely to the presence of space charge. Therefore the charge density at any radius r can be found by differentiating Eq. (2.41), with the result

$$\omega_p^2 = -\frac{\eta\rho}{\epsilon_0} = -\frac{1}{r}\frac{\partial}{\partial r}(rE_r) \tag{2.42}$$

Because for a laminar beam the radius r_c at which an electron left the cathode is proportional to r, it follows that

$$\omega_p^2 = -\frac{\eta^2}{2}\frac{B_c^2 r_c^4}{r^4} + \frac{\eta^2}{2r}\frac{\partial}{\partial r}\left[r\frac{\partial}{\partial r}(\hat{A}^2)\right] \tag{2.43}$$

From Eq. (2.43), the equilibrium charge density is determined by the radial variation of the fields. For small r, the results obtained are precisely those found earlier by the direct use of the paraxial equation. For larger values of r the results are somewhat more complicated, because $\hat{A}(r)$ varies as $I_1(2\pi r/L)$; when $2\pi r/L \gg 1$, the asymptotic form of the Bessel functions can be used. It can then be shown that, if $\hat{B}_z$ and $\hat{B}_r$ are, respectively, the rms values of B_z and B_r at a radius r, $\hat{B}_z \simeq \hat{B}_r \simeq 2\pi\hat{A}/L$ when $2\pi r/L \gg 1$. It follows, then, from Eq. (2.43), that for large r with zero magnetic field at the cathode,

$$\omega_p^2 = \frac{\eta^2\hat{B}_z^2}{2} = \frac{\hat{\omega}_H^2}{2} \tag{2.44}$$

where $\hat{\omega}_H$ is the rms value of the electron cyclotron frequency, and $\omega_H = \eta B_z$. Thus the charge density at large radius is proportional to the square of the magnetic field, the constant of proportionality being exactly the same as that for a small-diameter beam. It is only at intermediate radii that there is any difference from the conclusions that might be reached from paraxial theory.

Equation (2.44) implies that the equilibrium beam which is obtained from a shielded gun is highly nonuniform, with a maximum of charge density near the magnetic circuit, the charge-density variation being almost exponential; thus the beam is essentially a hollow one. It should be noted, however, that this is the situation only for a beam in perfect equilibrium. When the magnetic field is zero at the cathode, the forces due to the magnetic field on electrons near the center of the beam are negligible provided $2\pi a/L \gg 1$, where a is the radius of the beam. Consequently, it is possible for electrons to move back and forth through the cross section of the beam, and only a slight error in the entrance conditions is required for this to happen. The tendency is for the hollow beam to become a solid one, at least on the basis of the theory given here. The situation is not too clear in practice, for if the beam enters as a hollow beam, it receives an azimuthal component of motion; thus there is a small component of centrifugal force tending to keep the electrons near the outside of the beam.

A more reliable technique for obtaining a well-focused beam with small ripples is to use a magnetic field at the cathode. In this case, if B_c is finite, Eqs. (2.41) and (2.43) imply that, because the electron receives a spin about the axis after leaving the gun, there is an effective radial force pushing it outward. This is balanced by the inward force due to the magnetic field. Consequently, the two terms associated with these components of force in the right-hand side of Eq. (2.43) can be very large, each being far larger than the term due to space charge on the left-hand side of Eq. (2.43). In this case, the effect of space charge is small, the focusing action is very stiff, and the beam is well confined at an equilibrium radius determined by the equality of these two terms. For the situation when $2\pi r/L \gg 1$, the condition for space-charge balance becomes

$$\omega_p^2 = \frac{\hat{\omega}_H^2}{2}(1 - 2\mathcal{K}) \tag{2.45}$$

where
$$\mathcal{K} = \frac{r_c^4 B_c^2}{2\hat{B}_z^2 r^4} \tag{2.46}$$

When $\omega_p^2 \ll \omega_H^2/2$, the radius r of an electron trajectory is fixed very closely by the values of the magnetic field at the cathode and in the focusing system.

The situation dealt with here, in which the centrifugal force due to the initial spin of the beam is balanced against a highly nonuniform inward radial force due to the periodic focusing field, is very important; it enables the designer to fix the radial position of a beam accurately. It is only one example of many possible systems of this kind in which the basic principle is to balance two forces, each far stronger than that due to the space-charge field. The effect of the space-charge field is then negligible, so that the radius of the beam does not depend on the beam current. Another example of such a procedure involves using a rod placed coaxially inside a hollow beam. If this rod is made positive with respect to the potential of an electrode outside the beam, there is a radial field present tending to force electrons radially outward. This field can be balanced against a periodic focusing field, and strong focusing obtained.[7]

In all cases, the statements that are made with regard to strong focusing imply that the beam is stable. The condition for stability is basically that the period of the system should be extremely short so that the effective value of α may be small. Otherwise, a strong focusing system of the type described here would, by its nature, imply strong magnetic fields. Thus it is necessary, with such strong focusing schemes, to keep the period small.

Another serious difficulty which may be encountered in using a strong focusing system to focus a hollow electron beam is due to the variation of the z component of velocity of the individual electrons; this variation can be large through one period of the focusing system, and there may be a considerable difference between the z component of velocity of electrons at the outer edge of the beam and those at the inner edge of the beam. It can be shown from Eq. (2.36) that, for a cosinoidal variation of B_z,

$$\dot{\theta} = -\frac{\eta B_c r_c^2}{2r^2} + \frac{\sqrt{2}\,\eta \hat{A}}{r} \sin\left(\frac{2\pi z}{L}\right) \tag{2.47}$$

Thus the maximum value of $\dot{\theta}$ is at least $\omega_{Lc}(r_c^2/r^2)$, where ω_{Lc} is the Larmor frequency of the magnetic field of the cathode. In typical cases, when the beam is well confined, the radius r is nearly constant, and often such that $r \simeq r_c$. When the magnetic field in the drift region is of opposite sign to that near the cathode, then, from Eq. (2.47), $\dot{\theta} > \omega_{Lc}$. Consequently, if the space-charge fields are negligible and the potential is uniform throughout the beam, the axial component of velocity $\dot{z}$ is given by the relation

$$\dot{z} = (2\eta\phi_0 - \dot{\theta}^2 r^2)^{1/2} \tag{2.48}$$

so that $\dot{z}$ depends strongly on r when the term $(r_c^2\omega_{Lc}/r)^2 \simeq \omega_{Lc}^2 r_c^2$ is comparable to $2\eta\phi_0$. In fact, if this term is larger than $2\eta\phi_0$, there is a mirror effect, and the beam may be reflected. A discussion of this effect, which can lead to instabilities, is given in Sec. 9.3 of Chap. IV. Moreover, the electrons at different radii in the beam have different components of axial velocity; consequently, if $r^2\dot{\theta}^2 \simeq 2\eta\phi_0$, it would be difficult to obtain useful interaction with a microwave focusing structure. It is therefore important to check that the azimuthal component of velocity is small compared with the axial component of velocity in any strong-focusing-system design.

2.5. Tapering of a Periodic Magnetic Field. It was shown in Sec. 9.4 of Chap. IV that a change in the axial magnetic field strength of a uniform focusing field can be used to either compress or expand the diameter of a round beam. This is because the electrons tend to follow the magnetic field lines. Provided the taper is sufficiently slow, the radius of the beam at any point along the axis of the tapered system is given by the condition for focusing of a beam in a uniform magnetic field. Moreover, if the magnetic field is tapered sufficiently slowly, no ripple is induced in the beam motion by the presence of the taper, at least to the order of the approximation used. If the beam had an initial ripple when entering the magnetic field, the amplitude of this ripple changes through the taper. Two cases treated in Sec. 9.4 of Chap. IV, the beam with a completely shielded cathode and the strong-focused beam which carries negligible current, showed that the ripple amplitude δ varies so that $\delta \propto B^{-1/2}$. This implies that, because the radius of the beam decreases with increasing magnetic field, the fractional ripple δ/r increases with increasing magnetic field.

The same principles can be used to taper the diameter of a beam passing through a periodic magnetic focusing system. In this case, however, there are two parameters which may be varied, the strength of the magnetic field and the period of the focusing system. Two types of ripple must be considered: in one the initial ripple of the entering beam is due to the entrance conditions not being selected to match to the periodic system perfectly, and in the other the irreducible minimum ripple of the beam is caused by the fact that the focusing system is periodic.

It has already been shown in Sec. 2.2 that, to a good degree of approximation, the equilibrium conditions for beam focusing in a uniform periodic focusing system are equivalent to those for a beam flowing in a uniform magnetic field of the same value as the rms value of the periodic magnetic focusing field. It follows that, if the magnetic field strength is slowly tapered through the system, the conditions for rippling, stiffness, etc., are the same as those for the equivalent tapered nonperiodic magnetic field system. Consequently, when the cathode is shielded, or when the beam is strong-focused and the current is negligible, the amplitude of the ripple δ, due to poor matching to the periodic focusing system, is proportional to $\hat{B}^{-1/2}$, just as for the equivalent uniform field system.

Consider now the ripple-caused periodicity of the focusing system. A simple way to represent the tapering of the system is to imagine that the field has a sinusoidal variation through one period of the system, but that the periodic length L and the amplitude of the field can vary from period to period of the system. Thus we take

$$\begin{aligned} B &= \sqrt{2}\hat{B} \sin X \\ X &= \frac{2\pi z}{L} \end{aligned} \tag{2.49}$$

as before, with the possibility that $\hat{B}$ and L can vary slowly from one half-period to the next. It follows from Eq. (2.5) that anywhere in the system $\alpha \propto (\hat{B}L)^2$. The equilibrium condition for the beam in any section of the focusing field is given approximately by

$$\mathcal{P} = \alpha(1 - 2\mathcal{K}) \tag{2.50}$$

As $\mathcal{P}$ and $\mathcal{K}$ are functions of the average radius r, Eq. (2.50) is a condition which determines the average radius of the beam. For instance, if $\mathcal{K} = 0$, Eq. (2.50) implies that $\mathcal{P} = \alpha$, and hence $\lambda_p^2 = 2\lambda_H^2$ or $r_0^2 \hat{B}^2$ = constant; in this case σ has the same value at the end of each half-period of the system. Equation (2.50) is precisely the relation that would be used for the equivalent uniform beam and is equivalent to Eq. (4.2) of Chap. IV. In any half-periodic section of the system, Eq. (2.19) can be used to find the fractional ripple Δ in the form

$$\Delta = \frac{\alpha}{4}\left[\cos\left(2X\right) - 1\right] \tag{2.51}$$

At $X = 0$ and $X = \pi$, $\Delta = 0$. Thus there is no difficulty in matching between sections, and the fractional ripple can be calculated separately from half-period to half-period of the system. It is seen from Eq. (2.51) that the fractional ripple due to periodicity is such that $\Delta \propto \alpha$ or $\Delta \propto (\hat{B}L)^2$. Thus the fractional ripple due to periodicity increases as the square of the magnetic field and the square of the periodic length.

We have shown that a gradual increase in magnetic field decreases the absolute ripple due to poor initial matching, although it increases the fractional ripple. However, unless the period of the system is correspondingly decreased, the ripple due to the periodicity of the system also increases. Thus, if it is required to reduce the diameter of the beam by tapering a periodic magnetic focusing system, it is advisable to reduce the period of the system so that α or $\hat{B}L$ remains uniform.

3. PERIODIC ELECTROSTATIC FOCUSING OF BEAMS WITH A RECTILINEAR AXIS

3.1. Introduction. It has been shown in Section 2 that an electron beam can be focused by a periodic magnetic field. The net inward focusing force obtained is approximately equal to that of a uniform magnetic field of the same magnitude as the rms value of the periodic field. In a periodic magnetic field, however, there is always some beam rippling, and instabilities can occur because of overfocusing. The action of a periodic electrostatic focusing field is similar. A net inward focusing force is obtained which is proportional to the average value of the square of the electrostatic field. Again, it is not possible to obtain a completely ripple-free beam, and if the fields are too strong, instabilities may occur.

The physical action can be understood by a matrix analysis of the type given in Sec. 2.2. However, because an electrostatic field causes the beam velocity to change in the axial direction, the analysis is considerably more complicated. It is apparent that a periodic electrostatic focusing system can be regarded as a series of electric lenses whose end points are free of axial field. It was shown in Section 8 of Chap. III that each lens is convergent; therefore an array of lenses, arranged so that the exit point of one lens coincides with the entrance point of the next, must provide a net inward focusing force which can cancel space-charge forces. Because the focusing force varies with distance along the axis, there is, by the nature of the system, some rippling and the possibility of instabilities.

An important advantage of electrostatic focusing is that of ion drainage. No vacuum tube has a perfect vacuum. Consequently, when the electron beam collides with gas molecules, a certain number of ions are created; these ions tend to be trapped by the space charge of the beam. As the ions are massive, their motion is not affected much by a magnetic field. Consequently, in any magnetically focused electron tube there can be certain spurious effects present such as weak oscillations, because of trapped ions. An electrostatic focusing system has an advantage in this respect, since ions are drained off by the electrostatic focusing fields.

Electrostatic focusing systems also have decided disadvantages; one of the most obvious is that more than one applied potential may be required for the electrodes. This can complicate the power supply and partially nullify the weight savings over that of a magnetic focusing system. Another feature is that, for focusing a beam of the same perveance, a PPM focusing system gives less ripple than the equivalent electrostatic focusing scheme. A far more serious disadvantage is that the electrodes required for electrostatic focusing must be near the beam. For a traveling-wave-tube application, for instance, this means that the electrodes must be part of the r-f circuit. Consequently, certain compromises must be made in both the design of the r-f and the focusing systems to make them compatible. Alternatively, when the same idea is applied to an electrostatically focused klystron, the drift tubes can be replaced by a periodic focusing system without any serious disadvantage except that of mechanical difficulties; it may be hard, however, to maintain good focusing in the cavity gaps, particularly with a high-perveance beam at high r-f power levels. Typically, high electric fields are required for periodic electrostatic focusing. This can cause difficulties with breakdown across the insulators which are used to support the focusing system. For these reasons, periodic electrostatic focusing is not always practical, and magnetic focusing has had far wider application. In certain instances, electrostatic focusing has been used successfully in applications where the r-f circuit is compatible with the need for electrodes suitable for electrostatic focusing.

In this section we treat the properties of both strip-beam and round-beam focusing systems in a similar manner to the treatment of periodic magnetic focusing in Section 2. It is again convenient to use the appropriate paraxial-ray equations, making the assumption that the radial velocity of an electron is small compared with its velocity in the axial direction. In general, the analysis tends to be more complicated, because the axial and transverse velocity components of an electron vary with distance along the axis. To normalize the potential and other parameters of the system as in Section 2, we write

$$X = \frac{2\pi z}{L} \tag{3.1}$$

and $\quad r = \sigma r_0$ (3.2)

where L is the periodic length of the electrostatic focusing system, and r_0 is the radius or half-thickness of the beam at entrance into the focusing system; thus $\sigma = 1$ at $X = 0$. The potential anywhere along the beam axis is expressed as

$$\Phi = \phi_0 + \Phi_1 \tag{3.3}$$

where ϕ_0 is the average value of the potential, and Φ_1 is the periodic part of the potential. We write

$$\Phi_1 = \hat{\phi}\, f(X) \tag{3.4}$$

and take f(X) to be defined so that

$$\frac{1}{2\pi} \int_0^{2\pi} f'^2(X)\, dX = 1 \tag{3.5}$$

where the prime denotes differentiation with respect to X, and the normalization of the quantity f is carried out in terms of the electric field rather than the potential. This is because the focusing forces involved depend on the square of the electric field rather than on the square of the potential. By analogy with the definitions made for a periodic focusing magnetic field, we introduce a lens-strength parameter defined as

$$\gamma = \frac{\hat{\phi}}{\phi_0} \tag{3.6}$$

so that Eq. (3.4) becomes

$$\Phi_1 = \gamma \phi_0\, f(X) \tag{3.7}$$

For a cylindrical beam, just as in the periodic magnetic focusing case, the space-charge parameter $\mathcal{P}$ is defined by the relation

$$\mathcal{P} = \frac{IL^2}{16\pi^3 \epsilon_0 (2\eta)^{1/2}\, r_0^2 \phi_0^{3/2}} = \frac{1}{2}\left(\frac{L}{\lambda_p}\right)^2 \tag{3.8}$$

where λ_p is the space-charge wavelength of a beam of a radius equal to that of the beam entering the focusing system; the longitudinal velocity v_0 corresponds to the average potential ϕ_0. It will be seen that the parameter $\mathcal{P}$ can be defined also in terms of the perveance P of the beam by writing

$$P = 16\pi^3 \epsilon_0 (2\eta)^{1/2} \left(\frac{r_0}{L}\right)^2 \mathcal{P} = 2.62 \times 10^3\, \mathcal{P}\left(\frac{r_0}{L}\right)^2 \quad \text{micropervs} \tag{3.9}$$

For a strip beam a similar definition of $\mathcal{P}$ is

$$\mathcal{P} = \frac{IL^2}{16(2\eta)^{1/2}\,\phi_0^{3/2}\epsilon_0 \ell r_0 \pi^2} = \left(\frac{L}{\lambda_p}\right)^2 \tag{3.10}$$

where r_0 is now the half-thickness of the entering beam, and ℓ its width. The parameter $\mathcal{P}$ in this case is related to the perveance density p by the relation

$$p = 8(2\eta)^{1/2}\epsilon_0\pi^2 \frac{\mathcal{P}}{L^2}$$

$$= 415 \frac{\mathcal{P}}{L^2} \quad \text{micropervs/m}^2 \tag{3.11}$$

It would be more consistent with Chap. IV to discuss the perveance per square,

$$P_\square = 1630\,\mathcal{P}\left(\frac{r_0}{L}\right)^2 \quad \text{micropervs}$$

However, in periodic systems, p is a more natural unit than $P_\square$.

It follows from Eq. (2.25) of Chap. III that the normalized paraxial equation for electrostatic focusing ($\mathcal{B} = 0$) is

$$(1 + \gamma f)\sigma'' + \tfrac{1}{2}\gamma f'\sigma' + \tfrac{1}{4}\gamma f''\sigma = \frac{\mathcal{P}}{\sigma(1 + \gamma f)^{1/2}} \tag{3.12}$$

Similarly, the paraxial equation for a strip beam with a rectilinear axis [Eq. (6.19) of Chap. III] becomes, in normalized form,

$$(1 + \gamma f)\sigma'' + \tfrac{1}{2}\gamma f'\sigma' + \tfrac{1}{2}\gamma\sigma f'' = \frac{\mathcal{P}}{(1 + \gamma f)^{1/2}} \tag{3.13}$$

Another form of Eq. (3.13) is useful where the independent variable is normalized time T rather than distance X. Defining the normalized time variable T as

$$T = \int (1 + \gamma f)^{-1/2}\,dX \tag{3.14}$$

and writing the normalized velocity as

$$U = (1 + \gamma f)^{1/2} \tag{3.15}$$

the normalized form of the paraxial equation [Eq. (6.17) of Chap. III] is*

$$\frac{d^2\sigma}{dT^2} + \sigma\frac{\ddot{U}}{U} = \frac{\mathcal{P}}{U} \tag{3.16}$$

Both Eqs. (3.13) and (3.16) are linear ordinary differential equations for σ; consequently, the analysis of a strip beam is simpler than that of a cylindrical beam. The solution to the differential equation can be resolved into a particular and a complementary integral. Stability

*An alternative normalization, by which Eq. (3.6) simplifies further, is discussed in Sec. 4.2, e.g., Eq. (4.6).

is determined by the properties of the complementary solution of the equation; if this part of the solution indicates instability, any slight error in initial conditions leads to an unstable beam. This would be true even if the particular solution of the equations indicated stability.

By using the paraxial equation of motion [Eq. (3.16)] expressed in terms of time, it becomes relatively easy to illustrate the physical concepts of focusing described in the introduction to this chapter. Consider, for instance, the situation where the velocity is given by $U = 1 + \Gamma \cos T$, so that $\ddot{U} = -\Gamma \cos T$. In this case Eq. (3.16) becomes

$$\ddot{\sigma} - \frac{\Gamma\sigma \cos T}{1 + \Gamma \cos T} = \frac{\mathcal{P}}{U} \tag{3.17}$$

When cos T is positive, the second term of Eq. (3.17) yields an equivalent outward force on the electrons; i.e., the acceleration due to this term tends to be radially outward. But when cos T is negative, there is an equivalent inward force applied to the electrons. However, the magnitude of the second term of Eq. (3.17) is smaller when cos T is positive than when it is negative. Consequently, the average force applied to the electrons by the paraxial focusing action is always inward, and there is a net focusing force which can cancel out the effects of space charge.

Equation (3.17) is of the Hill type and has regions of stability and instability. It is difficult to determine the value of Γ, and hence the closely related value of the parameter γ, for which the beam becomes unstable. However, if the denominator of the second term of Eq. (3.17) is regarded as not differing much from unity, the equation becomes of the Mathieu type (Appendix D), and the instability begins in the neighborhood of $\Gamma > 1$; this in turn implies a negative beam velocity, which is a physically unreasonable situation. Thus the instability is likely to occur only in a range of impossibly high Γ or γ, where in any case the rippling of the beam would be too large for most applications.

3.2. Space-charge Balance Conditions for a Sheet Beam. The balance conditions for a strip beam may be determined in precisely the same way for a beam flowing in a periodic magnetic field. The parameters σ and $\mathcal{P}$ are expanded in different orders of γ by writing

$$\sigma = 1 + \gamma\sigma_1 + \gamma^2 \sigma_2 + \cdots \tag{3.18}$$

$$\mathcal{P} = \mathcal{P}_0 + \gamma \mathcal{P}_1 + \gamma^2 \mathcal{P}_2 + \cdots \tag{3.19}$$

and equating terms of the same order in γ. The zero-order solution is then $\mathcal{P}_0 = 0$. To first order in γ, Eq. (3.13) yields the result

$$\sigma_1'' + \tfrac{1}{2} f'' = \mathcal{P}_1 \tag{3.20}$$

The condition that σ_1 be periodic is $\mathcal{P}_1 = 0$. With $\mathcal{P}_1 = 0$, Eq. (3.20) can be integrated to yield the result

$$\sigma_1 = -\tfrac{1}{2}(f - f_0) \tag{3.21}$$

assuming that $\sigma_1 = 0$ and $f = f_0$, where $X = 0$.

Equating second-order terms in γ in Eq. (3.13), we find that

$$\sigma_2'' + f\sigma_1'' + \tfrac{1}{2}f'\sigma_1' + \tfrac{1}{2}\sigma_1 f'' = \mathcal{P}_2 \tag{3.22}$$

When Eq. (3.21) is substituted in Eq. (3.22), this yields the result

$$\sigma_2'' - \tfrac{3}{4}ff'' - \tfrac{1}{4}f'^2 + \tfrac{1}{4}f_0 f'' = \mathcal{P}_2 \tag{3.23}$$

The requirement for σ_2 to be periodic is that

$$\mathcal{P}_2 = -\frac{1}{2\pi}\int_0^{2\pi}(\tfrac{3}{4}ff'' + \tfrac{1}{4}f'^2)\,dX \tag{3.24}$$

i.e., the average value of the integrand of Eq. (3.24) taken over one period is equal to $\mathcal{P}_2$.

The fact that f is periodic can be used, and the first term in Eq. (3.24) integrated by parts. This yields the result

$$\mathcal{P}_2 = \tfrac{1}{2}\overline{f'^2} = \tfrac{1}{2} \tag{3.25}$$

Where $\bar{a}$ denotes the space average of a over one period, and we have defined f so that the rms value of f' is unity. Thus the focusing condition is

$$\mathcal{P} = \frac{\gamma^2}{2} \tag{3.26}$$

i.e., the current which is focused for minimum ripple is proportional to the average value of the square of the electric field. This is closely analogous to the focusing condition for a periodic magnetic focusing system, where we found that the current which could be focused was proportional to the average value of the square of the magnetic field.

In order to estimate the ripple of the beam, it is necessary to solve Eqs. (3.21) and (3.23) with an assumed form for f. We assume that f is a sinusoidal function so that

$$f = \sqrt{2}\cos X \quad \text{and} \quad f_0 = \sqrt{2} \tag{3.27}$$

In this case we find from Eq. (3.21) that

$$\sigma_1 = \frac{1}{\sqrt{2}}(1 - \cos X) \tag{3.28}$$

It follows similarly from Eq. (3.23) that

$$\sigma_2 = \tfrac{1}{4}[\cos(2X) - 1] - \tfrac{1}{2}(\cos X - 1) \tag{3.29}$$

where it is assumed that $\sigma_2 = 0$ when $X = 0$. Thus the ripple of the beam is given by the relation

$$r = r_0 \left\{1 + \frac{\gamma}{\sqrt{2}} (1 - \cos X) + \frac{\gamma^2}{4} [1 - 2 \cos X + \cos (2X)]\right\} \quad (3.30)$$

Unlike the magnetic-focusing case, there is a first-order ripple term, i.e., one which depends on the strength of field rather than on the square of the field, as well as a second-order term, very similar in nature to that obtained in the magnetic field focusing case. Thus, for small values of the parameter γ, the ripple of a beam of the same perveance tends to be higher in an electrostatic focusing system than it does with a periodic magnetic focusing system; the ripple in the electrostatic system may still be small, however. For purposes of comparison, it should be noted here that the parameter γ defined for a periodic electrostatic focusing system depends on the field rather than on the square of the field. The similar parameter α defined for a periodic magnetic focusing system depends on the square of the field.

The average value of the rippled-beam radius is slightly less than its initial entrance radius. The beam moves inward in regions where the potential is low and outward where the potential is high; the inward excursions are larger than the outward excursions from the initial beam radius.

3.3. Effect of Improper Entrance Conditions on the Beam Focusing. It has been shown in Sec. 3.2 that if the entrance conditions and current in the beam are chosen correctly, a beam with a small ripple can be obtained. No attempt was made in this analysis to determine the effect of incorrect entrance conditions and beam current; in this case, it would be expected that the ripple would be increased. For the purposes of tube design, it is obviously of great importance to determine the magnitude of the ripple caused by incorrect focusing conditions. A rough estimate of the ripple, which turns out to be substantially correct, may be made by extending the analysis already carried out in Sec. 3.2. In the treatment given there, it was found that two types of force are applied to the beam: The first, which arises from the first-order terms in γ, is a force component of the same period as the focusing system; this causes the beam to have a first-order ripple with a wavelength equal to the period of the system. There is also a second-harmonic ripple component arising from the second-order terms in the expansion. However, because of the second-order term, there is an average inward force applied to the beam which cancels the average space-charge force. If the beam radius varies slowly, so does this average force. It is possible, therefore, to make the assumption that the beam radius varies in a distance large compared with the period of the system, to set up a differential equation for this long-wavelength component of the ripple and to find its wavelength. It is seen from Eqs. (3.21) and (3.22) that the beam behaves as if an average normalized force component of magnitude $(\gamma^2/2)\overline{f'^2}$ is acting on it, where the averaging indicated by

$\overline{(\ )}$ is over a period. If this component is estimated for an electron at the outside of the beam, the force component $\mathfrak{F}$ that should be used is

$$\mathfrak{F} = -\frac{\gamma^2\sigma}{2}\overline{f'^2} = -\frac{\gamma^2\sigma}{2}$$

for it follows from Eq. (3.13) that all force components applied to the beam are proportional to radius. Consequently, to second order in γ, the equation of motion for the average radial position of an electron is

$$\sigma'' = -\frac{\gamma^2\sigma}{2}$$

This corresponds to simple harmonic motion with a period $2\pi/\mathcal{P}_F^{1/2}$ in the normalized system, where $\mathcal{P}_F = \gamma/\sqrt{2}$ is the value of $\mathcal{P}$ for optimum focusing. Thus the ripple wavelength of the beam is $\lambda_n = \lambda_{pF}$, the space-charge wavelength of an optimally focused beam. The total electron motion then consists of two parts: one is a short-wavelength ripple with a period equal to the period of the focusing system; the second has the periodicity of the space-charge wavelength of the optimally focused beam. The latter condition is obtained for most focusing systems, and is a consequence of the balance between space-charge and focusing forces. It follows, as we shall show later, that the stiffness of the system does not depend much on the detailed nature of the focusing scheme, but mainly on the space-charge wavelength of the optimally focused beam.

The assumptions made in obtaining the above results are somewhat loose. It is therefore of some interest to carry out the derivation more rigorously to determine how much the result is in error, and to illustrate the mathematical method of handling problems of this type. Consequently, we shall carry out a more exact analysis, based on a direct solution of the equation of motion, which makes use of the assumption that $\gamma \ll 1$; this in turn assumes that $\lambda_n, \lambda_{pF} \gg L$, the period of the system, an assumption also made implicitly above.

It is assumed that the potential at any point within the system is given by the relation

$$\Phi = \phi_0(1 + \sqrt{2}\,\gamma \cos X) \tag{3.31}$$

so that

$$f = \sqrt{2}\cos X \qquad \text{and} \qquad \gamma = \frac{\hat{\Phi}}{\phi_0} \tag{3.32}$$

The paraxial equation (3.13) can then be written in the form

$$\sigma''(1 + 2\Gamma\cos X) - \Gamma\sigma'\sin X - \Gamma\sigma\cos X = \frac{\mathcal{P}}{(1 + 2\Gamma\cos X)^{1/2}} \tag{3.33}$$

where $\Gamma = \frac{\gamma}{\sqrt{2}} = \mathcal{P}_F^{1/2}$

Equation (3.33) can be solved directly if the assumption $\gamma \ll 1$ or $\Gamma \ll 1$ is made. In this case, the complementary solution of Eq. (3.33) is found by assuming the form of the solution to be

$$\sigma = e^{j\mu X} \sum_n A_n e^{jnX} \tag{3.34}$$

Following exactly the same procedure as in Appendix D, only the A_0, A_1, and A_{-1} terms are retained. This yields the result

$$\sigma = [C_1 \cos(\Gamma X) + C_2 \sin(\Gamma X)](1 - \Gamma \cos X) \tag{3.35}$$

If it is assumed that $\mathcal{P}$ is $0(\gamma^2) = 0(\Gamma^2)$, as we have found in Sec. 3.2, the complete solution for the motion is

$$\sigma = \left[\frac{\mathcal{P}}{\Gamma^2} + C_1 \cos(\Gamma X) + C_2 \sin(\Gamma X)\right](1 - \Gamma \cos X) \tag{3.36}$$

If we suppose that, at $X = 0$, $\sigma = \sigma_0 = 1$ and $\sigma' = \sigma_0'$, the normalized radius of the beam at the plane X is given by the relation

$$\sigma = (1 - \Gamma \cos X)\left[\frac{\mathcal{P}}{\Gamma^2} + \left(1 + \Gamma - \frac{\mathcal{P}}{\Gamma^2}\right)\cos(\Gamma X) + \frac{1 + \Gamma}{\Gamma}\sigma_0' \sin(\Gamma X)\right] \tag{3.37}$$

This result is correct to first order in γ, and leads to the conclusion that if

$$\sigma_0' = 0 \qquad \text{and} \qquad \mathcal{P} = \mathcal{P}_F = \Gamma^2 = \frac{\gamma^2}{2} \tag{3.38}$$

the motion is given by the relation

$$\sigma = 1 - \Gamma[\cos X - \cos(\Gamma X)] \tag{3.39}$$

This result and the condition for optimum current agree to order Γ with the value obtained by simpler methods in Eqs. (3.28) and (3.30). Equation (3.39) is the minimum-ripple solution and is the particular integral. The entrance conditions are such that the beam is flowing parallel to the axis, and the current is at its optimum value corresponding to Eq. (3.38). If the current density is different from that which satisfies this minimum-ripple condition in the normalized system, there is an additional long-wavelength ripple of period $2\pi/\Gamma$ which modulates the short-wavelength ripple of period 2π. The long-wavelength ripple has a wavelength $\lambda = \lambda_{pF} = L/\gamma$ in unnormalized coordinates. If, in addition, the beam does not enter parallel to the axis, it will have a maximum-ripple amplitude of $\Delta_M = \sigma_0'(2 + 1/\Gamma)$ due to this effect, with the same wavelength for the ripple λ_{pF} as before. It should be noted that when the space-charge conditions of Eq. (3.38) are satisfied, the wavelength of the long-wavelength ripple is equal to the space-charge wavelength.

A measure of the stiffness of the beam is the maximum-ripple amplitude for a given entrance angle. The definition of stiffness of Eq. (4.18) of Chap. IV is no longer relevant, because there is in any case a ripple in the beam. A more meaningful definition of stiffness, the original one of Eq. (4.10) of Chap. IV, requires the σ due to the incorrect injection. We define stiffness by

$$\mathcal{S} = \frac{\sigma_0'}{(\sigma_B - \sigma_A)_M} \frac{2\pi}{L} \tag{3.40}$$

where σ_B is the σ of Eq. (3.37), and σ_A that of Eq. (3.37), with $\sigma_0' = 0$. Substitution of Eq. (3.39) into (3.40) gives

$$\mathcal{S} = \frac{1}{2(1 + 1/\Gamma)} \frac{2\pi}{L} \tag{3.41}$$

Thus the stiffness of an electrostatic focusing system of this kind is comparable with that of a magnetic or any other focusing system capable of focusing the same perveance beam. As might be expected, the beam stiffness can be increased by strengthening the focusing field (increasing Γ) or reducing the period. A particular case of interest is that of the strong-focused beam with negligible current ($\mathcal{P} = 0$). In this case, whatever the focusing conditions, the beam ripple is such that the outer electrons all pass through the axis of the system and the ripple is very large. However, a small change in space charge under these conditions ($\mathcal{P}/\mathcal{P}_F \ll 1$) makes very little difference to the shape of the electron trajectories, so the beam is strongly focused. In exactly the same way as in Sec. 4.3 of Chap. IV, the condition for a small ripple is that λ_{pF} be as small as possible; this in turn requires a small value of L, the focusing period, in order for Γ to remain small. In this case, although individual electrons may be passing back and forth through the axis, the beam is strongly held by the focusing system; because $\Gamma \ll 1$, the beam is stable despite the large-percentage ripple of the individual electron trajectories. Now, when a small amount of current is introduced into the system ($\mathcal{P} \ll \mathcal{P}_F$), the trajectory of Eq. (3.37), with $\mathcal{P} = 0$, applies to all electrons.

To summarize, we conclude that, when the beam current is chosen correctly and the beam enters with each trajectory parallel to the axis of the system, a beam of relatively small ripple can be obtained. This ripple is larger, however, than that in a magnetic focusing system capable of focusing the same perveance beam. On the other hand, when the current density is negligible, the ripple becomes large, for individual electrons pass through the axis. Nevertheless, such a beam is essentially strong-focused, because the presence of a small amount of space charge does not affect greatly the shape of the individual electron trajectories.

3.4. An Example of Strip-beam Focusing. A periodic electrostatic focusing system suitable for focusing a strip beam, illustrated

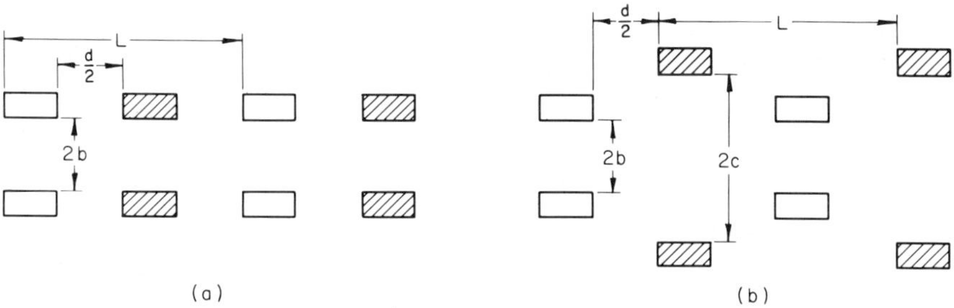

Fig. 5.12. Schematic of electrode systems for electrostatic periodic. The shaded rings have potentials Φ_a; the others Φ_b. (a) Electrode system with all rings at the same distance from the axis; (b) electrode system with alternate electrodes displaced relative to the intermediate electrodes.

in Fig. 5.12a, has a series of equally spaced plates on each side of the beam, the alternate plates being at potential Φ_a and Φ_b, respectively. With this configuration there is no transverse component of field on the central axis of the system. If $\Phi_b > \Phi_a$, the average potential on the axis of the system is

$$\phi_0 = \frac{\Phi_b + \Phi_a}{2} \tag{3.42}$$

and there is a periodic component of potential at the axis, having the magnitude $\Phi_1 \propto (\Phi_b - \Phi_a)$. For mechanical convenience it is often convenient to withdraw the electrodes at potential Φ_a a distance c from the axis as shown in Fig. 5.12b. In this configuration, it is possible to obtain a prescribed maximum variation of the potential Φ_1 on the axis and an average value of potential ϕ_0 on the axis and yet have this second set of electrodes, with potentials $\Phi_a = 0$. If it can be arranged, this eliminates one applied potential

In the theory given in Secs. 3.2 and 3.3, it was assumed that there is no field variation in a direction perpendicular to the z and r coordinates. The real beam has finite dimensions in this direction, so that there may be spreading due to space charge and the initial mismatch of the beam with a focusing system. Two common techniques for obviating this difficulty are shown in Fig. 5.13a and b. In the first case end plates at zero potential are used, which provide a small component of field to confine the beam and stop it moving toward the end plates. The effect of this field is felt only near the edges of the beam. An alternative technique is to form each focusing electrode as a slot in a metal sheet; each slot is shaped as shown in Fig. 5.13b. In this system there is also an inward force tending to stop the beam spreading in the axial plane because of the periodic-focusing effect at the edges of the beam.

The field on the axis of the system shown in Fig. 5.12a can be calculated by assuming that the potential can be expanded in the form

$$\phi(r,z) = \phi_0 + \sum_n A_n \cos\frac{2n\pi z}{L}\cosh\frac{2n\pi r}{L} \tag{3.43}$$

If the field is taken to be uniform between the metal plates at r = b, then, by the normal methods of Fourier analysis,

$$A_n \cosh\frac{2n\pi b}{L} = \frac{\Phi_b - \Phi_a}{n\pi}\,\frac{\sin\frac{2n\pi d}{L}}{\frac{2n\pi d}{L}} \qquad n = 1, 3, 5, \ldots \tag{3.44}$$

$$A_n = 0 \qquad n \text{ even}$$

Thus the potential on the axis is given by

$$\phi(0,z) = \phi_0 + \frac{\Phi_b - \Phi_a}{\pi}\sum_n \frac{\cos\frac{2n\pi z}{L}}{n\cosh\frac{2n\pi b}{L}}\,\frac{\sin\frac{2n\pi d}{L}}{\frac{2n\pi d}{L}} \qquad n \text{ odd} \tag{3.45}$$

It then follows from Eqs. (3.4) and (3.5) that

$$\hat{\phi}\; f(X) = \frac{\Phi_b - \Phi_a}{\pi}\sum_n \frac{\cos nX}{n\cosh\frac{2n\pi b}{L}}\,\frac{\sin\frac{2n\pi d}{L}}{\frac{2n\pi d}{L}} \tag{3.46}$$

so that

$$\hat{\phi} = \frac{\Phi_b - \Phi_a}{\sqrt{2}\,\pi}\left[\sum_n \frac{1}{\cosh^2\frac{2n\pi b}{L}}\left(\frac{\sin\frac{2n\pi d}{L}}{\frac{2n\pi d}{L}}\right)^2\right]^{1/2} \tag{3.47}$$

and

$$\gamma = \frac{\Phi_b - \Phi_a}{\sqrt{2}\,\pi\,\phi_0}\left[\sum_n \frac{1}{\cosh^2\frac{2n\pi b}{L}}\left(\frac{\sin\frac{2n\pi d}{L}}{\frac{2n\pi d}{L}}\right)^2\right]^{1/2} \tag{3.48}$$

where n is odd. Typically, if d/L is chosen so that the third-harmonic term of Eq. (3.48) is missing, the higher-order terms become relatively unimportant. A good approximation under most circumstances is, therefore, to keep only the fundamental term and to assume that the field varies sinusoidally on the axis. We can then write

$$\gamma = \frac{\Phi_b - \Phi_a}{\sqrt{2}\,\pi\,\phi_0\cosh\frac{2\pi b}{L}}\,\frac{\sin\frac{2\pi d}{L}}{\frac{2\pi d}{L}} \tag{3.49}$$

It follows that, as the equilibrium perveance density of the beam is determined by the relation $\mathcal{P} = \gamma^2/2$, then from Eqs. (3.11) and (3.49),

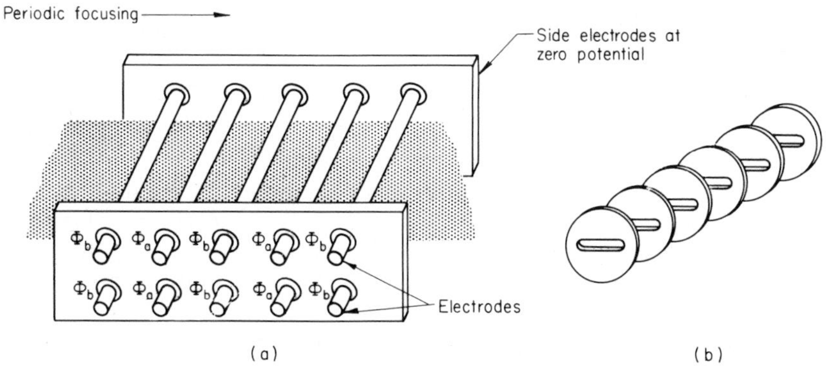

Fig. 5.13. Schematic of electrode systems used to counteract edge effects. (a) Electrode system with end plates; (b) electrode system with each electrode formed as a slot in a metal sheet.

$$p = \frac{10.5(\Phi_b - \Phi_a)^2}{L^2\phi_0^2 \cosh^2 \frac{2\pi b}{L}} \left(\frac{\sin \frac{2\pi d}{L}}{\frac{2\pi d}{L}} \right)^2 \tag{3.50}$$

The plasma wavelength of the equilibrium beam is, from Eqs. (3.8) and (3.49),

$$\lambda_p = 4.43L \left[\frac{\Phi_b - \Phi_a}{\phi_0 \cosh \frac{2\pi b}{L}} \; \frac{\sin \frac{2\pi d}{L}}{\frac{2\pi d}{L}} \right]^{-1} \tag{3.51}$$

The transverse oscillation frequency of the beam ω_n is equal to the plasma frequency $\omega_p = 2\pi\, v_0/\lambda_p$, and can be measured by r-f methods. This measurement, which provides a sensitive test of the validity of the theory, was carried out by Adler et al.[7] with good results. It should be noted that $\hat{\phi}$, the rms periodic part of the potential at the center of the focusing system, is much less than the difference in potential between the plates. Consequently, there may be large differences in potential between the plates, with only small values of the parameter γ. In some cases, it is reasonable to have $\Phi_a = 0$ even when the plates are level with each other. In practice, λ is a fairly small number, so that the fractional ripple $\gamma/\sqrt{2}$ under equilibrium conditions is also small.

3.5. Electrostatic Focusing of a Thick Beam. The paraxial theory for periodic electrostatic focusing that has been developed in this section is not valid for very thick beams. In just the same way as with PPM focusing, when the beam is very thick the periodic electrostatic focusing field will have a very large variation over the beam cross section. Consequently, the paraxial assumption for the transverse variation of field breaks down. However, the paraxial assumption for the nature of the electron motion is still a reasonable one, for it is valid to assume that the component of electron velocity perpendicular to the axis is small compared with the axial-velocity component. We may therefore modify the theory to take account of periodic focusing of a thick beam in much the same way as already done for the PPM focusing system.

It is not convenient to normalize the parameters for a thick beam without a detailed knowledge of the fields. Consequently, we work with an unnormalized theory. It is convenient to divide the potential into two parts: the potential due to the periodic focusing system, called ϕ_p, and the potential due to the space charge in the beam, called ϕ_s. The potential ϕ_p is Laplacian, and is defined as

$$\phi_p = \phi_0 + \xi\phi_1(x,y) \tag{3.52}$$

where x and y are the distances along and perpendicular to the axis of the rectilinear system, ϕ_0 is the average value of the electrode potential, and $\varphi_1(x,y)$ is taken to be of the same order of magnitude as ϕ_0, so that the parameter ξ is a quantity closely related, but not identical with the parameter γ defined earlier in Sec. 3.1. Thus we assume that $\xi \ll 1$ and expand the relevant equations in powers of ξ as before.

The equation of motion in the y direction is

$$\ddot{y} = -\eta E_y \tag{3.53}$$

The paraxial assumptions of Eq. (3.7) of Chap. III can be used to write this equation in the form

$$2\Phi y'' + \Phi' y' = -E_y \tag{3.54}$$

where $\Phi(x) = \phi(x,y_0)$, and the prime denotes d/dx. We assume that the space-charge-potential component ϕ_s, or at least its associated field E_{ys}, is of second order in ξ. Then y can also be expanded in powers of ξ by writing

$$y = y_0 + \xi y_1 + \xi^2 y_2 + \cdots \tag{3.55}$$

Substitution of Eqs. (3.52) and (3.55) in Eq. (3.54) yields the differential equation

$$y_1'' = \frac{1}{2\phi_0}\frac{\partial\phi_1}{\partial y_0} \tag{3.56}$$

In Eq. (3.56) the quantity $\partial\phi_1/\partial y_0$ denotes $\partial\phi/\partial y$ evaluated at $y = y_0$, and other such quantities are similarly defined. Equation (3.56) is correct to first order in ξ. It should be noted that the field E_y is the field at the position y of an electron, not the field at the position $y = y_0$; however, either assumption gives identical results with first order in ξ.

The field at the point (x,y) is given by

$$E_{yp} = E_{yp}(y_0) + \xi y_1 \frac{\partial E_{yp}}{\partial y_0} \tag{3.57}$$

From the Laplace equation, it follows that

$$E_{yp} = E_y(y_0) - \xi y_1 \frac{\partial E_{x0}}{\partial x}$$

$$= -\xi \frac{\partial \phi_1}{\partial y_0} + \xi^2 y_1 \Phi_1'' \tag{3.58}$$

where $\Phi_1 = \phi_1(x, y_0)$, and a prime denotes d/dx. Substitution of Eqs. (3.56) and (3.58) in Eq. (3.54) then yields the result

$$E_{ys} = -\overline{\xi^2(2\phi_0 y_2'' + 2\Phi_1 y_1'' + \Phi_1' y_1' + y_1 \Phi_1'')} \tag{3.59}$$

Following the procedure developed earlier in Sec. 2.4, we make the assumption that y_2 must be periodic, so that the equilibrium condition is that the space-charge field E_{ys} must be given by the relation

$$E_{ys} = -\overline{\xi^2(2\Phi_1 y_1'' + \Phi_1' y_1' + \Phi_1'' y_1)} \tag{3.60}$$

where $\overline{a}$ denotes, as usual, the average value of a. Equation (3.60) can be integrated by parts, and Eq. (3.56) substituted into it, to yield the result

$$E_{ys} = -\overline{2\xi^2 \Phi_1 \, y_1''} = -\frac{\xi^2}{\phi_0} \overline{\Phi_1 \frac{\partial \Phi_1}{\partial y_0}} \tag{3.61}$$

This can also be written in the form

$$E_{ys} = -\frac{1}{2} \frac{\xi^2}{\phi_0} \frac{\partial}{\partial y_0} \overline{\Phi_1^2} \tag{3.62}$$

Thus it appears as if the space-charge potential ϕ_s on $y = y_0$ is equivalent to a potential derived from the periodic focusing field, which is given by

$$\phi_s = \frac{\xi^2 \overline{\Phi_1^2}}{2\phi_0} \tag{3.63}$$

where the Φ_1^2 is averaged along the line $y_0 = $ constant. The similarity between Eqs. (3.62) and (3.63) and the equivalent results for PPM focusing of Eq. (2.41) are evident. For a strip beam the equivalent result for PPM focusing is

$$\phi_s = \frac{\eta A_z^2}{2} \tag{3.64}$$

where A_z is the magnetic vector potential of the periodic magnetic field, and it is assumed that the cathode is shielded. A mixture of a periodic magnetic and a periodic electrostatic field would give the sum of the results of Eqs. (3.63) and (3.64).

Consider now the focusing of a beam in the periodic electrostatic field described in Sec. 3.4. In this system

$$\phi(x,y) = \phi_0 + \xi\Phi_1(x,y_0) \tag{3.65}$$

where $\Phi_1(x,y_0)$ is given by

$$\xi\Phi_1 = \frac{\Phi_b - \Phi_a}{\pi}\sum_n \frac{\cos\frac{2n\pi x}{L}\cosh\frac{2n\pi y_0}{L}}{n\cosh\frac{2n\pi b}{L}}\left(\frac{\sin\frac{2n\pi d}{L}}{\frac{2n\pi d}{L}}\right) \tag{3.66}$$

It follows from Eqs. (3.63) and (3.66) that, on $y = y_0$, ϕ_s is given by

$$\phi_s = \frac{(\Phi_b - \Phi_a)^2}{4\pi^2\phi_0}\sum_n \frac{\cosh^2\frac{2n\pi y_0}{L}}{n^2\cosh^2\frac{2n\pi b}{L}}\left(\frac{\sin\frac{2n\pi d}{L}}{\frac{2n\pi d}{L}}\right)^2 \tag{3.67}$$

The equilibrium value of space-charge density ρ, which can be obtained in the electrostatic focusing system at any point y_0, is

$$\frac{\rho}{\epsilon_0} = -\frac{\partial^2\phi_s}{\partial y_0^2} \tag{3.68}$$

It follows that ρ is a rapidly varying function of y_0, so that the beam tends to have higher density on the outside near the electrodes of the focusing system. However, Eq. (3.62) indicates that those forces due to the focusing system which cancel space-charge effects are symmetric about the central axis of the system. Thus, if the space-charge forces are insufficient to cancel the focusing forces, electrons are always forced toward the central axis of the system and oscillate about it. When the space-charge forces are negligible, the electrons behave as if they are in a potential well of value $\phi = -\phi_s = -\xi^2\overline{\Phi_1^2}/2\phi_0$. If an electron is introduced into the system with a transverse velocity away from the axis v_y at the point $y = y_0$, the maximum distance it moves from the axis is $y_0 + \Delta y$, given by

$$v_y^2 + \eta\frac{\xi^2\Phi_1^2(y_0)}{\phi_0} = \frac{\eta\xi^2\Phi_1^2(y_0 + \Delta y)}{\phi_0} \tag{3.69}$$

If v_y is sufficiently small so that Δy is small, Eq. (3.69) can be reduced by a Taylor expansion to give the identity

$$\Delta y = \frac{v_y^2\,\phi_0}{2\eta\xi^2\,\Phi_1\frac{\partial\Phi_1}{\partial y_0}} = -\frac{v_y^2}{2\eta E_{ys}} \tag{3.70}$$

where E_{ys} is the effective focusing field given by Eq. (3.61). Thus, if the field is strong, the outward electron excursion is very small. Such a system is strong-focusing because it tends to keep the injected electrons properly focused near to the central axis. The stronger the field, the less the deviation of the electron path due to the effect of space charge.

3.6. Asymmetrical Sheet-beam Focusing. We have shown in the preceding section how a strong-focusing effect can be obtained by

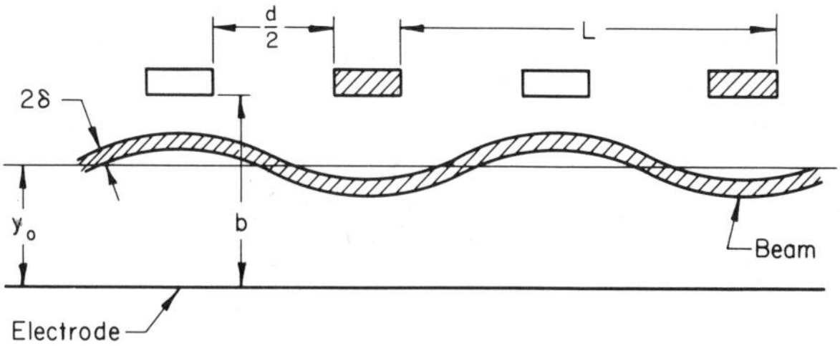

Fig. 5.14. Asymmetrical electrode system for focusing a sheet beam. The shaded electrodes have potential Φ_a; the others Φ_b. (Reproduced from Ref. 8, courtesy of the American Institute of Physics.)

the use of a symmetrical periodic focusing system in which a beam flows symmetrically along the central axis. In Section 2, it was shown how strong focusing could be obtained by balancing a uniform electric field, or the forces due to centrifugal motion of the electrons emitted from an unshielded cathode, against the periodic focusing field. In this case these force components are assumed to be strong compared with the space-charge field, and hence space charge only slightly affects the motion of the electrons.

Techniques similar to these can be used to obtain strong focusing in a sheet beam in a periodic electrostatic field. A system of this type is illustrated in Fig. 5.14. The system has been treated by Waters[8] in the sheet-beam form and by Johnson[9] in the annular-beam form and used in a microwave tube by Hogg.[10] The lower electrode in the system is negative with respect to the average potential of the periodic-focusing electrodes. Often it is at zero potential, thus giving rise to a uniform field E_0 in the focusing space. This field tends to push the electron toward the periodic-focusing electrodes. The periodic focusing system, on the other hand, tends to push the electrons in the opposite direction. Somewhere between the two sets of electrodes at a plane $y = y_0$ the two force components balance; this is the plane along which electrons tend to flow. The periodic-focusing fields must balance the two fields E_0 and E_{ys}. Thus we can generalize Eq. (3.62) and write

$$E_0 + E_{ys} = -\frac{\xi^2}{2\phi_0}\frac{\partial}{\partial y}\overline{\Phi_1^2} \tag{3.71}$$

If E_{ys} is such that $E_{ys} \ll E_0$, then the equilibrium position of the beam is given by the relation

$$E_0 = -\frac{\xi^2}{2}\frac{\partial}{\partial y_0}(\Phi_1^2)$$

$$= -\frac{(\Phi_b - \Phi_a)^2}{2\phi_0 \pi L}\sum_n \frac{\sinh\dfrac{4n\pi y_0}{L}}{n\cosh^2\dfrac{2n\pi b}{L}}\left(\frac{\sin\dfrac{2n\pi d}{L}}{\dfrac{2n\pi d}{L}}\right)^2 \tag{3.72}$$

where the lower electrode is located along the plane $y = 0$. This equation, in which only the first term is normally retained, gives a relation from which y_0 can be determined. Because $E_0 \gg E_S$, it might be expected that very strong beam focusing would be obtained, and that the equilibrium forces would be little affected by space charge. It follows from Gauss' law, applied to a symmetrical beam, that if the beam thickness is 2δ, then

$$\delta\rho \simeq E_0\epsilon_0 \tag{3.73}$$

so that the current I in the beam is

$$I \simeq E_0\epsilon_0\ell(2\eta\phi_0)^{1/2} \tag{3.74}$$

This is the equilibrium current which can flow in a thin beam whose central axis is at $y = y_0$. Further analysis indicates that the stiffness of the beam depends on the plasma wavelength λ_{pF} of the equilibrium beam in precisely the manner indicated in Sec. 3.3.

The method of focusing described here possesses the outstanding advantage that the electrode on one side of the beam is a unipotential one. In a microwave tube this electrode could be a microwave circuit such as a ladder line or interdigital circuit. It is necessary only that the circuit appear "smooth" in terms of the d-c potential. However, the system possesses the disadvantage of requiring three different d-c potentials and very critical beam-injection conditions. The first disadvantage can be obviated by placing the lower electrode, and one set of the periodic electrodes, at zero potential. The second disadvantage, however, is of great importance; if the beam is injected along the right plane $y = y_0$, it will be extremely stiff, but if it is injected along some other plane, it will tend to oscillate about the axis $y = y_0$. Thus stiffness, which indicates how much the beam is deflected because of an initial error in the entrance slope, is not always a good indication of the quality of the focusing system. With a system that has extremely high stiffness, there may be the greater disadvantage that if the electrons are injected into the wrong region of the focusing system, they will oscillate about the equilibrium position. One technique for obviating this latter difficulty is to taper the periodic focusing system. This, however, introduces considerable additional complications.

3.7. Space-charge Balance Conditions for a Round Beam. The space-charge balance conditions for a round beam can be determined by using the paraxial equation of flow (3.12),

$$(1 + \gamma f)\sigma'' + \tfrac{1}{2}\gamma f'\sigma' + \tfrac{1}{4}\gamma f''\sigma = \frac{\mathcal{P}}{\sigma(1 + \gamma f)^{1/2}} \tag{3.75}$$

The parameters σ and $\mathcal{P}$ are expanded to different orders in γ, as in Sec. 3.2, by writing

$$\sigma = 1 + \gamma\sigma_1 + \gamma^2\sigma_2 + \cdots \tag{3.76}$$

and $$\mathcal{P} = \mathcal{P}_0 + \gamma\mathcal{P}_1 + \gamma^2\mathcal{P}_2 + \cdots \tag{3.77}$$

Comparing terms of the same order in γ, the following results are obtained:

$$\sigma_1 = -\tfrac{1}{4}f \tag{3.78}$$

so that, to first order in γ,

$$\sigma = -\tfrac{1}{4}\gamma f \tag{3.79}$$

whereas, to second order in γ,

$$\mathcal{P} = \frac{3}{16}\gamma^2 \tag{3.80}$$

This latter result has the alternative form

$$\lambda_p^2 = \left[\frac{3}{8}\left(\frac{\hat{\phi}}{\phi_0}\right)^2\right]^{-1} L^2 \tag{3.81}$$

The similar result for a strip beam is

$$\lambda_p^2 = \left[\frac{1}{2}\left(\frac{\hat{\phi}}{\phi_0}\right)^2\right]^{-1} L^2 \tag{3.82}$$

From Eqs. (3.21), (3.78), (3.81), and (3.82), we can compare the properties of a strip beam and a cylindrical beam, focused by periodic focusing systems with the same value of γ, that is, $\hat{\phi}/\phi_0$, and field shape; the ripple and plasma frequency of the cylindrical beam are 50 per cent and 86 per cent, respectively, those of the strip beam.

3.8. The Effect of Improper Entrance Conditions on the Focusing of a Round Beam. The magnitude of the ripple caused by incorrect focusing conditions, and hence the stiffness, are not as easy to determine for a cylindrical beam as for a strip beam. This is because the paraxial equation of motion [Eq. (3.75)] is nonlinear. Therefore, to linearize the equation, it is necessary to make a small-ripple approximation and write

$$\sigma = 1 + \Delta \tag{3.83}$$

Then, to first order in Δ, Eq. (3.75) becomes

$$(1 + \gamma f)\Delta'' + \tfrac{1}{2}\gamma f'\Delta' + \left[\frac{\gamma}{4} f'' + \frac{\mathcal{P}}{(1 + \gamma f)^{1/2}}\right]\Delta = -\frac{\gamma}{4} f'' + \frac{\mathcal{P}}{(1 + \gamma f)^{1/2}} \tag{3.84}$$

We neglect, as for the strip beam, all terms of order 3 or higher in γ, and assume that $\mathcal{P} \sim 0(\gamma^2)$. This makes it possible to reduce Eq. (3.84) to the form

$$(1 + \gamma f)\Delta'' + \tfrac{1}{2}\gamma f'\Delta' + \left(\frac{\gamma}{4} f'' + \mathcal{P}\right)\Delta = -\frac{\gamma}{4} f'' + \mathcal{P} \tag{3.85}$$

With the same assumptions as for the strip-beam case, writing $f = \sqrt{2}\cos X$, the complementary solution of Eq. (3.85) is

$$\Delta = [C_1 \cos(\mu X) + C_2 \sin(\mu X)]\left(1 - \frac{\gamma}{2\sqrt{2}} \cos X\right) \tag{3.86}$$

where $\mu^2 = {}^3/_{16}\gamma^2 + \mathcal{P} = \mathcal{P}_F + \mathcal{P}$ (3.87)

and $\mathcal{P}_F$ corresponds to the equilibrium value of space charge. Thus the maximum ripple Δ_M due to a finite initial slope σ_0' is given by

$$\Delta_M = \left(1 + \frac{\gamma}{\sqrt{2}}\right)\frac{\sigma_0'}{\mu}$$

Using the same definition of stiffness $\mathcal{S}$ as for Eq. (3.40), $\mathcal{S}$ is given by

$$\mathcal{S} = \frac{2\pi}{L}\,\frac{(\mathcal{P} + \mathcal{P}_F)^{1/2}}{1 + \gamma/\sqrt{2}} \simeq \sqrt{2}\,\pi\left(\frac{1}{\lambda_{pF}^2} + \frac{1}{\lambda_p^2}\right)^{1/2} \tag{3.88}$$

Thus, as the injected current increases, so that $\mathcal{P}$ increases, the stiffness $\mathcal{S}$ also increases.

Thus the stiffness in an incorrectly injected beam increases as λ_p decreases to the value λ_{pF}. This results because the space-charge field hinders the beam moving toward the axis. As the beam is compressed, the field due to space charge increases, the opposite process occurring when the beam as a whole expands. As with the magnetically focused beam, Eq. (3.88) shows that the stiffness increases by a factor of $\sqrt{2}$ as $\mathcal{P}$ changes from zero space charge to its equilibrium value $\mathcal{P}_F$.

3.9. The Consequences of Nonlaminarity. It is important to note that the ripple theory given here and in the preceding sections is highly idealized; a laminar-flow beam is assumed, so that an electron which enters the system at the edge of the beam follows a geometrically similar path to one entering at some point within the beam. In reality, after passing some distance through the focusing system, the beam becomes nonlaminar in the same way as a beam focused by a uniform magnetic field, as is discussed in Sec. 6.2 of Chapter VI. Consider, for instance, an electron which enters the focusing system at some point within the cross section of the beam. If the ripple of the outside edge of the beam is small, the charge density at any region within the beam may be assumed to be virtually uniform in both the radial and the axial directions. In this case, the motion of electrons within the beam is governed by the type of paraxial equation described in Section 5 of Chap. III. For an electron within a round beam the correct paraxial equation is

$$r''\Phi + \frac{1}{2}\Phi' r' + \frac{1}{4}\Phi'' r + \frac{1}{4}\frac{\rho}{\epsilon_0} r = 0 \tag{3.89}$$

This equation can be normalized in just the same way as the paraxial equation of motion for electrons at the edge of the beam. For an electron entering at radius $r = r_0$, we put

$$r = r_0 \sigma \tag{3.90}$$

The distance along the axis is normalized in the same way as before, so that

$$\mathcal{P} = \frac{1}{2}\left(\frac{L}{\lambda_p}\right)^2 \tag{3.91}$$

as in Eq. (3.8). λ_p refers to the plasma wavelength at the entrance of the focusing system, $\lambda_p = 2\pi v_0/\omega_p = 2\pi(2\eta\phi_0)^{1/2}/\omega_p$. In the normalized system, Eq. (3.89) becomes

$$(1 + \gamma f)\sigma'' + \tfrac{1}{2}\gamma f'\sigma' + \sigma\left(\frac{\gamma}{4} f'' + \frac{\mathcal{P}}{\sigma_e}\right) = 0 \tag{3.92}$$

where σ_e is the σ of the beam edge. This equation is similar to the left-hand side of Eq. (3.85), the only difference being that $\mathcal{P}$ is replaced by $\mathcal{P}/\sigma_e$. Thus the solution is

$$\sigma = [C_1 \cos(\mu_1 X) + C_2 \sin(\mu_1 X)]\left(1 - \frac{\gamma}{2\sqrt{2}} \cos X\right) \tag{3.93}$$

where

$$\mu_1^2 = \frac{3}{16}\gamma^2 + \frac{\mathcal{P}}{\sigma_e} = \mathcal{P}_F + \frac{\mathcal{P}}{\sigma_e} \simeq \mathcal{P} + \mathcal{P}_F \tag{3.94}$$

with $f = \sqrt{2}\cos X$, and the assumption that $\mathcal{P} \sim 0(\gamma^2)$ as before. A comparison of Eqs. (3.87) and (3.94) shows that the long-wavelength ripple of the electrons within the beam is different from that of the electrons at the edge of the beam. Consequently, after traveling some distance through the periodic focusing system, the beam becomes nonlaminar. It will be observed, however, that as in the condition of small ripple ($\Delta \to 0$), the ripple wavelength of the electrons at the edge and the middle of the beam becomes identical; to this degree of approximation the beam stays laminar and Eqs. (3.86) and (3.94) are identical. In the limit of small space charge ($\mathcal{P} \to 0$), all electrons, whatever the entrance conditions, pass through the axis periodically. When the electrons enter the system with zero transverse velocity, they return to their original radial position at periodically spaced planes along the axis corresponding to the period of the long-wavelength ripple.

3.10. An Example of the Electrostatic Focusing of a Cylindrical Beam. One periodic electrostatic focusing system suitable for focusing a round beam consists of a series of equally spaced aperture disks. Alternate disks have potentials Φ_a and Φ_b, respectively. This system is illustrated in Fig. 5.15, where it is assumed the hole is of radius b. The analysis of the system is entirely analogous to that of Sec. 3.4. Following exactly the same procedure we find that

$$\gamma = \frac{\Phi_b - \Phi_a}{\sqrt{2}\,\pi\phi_0}\left[\sum_0^{\infty} \frac{I}{I_0^2\left[(2n+1)\dfrac{2\pi b}{L}\right]}\left(\frac{\sin\dfrac{(2n+1)\,2\pi d}{L}}{\dfrac{(2n+1)\,2\pi d}{L}}\right)^2\right]^{1/2} \tag{3.95}$$

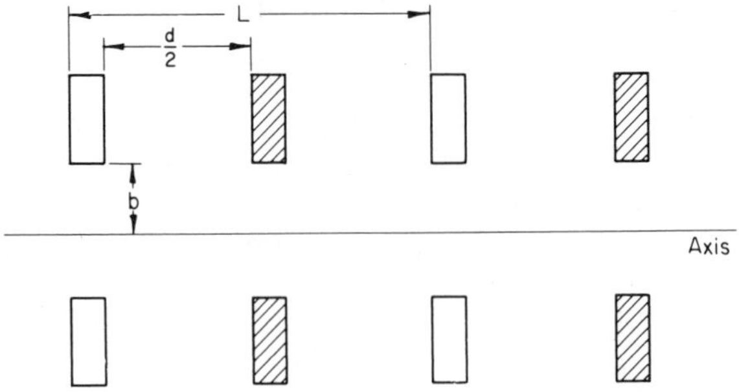

Fig. 5.15. Schematic of a periodic focusing system for focusing a cylindrical beam. The shaded rings have potential Φ_a; the others Φ_b.

A good approximation to this expression is obtained by keeping only the fundamental term, so that

$$\gamma = \frac{\Phi_b - \Phi_a}{\sqrt{2}\,\pi\phi_0} \frac{I}{I_0\left(\frac{2\pi b}{L}\right)} \frac{\sin\frac{2\pi d}{L}}{\frac{2\pi d}{L}} \tag{3.96}$$

By using the relation $\mathcal{P} = {}^3\!/_{16}\,\gamma^2$ and Eq. (3.9), it follows that the perveance of a beam of radius r_0 which can be contained by this system is

$$P = 26.9\left(\frac{\Phi_b - \Phi_a}{\phi_0}\right)^2 \left(\frac{r_0}{L}\right)^2 \frac{1}{I_0^2\left(\frac{2\pi b}{L}\right)} \left(\frac{\sin\frac{2\pi d}{L}}{\frac{2\pi d}{L}}\right)^2 \text{ micropervs} \tag{3.97}$$

From Eqs. (3.8) and (3.9) the plasma wavelength of the equilibrium beam is

$$\lambda_{pF} = 7.3\,\frac{\phi_0 L}{\Phi_b - \Phi_a}\, I_0\left(\frac{2\pi b}{L}\right) \left(\frac{\sin\frac{2\pi d}{L}}{\frac{2\pi d}{L}}\right)^{-1} \text{ meters}$$

It follows, from Eq. (3.88), that the stiffness of the beam is

$$\mathcal{S} = 0.61\,\frac{\Phi_b - \Phi_a}{\phi_0 L}\left[I_0\left(\frac{2\pi b}{L}\right)^{-1}\right] \frac{\sin\frac{2\pi d}{L}}{\frac{2\pi d}{L}} \left(1 + \frac{\lambda_{pF}^2}{\lambda_p^2}\right)^{1/2} \text{ meter}^{-1} \tag{3.98}$$

where it has been assumed that $\lambda_{pF} \gg L$. If, for the same focusing field, the beam current is reduced from the optimum value, $\lambda_p = \lambda_{pF}$, to zero, the ripple is reduced by a factor of 0.707.

It should be noted that under no circumstance can Eq. (3.97) predict a perveance much higher than 2. Let us assume that $r_0 = b$ with $\Phi_a = 0$, $\Phi_b = 2\phi_0$, and $d/L \ll 1$, so that the perveance has its maximum value. Equation (3.97) yields the maximum value of perveance when $2\pi b/L = 1.61$. This gives the result $P_M = 2.15$ micropervs. However, the derivation of this result is not quite accurate, because the value of $2b/L$ required for maximum perveance corresponds to neglecting the paraxial assumptions for the radial field variation near the edge of the beam. It does, however, provide an indication of the maximum perveance obtainable with a periodic electrostatic focusing system of this kind.

3.11. Periodic Electrostatic Focusing of a Thick Round Beam or a Hollow Beam. The analysis of Secs. 3.7 to 3.10 used the assumption that the fields of the electrostatic focusing system are paraxial in nature. Most focusing systems for round beams do not necessarily obey this assumption, because the focusing system itself is usually part of the microwave circuit, and its periodic length is short compared with the radius of the circuit. For this reason, electrostatic focusing is often used with a hollow beam rather than a solid round beam. The required thick-beam or hollow-beam theory can be derived in much the same manner as the thick-strip-beam theory of Sec. 3.5. Following that derivation, we write the equation of motion in the form

$$2\Phi r'' + \Phi' r' = -E_r \tag{3.99}$$

where $\Phi = \phi(r_0,z)$, and the periodic-focusing potential on $r = r_0$ is

$$\Phi_p = \phi_0 + \xi\Phi_1 \tag{3.100}$$

The position of an electron r is expanded in the form

$$r = r_0 + \xi r_1 + \xi^2 r_2 + \cdots \tag{3.101}$$

yielding the first-order result

$$r_1'' = \frac{1}{2\phi_0}\frac{\partial\Phi_1}{\partial r_0} \tag{3.102}$$

The procedure analogous to that used in Eqs. (3.57) and (3.58) yields the result

$$E_{rp} = -\xi\frac{\partial\Phi_1}{\partial r_0} + \xi^2 r_1\left(\Phi_1'' + \frac{1}{r_0}\frac{\partial\Phi_1}{\partial r_0}\right) \tag{3.103}$$

This equation differs from the equivalent expression for a strip beam [Eq. (3.58)] because of the last term in Eq. (3.103), which depends on the radius of the beam; the equivalent strip beam has an infinite radius. Substitution of Eqs. (3.102) and (3.99) yields the following second-order expression for the space-charge field:

$$E_{rs} = -\xi^2\overline{\left(2\Phi_1 r_1'' + \Phi_1' r_1' + \Phi_1'' r_1 + \frac{1}{r_0}\frac{\partial\Phi_1}{\partial r_0} r_1\right)} \tag{3.104}$$

The first three terms in this equation can be simplified by integration by parts in the same manner as for a strip beam. The last term, however, cannot be further simplified without making additional assumptions. We assume that the periodic part of the potential Φ_1 varies as $\cos(2\pi z/L)$; that is, the higher harmonics are missing. In this case, Eq. (3.102) can be integrated and the following result obtained:

$$r_1 = -\frac{L^2}{4\pi^2}\frac{1}{2\phi_0}\frac{\partial\Phi_1}{\partial r_0} \tag{3.105}$$

Integrating the first three terms by parts and making use of Eq. (3.105), Eq. (3.104) becomes

$$E_{rs} = -\frac{\xi^2}{\phi_0}\overline{\frac{\partial\Phi_1}{\partial r_0}\left(\Phi_1 - \frac{L^2}{8\pi^2 r_0}\frac{\partial\Phi_1}{\partial r_0}\right)} \tag{3.106}$$

Thus the effect of a finite radius is to decrease the effective focusing field. Where $2\pi r_0/L \gg 1$, $\partial\Phi_1/\partial r_0 \approx (2\pi/L)\Phi_1$, and the contribution of the second term of Eq. (3.106) is less than that of the first by a factor $L/4\pi r_0$. Consequently, for a hollow beam, its effect is not normally very important, and the strip-beam theory is often adequate to describe the properties of a hollow beam focused by periodic electrostatic fields. Near the axis, however, the second term of Eq. (3.106) becomes more important, because in this region $\Phi_1 \propto I_0(2\pi r_0/L)$; for $2\pi r_0/L \ll 1$, the last term is approximately $\frac{1}{4}\Phi_1$. Thus, near the axis, we obtain the result

$$\begin{aligned} E_{rs} &\simeq -\frac{3}{4}\frac{\xi^2}{\phi_0}\overline{\frac{\partial\Phi_1}{\partial r_0}\Phi_1} \\ &\simeq -\frac{3}{8}\frac{\xi^2 r}{\phi_0}\left(\frac{2\pi}{L}\right)^2\overline{\Phi_1^2(0)} \end{aligned} \tag{3.107}$$

Thus the last term serves to reduce the total focusing force available near the axis by a factor of 0.75.

We consider now the example of the disk structure dealt with in Sec. 3.10. Using only the first term of the series expansion for the periodic potential and inserting this result in Eq. (3.106), we find that

$$E_{rs} = -C\phi_0\left[\frac{\pi}{L}\, I_0\left(\frac{2\pi r}{L}\right) I_1\left(\frac{2\pi r}{L}\right) - \frac{1}{4r}\, I_1^2\left(\frac{2\pi r}{L}\right)\right] \tag{3.108}$$

where

$$C = \frac{1}{\phi_0}\left[\frac{\Phi_b - \Phi_a}{\pi}\,\frac{1}{I_0\left(\frac{2\pi b}{L}\right)}\,\frac{\sin\frac{2\pi d}{L}}{\frac{2\pi d}{L}}\right]^2 \tag{3.109}$$

From Gauss' law, the total current contained within a radius r is given by the relation

$$I = -(2\eta\phi_0)^{1/2}\, 2\pi r E_{rs}\epsilon_0 \tag{3.110}$$

It follows that the beam perveance is

$$P = \frac{104Cr}{L}\left[I_0\left(\frac{2\pi r}{L}\right) I_1\left(\frac{2\pi r}{L}\right) - \frac{L}{4\pi r} I_1^2\left(\frac{2\pi r}{L}\right)\right] \text{ micropervs} \qquad (3.111)$$

This expression reduces to Eq. (3.97) when $2\pi r/L \ll 1$. The charge density at any point within the beam is found by using the relation

$$\rho = \frac{1}{r}\frac{\partial}{\partial r}(rE_{rs}) \qquad (3.112)$$

When the radius of the beam is comparable with the periodic length, this leads to the conclusion that the charge density is highly nonuniform, being large near the periodic system and small near the axis; thus the beam is essentially a hollow one. As with the strip-beam system, if the charge density is not sufficient to counteract the periodic focusing forces, electrons tend to move back and forth through the axis of the system. If a thin hollow beam of the perveance given by Eq. (3.111), where r now refers to the outer radius of the beam, is introduced into the system, the inner electrons of the beam are not in balanced flow, and these electrons tend to be pushed inward by the focusing forces. Consequently, some electrons at the inside edge of the beam move back and forth across the focusing system. If the perveance of the hollow beam is far too low to satisfy Eq. (3.111), most of the electrons in the beam move back and forth across the axis in the system. Thus the beam becomes highly nonlaminar, and is not focused in a manner suitable for interaction with a microwave-tube circuit, which is also the periodic focusing system. One remedy for this situation is to apply a force in the radial direction to counteract the periodic focusing forces. Examples of this technique have already been described in Secs. 2.4 and 3.6.

A hollow-beam version of the asymmetrical sheet-beam focusing system described in Sec. 3.6 has been tested experimentally and found to give extremely strong focusing.[9] The basic technique is to use a central rod along the axis of the focusing system which is at a potential positive with respect to the average potential of the focusing electrodes. This gives rise to a radial field which tends to push the electrons outward against the inward forces of the focusing system, and hence produce a strong focusing. The basic theory of this technique is given in Sec. 3.6, and further details are given in Ref. 9.

3.12. The Bifilar Helix. An important practical electrostatic focusing system which cannot be treated directly by the methods already given uses a bifilar helix to focus a round electron beam. The helix is one of the commonest circuit structures employed in traveling-wave tubes. Consequently, the direct use of this microwave circuit for periodic focusing as well as r-f propagation is of great practical interest. The structure is arranged so that alternate turns of the helix are at the same potential; thus a bifilar-wound helix is necessary, as illustrated in Fig. 5.16a. This should be contrasted

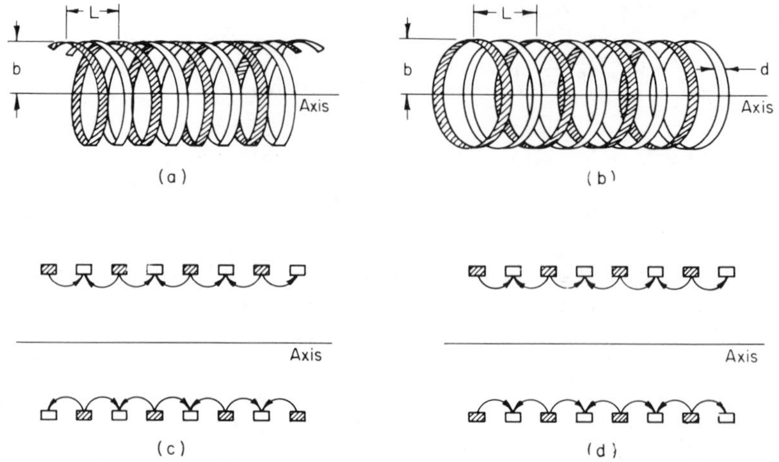

Fig. 5.16. Schematic of two bipotential periodic electrode systems used to form a cylindrical beam. The shaded electrodes have potential Φ_a; the others Φ_b. (a) Bifilar helix system; (b) system with annular rings; (c) schematic of the field configuration for the bifilar helix system; (d) schematic of the field configuration for the annular-ring system. (Reproduced from Ref. 11, courtesy of the Institute of Electrical and Electronics Engineers.)

with the use of annular rings of the same spacing as illustrated in Fig. 5.16b. It might be expected that both periodic focusing systems would yield approximately the same focusing forces. There is a slight difference between the two systems; for a helix there is a small θ component of field, so that there are additional terms giving rise to an azimuthal component of velocity, which in turn changes the effective focusing field by factors of the order of $(2\pi r/L)^2$ at a radius r. In addition, because of the azimuthal component of velocity, there is a small centrifugal force acting on an electron, of order $(2\pi r/L)^2$ compared with the main component. In many cases the result of Eq. (3.105) is sufficiently accurate to yield good estimates for the effective focusing fields. For completeness, however, we derive the correct results for a bifilar helix. It is necessary to work with equations of motion which take account of the azimuthal component of electron velocity.

The equation of motion in the radial direction is

$$\ddot{r} - r\dot{\theta}^2 = -\eta E_r \tag{3.113}$$

and the equation of motion in the θ direction is

$$\frac{1}{r}\frac{d}{dt}(r^2\dot{\theta}) = -\eta E_\theta \tag{3.114}$$

With the appropriate transformations, these become, respectively,

$$2\Phi r'' + \Phi' r' - 2\Phi r\theta'^2 = -E_r \tag{3.115}$$

and $2\Phi r\theta'' + \Phi' r\theta' + 4\Phi r'\theta' = -E_\theta$ (3.116)

By writing

$$\Phi p = \phi_0 + \Phi_1 \xi \quad (3.117)$$

$$r = r_0 + \xi r_1 + \xi^2 r_2 + \cdots \quad (3.118)$$

and $\theta = \theta_0 + \xi\theta_1 + \cdots$ (3.119)

we can solve Eqs. (3.115) and (3.116) to first order and obtain the results

$$r_1'' = \frac{1}{2\phi_0}\frac{\partial \Phi_1}{\partial r_0} \quad (3.120)$$

and $\theta_1'' = \dfrac{1}{2\phi_0 r_0^2}\dfrac{\partial \Phi_1}{\partial \theta_0}$ (3.121)

where Φ_1, r_1, etc., are evaluated on $r = r_0$ at $\theta = \theta_0$. The result analogous to Eq. (3.103) then becomes

$$E_{rp} = -\xi\frac{\partial \Phi_1}{\partial r_0} + \xi^2 r_1\left(\Phi_1'' + \frac{1}{r_0}\frac{\partial \Phi_1}{\partial r_0} + \frac{1}{r_0^2}\frac{\partial^2 \Phi_1}{\partial \theta_0^2}\right) - \xi^2\theta_1\frac{\partial^2 \Phi_1}{\partial \theta_0\,\partial r_0} \quad (3.122)$$

If the total radial field is given by $E_r = E_{rs} + E_{rp}$, where E_{rs} is the space-charge field, to second-order, E_{rs} is given by the expression

$$E_{rs} = -\xi^2\left(2\Phi_1 r_1'' + \Phi_1' r_1' - 2\phi_0 r_0 \theta_1'^2 + \Phi_1'' r_1 + \frac{r_1}{r_0}\frac{\partial \Phi_1}{\partial r_0} + \frac{r_1}{r_0^2}\frac{\partial^2 \Phi_1}{\partial \theta_0^2} - \theta_1\frac{\partial^2 \Phi_1}{\partial \theta_0\,\partial r_0}\right) \quad (3.123)$$

This is a general form for the space-charge field in an azimuthally varying periodic potential field. Following Tien[11] and the methods used earlier for finding the potential inside a focusing system, we write the potential inside the helix in the form

$$\Phi(r_0,\theta_0,z) = \phi_0 + \frac{2(\Phi_b - \Phi_a)}{\pi}\sum_m \frac{\sin\left[\frac{m\pi}{2}\left(1 - \frac{d}{L}\right)\right]}{\frac{m\pi}{2}\left(1 - \frac{d}{L}\right)}\,\frac{I_m\left(\frac{2m\pi r_0}{L}\right)}{I_m\left(\frac{2m\pi b}{L}\right)}\cdot\cos\left[m\left(\frac{2\pi z}{L} - \theta_0\right)\right] \quad (3.124)$$

In most cases, the terms for $m > 1$ can be neglected because they fall off very rapidly with distance from the helix. Consequently, the approximate form for the potential becomes

$$\Phi = \phi_0 + C\cos\left(\frac{2\pi z}{L} - \theta_0\right) I_1\left(\frac{2\pi r_0}{L}\right) \quad (3.125)$$

where

$$C = \frac{2(\Phi_b - \Phi_a)}{\pi} \frac{\sin\left[\frac{\pi}{2}\left(1 - \frac{d}{L}\right)\right]}{\frac{\pi}{2}\left(1 - \frac{d}{L}\right)} \frac{1}{I_1\left(\frac{2\pi b}{L}\right)} \tag{3.126}$$

and

$$\xi\Phi_1 = C \cos\left(\frac{2\pi z}{L} - \theta_0\right) I_1\left(\frac{2\pi r_0}{L}\right) \tag{3.127}$$

The use of Eqs. (3.125), (3.126), and (3.127) in Eq. (3.123) and integration by parts with respect to z makes it possible to simplify Eq. (3.123) to the form

$$E_{rs} = -\frac{C^2}{4\phi_0 r_0}\left\{I_1'(R_0)\left[2R_0 I_1(R_0) - I_1'(R_0) + \frac{2I_1(R_0)}{R_0}\right] - \frac{I_1^2(R_0)}{R_0^2}\right\} \tag{3.128}$$

where $R_0 = \frac{2\pi r_0}{L}$

The perveance of the beam may be derived from this formula in the same way as in Sec. 3.10. The result is

$$P = \frac{6.7C^2}{\phi_0^2} I_1'(R)\left\{\left[2R_0 I_1(R_0) - I_1'(R_0) + \frac{2I_1(R_0)}{R_0}\right] - \frac{I_1^2(R_0)}{R_0^2}\right\} \text{micropervs} \tag{3.129}$$

Equation (3.128) is very similar to the equivalent form for annular rings, Eq. (3.111), with additional terms to take account of the azimuthal component of motion.

An important practical obstacle has inhibited the wide use of bifilar-helix electrostatic focusing, namely, the problem of preventing arc-over between the helices. In almost all wave tubes using helices, stabilizing attenuators are often incorporated onto the dielectric supports of the helix; it is a very difficult engineering design problem to fashion such an attenuator to have suitable r-f properties, yet provide for reliable insulation between the helices. Nonetheless, some use has been made of this focusing system in practice.

The third term of this expression is the additional term due to centrifugal force, and the fourth term is the focusing force due to the θ component of the field. Further information on this focusing system, including plots of the function C, is given in Refs. 11 and 12.

4. PERIODIC DEFLECTION FOCUSING

4.1. Introduction. It was shown in Sec. 4.5 of Chap. IV that a hollow beam can be focused because of the nature of the electrostatic fields which are required to keep it on a circular path. The system of focusing using this principle is known as Harris flow. The basic focusing forces in such a system are proportional to the square of the curvature of the central trajectory. Consequently, if the curvature of the central trajectory is periodically reversed in sign, the

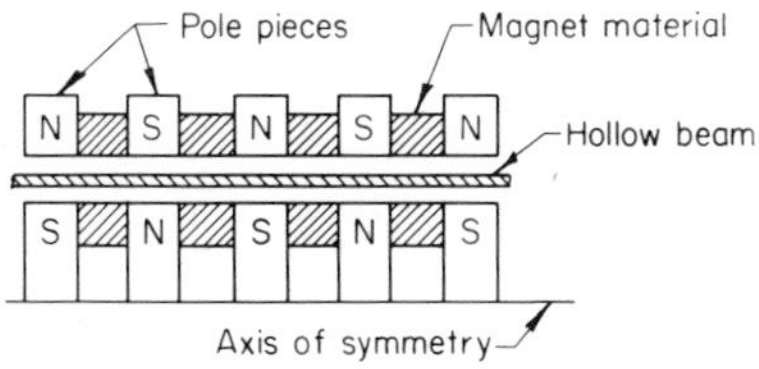

Fig. 5.17. Schematic of a hollow-beam PPM deflection focusing system.

beam can still be focused. This is the basic principle of deflection focusing of an electron beam.

The principle of periodic deflection focusing can be used with both electrostatic and magnetic systems. The basic theory required to treat one type of magnetic deflection focusing has already been dealt with in Sec. 2.4. There we considered the focusing of a hollow beam or thick round beam in a PPM focusing system; no restriction was made on the relative magnitudes of B_z and B_r. A particular PPM deflection focusing configuration which could be treated by this method is shown in Fig. 5.17. In this system a hollow beam flows between two sets of coaxial pole pieces arranged with a north pole opposite a south pole, so that the strongest component of magnetic field is radial. An electron passing through this system will, in accord with Eqs. (2.36) (Busch's theorem) and (2.38), gain a large azimuthal component of velocity which reverses in sign, if $B_c = 0$, every half-period. This large angular component of electron velocity interacts with the weak longitudinal component of magnetic field to yield a radial force which can balance the space charge of the beam. Thus the large deflection of the electrons in the θ direction is the basic reason why focusing takes place. This should be compared with the type of PPM focusing systems considered in Sec. 2, where the inward force on the beam arises because of the interaction of a small azimuthal component of electron velocity with a strong longitudinal component of magnetic field. The equilibrium focusing conditions for the deflection-focusing scheme described above are given by Eq. (2.43). Further study of the thin-beam approximation to Eq. (2.40) also yields stability conditions for this focusing system. Typically, large angular deflections of an electron trajectory of the order of 45° can be used.

We shall consider in this section the treatment required to deal with periodic electrostatic deflection focusing. The central axis of the beam is regarded as having a periodic variation of curvature with distance, and we derive formulas for beam perveance, beam stiffness, etc. Only the focusing of a sheet beam, infinite in the third direction, is discussed, but similar analyses can be made for hollow-beam configurations.[13]

The analysis leads to formulas which are very similar to those encountered in PPM focusing, so that the formalism developed in Section 2 can be used directly. It is shown that, for simple laws of periodicity of curvature, the same structure of alternate bands of instability disappear, but the electric fields required to produce these flows are not easy to fabricate or incorporate into practical circuits. One type of focusing system, slalom focusing, which has been demonstrated in the laboratory, is discussed.

We first determine the basic equations for electrostatic focusing, space-charge balance, and stability, in Sec. 4.2. We then show, in Sec. 4.3, how these results can be applied to slalom focusing and compare them with an exact theory for the slalom focusing system derived by another method.

4.2. The General Formulation for the Electrostatic Focusing of a Strip Beam Uniform in the z Direction. In this section we consider a strip beam flowing in purely electrostatic fields which are invariant in the z direction. Such a system could be of the kind illustrated in Fig. 5.14, where now the central axis of the beam is regarded as being curvilinear, and the z axis as normal to the direction of motion of the beam (i.e., into the paper). An approach of the kind given here provides an alternative method of dealing with such focusing systems as the asymmetric sheet-beam focusing type described in Sec. 3.6, in addition to those, to be described, for which it is most suited.

For a strip beam, the appropriate paraxial formula is Eq. (6.19) of Chap. III. For a beam in purely electrostatic fields this equation can be written

$$V^2 r'' + VV'r' + r(2V^2\kappa^2 + \eta\Phi'') = \frac{I\eta}{2\epsilon_0 \ell V} \tag{4.1}$$

where a prime denotes d/ds.

The paraxial equation (4.1) differs from the one for a rectilinear axis only in the introduction of an extra focusing term $2\kappa^2 V^2 r$. Thus the normalizations of s and $\mathcal{P}$ of Section 3 can be used as before.

Because we are interested, in this section, in demonstrating the basic effect of deflection focusing, we shall make the simplifying assumption that the potential along the ray axis is constant, so that $\Phi' = V' = \Phi'' = 0$. Thus Eq. (4.1) becomes

$$r'' + 2\kappa^2 r = \frac{I}{4\sqrt{2\eta}\,\epsilon_0 \ell \phi_0^{3/2}} \tag{4.2}$$

Equation (4.2) can be normalized by writing it in the form

$$\frac{d^2\sigma}{dX^2} + \xi\sigma f^2 = \mathcal{P} \tag{4.3}$$

$$\text{where} \quad \sigma = \frac{r}{r_0} \quad \text{and} \quad X = \frac{2\pi s}{L} \tag{4.4}$$

$$\mathcal{P} = \frac{IL^2}{16(2\eta)^{1/2}\phi_0^{3/2}\pi^2\epsilon_0 \ell r_0} = \left(\frac{L}{\lambda_p}\right)^2 \tag{4.5}$$

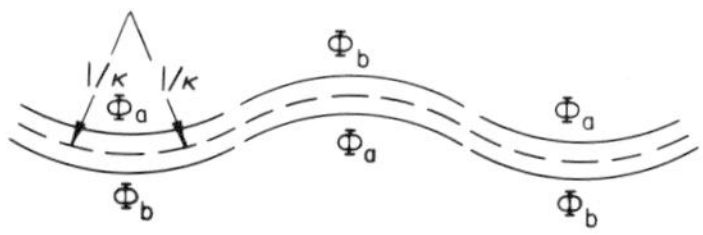

Fig. 5.18. Schematic of sheet-beam deflection focusing systems, made of a series of circular arcs. Electric system.

$$\xi = \frac{1}{2}\left(\frac{\hat{\kappa}L}{\pi}\right)^2 \tag{4.6}$$

and r_0 is half the beam thickness at entrance, whereas $\hat{\kappa}$ is the rms curvature given by

$$\kappa = \hat{\kappa}f \tag{4.7}$$

It will be seen that Eq. (4.3) is very similar in form to Eq. (2.8) if in that equation $\mathcal{K} = 0$, and is identical with it if $\mathcal{P} = 0$. Thus the results we have obtained for PPM focusing in Sec. 2 may be used directly to provide information on stability. An expansion to second order in ξ is equivalent to expanding to second order in σ in Eq. (2.8). In this case, the two forms of equations obtained are identical, and so the results of Sec. 2 may also be used directly to provide information of the perveance density which may be focused by an electrostatic deflection focusing system.

When this is done, we find that the equilibrium perveance density is

$$p = 21\,\hat{\kappa}^2 = 5.3\,\frac{\hat{E}_r^2}{\phi_0^2}\ \text{micropervs} \tag{4.8}$$

When the space charge is negligible and the curvature has a square-wave variation, then $f^2 = 1$ and, as shown in Sec. 2.2, focusing can be obtained and the beam is stable. For electrostatic deflection focusing this corresponds to the physical system shown in Fig. 5.18, which consists of a series of circular deflection plates. The beam flows along a circular path between any pair of deflection plates, and it is assumed that the sign of the field component normal to the axis changes very rapidly from section to section. In alternate sections the beam flows along circular paths with curvature of the opposite sign.

If, now, there is a field-free drift region between each set of plates, performance equivalent to that of the magnetic focusing system discussed in Sec. 2.2 should be obtained; now f is defined to have the value $f = (L/2d)^{1/2}$ for $0 < X < 2\pi d/L$; $f = 0$ for $2\pi d/L < X < L/2$; etc. This system has the same region of instability described by Eqs. (2.15) and (2.16).

In each case the lengths d and L refer to distances along the beam axis, not the distance between every other pair of plates.

Instability begins very near $\xi = 1$, which, from Eq. (4.6), implies that instability begins very near $\hat{\kappa}L = \pi\sqrt{2}$. Since the angular distance an electron travels in moving through one set of plates (length along central axis is L/2), is $\theta = \hat{\kappa} L/2$, the instability begins very near where $\theta = \pi/\sqrt{2}$ or where $\theta = 127°$. It was shown in Sec. 4.5 of Chap. IV that an electron leaving the axis under Harris-flow conditions returns to the axis after 127°, so that the instability begins at the point where an electron returns to the axis every half-period. The maximum angle that the electron path makes with the z axis is $\psi = 64°$.

Another interesting case is that for which the beam still follows an equipotential but the curvature of the ray axis has a sinusoidal variation. If the curvature is given by

$$F = f^2 - 1 = \cos 2X \tag{4.9}$$

the first unstable region lies in the range $0.66 < \xi < 1.75$. The equation of the ray axis is

$$\kappa = \sqrt{2}\,\hat{\kappa} \cos \frac{2\pi s}{L} \tag{4.10}$$

If ψ is the angle that the ray axis makes with the z axis, it follows that

$$\kappa = \frac{d\psi}{ds} = \sqrt{2}\,\hat{\kappa} \cos \frac{2\pi s}{L} \tag{4.11}$$

which can be integrated to yield the result

$$\psi = \frac{\sqrt{2}L}{2\pi}\,\hat{\kappa} \sin \frac{2\pi s}{L} \tag{4.12}$$

The maximum angle the ray axis makes with the z axis is

$$\psi_M = \frac{\hat{\kappa} L}{\sqrt{2}\pi} \tag{4.13}$$

Now $\hat{\kappa}$ is related to ξ by Eq. (4.6); therefore the width of the unstable region is

$$46.5° < \psi_M < 75.8° \tag{4.14}$$

4.3. Slalom Focusing. An electrostatic deflection focusing system which has received considerable attention is the slalom focusing type. The structure used consists of a row of equally spaced wires at the same potential placed midway between two parallel plates at another potential, usually zero, as shown in Fig. 5.19. The equipotential surfaces of this system are also plotted in this figure. Two equipotential surfaces intersect at the midpoint between adjacent wires, this point being a saddle point. It will be shown that one of these equipotential surfaces can be an electron trajectory. Because of the undulating nature of these trajectories, the system was called by its inventors a slalom focusing system.[14,15]

The fields in the system can be approximated by replacing each circular wire with a line charge. This is a reasonable mathematical approximation if the diameter of the wires is small compared with

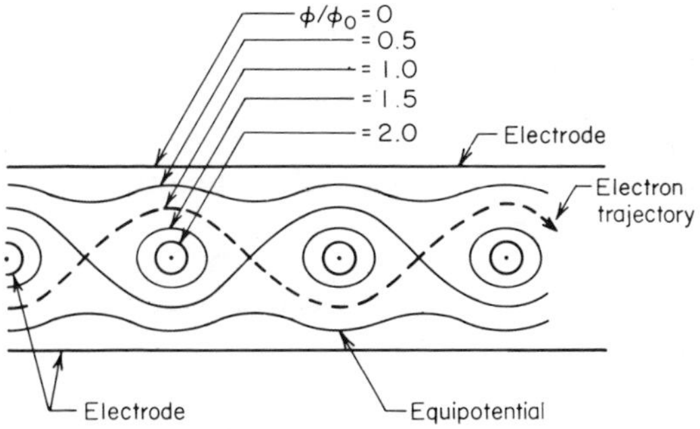

Fig. 5.19. Schematic of an electrode system for slalom focusing system. (Reproduced from Ref. 15 courtesy of the American Institute of Physics.)

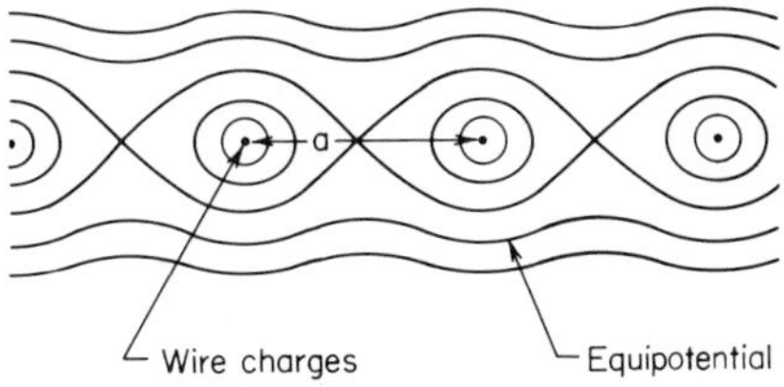

Fig. 5.20. Plot of equipotentials in an idealized slalom focusing system. (Reproduced from Ref. 15, courtesy of the American Institute of Physics.)

the center-to-center spacing. The array shown in Fig. 5.20 is a row of distinct line charges at the points 0, 0($\pm$a,0), ($\pm$2a,0), etc. The potential field is given by the relation

$$\phi = \phi_0\left[1 - \tfrac{1}{2}\ln \tfrac{1}{2}\left(\cosh\frac{2\pi y}{a} - \cos\frac{2\pi x}{a}\right)\right] \tag{4.15}$$

where ϕ_0 is the crossover potential. The crossover equipotentials are the loci of points for which $\phi = \phi_0$, and are therefore given by the expression

$$\cosh\frac{2\pi y}{a} - \cos\frac{2\pi x}{a} = 2 \tag{4.16}$$

which can be reduced to the form

$$\cos\frac{\pi x}{a} = \pm\sinh\frac{\pi y}{a} \tag{4.17}$$

The curvature of these equipotential surfaces is

$$\kappa = \frac{d^2y/dx^2}{[1 + (dy/dx)^2]^{3/2}} = \pm\frac{\pi}{\sqrt{2}\,a}\cos\frac{\pi x}{a} \tag{4.18}$$

This expression for curvature is identical with the value of $E_r/2\phi_0$ on the crossover equipotentials. Thus the crossover equipotentials are possible electron trajectories.

We take the crossover equipotential to be the axis of the system. It is necessary to express the curvature as a function of arc length along the axis in order to put the equations in the standard form required by the deflection focusing theory given in Sec. 4.2. Therefore the arc length is calculated as an explicit function of x by writing

$$s = \int_0^x \left[1 + \left(\frac{dy}{dx}\right)^2\right]^{1/2} dx = \int_0^x \frac{\sqrt{2}\, dx}{(1 + \cos^2(\pi x/a))^{1/2}} \tag{4.19}$$

which yields the result

$$s = \frac{a}{\pi}\, \mathfrak{F}\left(\frac{\pi x}{a}, \frac{1}{\sqrt{2}}\right) \tag{4.20}$$

where $\mathfrak{F}$ is an elliptic integral[16] of the first kind. This integral may be inverted to yield x as a function of s, and the result substituted into Eq. (4.18) to give κ as a function of s. The final form is

$$\kappa = \pi\ \mathrm{cn}\left(\frac{\pi s}{a}, \frac{1}{\sqrt{2}}\right) \tag{4.21}$$

where cn(a) is the Jacobi elliptic function.[16] From Eq. (4.21), the mean-square value of κ^2 is found to be given by the relation

$$\hat{\kappa}^2 = \frac{2.25}{a^2} \tag{4.22}$$

Hence it follows from Eq. (4.8) that the equilibrium perveance density of the beam which can be focused by the system is given by

$$p = \frac{47.8}{a^2} \text{ micropervs per unit area} \tag{4.23}$$

The instability of the focusing system can be examined by inserting Eq. (4.18) in the paraxial equation. When this is done, the paraxial equation reduces to a form of Lamé's differential equation.[17] Further details are given in Ref. 16. There is only one stable solution of this differential equation. A second solution possesses a linearly increasing component, an unfortunate fact which reveals the inherent instability of slalom focusing. Thus, when the central axis is chosen to be a crossover equipotential, the system is at the borderline of the instability region. This fact is a major deterrent to practical utilization of slalom focusing.

We obtain similar results by simpler means, by noting that a close approximation to Eq. (4.21) is a cosine function. If the cosine function is chosen to be such that $\psi_M = 45°$, and L chosen so that the central trajectory crosses the axis at points spaced distance a apart, then from Eq. (4.13),

$$\hat{\kappa}\, L = \frac{\sqrt{2}}{4}\, \pi^2 \tag{4.24}$$

From curvilinear geometry and Eq. (4.12) we write

$$\frac{dx}{ds} = \cos\psi = \cos\left(\frac{\sqrt{2}\,\hat{\kappa}L}{2\pi}\sin\frac{2\pi s}{L}\right) = \cos\left(\frac{\pi}{4}\sin\frac{2\pi s}{L}\right) \tag{4.25}$$

Thus the spacing between crossover points on the axis is given by the relation

$$a = \int_0^{1/2} \cos\left(\frac{\pi}{4}\sin\frac{2\pi s}{L}\right) ds \tag{4.26}$$

This expression gives the result[17]

$$a = \frac{L}{2} J_0\left(\frac{\pi}{4}\right) = 0.426L \tag{4.27}$$

where J_0 is a Bessel function of the first kind and zero order. After substituting Eq. (4.24) in Eq. (4.27), we find that

$$\hat{\kappa}^2 = \frac{2.23}{a^2} \tag{4.28}$$

which is essentially identical with the result of Eq. (4.22), obtained from the average value of the square of the elliptic function. Thus, when the curvature of the central axis is a sinusodial function of arc length, the same result for perveance is obtained. An almost identical result for the region where instability begins is also obtained, for Eq. (4.14) indicates that instability begins when $\psi_M = 46.5^\circ$.

It would appear, therefore, that the slalom focusing system cannot be used with one of the equipotential surfaces as a central axis, for this would result in instability. In order to carry the analysis further, it is necessary to resort to computer results.[15] It is found that, by increasing the initial electron energy, the beam can be made stable; the electron paths are no longer perfect equipotentials in this case. A deflection focusing system of this kind, however, is critical with respect to injection conditions.

The basic difficulty is similar to that which occurs with E-type or Harris-flow focusing. Slalom focusing permits no adjustment of lens strength, and there is only a limited range of paths which electrons can follow. Unfortunately, this range of paths is very near the instability range. The problem is common to most deflection focusing systems, making it difficult to devise a practical focusing system of this type suitable for use with microwave tubes.

An electrode system which has been used in a practical tube to give deflection focusing is shown in Fig. 5.21; the system has been used by Hogg to focus the beam of a backward-wave oscillator.[11] It should be noted, however, that the central-beam trajectory in this deflection focusing system is not an equipotential, although the assumption of an equipotential is a reasonable approximation. For a

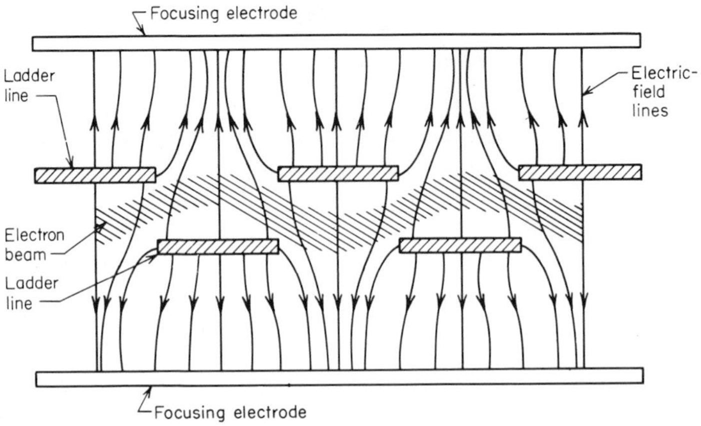

Fig. 5.21. Schematic of a deflection focusing system used by the Hogg electrode system. (Reproduced from Ref. 10, courtesy of the Institution of Electrical Engineers.)

correct attack on such a focusing problem all the terms in Eq. (4.1) must be included. Alternatively, the approach of Sec. 3.6 could be used. Further information on systems of this kind can be found in Refs. 10, 18, and 19.

REFERENCES FOR CHAPTER V

1. Glass, M. S.: Straight Field Permanent Magnets of Minimum Weight for T.W.T. Focusing: Design and Graphic Aids in Design, *Proc. IRE*, vol. 45, p. 1100, 1957.
2. Chang, K. K. N.: Confined Electron Flow in Periodic Electrostatic Fields of Very Short Periods, *Proc. IRE*, vol. 45, p. 66, 1957.
3. Palmer, J. L., and C. Susskind: Laminar Flow in Magnetically Focused Cylindrical Electron Beams, *Trans. IRE*, vol. ED-6, p. 262, 1959.
4. Sterret, J. E., and H. Heffner: The Design of Periodic Magnetic Focusing Structures, *Trans. IRE*, vol. ED-5, p. 35, 1958.
5. Harker, K. J.: Periodic Focusing of Beams from Partially Shielded Cathodes, *Trans. IRE*, vol. ED-2, p. 13, 1955.
6. Mendel, J. T., C. F. Quate, and W. H. Yocom: Electron Beam Focusing with Periodic Permanent Magnetic Fields, *Proc. IRE*, vol. 42, p. 800, 1954.
7. Adler, R., O. M. Kromhout, and P. A. Clavier: Resonance Behavior of Electron Beams in Periodically Focused Tubes for Transverse Signal Fields, *Proc. IRE*, vol. 43, p. 339, 1955.
8. Waters, W. E.: Electron Sheet Beam Focusing with Tape Ladder Lines, *J. Appl. Phys.*, vol. 31, p. 1814, 1960.
9. Johnson, C. C.: Periodic Electrostatic Focusing of a Hollow Electron Beam, *Trans. IRE*, vol. ED-5, p. 233, 1958.
10. Hogg, H. A. C.: Periodic Electrostatic Beam Focusing, *Proc. IEE*, part B, suppl. 10-12, p. 1016, 1958.
11. Tien, P. K.: Focusing of a Long Cylindrical Electron Stream by Means of Periodic Electrostatic Fields, *J. Appl. Phys.*, vol. 25, p. 1281, 1954.
12. Chang, K. K.: Biperiodic Electrostatic Focusing for High Density Electron Beams, *Proc. IRE*, vol. 45, p. 1522, 1957.

13. Sturrock, P. A.: Magnetic Deflection Focusing, *J. Electronics and Control*, vol. 7, p. 162, 1959.
14. Cook, J. S., R. Kompfner, and W. H. Yocom: Slalom Focusing, *Proc. IRE*, vol. 45, p. 1517, 1957.
15. Cook, J. S., W. H. Louisell, and W. H. Yocom: Stability of an Electron Beam on a Slalom Orbit, *J. Appl. Phys.*, vol. 29, p. 583, 1958.
16. Erdelyi, A., W. Magnus, F. Oberhettinger, and F. G. Triconi: "Higher Transcendental Functions," vol. 2, McGraw-Hill Book Company, New York, 1953.
17. Whittaker, E. T., and G. N. Watson: "Course of Modern Analysis," Cambridge University Press, London, 1952.
18. Sturrock, P. A.: Theory of Focusing of Sheet Beams in Periodic Focusing Systems, *J. of Electronics and Control*, vol. 7, p. 153, 1959.
19. Kirstein, P. T.: On the Determination of the Electrodes Required to Produce a Given Electric Field Distribution along a Prescribed Curve, *Proc. IRE*, vol. 46, p. 1716, 1958.

PROBLEMS

1.

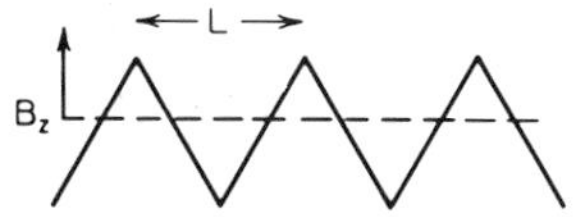

A PPM focusing system with a triangular-wave variation of the z component of magnetic field, as shown in the accompanying figure, is used to focus a thin cylindrical beam. Determine the stable region of operation for a space-charge-free beam by using matrix methods.

2. A PPM focusing system with a square-wave variation of field is used to focus a thin cylindrical beam. Taking space charge into account and assuming the beam is laminar, determine the motion of the edge electrons through a half-period of the focusing system. From this result find the motion through n half-periods of the focusing system. Determine the condition for minimum ripple and hence optimum focusing.

3. By expanding the magnetic field in terms of its components, show that the peak amplitude of the ripple of a cylindrical beam is proportional to the peak amplitude of the magnetic field, whereas current contained in equilibrium depends on the rms value of the magnetic field.

4. By using the rigorous methods given in Sec. (3.3), find the ripple and stiffness of a thin cylindrical beam in a PPM magnetic focusing system which has a sinusoidal variation.

5. The quadrupolar type of electrostatic focusing system has a potential profile near the axis which can be written in the form

$$\varphi = \varphi_0 + \varphi_1 r^2 \sin \frac{2\pi z}{L} \cos 2\theta$$

Working in a cartesian coordinate system and writing $x = r \cos \theta$, $y = r \sin \theta$, determine suitable paraxial equations to express the motion of an electron through the system. Suggest a suitable electrode system to produce the required potential.

6. With the conditions of Prob. 5, find the current in a cylindrical beam which can be focused in equilibrium by the system.

7. With the conditions of Prob. 5, find the stability region for a quadrupolar focusing system when the space charge is zero.

8.

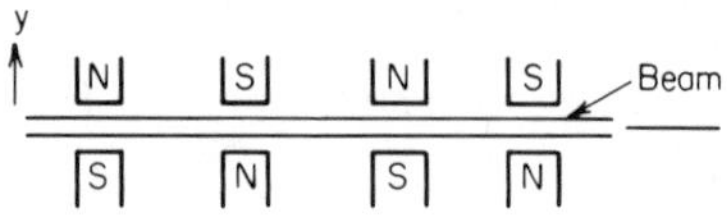

The PPM deflection focusing system illustrated in the accompanying figure, a strip-beam version of that described in Sec. 4.1., is used to focus a thin strip beam. By following the procedures given in Sec. 2.4, find the space-charge equilibrium conditions when the field on the central axis B_y has a variation given by

$$B_y = B_0 \sin \frac{2\pi x}{\ell}$$

and B_x, the field component parallel to the direction of motion of the beam, is taken to be zero.

9. For the same conditions as Prob. 8, find the stability range of the focusing system.

10. Assuming that the field variation on the axis of the deflection focusing system of Prob. 8 is square-wave, so that $B_y = \pm B_0$, find the stability range of the system.

11. Do Prob. 5 using the methods of Sec. 3.11.

12. Do Prob. 6 using the methods of Sec. 3.12.

13. A PPM-focused round beam has a radius of 1 mm, carries 50 ma of current, and has been accelerated through 2000 volts. If the cathode is magnetically shielded compute the peak magnetic field and the maximum safe period. Repeat if 20 gauss threads the cathode, which has a radius of 3 mm. Compute the average separation of electrons in the focused beam.

VI

Thermal Effects and Nonlaminar Flow

1. INTRODUCTION

In Chaps. II to V, many space-charge flows were discussed. In all cases, the effects of the spread in velocities of particles emitted from the cathode were ignored. This velocity spread ensures that the flow in the beam is nonlaminar. Not only do some particles cross, but at every point in the beam there is a distribution of particles with different velocities. It is no longer possible to describe the beam in terms of an action function, which could be used for most of the flows of Chap. II, or even by a finite number of single-valued action functions. The trajectories of the axis and edge of the beam were sufficient, in the paraxial solutions of Chaps. III to V, to describe the motion of all particles in the beam. In this chapter, it is necessary to use a phase-space-density distribution function n, which is a function of six variables—three of position and three of velocity—to describe the flow. The equation of conservation of charge $\nabla \cdot \mathbf{i} = 0$, is replaced by the equation of conservation of phase-space density, n = constant, known as Liouville's theorem, derived in Chap. I. The current density at any point P is obtained by integrating the current of all the individual particles, weighted by the phase-space density, which pass through P.

The velocity spread at the cathode is equivalent to potential differences of several tenths of volts. The final potential of the beam is usually several hundreds or thousands of volts. In spite of this disparity, thermal-velocity effects are often the factor limiting the possible convergence of the beam. In some applications, e.g., ion guns, it is necessary to estimate the current intercepted by the electrodes of the gun. For these reasons, it is important to be able to estimate thermal-velocity effects.

The problem of computing the effects of thermal-velocity spread in a general electrode system is too complex to be treated exactly. Several simplifications are always made. Only axially symmetric or sheet-beam geometries are treated, where all parameters of the flow are independent of either azimuthal angle θ or one direction z.

It is assumed, and this can be verified experimentally, that the distribution of particles emitted from any point of the cathode is Maxwellian (Section 2).

Basically, two types of problems can be solved, even with these simplified beams. In the first type, the electrodes are very simple shapes, e.g., planes or spheres. Thermal-velocity effects can be so severe that they completely change the potential distribution. These problems can be solved only for the simplest nonthermal beams, and the solutions have limited practical utility. Several solutions of this type are found in Refs. 1 to 3. The only such problem solved in this chapter is the flow from an infinite-parallel-plane diode. This problem is of great interest, for two reasons: It is a good illustration of the method for solving the problems exactly. More important, the parallel-plane-diode solution, which was treated in the absence of thermal velocities in Sec. 2.2 of Chap. II, is the basis for the boundary conditions used for space-charge-limited flow throughout the book. From the treatment of the problem in Section 2, which takes thermal-velocity effects into account, the limitations of the four-thirds-power law of Sec. 2.2 of Chap. II are found.

In the second type of problem, the electrodes and flows can be complex but the problem cannot be solved completely. In most applications, such as those discussed in Sections 3 to 7, it is adequate to assume that the electric fields are the same in nonthermal and thermal fields. The thermal spreading of the beam will alter the space-charge fields. This effect is ignored in the linear theories of Sections 3 to 7. In Section 3, some general results are derived for beams satisfying the paraxial equations of Chap. III. In Section 4, expressions are derived for the current density on the ray axis of a paraxial beam. In Section 5, the current density is determined anywhere in a cylindrical paraxial beam, and in Section 6 some applications are treated. In Section 7, the current density anywhere in a sheet beam with a (constant) crossed magnetic field is derived, and one application is discussed. The methods of Sections 3 to 7 can be extended to thick beams, where the paraxial equations are no longer valid. This extension is very mathematical, and it is difficult to get analytic results because of the complexity of the algebra. This extension is referred to at several points in the chapter.

In Section 8, the change in electric field, due to the change in space-charge distribution caused by thermal spreading, is discussed. Approximate expressions are given for correction to the results of Sections 3 to 7.

In this chapter we integrate continually over the possible velocities particles may have. In this integration, we assume always that the longitudinal and transverse velocities of particles are uncoupled (though we sometimes allow for some coupling via the conservation-of-energy equation). To the paraxial approximation, this assumption is certainly valid for a rectilinear ray axis. If the ray axis is not rectilinear, the analysis is still valid, provided the longitudinal velocity spread has negligible effect on the transverse motion; i.e., the terms in Ω and $\dot{\Omega}$ of Eq. (5.24) of Chap. III can be neglected. The longitudinal velocity spread in electron beams is typically of the order of a few tenths of electron volts [Eq. (2.8)]; provided the curvature is low in the cathode or low-voltage region, the results of this chapter should still be relevant. Thus, in normal Pierce-type guns, the formulas could be used, but with the crossed-field guns of Sec. 2.3 of Chap. II, the results would be more suspect.

To emphasize that the results can be used with confidence only for rectilinear axes, we adopt (x,y,z) or (r,θ,z) coordinates in most of this chapter. Since many of the results for cylindrical and sheet beams are identical, we adopt z as the longitudinal direction in both cases. So that (x,y,z) may still form a right-hand set, the transverse direction in sheet beams is in the x direction and all beam parameters are assumed constant in the y direction.

In Section 7 only sheet beams are considered, and comparison is made with Chap. III and IV. For this reason, and because the results may be applicable to curvilinear beams, we have adopted the same (s,r,z) notation in this section as in Chaps. III and IV. Now the beam is assumed uniform in the z direction. Those parts of Section 8 which refer to sheet beams use the same notation as Section 7.

2. THE PLANAR DIODE

2.1. Introduction. The analysis of the planar diode, taking thermal-velocity effects into account, is the most fundamental derivation given in this chapter. This problem is important for several reasons: First, its solution justifies the use of the boundary conditions of Section 6 of Chap. I; these boundary conditions are used throughout the book except in this chapter, and it is essential to recognize their limitations. Second, this example is the only one that can be solved exactly, and is conceptually the simplest; it is therefore a good introduction to the more complex examples given later in this chapter.

In addition to the presentation and solution of the relevant equations, some numerical examples are given. The conditions at the cathode itself are discussed in Sec. 2.2. In Sec. 2.3, the equations describing the flow are formulated in terms of an integrodifferential equation, and the limits of integration of the integral are derived. In Sec. 2.4, the resulting differential equation for the potential is solved; the solutions are presented both graphically and as approximate formulas. By suitable normalization, it is shown that the solution for the potential can be formulated as one universal curve. Finally, in Sec. 2.5, there is a discussion of how the formalism developed previously can be used to solve practical problems. Some relevant formulas are given, and several numerical examples evaluated.

2.2. The Boundary Conditions at the Cathode. The concept of phase-space density was discussed in Sec. 3.3 of Chap. I. This discussion is not repeated here. The reader who does not fully understand the concepts should reread that section before continuing with this chapter. The concepts of phase space, phase-space density, and phase-space-density distribution are used throughout this chapter. Also fundamental is the conservation of phase-space density by Liouville's theorem.

It has been predicted theoretically, and shown experimentally,[1,2,4] that the velocity distribution of electrons emitted from a cathode has a Maxwell-Boltzmann distribution.* This means that if N dS electrons are emitted from a region dS of cathode, the number with x velocity between v_x and $v_x + dv_x$, y velocity between v_y and $v_y + dv_y$, and z velocity between v_z and $v_z + dv_z$ is $n(\mathbf{v})\, dS\, dv_x\, dv_y\, dv_z$, where

$$n(\mathbf{v}) = C \exp - [\mathscr{b}^2(v_x^2 + v_y^2 + v_z^2)] \tag{2.1}$$

and C is a constant related to N. The value of C is discussed later. The parameter $\mathscr{b}$ is given by the relation

$$\mathscr{b} = \left(\frac{m}{2kT_c}\right)^{1/2} = 1.82 \times 10^{-4}/T_c^{\,1/2} \text{ meter}^{-1} \text{ sec} \tag{2.2}$$

where m = mass of the electron
k = Boltzmann's constant
T_c = temperature of the cathode

The emission phase-space-density distribution of Eq. (2.1) is called a Gaussian distribution.

If the z direction is chosen to be normal to the cathode, only positive values of v_z are possible in emitted particles, although v_x and v_y can also take negative values.

The z component of emitted current density i_{zc} is given by the expression

$$i_{zc} = -\int_0^\infty dv_z \int_{-\infty}^\infty dv_y \int_{-\infty}^\infty q\, C v_z \exp - (\mathscr{b}^2 v^2)\, dv_x = -\frac{\pi}{2}\, q\, \frac{C}{\mathscr{b}^4} \tag{2.3}$$

In Eq. (2.3), q is the electronic charge, and v is the total speed $(v_x^2 + v_y^2 + v_z^2)^{1/2}$ of an electron. Experimentally and theoretically it has been shown[1,2] that the maximum† total current density that can be drawn from a cathode is i_{cM}, given by

$$i_{cM} = AT^2 \exp - \left(\frac{q\Phi_0}{kT_c}\right) \tag{2.4}$$

where T_c = temperature
k = Boltzmann's constant

*The distribution of Eq. (2.1) is only a good approximation. The accurate emission phase-space-density distribution law is discussed in Ref. 1.

†By maximum, in this context, is meant maximum under normal conditions. If very high electric fields, in excess of 10^6 volts/cm, are present at the cathode, additional electrons can be drawn off by field emission. This shows itself in a reduction of the effective work function Φ_0 of the material.

A = a constant, for pure metals theoretically equal* to 1.2×10^6
Φ_0 = (almost constant) work function of the cathode.

For the purpose of this book, Eqs. (2.1) and (2.4) are assumptions; the interested reader may consult Refs. 1 and 2 for their justification. The current density i_{cM} is usually called the thermally limited cathode current density.

Comparing Eqs. (2.3) and (2.4), it is seen that C is given by the relation

$$C = -\frac{2}{\pi}\frac{i_{cM}}{q}\,\beta^4 \tag{2.5}$$

so that the n of Eq. (2.1) becomes

$$n_c(\mathbf{r}_c;\mathbf{v}_c) = -\frac{2}{\pi}\frac{i_{cM}(r_c)}{q}\,\beta^4 \exp - \beta^2(v_{xc}^2 + v_{yc}^2 + v_{zc}^2) \tag{2.6}$$

In Eq. (2.6), the subscript c on n denotes that this is the number density of particles just outside the cathode; since T_c and Φ_0 may vary over the cathode, i_{cM} is, in general, a function of position on the cathode. The n_c of Eq. (2.6) is fundamental to the discussion of the whole of this chapter.

In different parts of the book, the mean values of various quantities are required. If $a(\mathbf{r};\mathbf{n})$ is any parameter which varies with distance and velocity, the mean value of a is defined as $\bar{a}$, where

$$\bar{a}(\mathbf{r}) = \frac{\int_{v_x} dv_x \int_{v_y} dv_y \int_{v_z} a(\mathbf{r};\mathbf{v})n(\mathbf{r};\mathbf{v})\, dv_z}{\int_{v_x} dv_x \int_{v_y} dv_y \int_{v_z} n(\mathbf{r};\mathbf{v})\, dv_z} \tag{2.7}$$

The integrals in Eq. (2.7) are taken over all permissible velocities at $\mathbf{r}$. By permissible in this context, we mean the possible velocities which particles may have on reaching the point $\mathbf{r}$. The range of permissible $\mathbf{v}$ in particular instances is discussed later in this chapter; however, at the cathode, the permissible $\mathbf{v}_c$ are within the limits of integration of Eq. (2.3).

Using Eq. (2.7) with the n_c of Eq. (2.6), it can be shown that

$$\begin{aligned} \bar{v}_c &= \frac{2}{\sqrt{\pi}\,\beta}, \qquad (\overline{v_c^2})^{1/2} = \left(\frac{3}{2}\right)^{1/2}\frac{1}{\beta}, \qquad \overline{v_{zc}} = \frac{1}{\sqrt{\pi}\,\beta} \\ (\overline{v_{zc}^2})^{1/2} &= \frac{1}{\sqrt{2}\,\beta}, \qquad \overline{v_{\perp c}} = 0, \qquad (\overline{v_{\perp c}^2})^{1/2} = \frac{1}{\beta} \end{aligned} \tag{2.8}$$

In Eq. (2.8), $(\overline{v_c^2})^{1/2}$ is called the root mean square of the cathode ve-

*It should be noted that in the mks system i_{cM} has units of amperes per square meter. Usually A is quoted for pure metals as 120 in units of amperes per square centimeter. For practical cathodes, A may be an order of magnitude less than this value.

locity, and the other analogous quantities are defined similarly. The quantity $\overline{v}_{zc}$ is the mean initial velocity normal to the cathode, and $\overline{v}_{\perp c}$ is the mean velocity tangential to the cathode. The $\overline{v}_c$, etc., are denoted by $\overline{v}_{Tc}$ in other parts of the book, to show that they denote the cathode velocities due to thermal effects.

For the cathodes used in practice, these velocities are very small. For an oxide-coated cathode at 1000°K, $1/\mathscr{E} = 1.74 \times 10^5$ m/sec and $(\overline{v_{zc}^2})^{1/2} = 1.23 \times 10^5$ m/sec, corresponding to the velocity of an electron accelerated by a potential of 0.043 volt.

Both Eqs. (2.6) and (2.8) are valid, whatever the form of the cathode, if s is written for z, where s is in the direction normal to the cathode.

2.3. The Mathematical Formalism. In this section the problem of the planar diode is formulated. It is assumed that the electric fields are only in the z direction and that the current density of particles and all other parameters are independent of transverse directions. Under these circumstances Poisson's equation, [Eq. (2.12) of Chap. I] becomes

$$\phi''(z) = -\frac{q}{\epsilon_0} \int_{\mathbf{v}} n(z;\mathbf{v})\, dv_x\, dv_y\, dv_z \tag{2.9}$$

In Eq. (2.9) the double prime denotes d^2/dz^2; $n(z;\mathbf{v})$ is the density in phase space, and the integral over $\mathbf{v}$ means over all permissible velocities.

Since there are no x- or y-directed electric fields, the velocity of a particle in these directions remains unchanged; i.e.,

$$v_x = v_{xc}, \qquad v_y = v_{yc} \tag{2.10}$$

Using Eq. (2.10), the equation of conservation of energy, Eq. (2.27) of Chap. I becomes

$$v_z^2 - 2\eta\phi = v_{zc}^2 \tag{2.11}$$

In Eqs. (2.10) and (2.11) the subscript c denotes the value at the cathode, z = 0.

The conservation-of-charge condition can be used in the form of the invariance of the phase-space density, i.e., Liouville's theorem. Since the phase-space density is independent of x and y, Eq. (3.19) of Chap I can be written

$$n(z;v_{xc},v_{yc},v_z) = n_c(0;v_{xc},v_{yc},v_{zc}) \tag{2.12}$$

In Eq. (2.12) it is assumed that the particle which leaves the cathode with velocity components (v_{xc},v_{yc},v_{zc}) reaches the plane z with velocity (v_{xc},v_{yc},v_z). The invariance of the transverse velocities follows from Eq. (2.10).

In addition, the phase-space density at the cathode can be deduced from Eq. (2.6) in the form

$$n_c(0; v_{xc}, v_{yc}, v_{zc})$$

$$= -\frac{2}{\pi}\frac{i_{cM}}{q}\,\mathscr{b}^4 \exp - [\mathscr{b}^2(v_{xc}^2 + v_{yc}^2 + v_{zc}^2)] \tag{2.13}$$

Since uniform cathode current density is assumed, i_{cM} is constant.

The right side of Eq. (2.9) can be evaluated by substituting Eqs. (2.10) to (2.13). The only remaining problem is to determine the range of integration in Eq. (2.9). In the absence of space charge, assuming an anode-cathode spacing and potential difference of z_0 and ϕ_0, the potential variation in the anode-cathode region is shown in Fig. 6.1a. If the space charge produces a small amount of space-charge depression, the potential distribution has the form of Fig. 6.1b. If the space-charge depression is large, the situation of Fig. 6.1c is reached, where the minimum potential ϕ_m occurs at a position z_m.

For the moment it is assumed that a situation similar to the one depicted in Fig. 6.1c exists; that of Fig. 6.1b is treated as a special case later. For the potential distribution of Fig. 6.1c, some electrons have sufficient z velocity to pass the plane P; these electrons reach the anode A, and the rest of the electrons return to the cathode C. From Eq. (2.11), the criterion determining whether or not a particle can reach the Z_2 in region 2 of Fig. 6.1c is

$$v_{zc} > (-2\eta\phi_m)^{1/2} \tag{2.14}$$

In Eq. (2.14), it must be remembered that ϕ_m is negative for electrons.

If a particle can reach Z_2, it will reach the anode. Hence Eq. (2.14) can be used to obtain a relation between the emitted current density, the anode current density, and the potential minimum. The

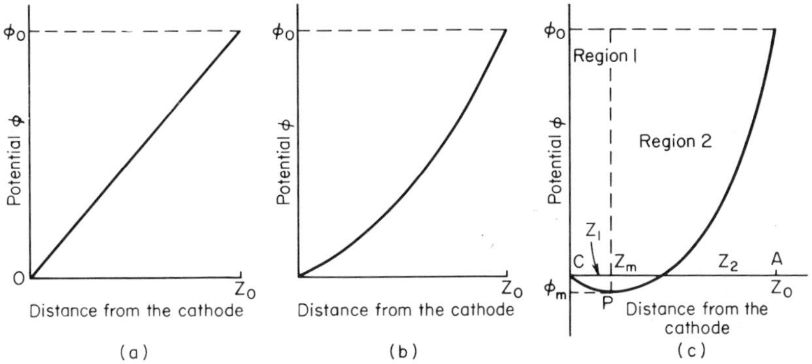

Fig. 6.1. Schematic of the potential distribution in a planar diode (a) in the absence of space charge; (b) with a small amount of space charge; (c) with a large amount of space charge, so that a potential minimum is formed.

anode current density i_A is given by

$$i_A(z_0) = -\iiint_V q v_z(z_0; v_x, v_y, v_z)\, dv_x\, dv_y\, dv_z$$

$$= -\int_{-\infty}^{\infty} dv_x \int_{-\infty}^{\infty} dv_y \int_{(-2\eta\phi_m)^{1/2}}^{\infty} q v_{zc} n_c(0; v_x, v_y, v_{zc})\, dv_{zc}$$

$$= 2 i_{cM}\, \delta^2 \int_{(-2\eta\phi_m)^{1/2}}^{\infty} v_{zc} \exp - (\delta^2 v_{zc}^2)\, dv_{zc} \qquad (2.15)$$

To derive Eq. (2.15), Eqs. (2.12) to (2.14) have been used; in addition, the integration over v_z has been changed into one over v_{zc}, where, from Eq. (2.11),

$$v_z\, dv_z = v_{zc}\, dv_{zc} \qquad (2.16)$$

The right side of Eq. (2.15) can be evaluated completely to give the relation

$$i_A(z_0) = i_{cM} \exp(2\eta\delta^2\phi_m), \quad \phi_m \leq 0 \qquad (2.17)$$

Equation (2.17) is very important, and shows how the transmitted current depends on the depth of the potential minimum in front of the cathode. If there is no potential minimum, as in Fig. 6.1b, all particles leaving the cathode reach the anode. Equation (2.17) must then be replaced by the simple equation

$$i_A(z_0) = i_{cM} \qquad (2.18)$$

For an electron to leave the cathode at all, it is necessary that $v_{zc} > 0$. Hence, using Eq. (2.11), electrons reach the plane Z_1, distant z_1 from the cathode with potential ϕ_1, on their way to P if

$$v_{zc} > (-2\eta\phi_1)^{1/2} \qquad (2.19a)$$

These electrons pass the plane Z_1 again, on their return to the cathode, if their initial velocity is insufficient to pass the plane P; this condition is, from Eq. (2.14),

$$v_{zc} < (-2\eta\phi_m)^{1/2} \qquad (2.19b)$$

From Eqs. (2.11) and (2.19), the possible v_z for electrons at Z_1 and Z_2 are:

At Z_1: $\quad -2\eta(\phi_1 - \phi_m) < v_z < \infty \qquad (2.20a)$

At Z_2: $\quad 2\eta(\phi_2 - \phi_m) < v_z < \infty \qquad (2.20b)$

In Eq. (2.20b), ϕ_2 is the potential at Z_2, and in both cases v_x, v_y can take all values in the ranges

$$-\infty < v_x,\ v_y < \infty \qquad (2.20c)$$

The v_x, v_y, v_z of Eqs. (2.20) determine the range of integration in Eq. (2.9).

The equations for the problem have now been stated completely. The potential ϕ satisfies Eq. (2.9); the density function is given by Eq. (2.12). It remains only to solve the differential equation subject to the boundary conditions, assuming a potential distribution as in Fig. 6.1c,

$$\phi = \phi_m \quad \text{and} \quad \frac{d\phi}{dz} = 0 \quad \text{at } z = z_m \tag{2.21}$$

Then ϕ_m and z_m can be obtained in terms of the anode voltage ϕ_0, the injected current density i_{cM}, the anode-cathode spacing z_0, and the parameter σ of Eq. (2.2).

2.4. The Solutions of the Equations for the Potential in Normalized Form. To solve the equations of Sec. 2.3, the following substitutions are useful:

$$\mathcal{V}_x = \sigma v_x, \quad \mathcal{V}_y = \sigma v_y, \quad \mathcal{V}_z = \sigma v_z, \quad \Upsilon = 2\eta\sigma^2(\phi - \phi_m) \tag{2.22}$$

Using Eqs. (2.12), (2.13), and (2.22), the term $n(z;\mathbf{v})$ becomes

$$n(z;\mathcal{V}_x,\mathcal{V}_y,\mathcal{V}_z) = -\frac{i_{cM}}{q}\frac{2}{\pi}\sigma^4 \exp-\left\{(\mathcal{V}_x^2 + \mathcal{V}_y^2 + \mathcal{V}_z^2 + \Upsilon - \Upsilon_c)\right\} \tag{2.23}$$

The incremental lengths in the $\mathbf{v}$ and $\mathcal{V}$ coordinate systems are related by

$$\sigma\, dv_x = d\mathcal{V}_x \cdots$$

so that Eq. (2.9) can be written

$$\frac{d^2\Upsilon}{dz^2} = \frac{4}{\pi}\frac{\eta N}{\epsilon_0} i_{cM}\,\sigma^3 \exp(\Upsilon - \Upsilon_c) \tag{2.24}$$

where N is given by

$$N = \int_{-\infty}^{\infty} d\mathcal{V}_x \exp-(\mathcal{V}_x^2) \int_{-\infty}^{\infty} d\mathcal{V}_y \exp-(\mathcal{V}_y^2) \int_{\mathcal{V}_{z0}}^{\infty} d\mathcal{V}_z \exp-(\mathcal{V}_z^2)$$

$$= \pi \int_{\mathcal{V}_{z0}}^{\infty} d\mathcal{V}_z \exp-(\mathcal{V}_z^2) \tag{2.25}$$

and $\mathcal{V}_{z0}$ has different values in the two regions, obtained from Eq. (2.10) by

$$\mathcal{V}_{z0} = \begin{cases} -\Upsilon^{1/2} & \text{in region 1} \\ \Upsilon^{1/2} & \text{in region 2} \end{cases} \tag{2.26}$$

The integral in Eq. (2.25) can be expressed in terms of the error function erf(u) defined by

$$\text{erf}(u) = \frac{2}{\sqrt{\pi}} \int_0^u e^{-\xi^2}\, d\xi \tag{2.27}$$

Using this definition, the N of Eq. (2.25) is given by

$$N = \frac{\pi^{3/2}}{2}\left[1 \pm \operatorname{erf}\left(\Upsilon^{1/2}\right)\right] \tag{2.28}$$

where the upper sign applies in region 1, the lower in region 2.

The substitution

$$\xi = \pm\left[4\pi^{1/2}\, i_{cM}\, \sigma^3 \frac{\eta}{\epsilon_0} \exp\left(-\Upsilon_c\right)\right]^{1/2} (z - z_m) \tag{2.29}$$

is now convenient; in this and the following equations the upper sign holds for region 1 of Fig. 6.1c, between the emitter and the potential minimum, and the lower sign in region 2. Thus ξ is increasing away from the potential minimum in either direction. Using Eqs. (2.28) and (2.29), Eq. (2.24) can be written

$$\frac{d^2\Upsilon}{d\xi^2} = \frac{1}{2}\left[1 \pm \operatorname{erf}\left(\Upsilon^{1/2}\right)\right] e^{\Upsilon} \tag{2.30}$$

and the boundary conditions (2.21) as

$$\Upsilon = \frac{d\Upsilon}{d\xi} = 0 \qquad \text{at } \xi = 0 \tag{2.31}$$

Using Eq. (2.31), Eq. (2.30) can be integrated once, after multiplying both sides by $2\, d\Upsilon/d\xi$, to give

$$\left(\frac{d\Upsilon}{d\xi}\right)^2 = \left(e^{\Upsilon} - 1\right) \pm \left[e^{\Upsilon} \operatorname{erf}\left(\Upsilon^{1/2}\right) - 2\left(\frac{\Upsilon}{\pi}\right)^{1/2}\right] \tag{2.32}$$

It is not possible to integrate Eq. (2.32) again in closed form. A graph of Υ verses ξ is given in Fig. 6.2.* Here ξ_1 refers to region 1, ξ_2 refers to region 2, of Fig. 6.1c. In Ref. 3, a more general problem is treated by the same methods; it is assumed that both the planes $z = 0$ and $z = z_0$ can emit electrons according to Eq. (2.4) but that the temperature of the two planes is different. This problem is not treated in this book.

Nottingham has shown, allowing for certain differences of notation, that in the region 2 beyond the potential minimum, the solution of Eq. (2.32) can be represented approximately by the solution, for large Υ,

$$\xi \simeq 1.255\Upsilon^{3/4}\left(1 + 1.413\, \Upsilon^{-0.475}\right)^{3/4} \tag{2.33}$$

which can be inverted and written

$$\Upsilon \simeq \frac{0.738\, \xi^{4/3}}{1 + 2.126\, \xi^{-2/3}} \tag{2.34}$$

The multiplying factors in Eqs. (2.33) and (2.34) are $(8\sqrt{\pi}/9)^{1/2}$ and

*The values are also tabulated in Ref. 1. However, the ξ of Eq. (2.29) differs from the χ of Eq. (36.1) of Ref. 1 by the relation $\xi = \sqrt{2}\,\chi$. This difference accounts also for the discrepancies between the formulas given in this section and those of Ref. 1.

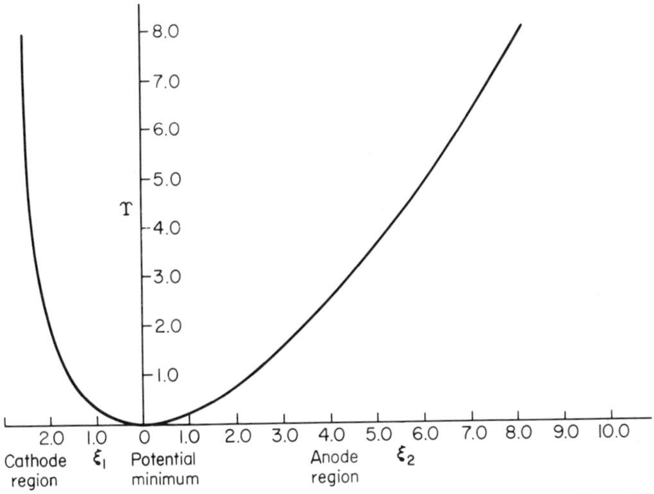

Fig. 6.2. The variation of potential in a planar diode. (Reproduced from Ref. 3, courtesy of the *Journal of Electronics and Control*.)

$(8\sqrt{\pi}/9)^{-2/3}$ in the numerator and denominator, respectively. In the region 1 between the cathode and the potential minimum, it is necessary to divide the region into two ranges; according to Nottingham,[1] approximate solutions are:*

$$\text{If } 0 \leq \xi \leq 2: \quad \Upsilon \simeq \frac{\xi^2}{4} + 0.6[\exp(0.107\xi^{3.17}) - 1] \tag{2.35a}$$

$$\text{If } 2 \leq \xi: \quad \Upsilon \simeq 2 \ln[\cos(0.707\xi - 0.235)]^{-1} \tag{2.35b}$$

It is seen that, as $\xi \rightarrow 2.544$, $\Upsilon \rightarrow \infty$. The inverses of Eqs. [2.35a) and (2.35b) are:

$$\text{If } 0 \leq \Upsilon \leq 2: \quad \xi^2 \simeq 4\Upsilon - 1.44\,\Upsilon^{1.46} \tag{2.36a}$$

$$\text{If } 2 \leq \Upsilon: \quad \xi^2 \simeq 2[\tan^{-1}(e^{\Upsilon} - 1)^{1/2} + 0.235]^2 \tag{2.36b}$$

In order to integrate Eq. (2.32), it is necessary to use the asymptotic expansions[5] for erf u:

$$\text{erf } u \simeq \begin{cases} 1 - \dfrac{1}{\sqrt{\pi}u} \exp(-u^2) & u \gg 1 \quad (2.37a) \\ \dfrac{2}{\sqrt{\pi}} u & u \ll 1 \quad (2.37b) \end{cases}$$

The most important case is in region 2, well away from the potential minimum; in this range $\Upsilon \gg 1$, and the negative sign is ap-

*There is a typographical error in Eq. (37.5) of Ref. 1; hence the sign in Eq. (2.36a).

plicable in Eq. (2.32). Using the asymptotic expansion of Eq. (2.37a), Eq. (2.32) becomes

$$\left(\frac{d\Upsilon}{d\xi}\right)^2 \simeq (e^{\Upsilon} - 1) - (e^{\Upsilon} + (\pi\Upsilon)^{-1/2}) + 2\,(\Upsilon/\pi)^{1/2} \simeq \frac{2}{\sqrt{\pi}}\,\Upsilon^{1/2} - 1 \qquad (2.38)$$

For large Υ the second term may be neglected, and Eq. (2.38) becomes

$$\frac{d\Upsilon}{d\xi} \simeq \left(\frac{2}{\sqrt{\pi}}\right)^{1/2} \Upsilon^{1/4} \qquad (2.39)$$

Equation (2.39) can be integrated with the boundary conditions of Eq. (2.31) to give

$$\Upsilon = \left(\frac{9}{8\sqrt{\pi}}\right)^{2/3} \xi^{4/3} \qquad (2.40)$$

Equation (2.40) agrees with the first term of Eq. (2.34). If, now, the definitions of Υ, ξ, and i_A of Eqs. (2.17), (2.22), and (2.29) are used, Eq. (2.40) becomes

$$\phi - \phi_m = \left(\frac{9}{4}\,\frac{i_A}{\epsilon_0(2\eta)^{1/2}}\right)^{2/3} (z - z_m)^{4/3} \qquad (2.41)$$

which is identical with Eq. (2.17a) of Chap. II, if z_m and ϕ_m are taken as the origin of position and potential. In Eq. (2.41) the definition of Υ was used to substitute for i_A from Eq. (2.17) by the relation

$$i_A = i_{cM} \exp(-\Upsilon_c) \qquad (2.42)$$

Although Eq. (2.41) is valid for large ξ in region 2, it is also instructive to investigate Eq. (2.32) for small ξ. Using Eq. (2.37b), Eq. (2.32) becomes, when Υ is assumed small, so that $e^{\Upsilon} \simeq 1 + \Upsilon$,

$$\left(\frac{d\Upsilon}{d\xi}\right)^2 \simeq \Upsilon$$

which has solution in either region,

$$\Upsilon = \frac{\xi^2}{4} \qquad (2.43)$$

Equation (2.43) is consistent with the first term of Eq. (2.35a), but not with Eq. (2.34). The disagreement occurs because Eq. (2.34) is valid only for large Υ. The importance of Eq. (2.43) is that, near the potential minimum, the potential varies quadratically with distance, not as the four-thirds-power law. Therefore the mathematical singularities in the space charge near the cathode disappear as soon as thermal velocities are taken into account. The correspondence between this result and those of Sec. 2.3 of Chap. II when the initial velocity is made finite should also be noted. With finite initial velocity the potential varies parabolically near the cathode. With thermal velocities, the true variation near the potential minimum is given, from Eq. (2.43) and the definitions of Υ and ξ, by

$$\phi - \phi_m = \frac{\pi^{1/2}\mathscr{C}}{2\epsilon_0} i_A (z - z_m)^2 \tag{2.44}$$

where $\mathscr{C}$ is given by Eq. (2.2). From Poisson's equation, the quadratic variation of ϕ shows that the charge density is constant near the potential minimum. Under some conditions, Eq. (2.44) is a better relation between potential and distance than Eq. (2.41), though not in the usual range of parameters, except in a magnetic field.

If the current density computed from Eq. (2.17) were to exceed i_{cM}, it is clear that Υ_c would have to be negative. In this case, there is no potential minimum, and the situation of Fig. 6.1b holds. Now the lower limit of integration in Eq. (2.25) is zero, and the boundary condition of Eq. (2.21) is not relevant. Instead, it is more convenient to choose the origin of the potential and the coordinates at the cathode, and one may then proceed in a manner similar to that given above to obtain the results for temperature-limited emission. Once more it is found that, for small Υ and ξ, with $\phi_m = z_m = 0$, Eq. (2.44) is again valid.

2.5. The Calculation of the Position and Effect of the Potential Minimum. The foregoing formalism can be used in many ways. For all of them, it is necessary first to express the various parameters in numerical form. In mks units, the expressions for $\mathscr{C}$, i_{cM}, i_A, Υ, and ξ are given, from Eqs. (2.2), (2.4), (2.17), (2.22), and (2.29), by

$$\mathscr{C} = 5.74 \times 10^{-6}\left(\frac{T_c}{1000}\right)^{-1/2} \tag{2.45}$$

$$i_{cM} = 1.2 \times 10^{12}\frac{T_c}{1000} A \exp -\left(\frac{11.600\Phi_0}{T_c}\right) \tag{2.46}$$

However, i_{cM} is best evaluated by measurement at the practical operating temperature of the cathode.

$$\Upsilon = 11.6\frac{1000}{T_c}(\phi - \phi_m) \tag{2.47}$$

$$i_A = i_{cM} \exp(-\Upsilon_c) \tag{2.48}$$

$$\xi = 3.76 \times 10^{11}\mathscr{C}^3 i_{cM} \exp(\Upsilon_c)^{1/2}(z - z_m) \tag{2.49}$$

Note that in mks units i is measured in units of amperes per square meter.

For Υ in region 2, $i_A(z - z_m)^2/(\phi - \phi_m)^{3/2}$ is given by the expression

$$\frac{i_A(z - z_m)^2}{(\phi - \phi_m)^{3/2}} = 2.34 \times 10^{-6} \tag{2.50}$$

One use of the formalism is to verify if, in a particular case, the potential minimum is sufficiently shallow and near the cathode to justify the zero-temperature assumptions that the potential minimum and the cathode are coincident. In this problem, it is assumed that the cathode parameters T_c, Φ_0, and the potential ϕ_0 at a point z_0, usually the anode, are known. First $\mathscr{E}$ and i_{cM} are computed from Eqs. (2.45) and (2.46); assuming z_m and ϕ_m are negligible, i_A is computed from Eq. (2.50), and hence Υ_c and ϕ_m from Eq. (2.48). Now Υ_A can be calculated from Eq. (2.47). By inspection of Fig. 6.2, or Eq. (2.34), it can now be seen whether the four-thirds-power law is still sufficiently accurate. Moreover, from Υ_c, Eq. (2.36), and Eq. (2.49), the position of the potential minimum can be found.

If the current density i_A, computed from Eq. (2.50), exceeds the i_{cM} from Eq. (2.48), there is no potential minimum, and the anode current must now be i_{cM}. If the i_A computed from Eq. (2.50) is less than i_{cM} and accurate values are required allowing for thermal effects, Eq. (2.50) cannot be used. Instead, it is necessary to adopt a method of successive approximations to find the position and depth of the potential minimum, and hence the current i_A.

3. PARAXIAL OPTICS FOR THERMAL BEAMS

3.1. Introduction. Except in one or two simple examples, e.g., the parallel-plane diode of Section 2, it is difficult to form a self-consistent solution for the flow from a thermally emitting cathode. Instead, the assumption is usually made that, at least for a first estimate, the fields within the beam are those which would exist in the equivalent beam emitted from a cathode at zero temperature. In addition, it is necessary to use paraxial theory. In most of this chapter we assume that the beam axis is rectilinear, although it is possible to generalize the analysis to take a curvilinear axis into account. According to the paraxial assumptions of Sec. 2.4 of Chap. III, if r is the distance from the beam axis, the components of electric and magnetic field in the r direction are proportional to r. This includes the forces due to space charge. This assumption is equivalent to saying that the effect of a transverse variation in charge density on the electric field is neglected. Since the space-charge term is itself usually a first-order term, variations in it are of second order. Thus it is not inconsistent to consider thermal effects in beams with nonuniform cathode emission to the paraxial approximation.

It was shown in Sections 5 and 6 of Chap. III that small changes in the longitudinal velocity of an electron do not affect its transverse position, at least if the axis of the paraxial system is rectilinear. Consequently, changes in the longitudinal velocity do not enter into our use of the paraxial equations. However, we must take account of the longitudinal motion in determining the total energy of an electron at a distance z from the cathode.* Because energy must be conserved, a negative energy may be required for a particle to reach a given plane with a given transverse velocity. The fact that this is physically impossible means that certain particles would not be able to reach the given plane z.

The basic paraxial analysis required is that for the electron trajectories within a beam, given in Sections 5 and 6 of Chap. III. It is assumed that the paraxial equation is valid for all electrons. In practice, of course, some electrons are emitted from the cathode in the direction almost parallel to its surface, and the paraxial equations are not strictly valid for such electrons. In the neighborhood of the cathode, however, the electric fields are almost perpendicular to its surface. Consequently, an electron is accelerated away from the cathode, with little change in its transverse velocity, i.e., velocity parallel to the cathode, until its longitudinal velocity is well above that corresponding to the average thermal speed. In practice, it is possible to regard the electrons as being emitted from a virtual cathode a short distance away from the real cathode (Section 2), and it is safe to use the paraxial equations to determine the transverse velocities of the electrons.

3.2. The Imaging Properties of Thermal Beams. In this section it is shown that a thermal beam can be treated optically; it has imaging properties similar to those of optical systems, with some differences due to the more general nature of electron-optical systems. Basically, this is because the ray paths in both systems obey paraxial equations. In Chap. III, Eqs. (5.10), (5.32), and (5.33), it was shown that, in a round axially symmetric beam, an electron arriving at the plane z obeys the relationship

$$\begin{pmatrix} w \\ v_w \end{pmatrix} = \begin{pmatrix} \mathfrak{M} & \mathfrak{N} \\ \dot{\mathfrak{M}} & \dot{\mathfrak{N}} \end{pmatrix} \begin{pmatrix} w(o) \\ v_w(o) \end{pmatrix} \tag{3.1}$$

with the condition

$$\mathfrak{M}\dot{\mathfrak{N}} - \dot{\mathfrak{M}}\mathfrak{N} = \exp 2j\vartheta \tag{3.2}$$

where the coordinates of an electron, x, y, are given by

$$w = x + jy, \qquad \dot{w} = v_x + jv_y = v_w \tag{3.3}$$

The parameter ϑ is related to the Larmor frequency ω_L, as follows:

$$\vartheta = \int \omega_L \, dt \tag{3.4}$$

and the moduli of $\mathfrak{M}$ and $\mathfrak{N}$ are given by

$$|\mathfrak{M}| = M \qquad \text{and} \qquad |\mathfrak{N}| = N \tag{3.5}$$

*See end of Section 1 for an explanation of the notation.

In a strip beam uniform in the y direction,* it was shown, in Eqs. (6.25) to (6.27) of Chap. III, that identical equations hold if

$$w = x, \qquad v_w = \dot{x}, \qquad \text{and} \qquad \vartheta = 0$$

Consider an electron leaving the axis at $w(0) = 0$ at the plane $z = 0$, which may be, but is not necessarily, the cathode. At some point along its path, at a plane z_1, the electron emitted from the axis will return to the axis; that is, $w = 0$. At this plane z, it is seen, from Eq. (3.1), that if $v_w(o) = 0$, $\mathfrak{N} = 0$. It follows, because $\mathfrak{N} = 0$, that another electron leaving the plane $z = 0$ at the point $w(o)$ will arrive at the point w, where

$$w(z_1) = \mathfrak{M}\, w(o) \tag{3.6}$$

Thus $w(z_1) \propto w(o)$ and is independent of the initial transverse velocity of the electron. Therefore, at the plane z_1, a perfect image, although possibly a rotated one, of the beam at the plane $z = 0$ is formed. In particular, Eq. (3.6) shows that a perfect image of the cathode is formed at the planes where an electron emitted from the axis returns to the axis. An image of the beam at $z = 0$ is formed at a plane called an image plane.

At an image plane, the magnification of the image is M, given by

$$M \equiv |\mathfrak{M}| = \left|\frac{w(z_1)}{w(o)}\right| \tag{3.7}$$

It follows from Eqs. (3.1), (3.2), and (3.4) that the transverse velocities of the axial-beam electrons at this plane z_1 are diminished by a factor

$$\left|\frac{v_w(z_1)}{v_w(o)}\right| = |\dot{\mathfrak{N}}| = \frac{1}{M} \tag{3.8}$$

An electron which leaves from a nonaxial point, with zero transverse velocity, does not, in general, have zero transverse velocity at the image plane. If this electron leaves from the cathode, it is convenient to call it a nonthermal electron. We call a similar electron which leaves from the cathode with an initial transverse velocity a thermal electron. Consider a thermal and a nonthermal electron emitted from the point w_c on the cathode, the nonthermal and thermal electrons having initial transverse velocities v_{w_1c}, v_{w_2c}, respectively. At the image plane it follows, from Eq. (3.7), that both electrons are focused to the same point w. Their transverse velocities, however, will be v_{w_1} and v_{w_2}, respectively. By using Eqs. (3.1) and (3.2), with $\mathfrak{N} = 0$, it is seen that

*In accordance with the notation for strip beams explained at the end of Section 1.

$$v_{w2} - v_{w1} = \dot{\mathfrak{M}}(v_{w2c} - v_{w1c}) = \frac{v_{w2c} - v_{w1c}}{\mathfrak{M} \exp(-2j\vartheta)} \tag{3.9}$$

If the difference in the transverse velocities of the thermal and nonthermal electrons at the same point is defined as v_T, then Eq. (3.9) implies that

$$|v_T| = \frac{|v_{Tc}|}{M} \tag{3.10}$$

Thus the transverse thermal velocity of an electron at the image plane is increased by a factor 1/M, that is, is inversely proportional to the magnification of the beam. The effective transverse temperature of the beam is defined as being proportional to $|v_T^2|$; it follows that compression of the beam increases the transverse temperature by $1/M^2$, and expansion decreases the effective transverse temperature of the beam by the same ratio. Therefore the transverse temperature at the image plane is inversely proportional to the area of the image.

The foregoing relationship can be stated in more general terms and, when used properly, applies at planes other than the image plane. Consider the situation shown in Fig. 6.3. Two electrons, a nonthermal electron and a thermal electron, are emitted from different points w_{1c} and w_{2c} at the cathode, and their trajectories intersect at a point w on the plane z. We shall determine the relationship between the initial transverse velocity of the thermal electron v_{Tc} leaving from the point w_{2c} and its thermal velocity v_T at the point w, defined to be $v_T = v_{w2} - v_{w1}$. It will be shown that $|v_T|$ is inversely proportional to the magnification M of the nonthermal trajectory.

It is sometimes convenient to use the inverted form of Eq. (3.1), which, because of Eq. (3.2), can be written

$$\begin{pmatrix} w(o) \\ v_w(o) \end{pmatrix} = \exp(-2j\vartheta) \begin{pmatrix} \dot{\mathfrak{M}} & -\mathfrak{M} \\ -\dot{\mathfrak{M}} & \mathfrak{M} \end{pmatrix} \begin{pmatrix} w \\ v_w \end{pmatrix} \tag{3.11}$$

It follows from Eq. (3.11) that, for the thermal and nonthermal electrons passing through the point w, the initial coordinates and trans-

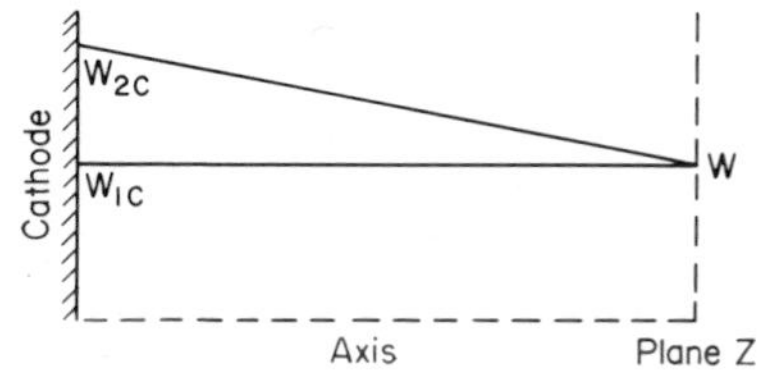

Fig. 6.3. Sketch of thermal and nonthermal trajectories from a planar cathode.

verse velocities at the cathode are related as follows:

$$\begin{aligned} w_{2c} - w_{1c} &= -\mathfrak{N}(v_{W2} - v_{W1}) \exp(-2j\vartheta) \\ &= -\mathfrak{N}\, v_T \exp(-2j\vartheta) \end{aligned} \tag{3.12a}$$

$$v_{Tc} = v_{W2c} - v_{W1c} = \mathfrak{M}\, v_T \exp(-2j\vartheta) \tag{3.12b}$$

so that

$$|v_T| = \frac{|v_{Tc}|}{M} \tag{3.13}$$

The relationship of Eq. (3.10) has been generalized to yield the result that compression of the beam increases the transverse temperature at any point of the beam. The transverse temperature of the beam is inversely proportional to the area of the image of the cathode formed by the nonthermal electrons. It should be noted, however, that the concept of transverse temperature must be used with care. The pitfalls in the use of this idea are discussed in detail in Sec. 4.3.

Another plane of interest is where the nonthermal electrons emitted from the cathode are focused to a point. It was demonstrated in Sec. 3.2 of Chap. I, by using Busch's theorem, that this condition can occur only if there is no magnetic field at the cathode. In accordance with the definition of Herrman,[8] the plane where the nonthermal electrons cross the axis is termed the crossover plane. At the crossover plane, by definition, it is seen that M = 0. Consequently, it follows from Eq. (3.1) that the radial position which thermal electrons reach at this plane is

$$r = |w| = N\,|v_{Tc}| \tag{3.14}$$

where N is given by Eq. (3.5).

Thus, if the transverse velocity distribution of the electrons at the cathode is Gaussian [see discussion following Eq. (2.1)], the density distribution of electrons with respect to radius at the crossover plane is also Gaussian. The radius which an electron reaches is dependent on the parameter $N = 1/\dot{M}$, which itself depends on the stiffness of the beam.

3.3. The Trajectories of Thermal Electrons. Most of the space-charge flows which have been analyzed in this book are zero-temperature flows. If the relevant paraxial equation has been solved, one linear combination of the $\mathfrak{M}$ and $\mathfrak{N}$ is known. For example, if the beam is parallel, with initial radius r_0, at t = 0, and the subsequent beam edge $r_e(t)$ is known, then $M = r_e(t)/r_0$. If $w_1(t)$ is a known solution and $w_2(t)$ an unknown one, of the paraxial equation inside the beam, then from Eq. (3.2), w_2 obeys the equation

$$\frac{\dot{w}_2 w_1 - \dot{w}_1 w_2}{w_1^2} = \frac{\exp(2j\vartheta)}{w_1^2} \tag{3.15}$$

This equation can be integrated to give

$$w_2(t) = w_1 \int_0^t \frac{\exp(2j\vartheta)}{w_1^2}\, dt_1$$

$$= w_1 \int_0^z \frac{\exp\left[2j \int_0^{z_1} \omega_L (2\eta\phi)^{-1/2}\, dz_2\right]}{\mathfrak{M}^2(2\eta\phi)^{1/2}}\, dz_1 \tag{3.16}$$

If $\quad w_1(o) = w_{1O} \quad$ and $\quad \dot{w}_1(o) = \dot{w}_{1O}$ (3.17)

then, from Eq. (3.16),

$$w_2(o) = 0 \qquad \text{and} \qquad \dot{w}_2(o) = \frac{1}{w_1(o)} \tag{3.18}$$

Thus $\mathfrak{M}$ and $\mathfrak{N}$ are given by

$$\mathfrak{M} = \frac{w_1(t)}{w_{1O}} - \dot{w}_{1O} w_2(t), \qquad \mathfrak{N} = w_{1O} w_2(t) \tag{3.19}$$

In the usual case where $\mathfrak{M}$ is known, $w_1(t) = \mathfrak{M}(t)$, so that $w_{1O} = 1$ and $\dot{w}_{1O} = 0$. In this case $\mathfrak{N}$ takes the simple form

$$\mathfrak{N} = \mathfrak{M}(t) \int_0^t \frac{\exp(2j\vartheta)}{\mathfrak{M}^2(t_1)}\, dt_1$$

$$= \mathfrak{M}(z) \int_0^z \frac{\exp\left[2j \int_0^{z_1} \omega_L (2\eta\phi)^{-1/2}\, dz_2\right]}{\mathfrak{M}^2(z_1)(2\eta\phi)^{1/2}}\, dz_1 \tag{3.20}$$

The determination of $\mathfrak{N}$ by this technique is somewhat simpler than the direct integration of the paraxial equation, since the paraxial equation is of second order.

Consider now a thermal and a nonthermal electron emitted from the same point, w_c on the cathode. From Eq. (3.1), the position reached by an electron emitted from this point is

$$w = \mathfrak{M} w_c + \mathfrak{N} v_{wc} \tag{3.21}$$

Since, for a nonthermal electron, $v_{wc} = 0$, and for the thermal electron, $v_{wc} = v_{Tc}$, from Eq. (3.17) the distance between the two electrons at the plane z is

$$w_T = \mathfrak{N} v_{Tc} \tag{3.22}$$

It follows that, if the value $\mathfrak{M}$ at any point is known, then substitution of Eqs. (3.20) and (3.22) yields the result

$$|w_T| = M\,|v_{Tc}| \left| \int_0^t \frac{\exp(2j\vartheta)}{\mathfrak{M}^2}\, dt_1 \right|$$

$$= M\,|v_{Tc}| \left| \int_0^z \frac{\exp\left[2j \int (2\eta\phi)^{-1/2}\, dz_2\right]}{\mathfrak{M}^2 (2\eta\phi)^{1/2}}\, dz_1 \right| \tag{3.23}$$

Thus the thermal electrons emitted from one point spread out in a Gaussian distribution about the path of the nonthermal electron emitted from the same point. This property is discussed further in Sec. 4.3.

As a simple example consider a Brillouin beam. In this beam, electrons with zero transverse velocity at the cathode stay at a constant radius, so that in the beam $\mathfrak{M} = \exp(j\theta)$. It follows that the distance between a thermal and a nonthermal electron in a Brillouin beam is

$$|w_T| = |v_{Tc}|\, t = |v_{Tc}| \frac{z}{v_0} \tag{3.24}$$

where v_0 is the (constant) longitudinal beam velocity. Thus a thermal electron is unconstrained in a Brillouin beam and free to move across it. In a system rotating at the Larmor frequency, it moves in the direction of v_{Tc}. It is seen that, in the presence of thermal electrons, a Brillouin beam is nonlaminar.

4. THE CURRENT DENSITY AT THE AXIS OF AN ELECTRON BEAM

4.1. Introduction. The discussion of focusing systems in Chaps. IV and V leads to the conclusion that space charge must necessarily limit the maximum current density obtainable in an electron beam. In many important cases, however, the major limitation on the current density is not that of space charge but that due to thermal velocities. This is because, as shown in Section 3, when the diameter of a beam decreases, the transverse velocity of the electrons within it increases. Consequently, there is a limitation on the maximum current density obtainable.

In this section, by using a method of analysis first given by Langmuir[9] and later extended by Pierce,[10] we evaluate limitations caused by thermal effects on the maximum current density which may be obtained in an electron beam. A limiting form, which is true whatever the type of focusing system, is obtained for a cylindrical beam in Sec. 4.2. In Sec. 4.3 limitations due to the nature of the focusing are considered, assuming that the focusing system is aberrationless, i.e., that paraxial theory is valid whatever the angles of divergence or transverse velocities of the electrons in the beam. Such a treatment is a little difficult to justify, since a paraxial theory of this kind might be expected to break down very near the cathode. One way of avoiding this difficulty, already discussed in Section 3, is to suppose that the initial plane is taken some short distance from the cathode; the transverse velocities are almost unchanged from their cathode values but the longitudinal velocities, i.e., the velocities of electrons normal to the cathode plane, have become much larger than their initial velocities. In this case the assumptions of the paraxial theory are valid for most of the thermal electrons. The results obtained are almost the same as if the paraxial theory were used from the cathode onward, on the assumption that it is valid throughout the beam.

The maximum-current limitations imposed by the theory to be given here are not necessarily those obtained in practice. For certain systems, such as the cathode-ray-tube beam where space-charge fields may be negligible, the considerations presented here give a good estimate of the current density that can be obtained in practice. In systems where lens aberrations are large or the perveance is high, these estimates may be limits that are difficult to reach; but whatever the considerations used, these limits can never be exceeded.

4.2. Langmuir's Bounding Expression for the Current Density on **the Axis of a Cylindrical System.** We now derive an upper bound for the current density on the axis of a cylindrical system, due to electrons which reach that axial position within a cone of half-angle α. It will be shown in Sec. 4.3 that, in a real focusing system, there may not be sufficient electrons of all velocity classes available from the cathode to yield the maximum current density within a cone of half-angle α.

We assume that the electrons emitted from the cathode have the Gaussian distribution of Eq. (2.6). For convenience, the expression for the phase-space density n_c of Eq. (2.6) and the normalization relations of Eqs. (2.2) and (2.22) are repeated here. Taking the cathode as z = 0, Eqs. (2.6), (2.2), and (2.22) become

$$n_c(x,y,o;v_{xc},v_{yc},v_{zc}) = -\frac{2}{\pi}\frac{i_c(x,y)}{q}\,\mathscr{b}^4 \exp - (\mathcal{V}_{xc}^2 + \mathcal{V}_{yc}^2 + \mathcal{V}_{zc}^2) \tag{4.1}$$

$$\text{where} \quad \mathscr{b} = \left(\frac{m}{2kT_c}\right)^{1/2} = 5.74 \times 10^{-6}\left(\frac{T_c}{1000}\right)^{-1/2} \tag{4.2}$$

$$\text{and} \quad \mathcal{V}_{xc} = \mathscr{b}\,v_{xc}, \quad \mathcal{V}_{yc} = \mathscr{b}\,v_{yc}, \quad \mathcal{V}_{zc} = \mathscr{b}\,v_{zc} \tag{4.3}$$

In Eq. (4.1), i_c is the total current density emitted normal to the cathode, and q is the electronic charge; in Eq. (4.2), m is the mass of the electron, k is Boltzman's constant, and T_c is the cathode temperature. For particles to leave the cathode, it is necessary that

$$\mathcal{V}_c \geq 0 \tag{4.4}$$

In the same way as in Section 2, the other normalizations of Eq. (2.22) are useful, namely,

$$\mathcal{V}_x = \mathscr{b}\,v_x, \quad \mathcal{V}_y = \mathscr{b}\,v_y, \quad \mathcal{V}_z = \mathscr{b}\,v_z \tag{4.5}$$

$$\text{and} \quad \Upsilon = -\frac{q\phi}{kT_c} = 2\eta\mathscr{b}^2\phi = 11.6\,\frac{1000}{T_c}\,\phi \tag{4.6}$$

In this and subsequent sections, the position of the <u>real</u> cathode is ignored; n_c and $z = 0$ refer to the virtual cathode. The virtual cathode at which Eq. (4.1) holds, as discussed in Section 2, coincides with the real cathode, if there is no potential minimum and the potential has the distribution of Fig. 6.1b. If the potential distribution has the form of Fig. 6.1c, the virtual cathode $z = 0$ is at $z = z_m$ in that figure. Equation (2.12) shows that the particle density at the plane $z = 0$ is still given by Eq. (4.1). Now, instead of i_{cM} in Eq. (2.6), the i_A of Eq. (2.15) must be written. Since, in the subsequent development, the current density transmitted across the potential minimum is treated as the "cathode current density," for i_A in Eqs. (2.15) or (2.16) we write i_c. In the problems treated in the rest of this chapter, z_m and ϕ_m are usually so small that they can be treated as zero. If in any particular case the validity of this assumption is questioned, it can be checked by evaluating z_m and ϕ_m from the equations of Sec. 2.5. For the rest of this chapter, and in all the book unless stated otherwise, the cathode means the virtual cathode.

Liouville's theorem, Eq. (3.28) of Chap. I, states that, as an electron moves from the cathode along the beam, the density in phase space about an electron which left the point $(x_c, y_c, 0)$ does not change; that is, $n(x,y,z;\ v_x,v_y,v_z) = n_c(x_c,y_c,0; v_{xc},v_{yc},v_{zc})$. Consequently, the current density at any plane z within the beam is

$$i(r) = \frac{2}{\pi} \int_{v_x} \int_{v_y} \int_{v_z} \mathscr{b}^4 v_z i_c(\mathbf{r}_c) \exp -[\mathscr{b}^2(v_{xc}^2 + v_{yc}^2 + v_{zc}^2)]\, dv_x\, dv_y\, dv_z \qquad (4.7)$$

where the current density at the cathode has been written $i_c(r_c)$, to show that the system is axially symmetric. It follows from the conservation-of-energy equation [Eq. (2.27) of Chap. I] that

$$v^2 = v_x^2 + v_y^2 + v_z^2 = v_{xc}^2 + v_{yc}^2 + v_{zc}^2 + 2\eta\phi \qquad (4.8)$$

Using Eqs. (4.5) and (4.6), Eq. (4.7) can be written in the form

$$i(r) = \frac{2}{\pi} \int_{\upsilon_x} d\upsilon_x \int_{\upsilon_y} d\upsilon_y \int_{\upsilon_z} i_c(\mathbf{r}_c)\, \upsilon_z \exp(\Upsilon - \upsilon^2)\, d\upsilon_z \qquad (4.9)$$

It should be noted that this expression is a general one, in that the axis of the system need not be rectilinear. In many cases, however, where the limits of the integral are determined by the optical properties of the system, the assumption of a rectilinear axis considerably simplifies the analysis.

It is now an easy matter to calculate a bounding expression for the current density reaching a point within a cone of half-angle α. We assume that the current density at the emitter is uniform, of value i_{co}, and that the cathode is infinite in extent. It is possible, in this case, to take $i_c(\mathbf{r}_c)$ outside the integral sign and perform the necessary integrations without reference to the value of $\mathbf{r}_c$.

For an axially symmetric system, the most convenient way of integrating Eq. (4.9) is to work in terms of spherical coordinates;

that is, $\mathcal{V}^2 = \mathcal{V}_x^2 + \mathcal{V}_y^2 + \mathcal{V}_z^2$. It is necessary that $\mathcal{V} > \Upsilon^{1/2}$, so that electrons leave the cathode at a speed greater than zero. We assume that the electrons arrive within a cone of half-angle α, so that $\theta < \alpha$. The limits of the integral are therefore

$$0 < \theta < \alpha \qquad \Upsilon^{1/2} < \mathcal{V} < \infty \tag{4.10}$$

Equation (4.10) can now be written in the form

$$i_{\alpha M} = 4i_{co} \int_{\mathcal{V}=\Upsilon^{1/2}}^{\infty} \int_{\theta=0}^{\alpha} \mathcal{V}^3 \cos\theta \sin\theta \exp(\Upsilon - \mathcal{V}^2)\, d\mathcal{V}\, d\theta \tag{4.11}$$

where $i_{\alpha M}$ is the maximum current available at the plane z, and i_{co} is the current density of the cathode. Integration of Eq. (4.11) yields the result that the maximum electron density which can reach a point within a cone of half-angle α is

$$i_{\alpha M} = i_{co}(1 + \Upsilon) \sin^2 \alpha \tag{4.12}$$

This relation, which is independent of the nature of the electromagnetic focusing system, provided that all fields are taken to be static, is known as Langmuir's bounding expression[9] for cylindrical beams.

4.3. The Current Density of the Axis of a Perfect Cylindrical Focusing System. The expression that has been obtained in Sec. 4.2 for the maximum current density $i_{\alpha M}$ has been derived without any consideration of the nature of the focusing system. Even with a perfect focusing system, the current density is below the value given by Eq. (4.12). This is because the assumption has been made that there are always electrons available at the point of interest within the cone of half-angle α. The focusing conditions may imply that, for the trajectory of a particle to intersect the axis at an angle ϑ, impossible conditions be fulfilled at the cathode, e.g., that the sine of the slope of the trajectory at the cathode be greater than unity. In this case, no thermal electron is available to arrive at the point of interest at the given angle. Consequently, the total current density obtained at the image point is, in general, less than the value given by the expression we have derived in Sec. 4.2.

In this section a correct value is found for the maximum current density on the axis of a perfect cylindrical focusing system. We assume that the equations of paraxial flow are valid, so that the analysis depends on using proper limits for the value of the angle of arrival of the electron at the plane z. It is convenient, as in Sec. 4.2, to work in spherical coordinates. It follows from Eq. (4.10) that the current density in the z direction contributed by those electrons within the speed limits ($\mathcal{V}$, $\mathcal{V} + d\mathcal{V}$), which arrive within an angle ϑ_0 of the axis, is $di_z(\mathcal{V})$, where

$$\begin{aligned} di_z(\mathcal{V}) &= 4i_{co} \int_0^{\vartheta_0} \mathcal{V}^3 \sin\vartheta \cos\vartheta \exp(\Upsilon - \mathcal{V}^2)\, d\vartheta\, d\mathcal{V} \\ &= 2i_{co} \mathcal{V}^3 \sin^2\vartheta_0 \exp(\Upsilon - \mathcal{V}^2)\, d\mathcal{V} \end{aligned} \tag{4.13}$$

Here we have assumed again that the current density at the cathode is uniform and of value i_{co} and that the cathode is infinite in extent.

In order to integrate Eq. (4.13) with respect to speed, it is necessary to determine the limits on $\mathcal{V}$. To do this, the relationship between the angle of arrival ϑ of an electron at the axial point z and the angle to the normal ϑ_c at which the electron left the cathode, must be found.

It was shown in Section 3 that the position and velocity of an electron leaving the cathode could be expressed in terms of its position and velocity at the plane z. The relation obtained, Eq. (3.10), is

$$\begin{bmatrix} w_c \\ v_{wc} \end{bmatrix} = \exp(-2j\vartheta) \begin{bmatrix} \dot{\mathfrak{N}} & -\mathfrak{N} \\ -\dot{\mathfrak{M}} & \mathfrak{M} \end{bmatrix} \begin{bmatrix} w \\ v_w \end{bmatrix} \tag{4.14}$$

An electron which arrives on the axis, w = 0, leaves the cathode from the point w_c with a velocity v_w given by

$$\begin{aligned} w_c &= -\mathfrak{N} v_w \exp(-2j\vartheta) \\ v_{wc} &= \mathfrak{M} v_w \exp(-2j\vartheta) \end{aligned} \tag{4.15}$$

On the axis, at the plane z, the magnitude of the transverse velocity of the electron is

$$v \sin \vartheta = |v_w| \tag{4.16}$$

where v is the total speed of the electron. At the cathode, the magnitude of the electron velocity parallel to the cathode is

$$v_c \sin \vartheta_c = |v_{wc}| \tag{4.17}$$

Consequently, after substitution of Eq. (4.15), it is found that

$$v_c \sin \vartheta_c = M |v_w| = Mv \sin \vartheta \tag{4.18}$$

We have now obtained the required relation between the angle at which an electron is emitted from the cathode and the angle at which it arrives at the axis. It is convenient to express Eq. (4.18) entirely in terms of the normalized speed, $\mathcal{V} = \mathscr{b}v$ of an electron at the plane z. To do this, the condition for conservation of energy, Eq. (4.8), and the defining equations, Eqs. (4.5) and (4.6), are used, with the result

$$\sin^2 \vartheta_c = \frac{M^2 \mathcal{V}^2 \sin^2 \vartheta}{\mathcal{V}^2 - \Upsilon} \tag{4.19}$$

If the left-hand side of this equation is less than unity or $\mathcal{V}^2 > \Upsilon/(1 - M^2 \sin^2 \vartheta)$, there are electrons available at the cathode which have a speed v on the axis at the plane z and which arrive at an angle ϑ with the axis. If $\mathcal{V}^2 < \Upsilon/(1 - M^2 \sin^2 \vartheta)$, however, the right-hand side of Eq. (4.19) will be greater than unity for the given value of ϑ. Since the maximum value of ϑ_c is $\pi/2$, it follows that, for an electron meeting the axis at an angle ϑ, if its speed is such that $\mho^2 < \Upsilon/(1 - M^2 \sin^2 \vartheta)$, then

$$\mho^2 \sin^2 \vartheta < \frac{\mho^2 - \Upsilon}{M^2} \tag{4.20}$$

There is the additional restriction that $\mho > \Upsilon^{1/2}$. If $M^2 \sin^2 \alpha < 1$, it follows that Eq. (4.16) must be integrated in two parts; the first integral is for $\Upsilon < \mho^2 < \Upsilon/(1 - M^2 \sin^2 \vartheta)$, with the condition of Eq. (4.20), and the second integral is for $\Upsilon/(1 - M^2 \sin^2 \alpha) < \mho^2 < \infty$, with $0 < \vartheta < \alpha$. With these ranges of integration, the total current density on the axis i_α becomes

$$i_\alpha = \frac{2i_{co}}{M^2} \int_{\Upsilon^{1/2}}^{[\Upsilon/(1 - M^2 \sin^2 \alpha)]^{1/2}} \mho\,(\mho^2 - \Upsilon) \exp\,(\Upsilon - \mho^2)\, d\mho$$
$$+ 2i_{co} \int_{[\Upsilon/(1 - M^2 \sin^2 \alpha)]^{1/2}}^{\infty} \mho^3 \sin^2 \alpha \exp\,(\Upsilon - \mho^2)\, d\mho \tag{4.21}$$

Equation (4.21) can be integrated to give the result

$$i_\alpha = \frac{i_{co}}{M^2}\left[1 - (1 - M^2 \sin^2 \alpha) \exp\left(-\frac{\Upsilon M^2 \sin^2 \alpha}{1 - M^2 \sin^2 \alpha}\right)\right] \tag{4.22}$$

for $M \sin \alpha < 1$. If, on the other hand, $M \sin \alpha > 1$, different considerations apply. In this case the maximum value of α is given by $M \sin \alpha = 1$, and all the current leaving the cathode arrives at the plane z.

At this point it is worthwhile discussing in more detail the concept of transverse temperature. It was shown in Sec. 3.2 that the transverse velocities of electrons leaving the cathode are inversely proportional to the value of M at the point of interest. This leads to the idea that the transverse temperature of the electrons is inversely proportional to M^2. The restrictions dictated by the use of Eq. (4.19), however, imply that, at least on the axis, electrons are not available in all velocity classes. As an extreme example, at the crossover plane, $M = 0$, and these concepts would predict infinite transverse temperature there. On the other hand, it follows from Eq. (4.19) that $\vartheta_c = 0$, so that only nonthermal electrons can reach the crossover point (which exists only if there is no magnetic field at the cathode). More generally, at any point of interest, part of the transverse velocity distribution is missing. If the velocity distribution were complete, the transverse temperature would be given by the foregoing arguments. The concept of transverse temperature gives information only on the way the transverse velocities of those electrons reaching the point of interest are changed after they leave the cathode.

The expression given by Eq. (4.22) applies anywhere along the axis of the beam, provided the parameters M and $\sin \alpha$ are known.

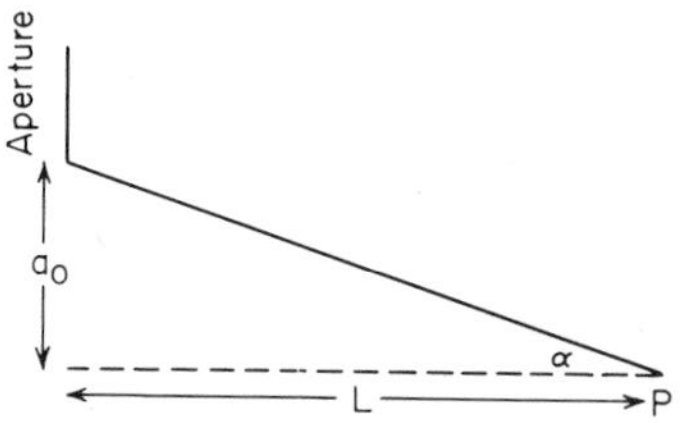

Fig. 6.4. Schematic of a ray passing through an aperture in an equipotential region.

The magnification M is given by the properties of the optical system, and may be calculated if the potential and magnetic field configurations are known. The angle α depends on the size of the aperture through which the beam passes. In the situation shown in Fig. 6.4, for example, an aperture of radius a_0 is placed a distance L from the point of interest P; the region between the pupil and P is taken to be an equipotential region. It is also assumed that there is no magnetic field present either at the cathode or in this region, so that the electrons are not rotating around the axis. The maximum angle α at which electrons can arrive at P is given approximately, if α is small, by

$$\sin \alpha = \frac{a_0}{L} \tag{4.23}$$

More generally, if this region is not an equipotential region, and even if there is a magnetic field present, the value of α can be deduced by using the relation given by Eq. (4.14), with w_c and v_{wc} replaced by their values at the aperture w_0, v_{w0}, and $\mathfrak{M}$, $\dot{\mathfrak{M}}$, $\mathfrak{N}$, $\dot{\mathfrak{N}}$ being the appropriate constants from the aperture to P. The expression analogous to Eq. (4.18) is

$$|w_0| = a_0 = |\mathfrak{N}|\ |v_W| = Nv \sin \alpha \tag{4.24}$$

or
$$\sin \alpha = \frac{a_0}{N(2\eta\Phi_z)^{1/2}} \tag{4.25}$$

where Φ_z is the potential on the axis at the plane z, not at the plane of the diaphram. Equation (4.23) or (4.25) is very convenient to use for determining the maximum current intensity that can be obtained on the spot at the screen of a cathode-ray tube, although the expression obtained applies anywhere along the axis of the system. If there were no magnetic field at the cathode, it would be possible to obtain a crossover, at a point corresponding to $\mathfrak{M} = 0$, where all electrons emitted from the cathode with zero velocity cross the axis. When $\mathfrak{M} = 0$, the limiting form of Eq. (4.22) is that given by Eq. (4.12), Langmuir's bounding expression. At the crossover point, however, the transverse density distribution is Gaussian in form, and a very large cathode would have to be used to obtain the limiting current density of Eq. (4.12). This would not be the most efficient method of cathode utilization.

It is more useful to choose the plane z as the image plane of the cathode. In this case the current density is uniform and of value given by Eq. (4.22). It has been seen that, whether or not magnetic field is present, for small values of M sin α, the current at the image plane can approach the limiting value given by Langmuir's bounding expression. On the other hand, as M sin $\alpha \rightarrow 1$, the current density obtained at the image approaches i_{c0}/M^2. This corresponds to the total current emitted from the cathode arriving at the image, a very efficient method of utilizing the cathode emission.

It should be emphasized that the foregoing calculations have been used and applied whatever the magnetic field present. It should be noted that no assumptions about the nature of the focusing system, except that it is a paraxial one, have been made. Consequently, all the results given here apply whether the focusing is by means of magnetic fields, electrostatic fields, or a combination.

5. THE CURRENT DENSITY AT ANY POINT IN A CYLINDRICAL BEAM

5.1. Introduction. We discussed in Section 4 the current which may be obtained on the axis of an electron beam. In many cases, this knowledge is not sufficient. For instance, in the design of an electron gun to produce a well-focused long electron beam, it is necessary to determine not only the current density obtainable at one particular point, but also the density distribution over the cross section of the beam and how it is changed by the presence of thermal velocities. It is also of interest to determine the change in the minimum diameter of the beam caused by thermal effects, and the distance of this plane in the beam from the cathode. A more detailed analysis than has been carried out before in this chapter is therefore needed.

As before, the analysis is based on the equations of paraxial flow and on the conservation of density in phase space dictated by Liouville's theorem. It is necessary to find a transformation which relates the velocity of a particle at a point (x,y,z) to the velocity and position it had on the cathode. The basic analysis then determines the current density at the point (x,y,z) by evaluating a weighted integral of the current density over the cathode.

It is possible to extend the analysis of this section to thick beams in which the paraxial equations are no longer valid. The analysis then relies on a linear perturbation treatment about the nonthermal flow.* The analysis is very mathematical, and beyond the scope of this book. The thick-beam treatment is particularly useful if a high-perveance high-convergence gun is being analyzed by the methods of Section 3 of Chap. VIII. The treatment allows thermal effects to be

*The range of validity of this method has not been fully established.

estimated in thick beams, on a computer, with little extra labor than required for the nonthermal problem. The details of the analysis are given in Ref. 11.

All the analyses of Sections 3 to 7 assume that the fields in the thermal case are the same as in the nonthermal case. In Section 8, we treat the case where this assumption is no longer valid.

In Sec. 5.2 the analysis is given for a cylindrical beam; some conclusions from the analysis pertaining to beams with very little velocity spread are given in Sec. 5.3. Examples of the use of the formulas obtained will be given in Section 6.

5.2. The Basic Integration to Find Current Densities. The current density at a radius r, in the presence of thermals, of an axially symmetric cylindrical beam was derived in Section 4. After Eq. (4.8) is substituted into Eq. (4.9), the following result is obtained:

$$i_z(r) = \frac{2}{\pi} \int_{\mathcal{V}_x} \int_{\mathcal{V}_y} \int_{\mathcal{V}_z} \mathcal{V}_z i_c(r_c) \exp -(\mathcal{V}_{xc}^2 + \mathcal{V}_{yc}^2 + \mathcal{V}_{zc}^2)\, d\mathcal{V}_x\, d\mathcal{V}_y\, d\mathcal{V}_z \tag{5.1}$$

The current density $i_z(r)$ at the radius r is composed of contributions from different points on the cathode $r = r_c$. It is of interest to express the integral in terms of the current density $i_c(r_c)$ at the point (x_c, y_c). It is necessary to eliminate the velocity terms and write them in terms of r and r_c. This is done by using the transformation

$$\begin{bmatrix} w \\ v_w \end{bmatrix} = \begin{bmatrix} \mathfrak{M} & \mathfrak{N} \\ \dot{\mathfrak{M}} & \dot{\mathfrak{N}} \end{bmatrix} \begin{bmatrix} w_c \\ v_{wc} \end{bmatrix} \tag{5.2}$$

It follows from Eq. (5.2) that

$$w = \mathfrak{M} w_c + \mathfrak{N} v_{wc} \tag{5.3}$$

$$\text{i.e.,}\quad v_{wc} = \frac{w - \mathfrak{M} w_c}{\mathfrak{N}} \tag{5.4}$$

It is convenient to write

$$w = r \exp(j\vartheta), \qquad w_c = r_c \exp(j\vartheta_c), \qquad \mathfrak{M} = M \exp(j\psi) \tag{5.5}$$

so that the following result is obtained:

$$N^2 \,|\, v_{wc} \,|^2 = (v_{xc}^2 + v_{yc}^2) N^2 = r^2 + r_c^2 M^2 - 2rr_c M \cos(\vartheta_c - \gamma) \tag{5.6}$$

where $\gamma = \vartheta + \psi$. Thus the speed parallel to the cathode has been expressed in terms of the coordinates at which the electron leaves the cathode and the coordinates of the point which it reaches.

In order to determine the total contribution to the current density from the current leaving the cathode, it is necessary to transform Eq. (5.1) into an integration over the cathode. To do this, $d\mathcal{V}_x$, $d\mathcal{V}_y$, $d\mathcal{V}_z$ must be expressed in terms of the element of area on the cathode and the velocity at which an electron leaves the cathode normal to it. We write, therefore

$$d\mathcal{V}_x\, d\mathcal{V}_y\, d\mathcal{V}_z = \mathcal{J}\, dx_c\, dy_c\, d\mathcal{V}_{zc} \tag{5.7}$$

where $\mathcal{J}$ is the Jacobian, given by the determinant

$$\mathcal{J} = \begin{pmatrix} \dfrac{\partial \mathcal{V}_x}{\partial x_c} & \dfrac{\partial \mathcal{V}_x}{\partial y_c} & \dfrac{\partial \mathcal{V}_x}{\partial \mathcal{V}_{zc}} \\ \dfrac{\partial \mathcal{V}_y}{\partial x_c} & \dfrac{\partial \mathcal{V}_y}{\partial y_c} & \dfrac{\partial \mathcal{V}_y}{\partial \mathcal{V}_{zc}} \\ \dfrac{\partial \mathcal{V}_z}{\partial x_c} & \dfrac{\partial \mathcal{V}_z}{\partial y_c} & \dfrac{\partial \mathcal{V}_z}{\partial \mathcal{V}_{zc}} \end{pmatrix} \tag{5.8}$$

Because $\mathcal{V}_x$ and $\mathcal{V}_y$ obey the paraxial equation, they are independent of $\mathcal{V}_{zc}$, and $\mathcal{J}$ becomes

$$\mathcal{J} = \frac{\partial \mathcal{V}_z}{\partial \mathcal{V}_{zc}}\left(\frac{\partial \mathcal{V}_x}{\partial x_c}\frac{\partial \mathcal{V}_y}{\partial y_c} - \frac{\partial \mathcal{V}_x}{\partial y_c}\frac{\partial \mathcal{V}_y}{\partial x_c}\right) \tag{5.9}$$

The first term of this equation can be found by using the equation of conservation of energy, in the form

$$\mathcal{V}_z^2 = \mathcal{V}_{zc}^2 + \mathcal{V}_{xc}^2 + \mathcal{V}_{yc}^2 + \Upsilon - \mathcal{V}_y^2 - \mathcal{V}_x^2 \tag{5.10}$$

It follows that

$$\frac{\partial \mathcal{V}_z}{\partial \mathcal{V}_{zc}} = \frac{\mathcal{V}_{zc}}{\mathcal{V}_z} \tag{5.11}$$

The most convenient way to find the terms in parentheses in Eq. (5.9) is to use the relation inverse to Eq. (5.2):

$$\begin{bmatrix} w_c \\ v_{wc} \end{bmatrix} = e^{-2j\vartheta}\begin{bmatrix} \dot{\mathfrak{N}} & -\mathfrak{N} \\ -\dot{\mathfrak{M}} & \mathfrak{M} \end{bmatrix}\begin{bmatrix} w \\ v_w \end{bmatrix} \tag{5.12}$$

from this expression, it is found that

$$w_c = (\dot{\mathfrak{N}} w - \mathfrak{N} v_w)\exp(-2j\vartheta) \tag{5.13}$$

from which it can be shown that

$$v_x + jv_y = v_w = \frac{\dot{\mathfrak{N}} w - w_c \exp(2j\vartheta)}{\mathfrak{N}} \tag{5.14}$$

It follows from the Cauchy-Riemann relations [Eq. (2.5) of Appendix B] that the term in parentheses in Eq. (5.9) can be written in the form

$$\left(\frac{\partial \mathcal{V}_x}{\partial x_c}\right)^2 + \left(\frac{\partial \mathcal{V}_y}{\partial x_c}\right)^2 = \left|\left(\frac{\partial \mathcal{V}_w}{\partial x_c}\right)^2\right| = \left|\left(\frac{\partial \mathcal{V}_w}{\partial w_c}\right)^2\right| = 6^2\left(\frac{\partial v_w}{\partial w_c}\right)^2 \tag{5.15}$$

After substitution of Eqs. (5.15) and (5.11) in Eq. (5.9) it is found that

$$\mathcal{J} = \frac{\mathscr{b}^2}{N^2} \frac{\mathcal{V}_{zc}}{\mathcal{V}_z} \tag{5.16}$$

where $\mathscr{b}$ is the $[m/(2kT_c)]^{1/2}$ of Eq. (2.2).

By using Eqs. (5.6) and (5.16) and writing

$$dx_c \, dy_c = r_c \, dr_c \, d\varphi_c \tag{5.17}$$

Eq. (5.1) can be written in the form

$$i_z(r) = \frac{1}{\pi\sigma^2} \int_{r_c} i_c(r_c) \, dr_c \int_{\mathcal{V}_{zc}} \mathcal{V}_{zc} \exp(-\mathcal{V}_{zc}^2) \, d\mathcal{V}_{zc} \times \int_0^{2\pi} \exp\left\{-\left(\frac{r^2 + M^2 r_c^2 - 2Mr\, r_c \cos\varphi_c}{2\sigma^2}\right)\right\} d\varphi_c \tag{5.18}$$

where the new parameter

$$\sigma = \frac{|\mathfrak{N}|}{\sqrt{2}\,\mathscr{b}} = \frac{N}{\sqrt{2}\mathscr{b}} = N\left(\frac{kT_c}{m}\right)^{1/2} \tag{5.19}$$

is the mean deviation from the axis of a thermal electron leaving the cathode on the axis. This definition is in accordance with that of Cutler and Hines.[12] Equation (5.18) can be integrated with respect to φ_c by using the relation[6] $\int_0^{2\pi} \exp(a \cos\theta)\, d\theta = 2\pi I_0(a)$,* to yield the result

$$i_z(r) = \frac{2}{\sigma^2} \int_{r_c} i_c(r_c)\, r_c \exp -\left(\frac{M^2 r_c^2 + r^2}{2\sigma^2}\right) I_0\left(\frac{Mr\, r_c}{\sigma^2}\right) dr_c \times \int_{\mathcal{V}_{zc}} \mathcal{V}_{zc} \exp(-\mathcal{V}_{zc}^2)\, d\mathcal{V}_{zc} \tag{5.20}$$

The limits of the integral over r_c are determined by the inside and outside diameters of the cathode. For a cylindrical cathode of radius a, the limits of the integral are given by the relation $0 < r_c < a$.

The limits on $\mathcal{V}_{zc}$ are more difficult to determine. In Section 4 an analysis was given which allowed for these limits in determining the current density at the axis of the beam. It is possible to carry out a similar analysis in this case to find the limits on $\mathcal{V}_{zc}$. Such an analysis is extremely complicated because the values of $|w_c|$ and $|w|$ enter into the computation and make the algebra extremely unwieldy. Instead, we assume that the integral may be taken be-

*Here $I_0(a)$ is, as usual, the modified Bessel function of the first kinda zero order.

tween the limits $0 < \upsilon_{zc} < \infty$. The implications of this assumption are discussed in more detail below.

Equation (5.18) is now integrated between the limits $0 < \upsilon_{zc} < \infty$, yielding the result

$$i_z(r) = \frac{1}{\sigma^2} \int_{r_c} i_c(r_c)\, r_c\, I_0\left(\frac{Mr\, r_c}{\sigma^2}\right) \exp -\left(\frac{r^2 + M^2 r_c^2}{2\sigma^2}\right) dr_c \tag{5.21}$$

Equation (5.21) is the basic equation for the current density at any point of a cylindrical beam emitted from a thermal cathode. It is possible to compute M from the trajectories of the nonthermal electrons; N, and hence σ, can be determined either by integration of Eq. (3.20) or directly from the paraxial equation. Then it is only necessary to integrate Eq. (5.21) to find the current density at any point. In the case when $i_c(r_c) = i_{co}$ is uniform over the cathode of radius a, Eq. (5.21) becomes

$$i_z(r) = \frac{i_{co}}{\sigma^2} \exp\left(-\frac{r^2}{2\sigma^2}\right) \int_0^a r_c\, I_0\left(\frac{Mr\, r_c}{\sigma^2}\right) \exp\left(-\frac{r^2 + M^2 r_c^2}{2\sigma^2}\right) dr_c \tag{5.22}$$

We normalize by writing

$$R_e = \frac{aM}{\sigma} = \frac{r_e}{\sigma} \qquad R_c = \frac{r_c M}{\sigma} \qquad R = \frac{r}{\sigma} \tag{5.23}$$

The parameter $r = r_c M$ is the radius of the path of a nonthermal electron which leaves the radius r_c on the cathode at $t = 0$ and arrives at the plane at time t. With these substitutions, Eq. (5.20) becomes

$$i_z(r) = \frac{i_{co}}{M^2} \exp\left(-\frac{R^2}{2}\right) \int_0^{R_e} R_c\, I_0(RR_c) \exp\left(-\frac{R_c^2}{2}\right) dR_c \tag{5.24}$$

The expression $i_{co}/M^2 = i_{z0}$ is precisely the current density of the equivalent nonthermal beam. The ratio $i_z(r)/i_{z0}$ is plotted as a function of $R = r/\sigma$ for different values of $R_e = r_e/\sigma$ in Fig. 6.5a. These curves are also plotted in a different manner in Fig. 6.5b. In this figure $i_z(r)/i_{co}$ is plotted with respect to r/r_e for different values of r_e/σ. To show that $i_z(r)/i_{z0}$ is a function of two variables, we often refer to it as $i_z(r,a)/i_{z0}$. For large values of r_e/σ, the current density at the center of the beam remains the same as for the nonthermal beam, but for a value of $r_e/\sigma = \sqrt{2}$, the current density at the center of the beam is reduced to 62 per cent of its value without thermal velocities. We conclude that, when $r_e/\sigma \gg 1$, the current-density variation within the beam remains substantially the same as that for the nonthermal beam. The only difference is in the current-density variation near the edge of the beam, which is discussed in Sec. 5.3. It should be noted that, although the current-density variation can remain unchanged, the beam temperature is

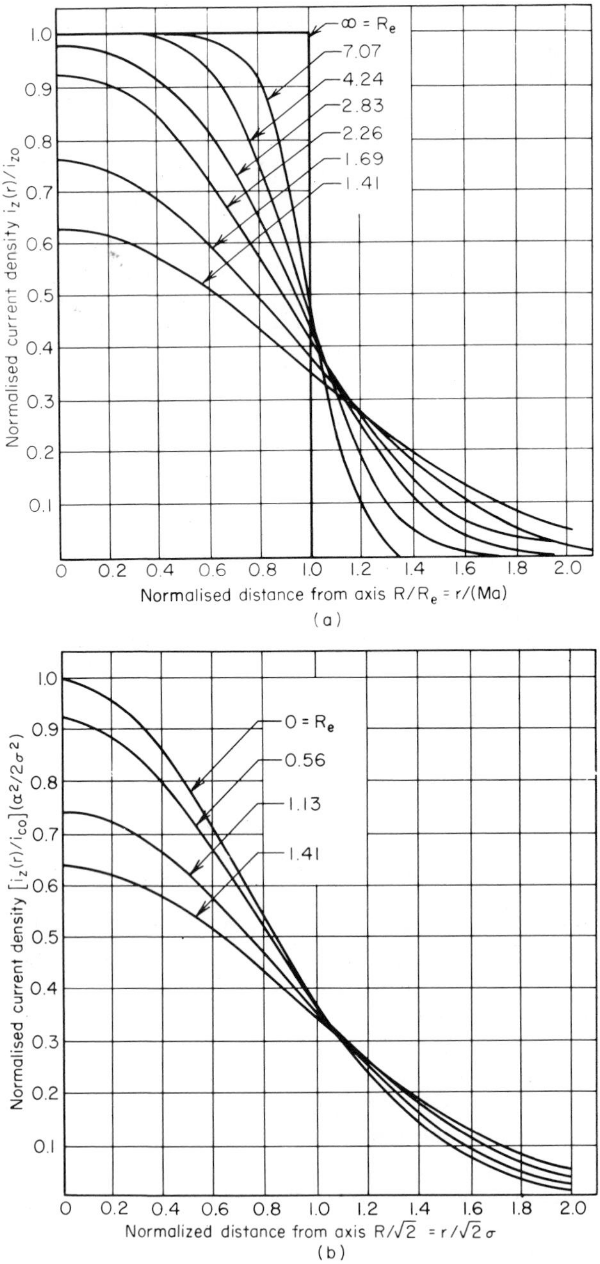

Fig. 6.5. Curves showing the character of the current-density variation in a cylindrical beam diffused by thermal velocities. (a) Curves suitable for $R_e \geq 1.41$; (b) curves suitable for highly convergent beams with $R_e \leq 1.41$. (Reproduced from Ref. 14, courtesy of the Institute of Electrical and Electronics Engineers.)

changed. It was shown in Sec. 3.2 that the temperature T at a plane z is $T = T_c(a/r_e)^2$. In many practical applications it is sufficient to treat the beam leaving the anode of a gun as being uniform in density, but with a temperature different from that at the cathode, the temperature being as given above.

It is interesting to compare the prediction of Eq. (5.22) for the current density at the center of the beam with the correct expression (4.22), obtained by evaluating the limits of the integration over $\mathcal{V}_{zc}$ properly. For R = 0, Eq. (5.24) can be integrated to show that

$$i_z(0) = \frac{i_{co}}{M^2}\left[1 - \exp\left(-\frac{M^2a^2}{2\sigma^2}\right)\right] \tag{5.25}$$

Equation (4.22) gives the result

$$i_z(0) = \frac{i_{co}}{M^2}\left[1 - (1 - M^2 \sin^2\alpha) \exp\left(-\frac{M^2 \sin^2\alpha}{1 - M^2\sin^2\alpha}\Upsilon\right)\right] \tag{5.26}$$

It follows from Eq. (4.25) that

$$\sin^2\alpha = \frac{a^2}{2N^2\phi\eta} = \frac{a^2}{2\sigma^2\Upsilon} \tag{5.27}$$

The two expressions yield the same value of current density if $M^2 \sin^2\alpha = (r_e/a)^2 \sin^2\alpha \ll 1$. This condition is usually satisfied for highly convergent beams. Thus, in most practical electron guns for use in beam-type tubes, it is possible to neglect the fact that the integration over the velocity in the z direction is taken from $0 < \mathcal{V}_z < \infty$ rather than over the correct, but more limited, range determined by the energy conditions.

It is seen also that, if $R_e = (r_e/\sigma) \ll 1$, it is possible to write $I_0(RR_c) \simeq 1$. In this case, Eq. (5.24) can be integrated to yield the result

$$i_z(r) = \frac{i_{co}}{M^2}\exp\left(-\frac{R^2}{2}\right)\left[1 - \exp\left(\frac{R_e^2}{2}\right)\right] \tag{5.28}$$

Thus, except for very large R, the current-density distribution is approximately Gaussian. This result, as has already been seen, is identically true when R_e and $M \to 0$, that is, at a crossover point. It is a good approximation to the truth for values of $R_e = r_e/\sigma < 1$.

It should be noted that it is very easy to determine the current density $i_z(r,a_1,a_2)$ in a hollow beam with uniform cathode current density and inner and outer radii of a_1 and a_2 by determining separately $i_z(r,a_1)$ for solid cathodes of these respective radii. The total current at radius r is

$$i_z(r,a_1,a_2) = i_z(r,a_2) - i_z(r,a_1) \tag{5.29}$$

Another situation of practical importance occurs when the current density at the cathode $i_c(r_c)$ is nonuniform. If it is assumed that the paraxial equations of flow give an accurate estimate for the form of the electron trajectories in this case, it is possible to use Eq. (5.22) to evaluate the current density at any point, whatever the form of $i_c(r_c)$. An example with nonuniform i_c is treated in Sec. 7.2 for a strip beam.

Another important quantity is the fraction of the total current $I_z(r)/I_z(\infty)$ inside the radius r. Here $I_z(r)$ is obtained by integrating Eq. (5.22) in the form, for uniform cathode current density,

$$I_z(r) = \frac{i_{c0}}{M^2} \int_0^r 2\pi r \exp\left(-\frac{r_1^2}{2\sigma^2}\right) dr_1 \int_0^{R_e} \left(\frac{r_c M}{\sigma}\right) I_0\left(\frac{Mr_c\, Mr_1}{\sigma^2}\right) \times \exp\left(-\frac{r_c^2 M^2}{2\sigma^2}\right) d\left(\frac{r_c M}{\sigma}\right) \tag{5.30}$$

Using the definitions of Eq. (5.23), Eq. (5.30) becomes

$$I_z(r) = I_z(\infty)\, \mathscr{I}(R, R_e) = I\mathscr{I}(R, R_e) \tag{5.31}$$

where I is the total current in the beam $i_c \pi a^2$ and

$$\mathscr{I}(R, R_e) = \frac{2}{R_e^2} \int_0^R R_1 \exp\left(-\frac{R_1^2}{2}\right) dR_1 \int_0^{R_e} R_c I_0(R_1 R_c) \exp\left(-\frac{R_c^2}{2}\right) dR_c \tag{5.32}$$

and R, R_e are given by Eq. (5.23). The $\mathscr{I}(R, R_e)$ form a two-parameter family of curves, plotted in Fig. 6.6.

5.3. The Density Variation for $r_e/\sigma \gg 1$. It is often of interest to determine the density variation near the beam edge of a well-collimated beam. For instance, if r_e/σ is large, then, as can be seen from Fig. 6.5a, the beam cross section is virtually that of a nonthermal beam. Nevertheless, the beam edge will have some thermal spread, and it is not possible to pass the beam through a hole in a diaphragm without losing a small fraction of the total beam current. In order to determine this fraction of current, it is necessary to determine how thermal velocities disperse the edge of the beam. By carrying out an integration of Eq. (5.24) for large R_e, for example, $(r_e/\sigma) > 10$, and using the asymptotic form of the Bessel function, it is possible to show that the current density is given by the formula

$$i_z(r) \simeq \frac{i_z(0)}{2}\left[1 - \operatorname{erf}\left(\frac{r - r_e}{\sqrt{2}\,\sigma}\right)\right] \tag{5.33a}$$

where erf y is the usual error function

$$\operatorname{erf} y = \frac{2}{\sqrt{\pi}} \int_0^y \exp(-t^2)\, dt \tag{5.34}$$

From its definition, it is clear that erf (−y) = −erf (y); therefore the solution for $r < r_e$ is more conveniently written

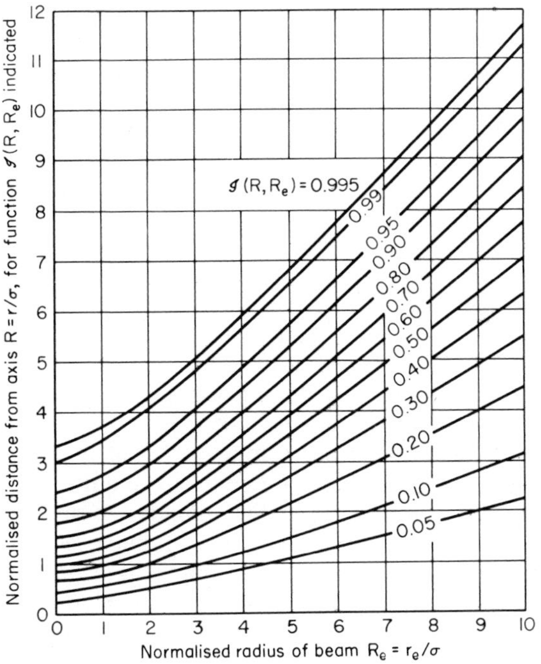

Fig. 6.6. Curve showing the fraction of the total beam current to be found within a radius r. (Reproduced from Ref. 15, courtesy of the *Bell System Technical Journal.*)

$$i_Z(r) \simeq \frac{i_Z(0)}{2}\left[1 + \operatorname{erf}\left(\frac{r_e - r}{\sqrt{2}\,\sigma}\right)\right] \tag{5.33b}$$

The approximation involved is clear from Eq. (5.28). If $r = 0$, the error is $[1 - \operatorname{erf}(r_e/\sqrt{2}\sigma)]$. It follows that the current density at the point corresponding to the edge of the nonthermal beam, if the beam is slightly diffused by thermal velocities, is one-half of the current density at its center. Equation (5.33a) shows that, for $(r - r_e)/\sigma = 2.58$, the current density is $i_Z(r) = 5 \times 10^{-3}\, i_Z(0)$. Using the approximate expression of Eq. (5.33a) for $i_Z(r)$, it is possible to find $I_Z(r)$, the current inside a radius r, by integration. After some algebra, the result is obtained, for $r > r_e$ and $r - r_e \gg \sigma$:

$$\begin{aligned} I_Z(r) &= \int_0^r 2\pi\, r_1 i_Z(r_1)\, dr_1 \\ &\simeq \pi i_Z(0)\,\sigma^2 \int_0^R R_1\left[1 - \operatorname{erf}\left(\frac{R_1 - R_e}{\sqrt{2}}\right)\right] dR_1 \\ &\simeq \pi i_Z(0)\,\sigma^2 R_e^2\left\{1 + \frac{1}{R_e^2} - \frac{\exp - [(R - R_e)^2/2]}{(2\pi)^{1/2} R_e^2 (R - R_e)}\right\} \end{aligned} \tag{5.35}$$

In deriving Eq. (5.35), the integral was performed exactly and the asymptotic expansion of Eq. (2.37a) was used both for erf $(R_e/\sqrt{2})$ and erf $[(R - R_e)/\sqrt{2}]$. The expression for $i_z(0)$ is itself in error by $\exp(-R_e^2/2)$, so that terms of this order were ignored. Finally, from Eq. (5.35), the following approximate expression for the $\mathcal{I}(R, R_e)$ of Eq. (5.31) is obtained:

$$\mathcal{I}(R, R_e) = \frac{I_z(r)}{I_z(\infty)} = 1 - \frac{\exp - [(R - R_e)^2/2]}{(2\pi)^{1/2}(R_e^2 + 1)(R - R_e)} \tag{5.36}$$

If, for example, we consider the previous example of $(r - r_e)/\sigma = R - R_e = 2.58$ and choose $r = 2r_e$, the value of the second term in Eq. (5.36) is 7×10^{-4}. If $R_e = 2.58$, but R is only 3.58, the second term is 3.2×10^{-2}. If the beam is passed through a diaphragm with space between the hole and the diaphragm $(r - r_e)$ of 2.58σ, equal to the nonthermal radius of the beam, only 0.07 per cent of the current is intercepted. If the same nonthermal radius of the beam is used, but $(r - r_e)/\sigma$ is only 1, then 3.24 per cent of the current will be intercepted. This result demonstrates that in order to reduce current intersection to extremely low values, the distance between the edge of the beam and the edge of a hole in a diaphragm through which it passes may be by no means negligible in comparison with the diameter of the beam, even at quite high voltages and with reasonable convergences.

6. SOME APPLICATIONS OF THE CYLINDRICAL-BEAM FORMULAS

6.1. Introduction. In Sections 4 and 5, expressions were derived for the current density in cylindrical beams. These expressions require the evaluation of the two parameters, the M and N of Eqs. (3.1) and (3.4b). In this section, the parameters are evaluated for several important applications.

In Sec. 6.2, we consider a beam from a shielded gun which suddenly enters a high magnetic field. In the analysis, space-charge effects are neglected. Another application, treated in Sec. 6.3, is that of a beam from an immersed parallel-flow gun, in which the magnetic field is increased adiabatically.

A focusing system frequently used is the Brillouin focusing system of Sections 3 and 4 of Chap. IV. In Sec. 6.4, the thermal spread of a beam in such a focusing system is discussed, both when the beam enters correctly (an unrippled beam) and when it is launched incorrectly (so that a rippled Brillouin beam results). Finally, in Sec. 6.5, expressions are derived for the increased spread in a drifting beam due to thermal effects.

In all the analyses of this section, it is assumed that the change in charge density caused by thermal effects does not appreciably affect the space-charge fields. A higher-order theory, which takes these changes into account, is developed in Section 8.

6.2. The Properties of a Cylindrical Beam Emitted from a Shielded Gun. It has been shown in Chap. IV that, under ideal conditions, in the absence of thermal effects, the minimum magnetic field required to focus a beam of given diameter is the Brillouin field. If thermal-velocity effects are present, it is necessary to use a higher magnetic field to obtain a beam in which a given fraction, e.g., 95 per cent, of the current is focused within a given diameter. It has been common practice to use a magnetic field several times the Brillouin value. In these circumstances, the effect of space charge becomes relatively unimportant, and the beam, even in the absence of thermal electrons, is highly nonlaminar.

We consider in this section the dynamics of such a beam, both with and without thermal electrons present. Space-charge fields are ignored, so that there are no electrostatic fields present, and the potential throughout the beam after it leaves the gun is uniform. Consequently, any differences in the longitudinal velocities of the individual electrons arise because their transverse velocities are different, although their total energies are the same. This effect is taken into account in determining the behavior of the beam, even though the longitudinal velocities of the individual electrons are different.

It was shown, in Eq. (5.36) of Chap. III, that the motion of the electrons in a uniform magnetic field B_0, when space charge is negligible, is given by the relation

$$\begin{pmatrix} w(t) \\ v_w(t) \end{pmatrix} = \begin{bmatrix} 1 & \frac{j}{2\omega_L}[1 - \exp(2j\omega_L t)] \\ 0 & \exp(2j\omega_L t) \end{bmatrix} \begin{pmatrix} w(0) \\ v_w(0) \end{pmatrix} \tag{6.1}$$

We assume that electrons enter this uniform magnetic field region from a gun which is perfectly shielded and that the magnetic field begins very suddenly at the plane $z = 0$, which is the anode of the gun. An electron entering at the point $w(0)$ with a transverse velocity $v_w(0)$ crosses magnetic field lines, so that it will suddenly receive an extra spin about the axis of the Larmor frequency ω_L in addition to its original transverse velocity. If the field is regarded as beginning infinitely suddenly, the radial position of an electron will be unchanged as it passes through the plane $z = 0$. It follows that

$$\begin{bmatrix} w^+(0) \\ v_w^+(0) \end{bmatrix} = \begin{bmatrix} 1 & 0 \\ j\omega_L & 1 \end{bmatrix} \begin{bmatrix} w^-(0) \\ v_w^-(0) \end{bmatrix} \tag{6.2}$$

where the superscripts + and − are used to indicate the value of v_w in regions just beyond and just before the plane $z = 0$.

Substituting Eq. (6.2) in Eq. (6.1) and taking the product of the matrices then yields the result

$$\begin{bmatrix} w(t) \\ v_w(t) \end{bmatrix} = \exp(j\omega_L t) \begin{bmatrix} \cos(\omega_L t) & \dfrac{\sin(\omega_L t)}{\omega_L} \\ j\omega_L \exp(j\omega_L t) & \exp(j\omega_L t) \end{bmatrix} \begin{bmatrix} w^-(0) \\ v_w^-(0) \end{bmatrix} \tag{6.3}$$

An electron entering this uniform magnetic field region at a radial position $r = r_0 = |w^-(0)|$ with no transverse component of velocity is a nonthermal electron. For this electron $v_w^-(0) = 0$, so that, from Eq. (6.3),

$$r(t) = |w| = r_0 \,|\cos(\omega_L t)| \tag{6.4}$$

At times given by $\omega_L t = (n + \frac{1}{2})\pi$, all nonthermal electrons cross the axis, whatever their initial radial position. This does not imply that all the electrons cross at one point on the axis. If the applied potential is ϕ_0, it follows, from Eq. (6.3), that the longitudinal velocity v_z of an electron is given by the relation

$$v_z^2 + \omega_L^2 [w(0)]^2 = 2\eta\phi_0$$

or

$$v_z^2 + \omega_L^2 r_0^2 = 2\eta\phi_0 \tag{6.5}$$

where ϕ_0 is the applied potential in the uniform magnetic field region. Thus different electrons entering at different radial positions have different longitudinal velocities. The axial position z, which an electron reaches after a time t, is

$$z = v_z t = t(2\eta\phi_0 - r_0^2\omega_L^2)^{1/2} \tag{6.6}$$

An electron entering at radius r_0 crosses the axis at a position given by

$$z = \left(n + \frac{1}{2}\right)\frac{\pi}{\omega_L}(2\eta\phi_0 - \omega_L^2 r_0^2)^{1/2} \tag{6.7}$$

Individual electrons do not cross the axis at the same point; the crossover points become farther apart for electrons starting at different radial positions, as the distance along the beam is increased. Consequently, even in the absence of thermals the beam is nonlaminar.

The density profile of a thermally spread beam can be determined by using Eq. (5.24), which was derived from Liouville's theorem. With no thermal electrons present, it is possible, by making the assumption that σ approaches zero, to derive the required results directly. We adopt an easier method, however, using the equation of continuity of current.

Let the current density at the plane $z = 0$ be $i_{z0}(r_0)$ at a radius r_0, and the radius of the electrons, which were at radius r_0 at $t = 0$, be r after time t. Then the total current flowing through a ring between r and r + dr must be equal to the total current leaving the ring between r_0 and $r_0 + dr_0$ at time t = 0. It follows that, since current must be conserved,

$$2\pi r i_z(r)\, dr = 2\pi r_0 i_{z0}(r_0)\, dr_0 \tag{6.8a}$$

or

$$i_z(r) = \frac{r_0}{r} i_{z0}(r_0) \frac{dr_0}{dr} \tag{6.8b}$$

The substitution of Eq. (6.4) in (6.8b) then yields the result

$$i_z(r) = \frac{i_{z0}(r_0)}{\cos(\omega_L t)[\cos(\omega_L t) - \omega_L r_0 \sin(\omega_L t)\,(dt/dr_0)]} \tag{6.9}$$

To write this expression in terms of the distance z along the axis, it is convenient to call the velocity of the electrons which enter at the center of the beam v_0, where $v_0^2 = 2\eta\phi_0$. We assume that, for all electrons, $v_0^2 \gg r_0^2\omega_L^2$, that is, that the transverse energy of the electrons is much less than their longitudinal energy. In this case, from Eq. (6.6),

$$t \simeq \frac{z}{v_0}\left(1 + \frac{\omega_L^2 r_0^2}{2v_0^2}\right) \tag{6.10}$$

from which it follows that

$$\frac{dt}{dr_0} = \frac{\omega_L^2 r_0 z}{v_0^3} \tag{6.11}$$

Equations (6.10) and (6.11) can be substituted in Eq. (6.9) to yield the result

$$i_z(r) = i_{z0}(r_0)\left| \cos\left(\beta_L z + \frac{pr_0^2}{2a^2}\right)\left[\cos\left(\beta_L z + \frac{pr_0^2}{2a^2}\right) - \frac{pr_0^2}{a^2}\sin\left(\beta_L z + \frac{pr_0^2}{2a^2}\right)\right]\right|^{-1} \tag{6.12}$$

where $\beta_L = \omega_L/v_0$, which can be called the Larmor wave number, a is taken to be the outer radius of the beam, and $p = \beta_L^3 a^2 z$ is the total phase shift between the center and the outer edge of the beam at the plane z. If the phase difference between the outside and the inside of the beam is assumed negligible, that is, $p \simeq 0$, then $i_z(r)$ becomes infinite when $\cos \beta_L z = 0$, i.e., at the crossover points, as might be expected.

If the current density distribution $i_0(r_0)$ at the plane z = 0 is known, it is possible to calculate the current density distribution at any other plane by using Eq. (6.12). For the case when p = 0 and the current density is uniform at z = 0, the beam density distribution for different values of $\beta_L z$ is shown by the dotted lines in Fig. 6.7. For $\beta_L z = 0$, the beam is of uniform density and radius a. At other planes the beam successively broadens and diminishes in diameter, re-

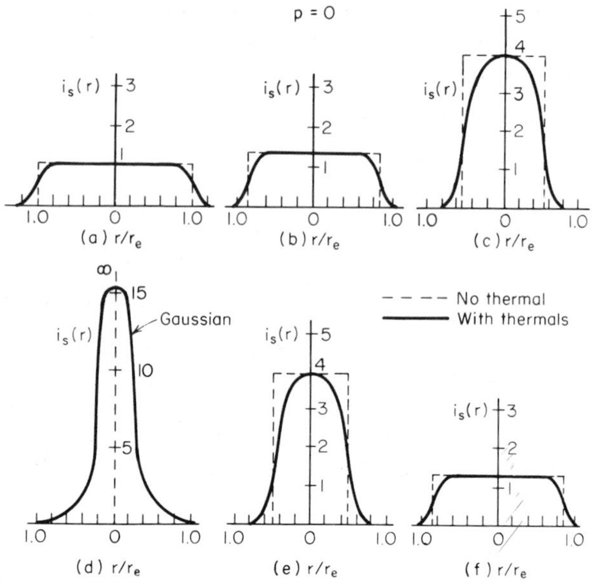

Fig. 6.7. The calculated current density distribution with and without thermals for the case of zero-phase shift p = 0 at different planes z through one rippling wavelength. (a) $\beta_L z = 0$; (b) $\beta_L z = \pi/3$; (c) $\beta_L z = 2\pi/3$; (d) $\beta_L z = \pi$; (e) $\beta_L z = 4\pi/3$; (f) $\beta_L z = 5\pi/3$. (Reproduced from Ref. 13, courtesy of the American Institute of Physics.)

maining of uniform density, although at the crossover points its density becomes infinite. When $p \neq 0$, so that there is a $\pi/2$ phase delay between the inside and outside electrons of the beam, the current density distribution of Fig. 6.8 results. In this case, the beam shape is shown by the dotted lines, as before, for the different values of $\beta_L z$. Overtaking of one electron by another considerably alters the form of the beam. The situation becomes still more extreme for larger values of phase difference. This is seen, for instance, for the situation depicted in Fig. 6.9, with $p = 2\pi$.

For very large distances from the cathode, the current density may have more than one peak, as when there are several rings of charge which coincide at p = 0 but move through the beam as p increases. The picture becomes increasingly more complicated for large values of p. Near the origin the electrons cross virtually at one point. Farther from it, the points where the electrons cross the axis are different, because there are more crossovers of electron trajectories as the distance from the origin increases.

When there are thermal electrons present, Eq. (5.21) must be used to determine the current at the plane z. In this case we write, using the definition of Eq. (5.19),

$$\sigma^2 = \frac{N^2}{2\mathscr{E}} = \frac{kT \sin^2 \omega_L t}{m\omega_L^2} \tag{6.13}$$

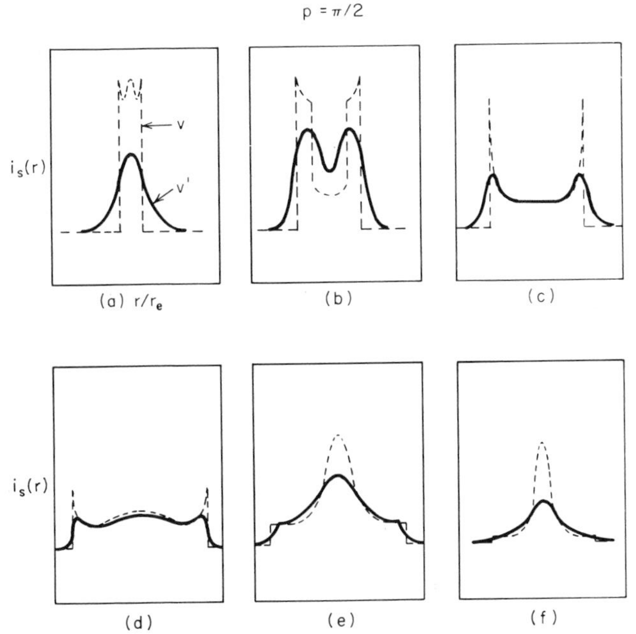

Fig. 6.8. The calculated current density distribution with and without thermals for the case of $p = \pi/2$, at different planes s through one rippling wavelength. (a) $\beta_L z = 2\pi/3$; (b) $\beta_L z = \pi/3$; (c) $\beta_L z = 0$; (d) $\beta_L z = 5\pi/3$; (e) $\beta_L z = 4\pi/3$; (f) $\beta_L z = \pi$. (Reproduced from Ref. 13, courtesy of the American Institute of Physics.)

where T is the temperature of the electrons at the entrance plane $z = 0$, and N is given by Eq. (6.3). It is necessary to substitute for the time t in terms of z, as was done in the zero-temperature case. If Eqs. (6.10) and (6.13) are substituted into Eq. (5.24) to find an expression for the current density at any radius, a complicated, but nevertheless integrable, expression is obtained.

The resultant expression has been evaluated by Ashkin.[13] For the three cases already described, the current densities as a function of radius are plotted as full lines in Figs. 6.7 to 6.10, to compare with the zero-temperature situation.

As might be expected, when $p = 0$, i.e., when there is no phase shift between the outside and inside electrons, the presence of thermals tends to spread the beam out slightly. A Gaussian variation of density is formed at the crossover plane, and the density variation is rounded off at the edges of the beam at other planes. When $p = \pi/2$, the density variation is somewhat similar to that at zero temperature, except that the peaks are rounded off. This result should be compared with the results shown in Fig. 6.10, which are experimental measurements taken under the same conditions as given by the theory. There is excellent agreement between the

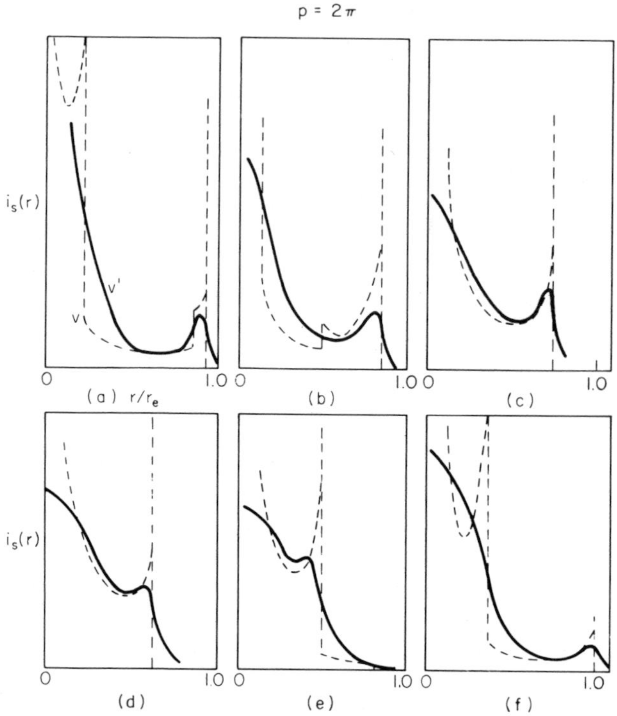

6.9. The calculated current density distribution with and without thermals for six different planes z through one rippling wavelength. (a) $\beta_L z = \pi/3$; (b) $\beta_L z = 2\pi/3$; (c) $\beta_L z = \pi$; (d) $\beta_L z = 4\pi/3$; (e) $\beta_L z = 5\pi/3$; (f) $\beta_L z = 0$. (Reproduced from Ref. 13, courtesy of the American Institute of Physics.)

theory and the experiment, thus giving us confidence in the theoretical results. For the case of still larger p, with p = 2π, the density variations become far less extreme with thermals than without thermals. For large distances along the beam, the scalloping effect tends to be washed out by the presence of the thermals.

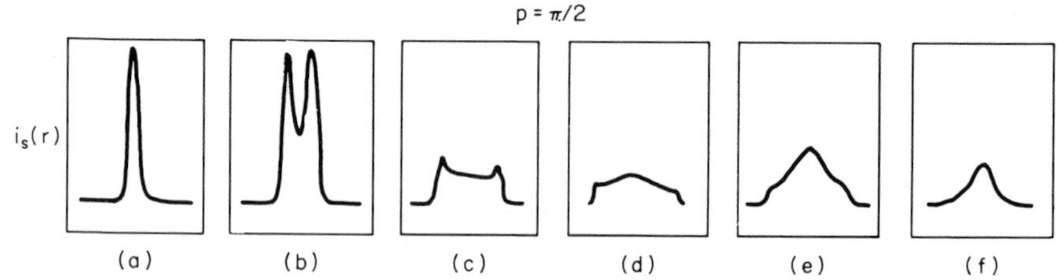

Fig. 6.10. Experimental current density distribution for λ/2 phase shift, p = π/12, measured at different planes s through one rippling wavelength. (a) $\beta_L z = 2\pi/3$; (b) $\beta_L z = \pi/3$; (c) $\beta_L z = 0$; (d) $\beta_L z = 5\pi/3$; (e) $\beta_L z = 4\pi/3$; (f) $\beta_L z = \pi$. (Reproduced from Ref. 13, courtesy of the American Institute of Physics.)

The same theory can be carried out in the case when there is a magnetic field at the cathode, but it is still more complicated. One big difference would be, of course, that nonthermal electrons could not cross the axis. When there are thermals present, some electrons can cross the axis, but not as many as before. The use of this property yields a very sensitive test of whether there is magnetic field at the cathode. The scalloping of the beam is measured, and the point where the current density appears to be a maximum at the axis is determined. A slight change in magnetic field at the cathode radically affects the axial current density at this point. Consequently, by this means it is possible to detect magnetic fields at the cathode of the order of a few gauss, in comparison with a total field of several hundred gauss.

6.3. The Properties of a Thermally Diffused Cylindrical Beam in a Planar Diode. It is apparent from the formulas derived in Section 5 that the beam emitted from a shielded cathode tends to diffuse radially as the distance from the cathode increases. If, on the other hand, the cathode is immersed in a uniform magnetic field, normal to the cathode, it would be expected that the radial diffusion of electrons due to thermal velocities would be inhibited. Physically, we should expect that the radius of gyration of a thermal electron, about the path of a nonthermal electron emitted from the same point, is of the order v_T/ω_H; here v_T is the transverse velocity of the electron emitted from the cathode, and the projection of the electron path on the cathode is of the form shown in Fig. 6.11. Thus, if, at least for most of the electrons, v_T/ω_H were very small compared with the radius of the beam, not much thermal spreading of the beam would be expected. In this section, we give a more exact analysis, which makes it possible to place this hypothesis on a quantitative basis, and also illustrates the use of the formulas derived in earlier sections.

We consider a beam emitted from a cathode of radius a immersed in a uniform magnetic field of Larmor frequency ω_L. If the gun is a

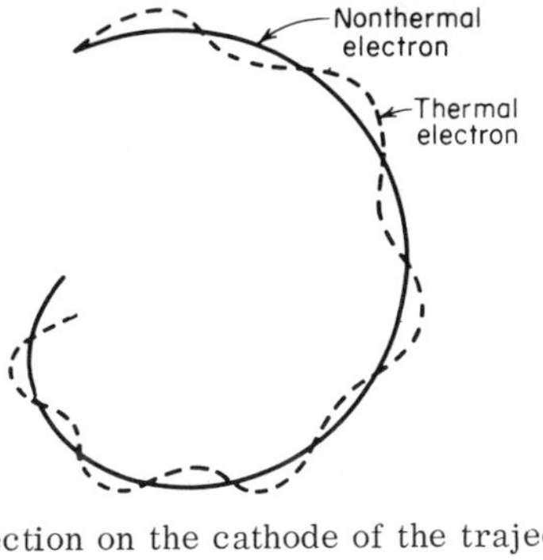

Fig. 6.11. The projection on the cathode of the trajectory of a particle in a magnetic field.

Pierce gun, designed so that the beam is in rectilinear flow, the trajectory of a nonthermal electron is a constant distance from the axis. Thus the magnification $\mathfrak{M}$ is unity. The parameter $\mathfrak{N}$ is, from Eq. (3.16),

$$\mathfrak{N} = \mathfrak{M} \int_0^t \frac{\exp(2j\vartheta)}{\mathfrak{M}^2}\, dt \qquad \text{where } \vartheta = \int \omega_L\, dt \tag{6.14a}$$

or

$$\mathfrak{N} = \frac{\exp(2j\omega_L t) - 1}{2j\omega_L} \tag{6.14b}$$

The $\mathfrak{N}$ of Eq. (6.14b) is exactly that of Eq. (5.36) of Chap. III. This is because, for the case considered here, there is no radial electrostatic field. Thus the results without space charge and no radial field correspond to the results with space charge and acceleration terms which cancel out the space charge field terms.

In order to evaluate the current density at any point, it is necessary to know the parameters M and σ of Eq. (5.22). From Eqs. (5.19) and (6.14) it is seen that

$$\sigma = \left(\frac{kT_c}{m}\right)^{1/2} \tag{6.15a}$$

$$\sigma = \left(\frac{kT_c}{m}\right)^{1/2} \frac{|\sin(\omega_L t)|}{\omega_L} \tag{6.15b}$$

For this gun, M = 1 and $r_e = a$, so that the R_e of Eq. (5.23) is given by

$$\frac{r_e}{\sigma} = \frac{aM}{\sigma} = \frac{\omega_L a}{|\sin(\omega_L t)|}\left(\frac{m}{kT_c}\right)^{1/2} \tag{6.16}$$

The transit time t of an electron in the gun can be determined easily from the relations for the plane diode given in Sec. 2.2 of Chap. II. It is apparent, however, that the maximum value of (r_e/σ) is $(r_e/\sigma)_M = \infty$. The minimum value of (r_e/σ) is $(r_e/\sigma)_m = \omega_L a(m/kT_c)^{-1/2}$. At any plane z, the profile of the beam can be determined by using Eq. (5.24). The possible beam shapes have been plotted in terms of r_e/σ in Fig. 6.5a and 6.5b.

It was shown in Section 5 that there is very little thermal spread for large values of r_e/σ. From the above physical reasoning, it is apparent that, when $\omega_L a(m/kT_c)^{-1/2} \gg 1$, i.e., is greater than about 10, the thermal spread of the beam is negligible.

It is interesting to consider what happens if the magnetic field is tapered to increase the beam density after the beam leaves the gun. We consider here a simplified case in which it is assumed that:

1. The gun is gridded; so there are no lens effects at the anode of the gun.

2. The magnetic field is so strong that space charge may be ignored after the beam leaves the gun.

3. The tapering is so slow that the nonthermal beam decreases in diameter adiabatically; i.e.; the nonthermal electrons follow magnetic field lines.

Because magnetic flux must be conserved, that is, $\nabla \cdot \mathbf{B} = 0$, it follows that, for a slow taper of the magnetic field,

$$r^2 B = \text{constant} \tag{6.17}$$

where r is the radius of a particular flux line along which a nonthermal electron moves.

Consequently, for a nonthermal electron leaving the edge of the cathode,

$$r_e^2 \omega_L = a^2 \omega_{Lc} \tag{6.18}$$

where ω_{Lc} is the Larmor frequency of the magnetic field at the cathode. It follows from Eq. (6.18) that

$$\mathfrak{M} = \left(\frac{\omega_{Lc}}{\omega_L}\right)^{1/2} \tag{6.19}$$

From Eq. (6.14a) $\mathfrak{N}$ is given by

$$\mathfrak{N} = \left(\frac{\omega_{Lc}}{\omega_L}\right)^{1/2} \int_0^{\vartheta} \exp(2j\vartheta) \frac{d\vartheta}{\omega_{Lc}} \tag{6.20a}$$

so that

$$N = |\mathfrak{N}| = (\omega_L \omega_{Lc})^{-1/2} \left| \frac{1}{2j} [\exp(2j\vartheta) - 1] \right| = (\omega_{Lc} \omega_L)^{-1/2} |\sin \vartheta| \tag{6.20b}$$

The value of r_e/σ is found by substituting Eqs. (6.18) and (6.20b) in (6.15a):

$$\frac{r_e}{\sigma} = \frac{a\omega_{Lc}}{|\sin \vartheta|} \left(\frac{m}{kT_c}\right)^{1/2} \tag{6.21}$$

Equation (6.21) demonstrates the important result that the minimum value of r_e/σ is unaltered by adiabatic tapering of the magnetic field; at the points where $\vartheta = (n + 1)\pi/2$, if space charge is ignored, the beam profile remains unaltered.

The current density at the center of the beam, $i_z(0)$, may be found by using Eqs. (5.25) and (6.21):

$$i_z(0) = i_{co} \frac{\omega_L}{\omega_{Lc}} \left[1 - \exp\left(-\frac{1}{2} \frac{m}{kT_c} a^2 \omega_{Lc}^2\right)\right] \tag{6.22}$$

Thus, in order to obtain the maximum current density at the center of the beam, it is necessary to have a sufficiently large magnetic field at the cathode, to make the second term in Eq. (6.22) negligible. In this case, as might be expected, the current density within the beam is

$$i_z(0) = i_{co} \frac{\omega_L}{\omega_{Lc}} \tag{6.23}$$

It should be noted that the conditions obtained here are independent of the applied potential. In this case, the applied potential becomes important only when it is so small that the conditions on longitudinal velocities, required by the paraxial equation, are no longer valid.

6.4. The Properties of a Thermally Diffused Cylindrical Beam in a Brillouin Focusing System. It is not difficult to apply the formalism of Section 5 to a beam which enters a Brillouin focusing system so that no rippling occurs. As an exercise, we consider now both an unrippled and a slightly rippled Brillouin beam.

In order to determine the M and N of Eqs. (5.18) and (5.19), it is simplest to determine first the μ and ν of Eqs. (5.22) of Chap. III; the M and N can be deduced from these μ and ν by using Eq. (5.31) of Chap. III; i.e.,

$$M = (\mu^2 + \nu^2 \omega_{L0}^2)^{1/2} \qquad \text{and} \qquad N = \nu \tag{6.24}$$

Using Eqs. (5.2) and (5.12) of Chap. III and remembering that, in a Brillouin focusing system, the potential of the beam is a constant ϕ_0, we see that μ and ν satisfy

$$\ddot{\Gamma} + \Gamma\,(\omega_{L0}^2 - \tfrac{1}{2}\omega_p^2) = 0 \tag{6.25}$$

where ω_{L0} and ω_p are the Larmor and plasma frequencies

$$\omega_L = \omega_{L0} = \eta B_0 \qquad \text{and} \qquad \omega_p^2 = -\frac{\eta\rho_0}{\epsilon_0} \tag{6.26}$$

where B_0 is the constant Brillouin field.

From Eqs. (5.19) to (5.22) of Chap. III, the μ and ν are the solutions of Eq. (6.25), satisfying

$$\dot{\Gamma}(0) = 0 \qquad \text{and} \qquad \Gamma(t) = \mu(t) \qquad \text{if } \Gamma(0) = 1 \tag{6.27a}$$

and

$$\dot{\Gamma}(0) = 1 \qquad \text{and} \qquad \Gamma(t) = \nu(t) \qquad \text{if } \Gamma(0) = 0 \tag{6.27b}$$

If it is assumed that the nonthermal beam has no rippling, ρ_0 is a constant ρ_{00}, and therefore

$$\omega_p^2 = \omega_{p0}^2 = 2\omega_{L0}^2 \tag{6.28}$$

The μ and ν in this case are the simple functions, from Eqs. (6.25) and (6.27),

$$\mu(t) = 1 \qquad \nu(t) = t$$

The M and N are therefore

$$M = (1 + \omega_{L0}^2 t^2)^{1/2} \qquad \text{and} \qquad N = t \tag{6.29}$$

and the formalism of Sections 4 and 5 can be applied. Note that, even though the beam edge remains at a constant radius, M is not unity.

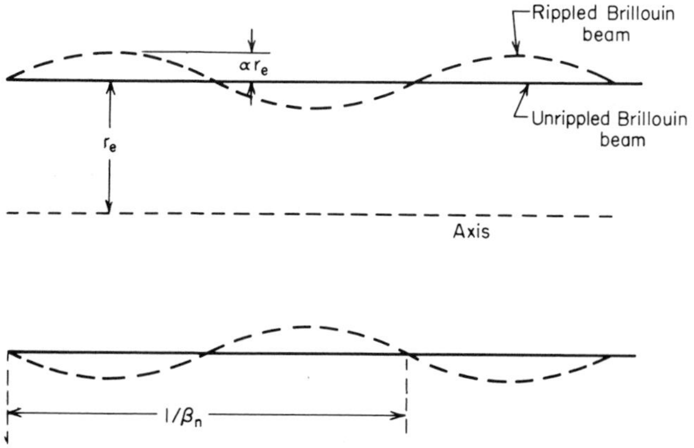

Fig. 6.12. The beam edge of rippled and unrippled beams in a uniform axial magnetic field.

The difference arises because the electron at the beam edge has an initial angular velocity ω_{L0}.

If there is beam rippling, ω_p is no longer constant, and the problem becomes more difficult. It is necessary to obtain, first, the nonthermal radius of the beam. This radius can be used to derive ω_p^2. Using the ω_p, Eq. (6.25) can be integrated, so that μ and ν are found.

In the general case, the algebra becomes very involved. If, however, the rippling is small, the M and N can be found in terms of elementary functions. The equation for the radius of the beam as a function of position has been derived in Sec. 4.3 of Chap. IV. If r_e and r_b are the two special radii defined by Eqs. (4.3) to (4.6) of Chap. IV, the radius of the nonthermal beam is, for small rippling,

$$r = r_e + r_1 \tag{6.30}$$

where, from Eq. (4.17) of Chap. IV,

$$\ddot{r}_1 + r_1\omega_n^2 = 0 \tag{6.31}$$

and
$$\omega_n^2 = 4\omega_{L0}^2\left(1 - \frac{r_b^2}{2r_e^2}\right) \tag{6.32}$$

A solution of Eqs. (6.30) to (6.32) is

$$r = r_e\,(1 + \alpha \cos \omega_n t) \tag{6.33}$$

where α is the rippling factor, which is assumed to be small. The beam edge is sketched in Fig. 6.12. Note that it is possible, since the axial velocity is constant, to transfer from time to axial distance as independent variable by using

$$\beta = \frac{\omega}{(2\eta\phi_0)^{1/2}} \tag{6.34}$$

where β and ω can be written β_n, ω_n or β_p, ω_p, etc. If the beam edge is given by Eq. (6.33), ρ_0, and therefore ω_p, are given by

$$\omega_p^2 = -\frac{\eta\rho_0}{\epsilon_0} = \omega_{p0}^2 \frac{r_e^2}{r^2} = 2\omega_{L0}^2 \left[1 - 2\alpha \cos(\omega_n t)\right] \tag{6.35}$$

Using the ω_p of Eq. (6.35), Eq. (6.25) becomes

$$\ddot{\Gamma} + \Gamma\left[2\alpha\omega_{L0}^2 \cos(\omega_n t)\right] = 0 \tag{6.36}$$

where ω_n is given by Eq. (6.32).

Equation (6.36) is the Mathieu equation, discussed in Appendix D. For small α it can be verified that the solutions of Eq. (6.36) which satisfy Eqs. (6.27a) and (6.27b) are

$$\Gamma(t) = \mu(t) = 1 - 2\alpha \frac{\omega_{L0}^2}{\omega_n^2}\left[1 - \cos(\omega_n t)\right] \tag{6.37a}$$

and

$$\Gamma(t) = \nu(t) = t + \frac{2\alpha\omega_{L0}^2}{\omega_n^2}\left[t \cos(\omega_n t) - t - \frac{2}{\omega_n}\sin(\omega_n t)\right] \tag{6.37b}$$

From Eq. (6.24), N is the modulus of the right side of Eq. (6.37b), and M is given by

$$M = (1 + \omega_{L0}^2 t^2)^{1/2}\left\{1 - 2\alpha\frac{\omega_{L0}^2}{\omega_n^2}\left[1 - \cos(\omega_n t) - \frac{2\,\omega_{L0}^4 t \sin(\omega_n t)}{\omega_n^3(1 + \omega_{L0}^2 t^2)}\right]\right\} \tag{6.38}$$

Thermal effects in rippled Brillouin beams can be estimated from Eqs. (5.19), (5.23), and (5.24), with the M and N of Eqs. (6.37b) and (6.38). Note that, in the limiting case of $\alpha \to 0$, the expressions for M and N reduce simply to the expressions in the unrippled beam [Eq. (6.29)].

6.5. A Linear Treatment of the Thermal Spread in a Round Drifting Beam. A last example, which is of practical use, is the thermal spread in a drifting beam. In the absence of thermal effects, this problem has been treated in Sec. 3.10. It was shown that the spread of a beam, initially parallel and of radius r_0, follows the law [Eqs. (10.3) and (10.4) of Chap. III]

$$k\frac{z}{r_0} = F(r) \tag{6.39}$$

$$k^2 = \frac{P}{8\pi\epsilon_0(2\eta)^{1/2}} = 7.6 \times 10^{-3}\,P \tag{6.40}$$

where P is in micropervs and

$$F(r) = \int_0^{\log(r/r_0)} \exp(u^2)\,du \tag{6.41}$$

Here it is assumed that the current density is uniform across the beam, there is no magnetic field, and the initial plane is at the waist of the beam.

It can be shown by a series expansion that a good approximation to Eqs. (6.39) and (6.41) is

$$M = \frac{r}{r_0} = 1 + K^2 \tag{6.42}$$

where $$K = \frac{kz}{r_0} \tag{6.43}$$

This expression is in error by 8 per cent for $kz = r_0$.

Since we assume there is no magnetic field, the r/r_0 of Eq. (6.42) gives M directly. The axial velocity is a constant, $(2\eta\phi_0)^{1/2}$, so that N is given, from Eq. (3.20), by

$$\begin{aligned} N &= \left[1 + \left(\frac{kz}{r_0}\right)^2\right] \int_0^z \frac{1}{(2\eta\phi_0)^{1/2}} \left[1 + \left(\frac{kz_1}{r_0}\right)^2\right]^{-2} dz_1 \\ &= \frac{z/2}{(2\eta\phi_0)^{1/2}} \left(1 + \frac{1 + K^2}{K} \tan^{-1} K\right) \end{aligned} \tag{6.44}$$

The integral leading to Eq. (6.44) can be found in Ref. 7.

With the M and N of Eqs. (6.42) and (6.44), it is again possible to use the methods of Section 5; in particular, i(r) can be found from Fig. 6.5.

In all the analyses of Section 6, it is assumed that the thermal-velocity effects do not affect the space-charge fields. The higher-order theory, taking changes in the space-charge fields into account, is considered in Section 8.

7. THE CURRENT DENSITY AT ANY POINT IN A SHEET BEAM

7.1. Introduction. If the beam is axially symmetric, the most useful applications in practice are the ones in which the axis is rectilinear. In sheet beams, however, curvilinear axes are usually employed. In curvilinear beams there is a coupling between the longitudinal and transverse motion, which leads to awkward algebraic complexity. In the examples given in this section, the coupling is ignored. For this reason, the treatment is valid only when the central trajectory is rectilinear in the gun region. If the beam is accelerated in a straight line until the longitudinal velocity is much greater than the longitudinal velocity spread, the theory is valid even if the beam is later curvilinear. The discussion is limited, in this section, to a linear paraxial treatment. A nonlinear correction, to allow for the fact that thermal spreading affects the space-charge fields, is given in Section 8. The extension to a linear treatment of thick beams is discussed in Ref. 11. In Sec. 7.2 the general expressions for the current density in a sheet beam are derived. The particular case where there is a linear (with its special case of constant) cathode current density is integrated explicitly. In Sec. 7.3 one application is considered, the spreading of a sheet beam when both space-charge spreading and thermal effects are taken into account.

7.2. The Basic Integration to Compute Final Current Densities. If the coupling between longitudinal and transverse velocities is ignored, the derivation of $i_s(r)$ follows exactly the same lines as that of Sec. 5.2 for cylindrical beams.* Although the derivation with arbitrary magnetic field is possible, for algebraic simplicity the problem of Section 6 of Chap. III will be considered. In this case the flow is uniform in the z direction, and the magnetic field is a constant B directed in the z direction. Under these conditions the r and v_r at the plane s are related to their values at the initial plane by the relation [Eqs. (3.1) to (3.4)]

$$\begin{pmatrix} r \\ v_r \end{pmatrix} = \begin{pmatrix} \mathfrak{M} & \mathfrak{N} \\ \dot{\mathfrak{M}} & \dot{\mathfrak{N}} \end{pmatrix} \begin{pmatrix} r(0) \\ v_r(0) \end{pmatrix} \tag{7.1}$$

where $\mathfrak{M}\dot{\mathfrak{N}} - \dot{\mathfrak{M}}\mathfrak{N} = 1$ (7.2)

and $v_r = \dot{r}$ (7.3)

In this section, the same assumptions are made as in Section 6 of Chap. III. The coordinate system is (s,r,z), and the beam parameters do not depend on z. The magnetic field is (0,0,B), where B is a constant. The explicit expressions for $\mathfrak{M}$, $\mathfrak{N}$, $\dot{\mathfrak{M}}$, $\dot{\mathfrak{N}}$ can be obtained from Eqs. (6.23) to (6.25) of Chap. III.

The expression for the current density [Eq. (5.1)] can be integrated immediately once over v_{zc}, since i_c depends only on r. The expression for $i_s(r)$ becomes

$$i_s(r) = \frac{2}{\pi} \int_{\mathcal{V}_r} d\mathcal{V}_r \int_{\mathcal{V}_s} d\mathcal{V}_s \int_{\mathcal{V}_z} d\mathcal{V}_z \, \mathcal{V}_s \, i_c(r_c) \exp - (\mathcal{V}_{sc}^2 + \mathcal{V}_{rc}^2 + \mathcal{V}_{zc}^2) \tag{7.4}$$

where the initial plane is taken at the cathode; hence the subscript c. In Eq. (7.4), the same normalization is made as in Eq. (5.1), but now (s,r,z) is written for the (x,y,s) of Section 5. The same choice of cathode phase-space density is made, i.e., that of Eq. (2.6).

It is possible to make substitutions similar to those in Sec. 5.2.

$$\mathcal{V}_{rc} = \mathscr{b} v_{rc} = \mathscr{b}\,\frac{r - \mathfrak{M} r_c}{\mathfrak{N}} = \frac{r - \mathfrak{M} r_c}{\sqrt{2}\,\sigma} \tag{7.5a}$$

and $$\sigma = \frac{\mathfrak{N}}{\sqrt{2}\,\mathscr{b}} = N\left(\frac{kT_c}{m}\right)^{1/2} \tag{7.5b}$$

*As explained in Section 1, in this section we use (s,r,z) coordinates, with the beam uniform in the z direction.

and $$d\mathcal{V}_s\, d\mathcal{V}_r\, d\mathcal{V}_z = \frac{\mathcal{V}_{sc}}{\sqrt{2}\,\sigma \mathcal{V}_s}\, d\mathcal{V}_{sc}\, dr_c\, d\mathcal{V}_{zc} \tag{7.5c}$$

The integral over $\mathcal{V}_{zc}$ may be performed at once, since $-\infty < \mathcal{V}_{zc} < \infty$, and Eq. (7.4) becomes

$$i_s(r) = \frac{2}{\sqrt{\pi}}\frac{1}{\sigma}\int_{r_c} i_c(r_c)\exp -\left[\frac{(r - Mr_c)^2}{2\sigma^2}\right]dr_c \int_{\mathcal{V}_{sc}} \mathcal{V}_{sc}\exp - \mathcal{V}_{sc}^2\, d\mathcal{V}_{sc} \tag{7.6}$$

As in Sec. 5.2, it is assumed that all particles which leave the cathode normally reach the plane s, so that the limits of integration for $\mathcal{V}_{sc}$ are $0 < \mathcal{V}_{sc} < \infty$. If the cathode is the strip $-a < r_c < a$, the cathode current distribution can be written in a dimensionless form,

$$i_c = i_c\left(\frac{r}{a}\right) \tag{7.7}$$

and Eq. (7.6) becomes[14]

$$i_s(r) = (2\pi)^{-1/2}\frac{1}{M}\int_{-R_e}^{R_e} i_c\left(\frac{R_c}{R_e}\right)\exp -\left[\frac{(R - R_c)^2}{2}\right]dR_c \tag{7.8}$$

where, as in Sec. 5.2,

$$R_e = \frac{aM}{\sigma}, \qquad R_c = \frac{r_c M}{\sigma}, \qquad R = \frac{r}{\sigma} \tag{7.9}$$

Equation (7.8) is the sheet-beam equivalent to Eq. (5.24) for the cylindrical beam.

Unlike Eq. (5.24), it is possible to integrate Eq. (7.8) explicitly for certain simple choices of $i_c(r/a)$. If there is a curvature of the ray axis at the cathode, it was shown in Sec. 3.2 of Chap. II that a linear variation of current density at the cathode results. If i_c has the variation

$$-a < r < a \quad i_c\left(\frac{r}{a}\right) = i_{co}\left(1 + \alpha\frac{r}{a}\right) \tag{7.10}$$

then

$$\frac{i_s(r)}{i_{co}} = \frac{1}{2M}\left\{\left(1 + \alpha\frac{R}{R_e}\right)\left[\operatorname{erf}\left(\frac{R + R_e}{\sqrt{2}}\right) - \operatorname{erf}\left(\frac{R - R_e}{\sqrt{2}}\right)\right] + \left(\frac{2}{\pi}\right)^{1/2}\frac{\alpha}{R_e}\left(\exp -\left[\frac{(R - R_e)^2}{2}\right] - \exp -\left[\frac{(R + R_e)^2}{2}\right]\right)\right\} \tag{7.11}$$

where erf x is the usual error function of Eq. (4.14). The $i_s(r)/i_{co}$ of Eq. (7.11) have been plotted, with R_e as a parameter, in Figs. 6.13 and 6.14. The curves of Fig. 6.13 are more suitable for large R_e, that is, small thermal effects, whereas those of Fig. 6.14 are better for small R_e. The limiting case of $R_e = \infty$ corresponds to the

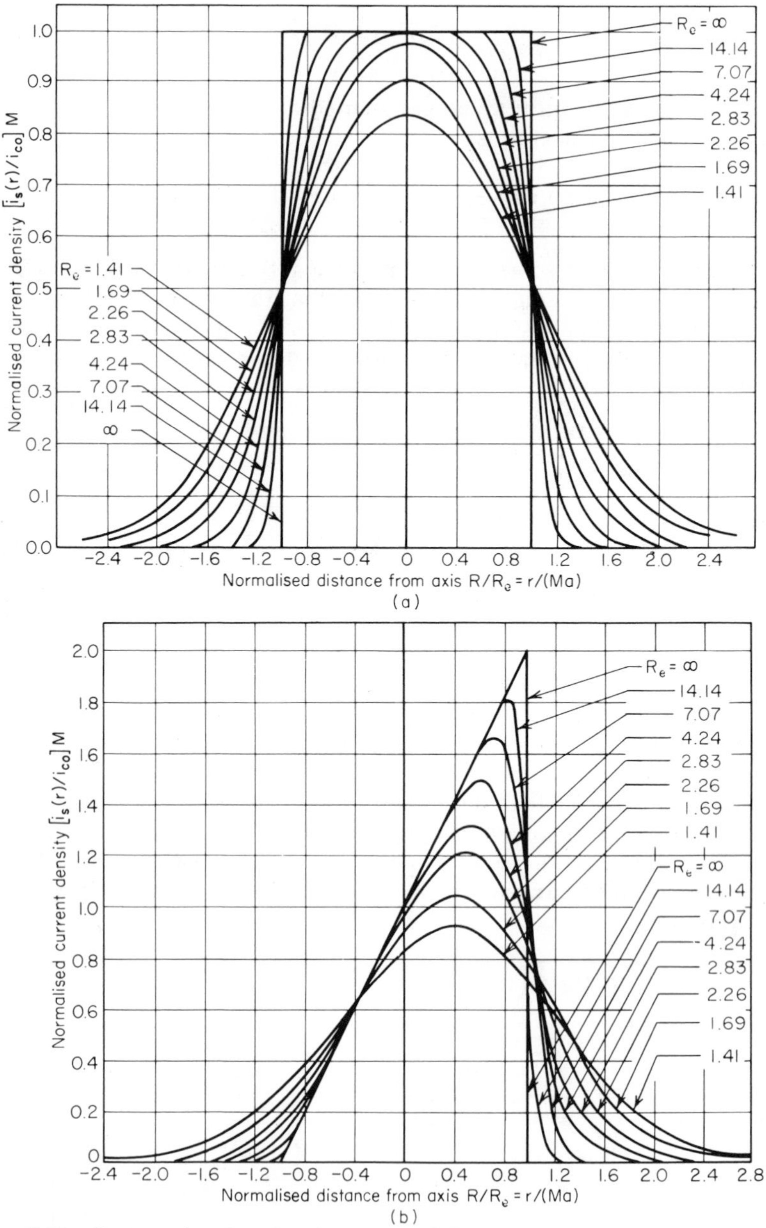

Fig. 6.13. Curves showing the character of the current density variation in a sheet beam with linear-current-density variation at the cathode dispersed by thermal velocities. The ratio of maximum to minimum current density at the cathode is $(1 + \alpha)/(1 - \alpha)$. These curves are suitable for $R_e \geq 1.41$. (a) Constant current density $\alpha = 0$; (b) linear current density $\alpha = 1$. (Reproduced Ref. 14, courtesy of the Institute of Electronic and Electrical Engineers.)

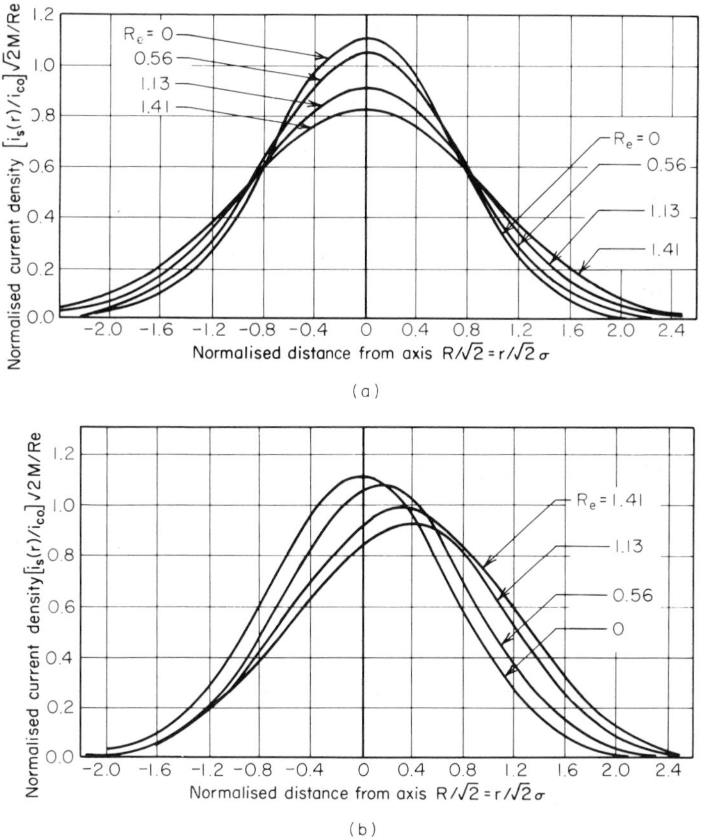

Fig. 6.14. Curves showing the character of the current-density variations in a sheet beam dispersed by thermal velocities as in Fig. 6.13. These curves are more suitable for highly convergent beams with $R_e \leq 1.41$. (a) Constant current density $\alpha = 0$; (b) linear current density $\alpha = 1$. (Reproduced from Ref. 14, courtesy of the Institute of Electronic and Electrical Engineers.)

cathode current density, and is reproduced at any cathode image. Figures 6.13a and 6.14a are for a constant current density ($\alpha = 0$), and those of Figs. 6.13b and 6.14b are for $\alpha = 1$. The ratio of maximum to minimum current density is $(1 + \alpha)/(1 - \alpha)$. The current density for any different α can be calculated by a suitable combination of Fig. 6.13a and b or 6.14a and b.

On the axis, where R = 0, Eq. (7.11) takes the value

$$\frac{i_s(0)}{i_{c0}} = \frac{1}{M}\,\mathrm{erf}\,\frac{R_e}{\sqrt{2}} \tag{7.12}$$

R_e is given, from Eqs. (5.19) and (5.23), by

$$R_e = \frac{aM}{\sigma} = \frac{\sqrt{2}\, aM\, \mathscr{b}}{N} \tag{7.13}$$

Finally, it is important to compute $I_s(r)$, the current between the planes $r = 0$ and r. $I_s(r)$ can be integrated explicitly[6] to give

$$I_s(r) = \int_0^r i_s(r)\, dr = \frac{aM}{R_e}\int_0^R i_s(r)\, dR$$

$$= \frac{I}{\sqrt{2}R_e}\left\{\frac{1-\alpha}{2} F_2\left(\frac{R+R_e}{\sqrt{2}}\right) - \frac{1+\alpha}{2} F_2\left(\frac{R-R_e}{\sqrt{2}}\right) + \alpha F_2\left(\frac{R_e}{\sqrt{2}}\right)\right. \tag{7.14}$$

$$\left. + \frac{\alpha}{\sqrt{2}R_e}\left[F_1\left(\frac{R+R_e}{\sqrt{2}}\right) - F_1\left(\frac{R-R_e}{\sqrt{2}}\right) - 2F_1\left(\frac{R_e}{\sqrt{2}}\right)\right]\right\}$$

where

$$F_1(x) = \tfrac{1}{2}(x^2 - \tfrac{3}{2})\, \text{erf}\,(x) + \frac{x}{2\sqrt{\pi}} \exp\,(-x^2) \tag{7.15a}$$

$$F_2(x) = x\, \text{erf}\,(x) + \frac{1}{\sqrt{\pi}} \exp\,(-x^2) \tag{7.15b}$$

and $I = 2ai_{co}$ = total current in the beam = $I_s(\infty)$ of Sec. 5.2. The $I_s(r)$ of Eq. (7.15) is plotted in Fig. 6.15. Figure 6.15 is for the constant current density, $\alpha = 0$; Fig. 6.15b, for $\alpha = 1$. If the current density is constant and $Ma/\sigma = R_e$ is 1.4, Fig. 6.15a shows that 30 per cent of the beam is outside the nonthermal radius.

Approximations can be derived for the expressions of this section, but it is more convenient to use the appropriate figures.

7.3. A Linear Treatment of the Current Density in a Drifting Sheet Beam. It is possible to give a large number of applications of the formalism of Sec. 7.2. The formulas are applied exactly as those of Section 5 were applied in Section 6, and a new set of applications would be repetitious. However, one single problem will be considered in detail, because it is needed in Section 8.

A useful practical example is the thermal spread in a drifting sheet beam. In the absence of thermal effects, this problem has been treated in Sec. 3.10. It was shown that the spread of a sheet beam, initially parallel with uniform current density and of radius r_0, follows the law [Eqs. (10.8) and (10.9) of Chap. III],

$$\frac{r}{r_0} = 1 + \left(\frac{ks}{r_0}\right)^2 \tag{7.16}$$

where

$$k^2 = \frac{P_\square}{16\epsilon_0(2\eta)^{1/2}} = 1.19 \times 10^{-2}\, P_\square \tag{7.17}$$

and $P_\square$ is the perveance per square in micropervs (Section 10 of Chap. III). Equation (7.16) is identical with the approximate relation

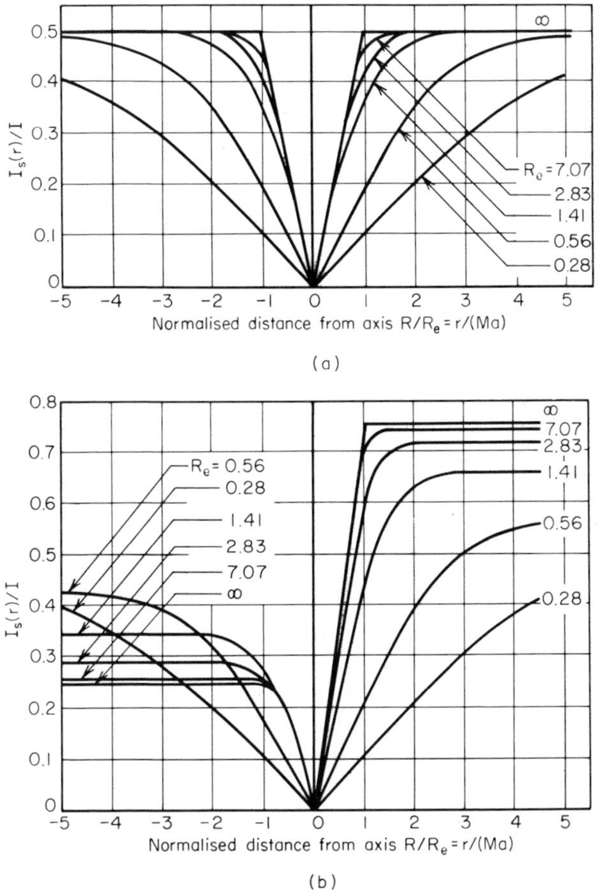

Fig. 6.15. Curves showing the per cent of the total beam current to be found between the planes r = 0 and r = r in a sheet beam dispersed by thermal velocities. (a) Constant current density $\alpha = 0$; (b) linear current density $\alpha = 1$. (Reproduced from Ref. 14, courtesy of the Institute of Electronic and Electrical Engineers.)

Eq. (6.42) for the cylindrical beam. Hence the same integral can be performed as in Sec. 6.5 to give the same values for M and N [Eqs. (6.42) to (6.44)].

$$M = 1 + K^2, \qquad N = \frac{s/2}{(2\eta\phi_0)^{1/2}}\left(1 + \frac{1 + K^2}{K}\tan^{-1} K\right) \tag{7.18}$$

where $K = \dfrac{ks}{r_0}$

and ϕ_0 is the potential in the drifting beam. With these M and N, Figs. 6.13a, 6.14a, and 6.15a can be used to find $i_S(r)$ and $I_S(r)$ anywhere in the beam.

For example, if a 10-volt, 2-mm-thick sheet beam, with a $P_\square$ of 1, drifts for 1 cm,

$$M = 2.19 \qquad \text{and} \qquad N = 7.3 \times 10^{-9}$$

If the cathode temperature is 2000°K, $\mathscr{E}$ is, from Eq. (2.2), 4.05×10^{-6}, so that σ is given, from Eq. (5.19), by

$$\sigma = 1.3 \times 10^{-3}$$

Using Eq. (7.9), we obtain

$$R_e = \frac{2.19 \times 10^{-3}}{1.3 \times 10^{-3}} = 1.7 \qquad R = \frac{r}{1.3 \times 10^{-3}} \tag{7.19}$$

Thus, in this distance, the nonthermal space-charge spreading would be to 4.38 mm. At the nonthermal edge of the beam, $R_e = 1.7$, $R/R_e = 1$, and from Fig. 6.15a about 24 per cent of the beam is outside this distance (at $R_e = 1.7$, $R/R_e = 1$, $\alpha = 0$, $I_S/I = 0.38$, which means that 12 per cent of the current is at $R > R_e$ and 12 per cent at $R < -R_e$).

8. THE MODIFICATION OF THE THERMAL-SPREAD FORMULAS DUE TO THE CHANGE IN SPACE-CHARGE FORCES

8.1. Introduction. For almost all the flows considered in this chapter, the nonthermal solutions are based on paraxial theories. In the paraxial formulation, the effect of transverse variations in space-charge density on the electric fields are ignored. It would be inconsistent, therefore, to consider these transverse effects in thermally diffused beams. However, the fact that, in thermally diffused beams, the current density and the space-charge density are reduced on the ray axis can be estimated simply as described in Sec. 8.2.

In two important flows considered in this chapter, a drifting cylindrical beam and a drifting sheet beam, the equations of flow are valid far from the nonthermal beam. In Sec. 8.3, a method is given for estimating the correction to the flow, due to the transverse variation in charge density caused by thermal diffusion in drifting beams. The method can be extended to other problems. Since, however, even the linear theories of this chapter have been limited to paraxial flows, it would be inconsistent to consider more general nonlinear corrections.

8.2. The Modification in a Paraxial Beam. In the computation of M and N for paraxial flows, the effects of transverse variation of space-charge density were ignored. The formulas used for computing M and N were, from Eqs. (5.2), (5.8), (6.23), and (6.24) of Chap. III,

$$\ddot{w} - 2\,j\omega_L\dot{w} + \left(\tfrac{1}{2}\eta\Phi'' - j\dot{\omega}_L\,w + \frac{\eta\rho_0}{2\epsilon_0}\right)w = 0 \tag{8.1a}$$

and

$$\ddot{r} + \left(2V^2\kappa^2 - 2\eta\kappa VB_Z + \eta^2 B_Z^2 + \eta\Phi'' + \eta^2 \mathcal{a}_1^2 - \eta^2 \mathcal{a}\mathcal{a}'' + \frac{\eta\rho_0}{\epsilon_0}\right) = 0 \tag{8.1b}$$

for cylindrical and sheet beams, respectively. Here Φ, V, and κ are the potential, velocity, and curvature of particles on the ray axis, and B_Z, $\mathcal{a}$, and $\mathcal{a}_1$ are related to the magnetic field on the ray axis in Sections 5 and 6 of Chap. III; ρ_0 is the space-charge density on the axis given for cylindrical beams by

$$\rho_0 = -\frac{I}{\pi r_e^2 V} \tag{8.2a}$$

and for sheet beams by

$$\rho_0 = -\frac{I}{2r_e \ell V} = \frac{I_\square}{4r_e^2 V} \tag{8.2b}$$

where ℓ = beam width
I = total current in the beam
$I_\square$ = current per square [Section 7 of Chap. IV]
r_e = radius of the edge of the nonthermal beam

The $\mathfrak{M}$ and $\mathfrak{N}$ are computed from Eq. (8.1a), with the boundary conditions:

$$\text{If } w = \mathfrak{M}: \quad w(0) = 1, \qquad \dot{w}(0) = 0 \tag{8.3a}$$

$$\text{If } w = \mathfrak{N}: \quad w(0) = 0, \qquad \dot{w}(0) = 1 \tag{8.3b}$$

The $\mathfrak{M}$ and $\mathfrak{N}$ for sheet beams are computed the same way from Eq. (8.1b).

If the beams are diffused by thermal spreading, it was shown that the current density, and hence space-charge density, are reduced by a factor γ on the axis over their nonthermal values. From Eqs. (5.25) and (7.12), γ has the value, for cylindrical beams,

$$\gamma = 1 - \exp(-\xi^2) \tag{8.4a}$$

and for sheet beams,

$$\gamma = \operatorname{erf} \xi \tag{8.4b}$$

$$\text{where} \quad \xi = \frac{aM}{\sqrt{2}\,\sigma} = \frac{aM\mathscr{6}}{N} \tag{8.5}$$

The symbol $\mathscr{6}$ is, as usual, $(m/2kT_c)^{1/2}$. More accurate values of γ, including longitudinal effects ignored in Sections 5 to 7, are derived from Eqs. (4.25) and (4.22):

For cylindrical beams:

$$\gamma = 1 - \zeta^2 \exp\left(-\frac{\xi^2}{\zeta^2}\right) \tag{8.6a}$$

For sheet beams the equivalent result is*

$$\gamma = \operatorname{erf}\left(\frac{\xi}{\zeta}\right) + e^{\Upsilon} (1 - \zeta^2)^{1/2} \left[1 - \operatorname{erf}\left(\frac{\Upsilon}{\zeta}\right)\right]^{1/2} \tag{8.6b}$$

where

$$\zeta = \left(1 - \frac{M^2 a^2 \sigma^2}{N^2 \Upsilon}\right)^{1/2} \quad \text{and} \quad \Upsilon = 2\eta\sigma^2 \phi_0 \tag{8.7}$$

and ϕ_0 is the potential of the drifting beam

For large Υ, $\zeta \to 1$, and the γ of Eq. (8.6) tend to those of Eq. (8.4). If the potential is sufficiently low so that there are significant differences between the γ of Eqs. (8.4) and (8.6), the latter should be used.

In order to calculate accurately the current density in the thermally diffused beam, an iteration procedure can be set up. To compute M and N, Eq. (8.1) is integrated with ρ_0, given by Eq. (8.2), but with the beam current $\bar{I}^1$, where

$$\bar{I} = \gamma I \tag{8.8}$$

First, with $\gamma = 1$, the usual M and N are computed; these we call M_1 and N_1. Using these M_1 and N_1, a γ_1 is computed from Eq. (8.4) or (8.6). With this γ_1, a new M_2 and N_2 are computed, which can be used to compute a new γ_2, etc., if required. Usually, one iteration cycle is adequate. If thermal effects are very important, more cycles may be required. The test whether sufficient cycles have been achieved is the size of the change in γ between iterations.

The final M and N obtained can then be used to compute the beam parameters in the thermally diffused beam.

8.3. Application of the Method of Sec. 8.2 to a Drifting Sheet Beam. As an illustration of the method, we can consider the drifting sheet beam of Sec. 7.3.

The exact equation of motion can be deduced from Gauss' law, and is

$$r'' = 4k^2 \frac{I_S(r)}{I} \tag{8.9}$$

where

$$k^2 = \frac{P_\square}{16\epsilon_0(2\eta)^{1/2}} = 1.19 \times 10^{-2} P_\square \tag{8.10}$$

and, as usual, $I_S(r)$ is the total current between the plane $r = 0$ and $r = r$. In Eq. (8.9), it is assumed that, even with thermal spreading, the function $I_S(r)$ is symmetric in r. If the nonthermal value is used for $I_S(r)$ [that is, $I_S(r) = I/2$] and if r is an electron at the beam edge $(r - r_e)$, then Eq. (8.9) gives the usual space-charge-spreading equa-

*See problem 3.

tion [Eq. (10.2) of Chap. III] from which the results of Sec. 7.3 were obtained. The solutions of Eq. (8.9) with $I_s(r) = I/2$ are equivalent to putting the γ of Eq. (8.5) equal to unity. The resulting M and N were obtained in Eq. (7.18), and are $M_1 = 1 + K^2$

$$N_1 = \frac{s/2}{(2\eta\phi_0)^{1/2}}\left(1 + \frac{1 + K^2}{K}\tan^{-1} K\right) \tag{8.11}$$

where $K = \dfrac{ks}{r_0}$

Using Eqs. (8.4) and (8.5), γ_1 is given by

$$\gamma_1 = \text{erf}\left(\frac{r_0 M_1 \mathscr{E}}{N_1}\right) \tag{8.12}$$

In order to use the method of Sec. 8.2, we approximate $I_s(r)$ by the relation, using Eq. (8.8),

$$I_s(r) = \tfrac{1}{2}\gamma_1 I \tag{8.13}$$

The error in this approximation will be discussed in Sec. 8.4. To obtain M_2, it is necessary to integrate Eq. (8.9) with the $I_s(r)$ of Eq. (8.13). For the edge electron, the differential equation is

$$r_e'' = 2k^2 \text{ erf } (\gamma_1) \tag{8.14}$$

with the initial conditions

$$r_e(0) = r_0, \qquad r_e'(0) = 0 \tag{8.15}$$

Equation (8.14) cannot be integrated in general. However, if

$$ks \ll r_0 \qquad \text{and} \qquad s \ll 2(2\eta\mathscr{E}^2\phi_0)^{1/2} \tag{8.16}$$

Eq. (8.14) becomes, from Eqs. (8.11), (8.12), and the asymptotic expression for erf x of Eq. (2.37a),

$$r_e'' \simeq 2k^2\left[1 - \frac{\exp - (\alpha^2/s^2)}{\sqrt{\pi}\ \alpha/s}\right] \tag{8.17}$$

where $\alpha = (2\eta\mathscr{E}^2\phi_0)^{1/2} r_0$ (8.18)

For $s \ll \alpha$, as in Eq. (8.16), an approximate integral of Eq. (8.17) is

$$\frac{r_e}{r_0} \simeq 1 + \left(\frac{ks}{r_0}\right)^2 - \frac{k^2\alpha^2}{2\sqrt{\pi}}\left(\frac{s}{\alpha}\right)^7 \exp - \left(\frac{\alpha^2}{s^2}\right) \tag{8.19a}$$

M_2 is given by the right side of Eq. (8.19a), and N_2 is obtained by integration; using Eq. (3.20), N_2 is given by

$$N_2 = M_2 \int_0^s \frac{(2\eta\phi_0)^{1/2}\, ds}{M_2^2} \tag{8.19b}$$

Clearly, M_2 and $N_2 \to M_1$ and N_1 very rapidly as $s \to 0$.

Usually, the integral analogous to Eq. (8.14) is performed numerically. The algebraic expressions are included here as an example and to give an indication of the correction in M and N which results from the use of this method.

8.4. An Alternative Analysis of the Current Density in a Thermally Diffused Drifting Beam. In a drifting beam, the equations of motions are exact. It is therefore meaningful to consider the effects of transverse variations of current density on the space-charge fields. The analysis is carried out in detail for the cylindrical beam, and the results for the sheet beam are quoted without proof. The analysis is approximate, and is due to Danielson et al.[15]

The equations of motion for a particle in a cylindrical beam of potential ϕ_0 is, from Eq. (10.1) of Chap. III,*

$$r'' = \frac{k^2}{r}\frac{I_z(r)}{I} \tag{8.20}$$

where $I_z(r)$ is the current within the radius r, I is the total current in the beam, and

$$k^2 = \frac{P}{4\pi\epsilon_0(2\eta)^{1/2}} \tag{8.21}$$

In the paraxial theories of Sections 4 to 6, the value assumed for $I_z(r)$ in the integration is

$$I_z(r) = \frac{Ir^2}{M^2a^2} \tag{8.22}$$

where a is the radius of the beam at the cathode. In Section 5 more accurate expressions were developed for $I_z(r)$, which took the thermal spreading of the beam into consideration. The formulas were developed in terms of r_e and σ, where

$$r_e = Ma \qquad \text{and} \qquad \sigma = N\left(\frac{kT_c}{m}\right)^{1/2} = \frac{N}{\sqrt{2}\,\mathscr{C}} \tag{8.23}$$

The parameter $r_e(z)$ corresponds to the trajectory of an electron on the edge of the nonthermal beam, and σ of an electron which starts from the axis with an average transverse velocity. The initial transverse velocity of the σ electron is average in that it is the standard deviation of the transverse velocities defined by

$$\dot{\sigma}^2 = \frac{\int n_c v_\perp^2\, dv_r\, dv_\theta\, dv_z}{\int n_c\, dv_r\, dv_\theta\, dv_z} \tag{8.24}$$

and the integral is taken over all initial velocities at the cathode. It can be verified from Eq. (2.8) that $\dot{\sigma}$ at the cathode is just $(kT_c/m)^{1/2}$.

*Here we use ordinary cylindrical polar coordinates.

The assumption is now made that r_e and σ are sufficiently representative and that a new M and N can be computed based on the motion of the particular r_e and σ electrons. This assumption is only approximately true, but does allow a correction to the M and N to be calculated. The new M and N can then be used to calculate the beam parameters by the methods of Sections 4 to 7.

The equations of motion for the r_e and σ electrons are, from Eqs. (8.20),

$$r_e'' = \frac{k^2}{r_e}\, \mathcal{G}\left(\frac{r_e}{\sigma}, \frac{r_e}{\sigma}\right) \triangleq \frac{2k^2}{r_e} F_{r_e} \tag{8.25}$$

and

$$\sigma'' = \frac{k^2}{\sigma}\, \mathcal{G}\left(1, \frac{r_e}{\sigma}\right) \triangleq \frac{2k^2}{\sigma} F_\sigma \tag{8.26}$$

In Eqs. (8.25) and (8.26), $\mathcal{G}(R, R_e)$ is the function defined in Eqs. (5.30) and (5.31) and illustrated in Fig. 6.7. The initial conditions for Eqs. (8.25) and (8.26) are

$$r_e(0) = a \qquad \text{and} \qquad \dot{r}_e = 0 \tag{8.27}$$

and
$$\sigma(0) = 0 \qquad \text{and} \qquad \dot{\sigma}(0) = \left(\frac{kT_c}{m}\right)^{1/2} \tag{8.28}$$

In Eq. (8.27), it is assumed that, at z = 0, the nonthermal beam is parallel. Equations (8.25) and (8.26) are a coupled set of differential equations, which can be integrated by the methods of Sec. 9.5 of Chap. IX. A corrected M and N can be computed from the r_e and σ which are the solutions of Eqs. (8.25) and (8.26).

The F_{r_e} and F_σ are plotted in Fig. 6.16a and b. Equations (8.25) and (8.26) can be integrated only numerically, but the method can be extended to more general problems. It is for this reason that the curves are presented.

The analysis for sheet beams is very similar. The relevant equation of motion is, from Eq. (8.9),

$$r'' = 4k^2 \frac{I_s(r)}{I} \tag{8.29}$$

where
$$k^2 = \frac{P_\square}{16\epsilon_0(2\eta)^{1/2}} \tag{8.30}$$

and $P_\square$ is the perveance per square of the beam. This equation can be integrated in the same way for r_e and σ electrons. The relevant $I_s(r)$ is given in Eq. (7.14).

8.5. **The Spherical Diode.** The formalism of Sec. 8.4. can be combined with the anode-aperture-lens formulas of Sec. 8.4, of Chap. III to derive a comprehensive set of design curves for the spherical diode. The theory used to derive these curves is given in Ref. 15, and this section is largely based on that paper. It can be shown[15,16]

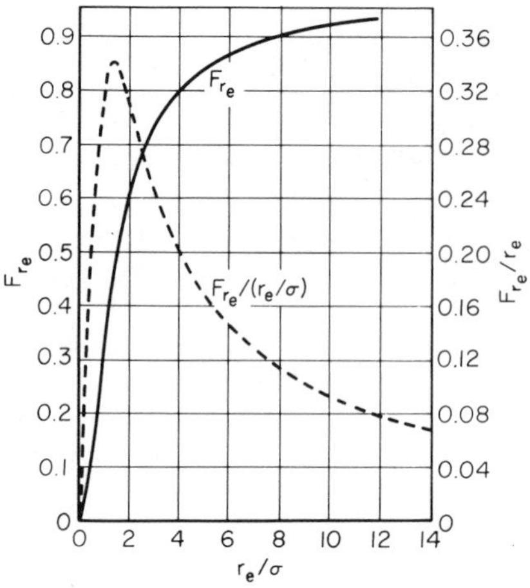

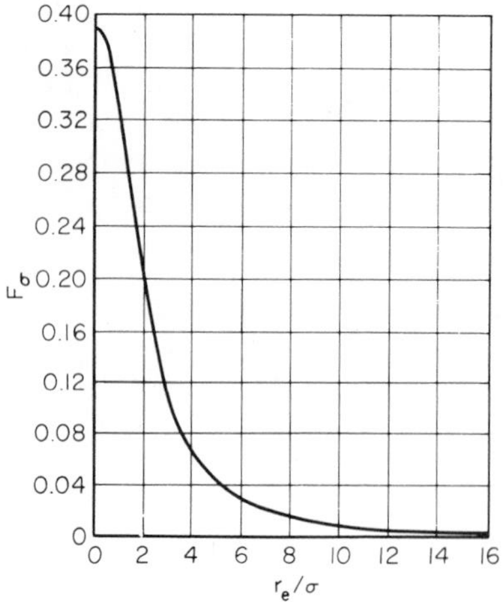

Fig. 6.16. Fraction of the total current contained within the radius of two representative electrons in a cylindrical beam. (a) Fraction inside the radius of the r_e electron; (b) fraction inside the radius of the σ electron. (Reproduced from Ref. 15, courtesy of the *Bell System Technical Journal.*)

that the characteristics of a spherical-diode Pierce gun are completely determined by four parameters, R_C/R_A, P, Φ_A/T_C, and Γ; here R_C and R_A are the cathode and anode radii, P is the beam perveance, Φ_A is the anode voltage, T_C is the cathode temperature, and Γ is the correction which must be made to the anode-lens formula of Eq. (8.12) of Chap. III. For most of the gun parameters used in practice, the transverse scaling laws of Sec. 7.3 of Chap. I are valid, so that the beam parameters depend not on P and Φ_A/T_C separately, but only on Λ, where Λ is defined as

$$\Lambda = \frac{P\Phi_A}{T_C} \tag{8.31}$$

The parameter Γ is defined as

$$\Gamma = \frac{f_L}{f} \tag{8.32}$$

where f is the focal length of the anode lens of the actual gun geometry, and f_L is the f of the ideal spherical diode given by Eq. (8.12) of Chap. III, namely,

$$f_L = -\frac{4\Phi}{\Phi'} \tag{8.33}$$

where Φ' is the rate of change of Φ at the plane of the anode hole. For the spherical diode, the variation of Φ is given, from Eq. (9) of Appendix E, by

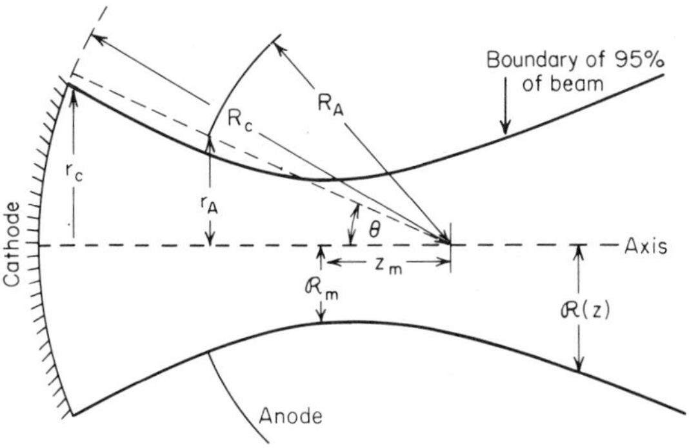

Fig. 6.17. Schematic of a spherical-diode gun.

$$\frac{\Phi}{\Phi_A} = \left(\frac{P}{29.34}\right)^{2/3} (-\alpha)^{4/3} \tag{8.34}$$

where P is the perveance in micropervs, and α is a function of R_c/R given in Table E.1.* Thus f_L is given by

$$f_L = -4\left\{\frac{(-\alpha)^{4/3}}{d[(-\alpha)^{4/3}]/d(R_c/R)}\right\} \tag{8.35}$$

The quantity in parentheses is tabulated in the last column of Table E.1.

Various methods of determining Γ are given in Ref. 15, but for the usual range of parameters, a value of 1.1 for Γ is a good approximation. Using the notation of Fig. 6.17, $\mathcal{R}$ is defined as the radius containing 95 per cent of the beam, and $\mathcal{R}_m$ is its minimum value; z_m is the corresponding axial distance of the plane, where $\mathcal{R} = \mathcal{R}_m$ from the anode hole. For $\Gamma = 1.1$, the beam profiles for various values of R_c/R_a and $\Lambda = P\Phi_A/T_c$ are shown in Fig. 6.18. From these curves, the positions of the minimum radii can be found. Plots of $\mathcal{R}_m$ and the corresponding z_m are shown in Fig. 6.19a and b; the values of r_e and σ at the same plane z_m are shown in Fig. 6.19c and d.

To design a gun based on these curves, it is usual to specify $\mathcal{R}_m$, Φ_A, and I_c. Since the cathode temperature T_c usually depends only on the cathode material, Φ_A and I_c are sufficient to specify Λ. The cathode radius r_c can usually be determined from the emission requirements, so that R_c/R_a is determined by Fig. 6.19a. The cathode and anode radii of curvature, R_c and R_a, and the gun half-angle θ are then derived from Eqs. (9) and (11) of Appendix E,

$$\frac{r_c}{R_c} = \frac{r_a}{R_A} = \theta = \left[\frac{P(-\alpha^2)}{7.335}\right] \tag{8.36}$$

*Note that the R, R_c, etc., of this section correspond to r, r_c, etc., in Appendix E.

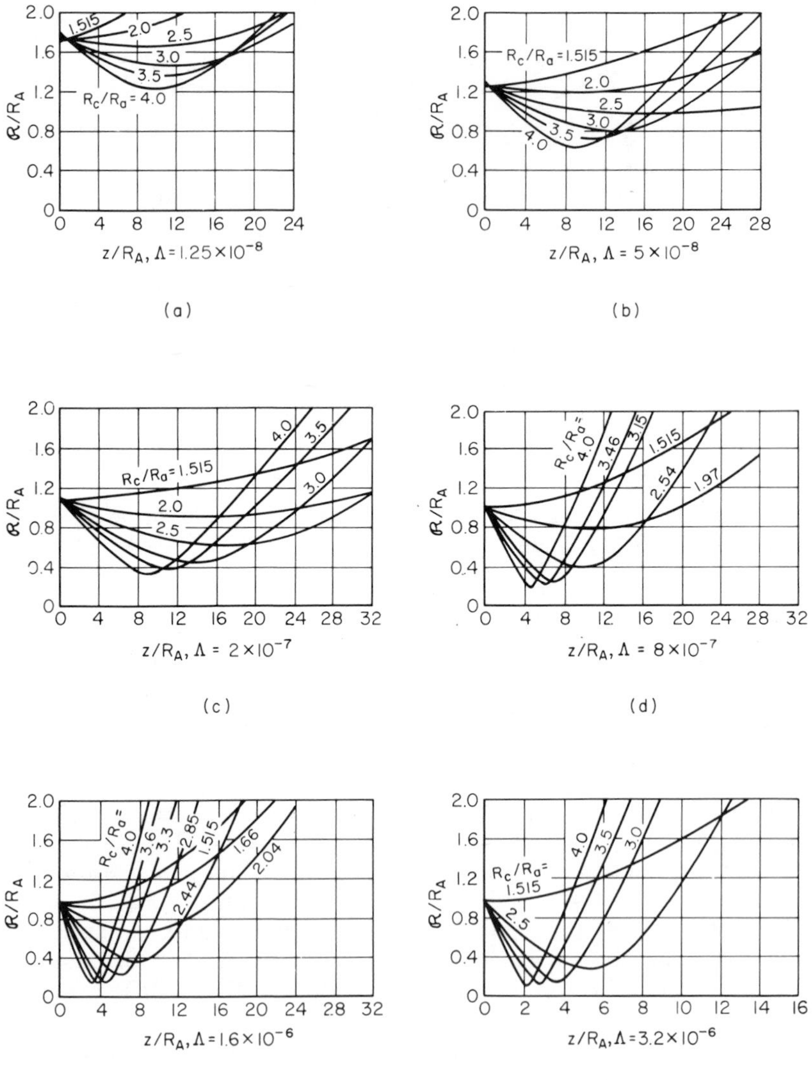

Fig. 6.18. Beam profiles for 95 per cent of the beam in a spherical diode for various $\Lambda = P\Phi_A/T_c$ with r_c/r_a as parameter. (a) $\Lambda = 0.0125$; (b) $\Lambda = 0.05$; (c) $\Lambda = 0.2$; (d) $\Lambda = 0.8$; (e) $\Lambda = 1.6$; (f) $\Lambda = 3.2$.

and P is the perveance in micropervs. Note that this derivation is valid only for small θ, where $\sin\theta \simeq \theta$; for larger half-angle than about 30°, the transverse scaling is no longer sufficiently accurate, and the reader should use the curves of Ref. 15. From Fig. 6.19b to d, one can find z_m and then r_c/σ and σ/R_s at the plane z_m.

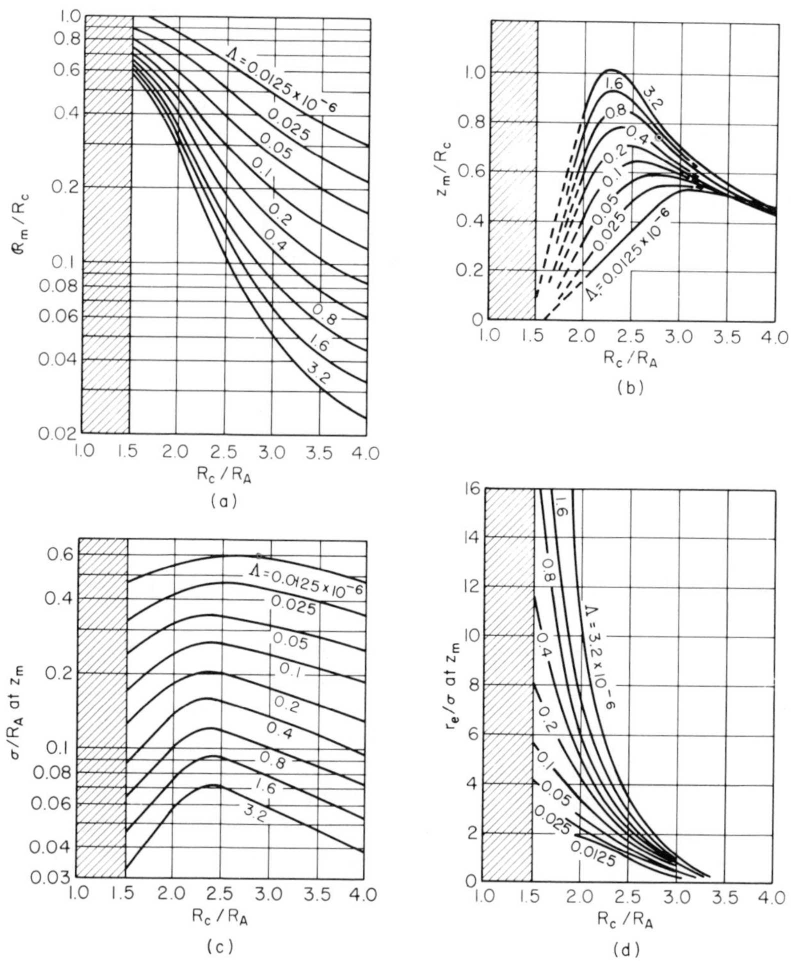

Fig. 6.19. Design curves for Pierce-type spherical diodes, considering thermal effects with $\Lambda = P\Phi_A/T_c$ as a parameter and the ratio of cathode to anode radii R_c/R_a as abscissa. (a) Minimum radius for 95 per cent of the beam, R_m; (b) axial position z_m of R_m; (c) r_e/σ at axial position z_m; (d) σ/R_A at axial position z_m. (Reproduced from Ref. 16, courtesy of the American Institute of Physics.)

The agreement between theory and experiment is illustrated in Fig. 6.20. Here A represents an experimental curve, B a beam profile obtained using the curves of Figs. 6.18 and 6.19, and C a beam profile using the simple linear methods of Section 5, and D is a beam profile using the universal beam-spreading curve of Section 10 of Chap. III. Figure 6.20 shows that, in this particular case, the theory leading to Figs. 6.18 and 6.19 predicts $\mathcal{R}_m$ very accurately, but not z_m. This is a characteristic of the method. Luckily, z_m is not usually required so accurately, because the matching between the

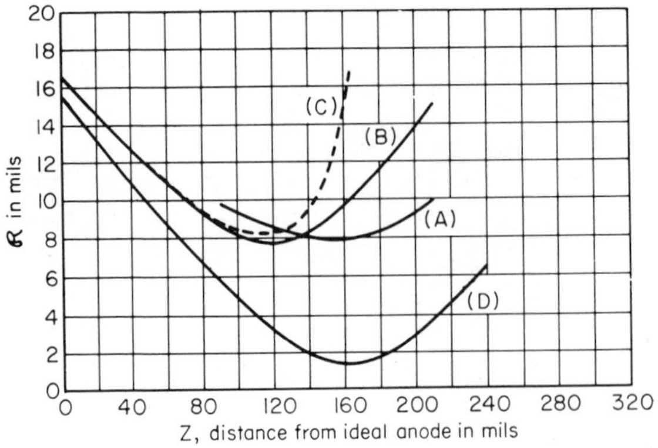

Fig. 6.20. Agreement between different theories and experiment for a particular Pierce gun with $R_c/R_a = 2.8$, $\theta = 13.7°$, $P\Phi_A/T_c = 0.2$, $R_c = 0.043$ in. Curve A is experimental; curve B is according to the curves of this section; curve C is based on the theory of Section 5; curve D is based on the universal beam-spread curve of Section 10 of Chap. III. (Reproduced from Ref. 15, courtesy of the *Bell System Technical Journal.*)

electron gun and the magnetic focusing field in the rest of a microwave tube is developed somewhat empirically.

Figures 6.18 and 6.19 were derived assuming a Γ of 1.1. The effect on the beam profile of changing the anode-lens correction for a typical gun is shown in Fig. 6.21. A change of ± 10 per cent in Γ from 1.1 is larger than is encountered for most applications.

In general, the calculations of the method of Section 5 will always predict, for a given set of gun parameters, an $\mathcal{R}_m$ which is larger than that predicted by those of this section. Nevertheless, in many cases the difference in the $\mathcal{R}_m$ predicted by the two theories is negligible. When r_c/σ, calculated from Section 5, remains greater than about 2 throughout the range of interest, the differences between the

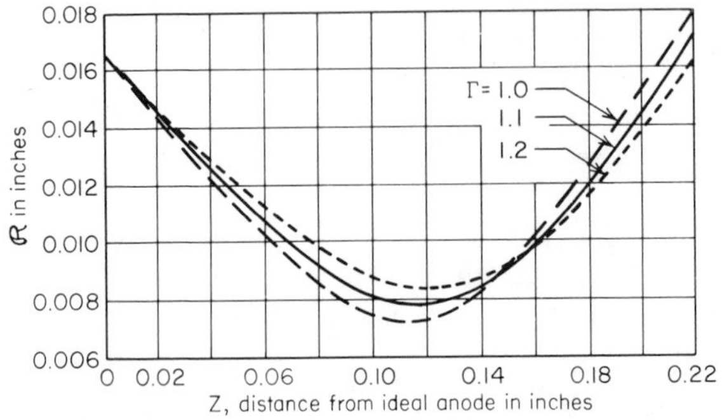

Fig. 6.21. Beam profiles for one particular gun as obtained from the methods of this section but using different lens corrections Γ. The different profiles correspond to different values of Γ. (Reproduced from Ref. 15, courtesy of the *Bell System Technical Journal.*)

corresponding values of $\mathcal{R}$ will be less than a few per cent. If, however, r_c/σ becomes much less than unity, the method of this section will give more accurate results.

REFERENCES FOR CHAPTER VI

1. Nottingham, W. D.: Thermionic Emission, *Handbuch der Physik*, vol. 21, Springer Verlag OHG, Berlin, 1956.
2. Lindsay, P. A.: Velocity Distribution in Electron Streams, *Advances in Electronics and Electron Physics*, vol. 13, Academic Press Inc., New York, 1960.
3. Lindsay, P. A., and F. W. Parker: Potential Distribution between Two Plane Emitting Electrodes, *J. Electronics and Control*, vol. 7, p. 289, 1959.
4. Spangenberg, K. R.: "Vacuum Tubes," McGraw Hill Book Company, New York, 1948.
5. Flugge, W.: "Four Place Tables of Transcendental Functions," McGraw-Hill Book Company, New York, 1954.
6. Ryshik, I. M., and I. S. Gradstein: "Tables of Series, Products and Integrals," Deutscher Verlag der Wissenschaften, Berlin, 1957.
7. Peirce, B. O.: "A Short Table of Integrals", Ginn and Company, Boston, 1929.
8. Herrman, G.: Optical Theory of Thermal Velocity Effects in Cylindrical Electron Beams, *J. Appl. Phys.*, vol. 29, p. 127, 1958.
9. Langmuir, D. B.: Theoretical Limitations of Cathode Ray Tubes, *Proc. IRE*, vol. 25, p. 977, 1937.
10. Pierce, J. R.: "Theory and Design of Electron Beams," D. Van Nostrand Company, Inc., Princeton, N. J., 1954.
11. Kirstein, P. T.: The Estimation of Thermal Velocity Effects in Thick Steady Beams, *J. Electronics and Control*, vol. 17, p. 521, 1964.
12. Cutler, C. C., and M. E. Hines: Thermal Velocity Effects in Electron Guns, *Proc. IRE*, vol. 43, p. 307, 1955.
13. Ashkin, A.: Dynamics of Electron Beams from Magnetically Shielded Guns, *J. Appl. Phys.*, vol. 29, p. 1594, 1958.
14. Kirstein, P. T.: On the Effect of Thermal Velocities in Two-dimensional and Axially Symmetric Beams, *Trans. IEEE*, vol. ED-10, p. 69, 1963.
15. Danielson, W. E., J. L. Rosenfeld, and J. A. Saloom: A Detailed Analysis of Beam Formation with Electron Guns of the Pierce Type, *Bell System Tech. J.*, vol. 35, p. 375, 1956.
16. Herrman, G.: Transverse Scaling of Electron Beams, *J. Appl. Phys.*, vol. 28, p. 474, 1957.

PROBLEMS

1. Determine the current density and the voltage and position of the potential minimum in a closely spaced diode with anode-cathode spacing 0.1 mm, cathode temperature 1100°K, and current density emitted at the cathode 1 amp/cm^2 when (a) the anode-cathode potential is 1 kv, and (b) the anode-cathode potential is 1 volt.

A method of successive approximations will be needed for case b, using as a first guess Eq. (2.49), with $z_m = 0$, $\phi_m = 0$.

2. Show that the expression for the bounding current density in a strip beam analogous to that of Eq. (4.12) is

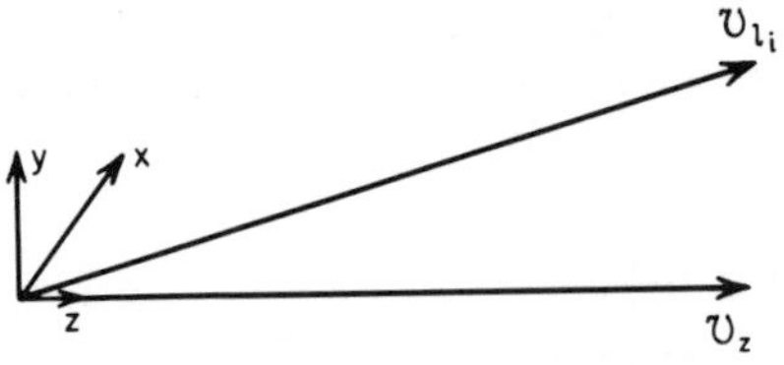

Fig. 6.22. Diagram of cylindrical polar coordinates in the (x,y,z) coordinate system.

$$i_{\alpha M} = \frac{2}{\pi} i_{co} \int_{-\infty}^{\infty} d\upsilon_x \int_{\Upsilon^{1/2}}^{\infty} d\upsilon_\ell \int_{-\alpha}^{\alpha} \upsilon_\ell^2 \exp\,(\Upsilon - \upsilon_\ell^2 - \upsilon_y^2) \cos\theta \, d\theta$$

$$= i_{co}\left[\frac{2}{\sqrt{\pi}} \Upsilon^{1/2} + \exp \Upsilon \left(1 - \operatorname{erf} \Upsilon^{1/2}\right)\right] \sin\alpha$$

where erf y is the error function of Eq. (2.27).

Show that, for a practical electron gun with $T_c = 1000°K$ and $\phi > 1$ volt, the second term of this equation can be neglected and it simplifies to the result

$$i_{\alpha M} = \frac{2}{\sqrt{\pi}} i_{co} \Upsilon^{1/2} \sin\alpha$$

It is convenient to work in the cylindrical polar coordinate system of Fig. 6.22, where $\upsilon^2 = \upsilon_\ell^2 + \upsilon_y^2$, with $\upsilon_z = \upsilon_\ell \cos\theta$, and to assume that there is no potential variation in the y direction.

3. By using the same assumptions and coordinate system as in Prob. 2, show that the current density on the axis of a perfect strip-beam focusing system is

$$i_\alpha = \frac{i_{co}}{M}\left(\operatorname{erf}\left[\frac{M^2 \Upsilon \sin^2\alpha}{1 - M^2 \sin^2\alpha}\right]^{\frac{1}{2}} + Me^{\Upsilon} \sin\alpha \left\{1 - \operatorname{erf}\left[\frac{\Upsilon}{1 - M^2 \sin^2\alpha}\right]^{\frac{1}{2}}\right\}\right)$$

where erf y is the error function of Eq. (2.27). It is convenient to assume that the axis is rectilinear and that there is no magnetic field. If the beam had a curved central axis or if there were a component of magnetic field parallel to the cathode, the thermal velocity component along the axis would deflect an electron in a direction perpendicular to the axis.

VII

Analytical Methods of Electrode Design

1. INTRODUCTION

The usual problem in electron optics is to determine the sort of flow pattern which will result from a prescribed electrode configuration, usually neglecting space-charge effects. These electrodes are then varied to increase focusing, reduce aberrations, compensate for chromatism, etc. We wish to solve a quite different problem; the expressions for the physical parameters of flow inside the beam are known, whereas the electrodes required to produce these distributions have unknown geometrical shapes, positions, and potentials.

The first problems of this kind were those encountered in the Pierce gun.[1] The flow in this gun is described in Sec. 2.2 of Chap. II and in Appendix E, and is called Langmuir flow. The flow is in straight lines and, in the simplest case, is from a planar cathode. The electrodes for this simplest case were derived in Pierce's paper by theoretical methods. Attempts to design analytically the electrodes for the other kinds of Langmuir flow met with mixed success, until Radley[2] wrote a detailed paper on the subject. The earlier methods used series developments, or numerical integration, of doubtful validity and with limited success. A summary of the references, methods, and results obtained before 1957 is provided by Radley's paper. In 1957, Lomax[3] developed a theoretically exact method which allowed the analytic design of electrodes, given the field on the beam edge, for a strip beam infinite in the third direction. Radley,[2] in 1958, developed a method using integral equations which solves for the potential when the boundaries are any level lines of a coordinate system for which Laplace's equation is separable. Finally Harker,[4] in 1960, developed an elegant and powerful method for solving axially symmetric problems under the same boundary conditions as Lomax's solutions for planar problems.

The limited success of some of the earlier analytic methods of solving the problem of electrode design is due to the fact that Laplace's equation is solved under "improper" boundary conditions. With "proper" boundary conditions for an elliptic partial differential equation, such as Laplace's equation, some combination of the potential and the normal field must be prescribed on a closed boundary.

This problem can be solved numerically by the relaxation methods of Section 3 of Chap. IX. The lack of success in solving Laplace's equation for the boundary conditions in which both the potential and the normal field are prescribed on an open boundary, the Cauchy conditions, is due to the theoretical instability of the solution by numerical methods. By instability, in this context, we mean that the difference equation, derived from the exact differential equation, does not converge uniformly to a solution as the mesh size is indefinitely decreased. This result, which is described by Richtmeyer,[5] leads to the fact that straightforward integration away from the beam boundary has an uncertain range of validity. For this reason it is necessary to develop methods which either allow analytic electrode designs, or put the design problem in a form which is tractable by straightforward numerical means.

In this chapter several different methods of solution are developed. In the discussion of methods, equations for the required potential function are derived. Little attention is given to the numerical techniques which must be used to obtain an electrode configuration. For example, in one method, that of Harker in Section 5, a hyperbolic partial differential equation is obtained. The solution of such a differential equation by difference-equation techniques is adequately described in books on numerical methods.[5]

The electrode configurations which arise from purely theoretical considerations usually will not lead to structures which are easy to fabricate. The problem of obtaining shapes that are physically more suitable is usually better solved by approximate than by theoretically exact means. Such methods are described in the following two chapters. As a general rule, theoretically exact methods are easier to use with complicated equations but simple boundaries; approximate methods come into their own with complicated boundaries. There have been attempts to solve interior-boundary-value problems by using Fourier analysis in one direction.[6] These methods have been successful only with rectangular or other simple boundaries. Problems of designing electrode configurations in such a way as to leave unchanged the fields in the vicinity of the beam are very awkward to solve by theoretically exact methods.

Many institutions have available large, fast digital computers, but possess no analog facilities. In such cases, it is more convenient to use even lengthy and awkward numerical techniques than to build specialized analog equipment. In Chap. VIII we shall outline some of the possible iterative techniques which may be used to vary, numerically, the beam boundary, until the required potential distribution in the beam vicinity is obtained. These techniques are applicable whether the relevant equations are solved by analog or numerical means.

There is a further consequence of the instability of Laplace's and Poisson's equations under Cauchy conditions. For high-perveance guns, the length of the gun is of the same order as the width. The theoretical electrodes would usually pass through the beam, a possibility which could be realized only with grids. In many applications grids are unusable, because they intercept charge and have a low thermal conductivity; hence, in high-power applications, grids may easily be melted. Moreover, in order to synthesize the potentials accurately across the beam, the grid must be finely spaced, adding to the interception problem. Even if grids were used, any departure in shape from the theoretical electrode which would produce only slight errors on the beam edge might become magnified in the beam interior, producing severe errors in electron emission at the cathode. This point is demonstrated in Sec. 2.3. For these reasons, the purely analytic methods of designing electrodes, in which only potentials outside the beam boundary are considered, must be used with extreme care; they are of little use in the design of high-perveance guns. In this context, high-perveance guns are defined as having a microperveance above 1, for solid beams, and near unity ratio of anode-cathode spacing to cathode width, for hollow beams. In Figs. 7.1 to 7.3 are sketched typical low- and high-perveance strip, solid, and hollow beams. Clearly, the accuracy with which the potentials may be computed in the beam interior has some relation to the ratio of the length of beam boundary over which the potential

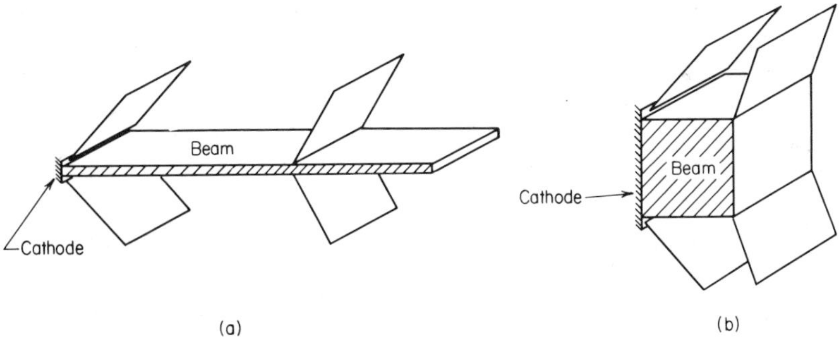

Fig. 7.1. Sketch of low- and high-perveance strip beams.

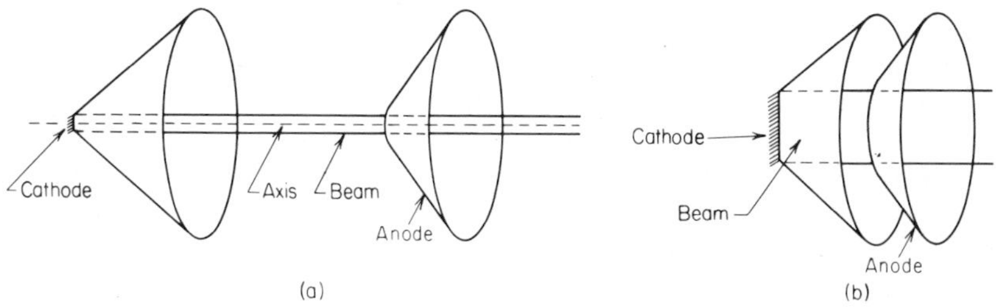

Fig. 7.2. Sketch of low- and high-perveance solid beams.

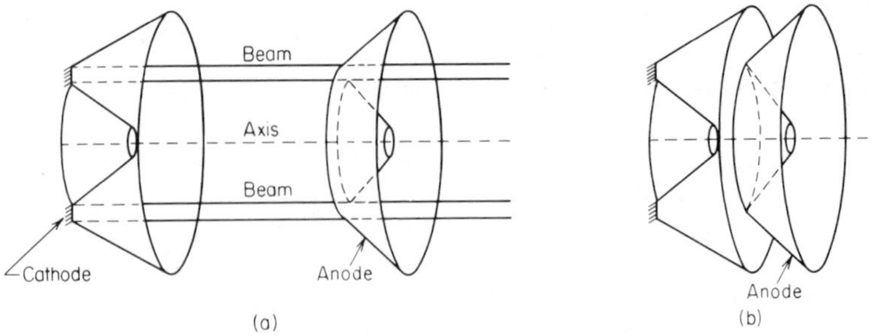

Fig. 7.3. Sketch of low- and high-perveance hollow beams.

is given to the minimum distance from the beam boundary to the cathode center. The errors introduced may be much more serious in high-perveance than in low-perveance applications. For such problems, it is better to trace trajectories inside the beam. This procedure is discussed in Chap. VIII.

In Section 2, we describe the different boundary conditions which arise in the problem of electrode design; the instability of the solution is illustrated by a simple example showing how small errors build up away from the beam boundary.

In Section 3, the method of Lomax for a strip beam is presented; several applications to actual problems are discussed, and some pitfalls to be avoided are pointed out. In Section 4, Radley's method of solving axially symmetric problems is described. Finally, in Section 5, Harker's method of solving axially symmetric problems is developed. Radley's method, in its simpler form, is applicable only with simple beam boundaries. Harker's technique is far more general, but more lengthy to apply.

2. SOME SIMPLE SOLUTIONS OF TWO-DIMENSIONAL BOUNDARY-VALUE PROBLEMS

2.1. Introduction. This chapter treats the problem of determining the electrodes required outside a beam to produce a specified electric field configuration at the beam edge. It is therefore concerned with solving Laplace's, or sometimes Poisson's, equation, which the electrostatic potential of the beam must satisfy. Formally, if the electric field is known at a beam edge, and if the potential distribution obeys Laplace's equation outside the beam, it is simple to determine the potential outside the beam. Laplace's equation may be replaced by a difference equation, which may be solved with comparatively little effort on a digital computer. Unfortunately, when this procedure is applied to the problems with known solutions, the results are often seriously in error. Finite-difference procedures cannot blindly be applied to the solution of partial difference equations; some procedures produce the correct solution of the differential equations when the difference mesh size is indefinitely reduced; others do not. In a finite-difference procedure, numerical errors creep in which are caused by working only to a specified number of significant figures, and by the imperfect simulation of the differential by a difference equation. In some cases these errors are not serious in practice; in others they can completely invalidate the results. It is necessary to look carefully at the original equation and to see how errors in its solution may build up as the solution is continued. To understand the reasons for the success of some methods and the failure of others, it is necessary to investigate the equations under the different boundary conditions we might like to impose.

In a mathematical text, a general and rigorous analysis of the efficacy of the procedure of solution would now be necessary. This analysis has been made elsewhere.[7,8] The boundary condition we should like to impose as the specification of the electric field on an open boundary, i.e., the beam edge, has been shown to be a dangerous one. The different possible boundary conditions are illustrated in this section by simple examples and particular instances. Generalizations are made without proof, which can be verified elsewhere[7,8] from the behavior of the simple problems considered here, about problems with more general boundaries and boundary conditions. For the purpose of this analysis, the physical concepts of electric field, beam boundary, etc., are immaterial. It is sufficient to discuss the behavior of the solution of Laplace's equation, under different boundary conditions for ϕ and its derivations on specified curves. Only the two-dimensional Laplace's equation will be considered; the conclusions can be shown to be valid for three-dimensional systems also. For illustration, only one simple configuration will be considered, that in which the region of interest is bounded by two concentric circles. However, cases are discussed where one circle may have an infinitely large or small radius. On the boundaries, simple variations of the potential and electric fields are assumed.

In Sec. 2.2 the solutions are considered with the four common types of boundary conditions; the Dirichlet conditions, where the potential ϕ is specified on both circles, the Neumann condition, where the normal derivative of ϕ is specified on both circles, the mixed condition, where combinations of ϕ and its derivatives are prescribed on both circles, and finally the Cauchy condition, where ϕ and its normal derivative are prescribed on one circle. In Sec. 2.3 the behavior of each of these solutions is investigated, when the value of the function is slightly varied at the boundary. In the first three types of boundary conditions, the potential is found to change the most at the boundary; in the fourth the difference increases at points farther from the boundary. From this result, it may be concluded that numerical procedures based on the first three boundary conditions may be applied with reasonable safety; those based on the last are dangerous.

In Section 5 a method is developed for transforming Laplace's equation, which is elliptic, into a hyperbolic equation. This latter type of equation is stable under Cauchy conditions. When the boundary conditions are known only to finite accuracy, the difference between the true and approximate potential is maximum on the boundary, and less than this value up to a certain distance from it. This result is illustrated in Sec. 2.4 by considering a simple hyperbolic equation twice; first the equation is solved with boundary conditions given on a circle, and then again with a slightly different prescribed potential and normal derivative on the boundary.

The conclusion that the solutions of Laplace's equation are stable under Dirichlet, and unstable under Cauchy, boundary conditions has two important corollaries. If the potentials on an electrode system far from the beam are specified, the boundary conditions are of the Dirichlet form. Even if the electrode system is changed considerably, the fields in the vicinity of the beam may be only slightly altered. It is this fact which, under certain conditions, allows the design of widely different electrode shapes to simulate the same beam. Conversely, if electrodes are being designed by integrating away from the beam boundary, a solution under Cauchy conditions, even a slight error in the value of the boundary conditions for ϕ and $\partial\phi/\partial n$ at the beam boundary may cause radical changes in the possible electrode shapes. The choice of electrodes may not be as wide as it might seem, because the potentials set up inside the beam may not be correct; the errors are greatest for a high-perveance gun which has its thickness or diameter comparable with its length. If the potentials within the beam are incorrect, the emission from the cathode is also liable to be drastically different from its correct value.

2.2. Solution under Different Boundary Conditions. In the first problem considered, the potential ϕ satisfies Laplace's equation in two dimensions in the annulus between two circles, $r = a$ and $r = b$, as shown in Fig. 7.4. In circular polar coordinates, using the expressions for the Laplacian derived in Appendix A, Eq. (3.8), the potential satisfies the equation

$$\frac{\partial^2\phi}{\partial r^2} + \frac{1}{r}\frac{\partial\phi}{\partial r} + \frac{1}{r^2}\frac{\partial^2\phi}{\partial\theta^2} = 0 \qquad (2.1)$$

In addition, the boundary conditions

$$\phi = \sin n\theta \quad \text{on } r = a \quad \text{and} \quad \phi = 0 \quad \text{on } r = b \qquad (2.2)$$

are imposed. These boundary conditions, in which ϕ is defined on a closed boundary, are called Dirichlet conditions.

By use of the method of separation of variables, Eq. (2.1) may be solved under the boundary conditions of Eq. (2.2) with a ϕ of the form

$$\phi = \left(Ar^n + \frac{B}{r^n}\right)\sin n\theta \qquad (2.3)$$

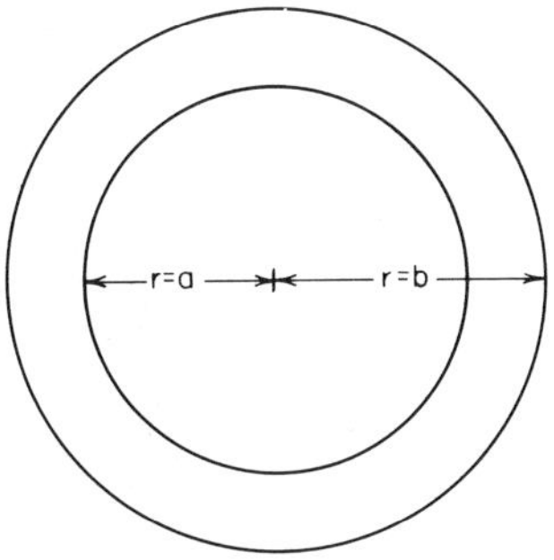

Fig. 7.4. Two circles to illustrate boundary-value problems.

Substitution into Eq. (2.2) yields the formulas

$$A\,a^n + \frac{B}{a^n} = 1 \quad \text{and} \quad A\,b^n + \frac{B}{b^n} = 0 \tag{2.4}$$

so that

$$A = \frac{a^n}{\Delta} \quad \text{and} \quad B = -\frac{a^n b^{2n}}{\Delta} \tag{2.5}$$

where $\Delta = a^{2n} - b^{2n}$. Thus the problem posed by the solution of Laplace's equation under the Dirichlet conditions of Eq. (2.2) is easily soluble.

If we apply, instead of the conditions of Eq. (2.2), the Neumann conditions, in which the normal derivative of ϕ is specified on the boundary in the form

$$\frac{\partial \phi}{\partial r} = \sin n\theta \quad \text{on } r = a \quad \text{and} \quad \frac{\partial \phi}{\partial r} = 0 \quad \text{on } r = b \tag{2.6}$$

a simple substitution of a ϕ of the form of Eq. (2.3) yields the straightforward solution

$$A = \frac{a^{n+1}}{\Delta} \quad \text{and} \quad B = \frac{a^{n+1}\,b^{2n}}{\Delta} \tag{2.7}$$

where $\Delta = (a^{2n} - b^{2n})n$.

Finally, if the boundary values are prescribed in a mixed form, so that some linear combination of ϕ and $\partial\phi/\partial r$ is prescribed, for example,

$$\phi + k_1 \frac{\partial \phi}{\partial r} = \sin n\theta \qquad \text{on } r = a$$

$$\text{and} \quad \phi + k_2 \frac{\partial \phi}{\partial r} = 0 \qquad \text{on } r = b \tag{2.8}$$

it may be verified that the solution again has the form of Eq. (2.3), with

$$A = \frac{b^{-n} - nk_2 b^{-n-1}}{\Delta} \qquad \text{and} \qquad B = -\frac{b^{n} + nk_2 b^{n-1}}{\Delta}$$

$$\Delta = (a^{n} + nk_1\, a^{n-1})(b^{-n} - nk_2\, b^{-n-1}) - (a^{-n} - nk_1 a^{-n-1})(b^{n} - nk_2 b^{n-1}) \tag{2.9}$$

The solutions of Eqs. (2.5) and (2.7) are special cases of those of Eq. (2.9). This can be seen from the form of the boundary condition. The boundary condition of Eq. (2.8) indicates that the boundary function specified may be different at different parts of the boundary.

These examples show how a very simple problem may be solved under the usual boundary conditions for this type of problem, namely the Dirichlet conditions, where ϕ is defined, the Neumann conditions, where the normal derivative of ϕ is defined, and the mixed conditions, where a combination of ϕ and its normal derivative are defined on the boundary.

The radius of the outer circle, $r = b$, can become infinitely large, that is, $b \to \infty$, and the problem is still well defined. The boundary conditions are now given on a contour, i.e., at $r = a$, and at infinity; the solutions of Eqs. (2.5), (2.7), and (2.9) are still valid if the limits of the solutions are taken as $b \to \infty$.

In the solutions just derived, two conditions were imposed on linear combinations of ϕ and its normal derivative. In the examples considered, one linear combination of these quantities was specified on two separate curves. Alternatively, we could specify two linear combinations of them on one closed curve, for example,

$$\phi = \sin n\theta \qquad \text{and} \qquad \frac{\partial \phi}{\partial r} = 0 \qquad \text{on } r = a \tag{2.10}$$

In this case, substitution of a solution of the type of Eq. (2.3) yields

$$\phi = \frac{1}{2}\left[\left(\frac{r}{a}\right)^{n} + \left(\frac{a}{r}\right)^{n}\right] \sin n\theta \tag{2.11}$$

We have thus shown that this problem may also be solved under the conditions in which ϕ and its normal derivative are defined separately on a curve. This is known as the exterior-boundary-value problem, or the solution under Cauchy boundary conditions.

2.3. The Instability of Solutions under Cauchy Conditions and the Stability under Dirichlet Conditions. The solution of Laplace's equation under Dirichlet conditions is always stable. By this we mean that, if there is a slight change in ϕ on the boundary, the change in ϕ in the interior will always be less than the largest change on the boundary. This result is also valid for solutions under Neumann and mixed conditions, but not under Cauchy conditions. With the latter type of boundary condition slight changes or errors in the boundary conditions give increasingly large changes or errors in potential as the distance from the boundary is increased.

The foregoing result on the stability of Laplace's equation can be proved easily. Let ϕ_1 be the potential satisfying Laplace's equation at any point within a closed contour $\mathcal{C}$, with

$$\phi_1 = \Phi_1 \quad \text{on } \mathcal{C} \tag{2.12}$$

If $\psi = \phi_1 + \phi_2$ is a potential distribution satisfying the boundary conditions

$$\psi = \phi_1 + \phi_2 = \Phi_1 + \epsilon\, \Phi_2 \quad \text{on } \mathcal{C} \tag{2.13}$$

then ψ and ϕ_2 satisfy Laplace's equation inside $\mathcal{C}$. The term ϕ_2 has the value $\epsilon\, \Phi_2$ on $\mathcal{C}$. But no solution of Laplace's equation can have a maximum at an interior point;[7] hence $|\phi_2| < |\epsilon\, \Phi_2|$. A similar argument is also valid for Neumann or mixed boundary conditions. Thus with Dirichlet, Neumann, or mixed boundary conditions the change in potential within a closed boundary is always less than the change or error in potential at the boundary.

The result may be verified by considering the situation when

$$\begin{aligned} &\phi_1 = \sin\theta \qquad \psi = \sin\theta + \epsilon \sin n\theta && \text{on } r = a \\ \text{and} \quad &\psi = \phi_1 = 0 && \text{on } r = b \end{aligned} \tag{2.14}$$

This case is sufficiently general for our purposes, because any error in the potential at the boundary can be Fourier-analyzed as the sum of a number of terms of the form $\epsilon \sin n\theta$. Using the superposition of two solutions of the type of Eq. (2.5), it is seen that

$$\phi_2 = \psi - \phi_1$$

$$\phi_2 = \begin{cases} \epsilon \sin n\theta & \text{on } r = a \\ 0 & \text{on } r = b \end{cases} \tag{2.15}$$

and inside the region bounded by the circles $r = a$ and $r = b$,

$$\phi_2 = \frac{\epsilon}{\Delta}\left(a^n r^n - \frac{a^n b^{2n}}{r^n}\right)\sin n\theta \tag{2.16}$$

where $\Delta = a^{2n} - b^{2n}$. It can be easily verified that $|\phi_2|$ is minimum at $r = b$, and greater at $r = a$, $\theta = a/2n$, than anywhere with $a < r < b$. The result may be verified in a similar way for the other types of boundary conditions.

Under Cauchy conditions, such as those of Eq. (2.10), the solution of Laplace's equation still has a maximum value on the boundary. However, the region involved must be bounded. The solution of Eq. (2.11) takes its largest values on the boundaries; for the inside of the circle, these are at $r = 0$, for the outside at $r = \infty$. In either case, the potential becomes infinite.

For example, in the problem

$$\phi_1 = \sin\theta \qquad \psi = \phi_1 + \phi_2 = \sin\theta + \epsilon \sin n\theta$$

and (2.17)

$$\frac{\partial\psi}{\partial r} = \frac{\partial\phi_1}{\partial r} = \frac{\partial\phi_2}{\partial r} = 0 \qquad \text{on } r = a$$

the solution for ϕ_2 away from $r = a$ takes the form of Eq. (2.11). Inspection of Eq. (2.11) shows that, if the potential is slightly in error, by $\epsilon \sin n\theta$, on $r = a$, this error will build up indefinitely, as r is increased or decreased from the value $r = a$. This fact has a strong influence on methods of solution which work out from the beam edge. With an arbitrary error of potential at the boundary of the form $\phi_2 = \Sigma\, \epsilon_n \sin n\theta$, each one of the Fourier components of the error potential increases in magnitude with distance from the boundary, and in general the total error in the potential becomes arbitrarily large.

2.4. The Stability of Solutions of Hyperbolic Equations under Cauchy Conditions. As a physical example, we consider the use of an electrolytic tank (discussed more fully in Chap. IX) to find the potentials outside a circular boundary of radius a. For the case given here, 2n probes spaced at angles π/n apart could be used. However accurately the potentials are defined at the probes, there is an error in potential with a fundamental component of the form $\epsilon \sin n\theta$ around the circle. Hence there are large errors in the potentials determined both inside and outside the radius $r = a$. Doubling the number of probes and spacing them at angles $\pi/2n$ apart would not help, and could lead to worse errors. If we assume that the magnitude of the error at the boundary is the same as before, so that the fundamental error component is of the form

$$\phi_2 = \epsilon \sin 2n\theta \tag{2.18}$$

at $r = a$, then, at any other point,

$$\phi_2 = \left[\left(\frac{r}{a}\right)^{2n} + \left(\frac{a}{r}\right)^{2n}\right] \frac{\varepsilon \sin 2n\theta}{2} \tag{2.19}$$

Now the errors increase in magnitude with distance from the boundary more rapidly than before. Similar difficulties arise in an analysis which uses an nth-order polynomial approximation to the correct potential at the boundary accurate at n points. The same troubles also occur with numerical methods based on the use of difference equations, or with resistance networks.

For high-perveance guns, therefore, in which the distance from the beam edge to the cathode is comparable with the anode-cathode spacing, direct methods of solution which work out from a beam edge of finite length are of doubtful validity. Not only would the potentials, and hence the electrodes, outside the beam be suspect, but also the potentials within the interior of the beam could be radically in error. Possible guns in which such difficulties might arise are illustrated schematically in Figs. 7.1b and 7.2b.

In this section we consider, as an example, a type of hyperbolic differential equation, the wave equation in cylindrical polar coordinates, and show that, with Cauchy conditions, its solutions are stable; i.e., the error in potential is always less than or equal to that on the boundary. This situation is quite different from the one derived in the preceding section for an elliptic differential equation, i.e., Laplace's equation, and confirms the general result that hyperbolic equations can be solved under Cauchy's conditions.[8]

The solution of the hyperbolic equation

$$\frac{\partial^2 \phi}{\partial r^2} + \frac{1}{r}\frac{\partial \phi}{\partial r} - \frac{1}{r^2}\frac{\partial^2 \phi}{\partial \theta^2} = 0 \tag{2.20}$$

with the same boundary conditions as were taken for Laplace's equation [Eq. (2.1)],

$$\phi = \sin(n\theta) \qquad \text{and} \qquad \frac{\partial \phi}{\partial r} = 0 \qquad \text{on } r = a \tag{2.21}$$

is

$$\phi = \cos\left[n\,\ell n\,\frac{r}{a}\right]\sin n\theta \tag{2.22}$$

When the potential at the point (r,θ) is compared with its value at the point (a,θ), it is seen that

$$|\phi(r,\theta)| \leqq |\phi(a,\theta)| \tag{2.23}$$

Consequently, a change or error in the potential at the boundary $r = a$ gives rise to smaller changes or errors in potential at points outside or inside the boundary.

Numerical calculation performed on hyperbolic equations with such boundary conditions may therefore be expected to be accurate.

3. THE SOLUTION OF THE TWO-DIMENSIONAL EXTERIOR-BOUNDARY-VALUE PROBLEM

3.1. Introduction. In this section we give an exact solution to the problem of solving Laplace's equation in two dimensions when ϕ and its normal derivatives are prescribed on some curve. In practice, this curve would normally be the beam boundary. The method used, that of analytic continuation, gives an exact solution and is free from most of the pitfalls which arise from purely numerical solutions of the problem. The method given here was used first by Pierce[1] to determine analytically the potential distribution outside a parallel rectilinear beam. Lomax[9] and Kirstein[10] extended the method to find the potentials outside curved beams; Lomax used his method to determine the electrode for the circular flow of Chap. II, Sec. 3.4.

We first solve a very common problem in which ϕ is defined in a particular way, on a straight line, with zero normal derivative. The solution is extended to the case where ϕ and its normal derivative are defined by arbitrary analytic functions on a straight line; and finally, we treat the problem of finding ϕ, when the potential and its normal derivative are given by arbitrary analytic functions on a

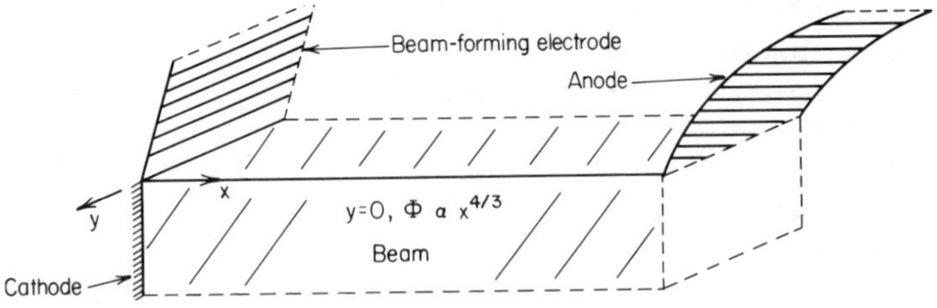

Fig. 7.5. Configuration for a parallel beam.

parametrically represented analytic curve. Some particular problems are solved to demonstrate the use of the method and to illustrate the possible pitfalls to be encountered in its application. Finally, the method is extended to problems in which neither the arbitrary curve nor the gradient of potential on it is defined in terms of analytic functions.

3.2. Electrodes to Maintain a Parallel Beam. The first electron-flow problem considered, that of maintaining a parallel flow of electrons from a space-charge-limited cathode, is of great importance in gun design. The physical situation is shown in Fig. 7.5, with the beam flowing in the x direction. It has been shown in Sec. 2.2 of Chap. II that the potential must vary as $x^{4/3}$ in the beam. Using the coordinates shown in Fig. 7.5, the solution is required for the potential outside the beam. This corresponds, mathematically, to solving the exterior-boundary-value problem, under Cauchy conditions, defined by the relation

$$\phi = x^{4/3} \quad \text{and} \quad \frac{\partial \phi}{\partial y} = 0 \quad \text{on } y = 0 \tag{3.1}$$

We now consider the (x,y) plane as part of the w plane, where

$$w = x + jy \tag{3.2}$$

It is more usual to use the notation z for w. To avoid confusion with the third coordinate direction, however, the symbol w is used. A fuller discussion of the meaning of such complex planes, and of the algebra associated with them, is given in Appendix B. It is shown in Appendix B, Section 3, that both real and imaginary parts of any function of w satisfy Laplace's equation so that, if complex functions χ and ψ are defined by the relations

$$\chi(w) = \phi(x,y) + j\psi(x,y) \tag{3.3}$$

ϕ satisfies Laplace's equation. Now since χ is a function only of w, it satisfies the Cauchy-Riemann equation [Eq. (2.5) of Appendix B]

$$\frac{\partial \phi}{\partial x} = \frac{\partial \psi}{\partial y} \quad \text{and} \quad \frac{\partial \phi}{\partial y} = -\frac{\partial \psi}{\partial x} \tag{3.4}$$

so that $\partial\phi/\partial y$ is given by

$$\frac{\partial\phi}{\partial y} = -\frac{\partial\psi}{\partial x} = -\text{Im}\left(\frac{\partial\chi}{dw}\right) \tag{3.5}$$

Consider the function

$$\chi = w^{4/3} \tag{3.6}$$

On the line y = 0, Re χ, that is, ϕ, has the value $x^{4/3}$, whereas from Eq. (3.5) the normal derivative of ϕ, that is, $\partial\phi/\partial y$, is zero. Hence the function

$$\phi = \text{Re}\left(w^{4/3}\right) \tag{3.7}$$

satisfies Laplace's equation and the boundary condition of Eq. (3.1).

We wish to solve this problem in order to determine the correct electrodes. The equation of the electrodes may be obtained easily from Eq. (3.7) since the electrodes lie along the equipotentials, ϕ = constant. In circular coordinates centered at x = y = 0, the equipotentials are given, from Eq. (3.7), by

$$r^{4/3} \cos\left(\tfrac{4}{3}\theta\right) = \text{constant} \tag{3.8}$$

The equipotentials arising from the evaluation of Eq. (3.8) are shown in Fig. 7.6.

The equation for the equipotentials may also be obtained in another form, which is capable of extension to more complicated problems. The total rate of change of ϕ with x is given by

$$\frac{d\phi}{dx} = \frac{\partial\phi}{\partial x} + \frac{\partial\phi}{\partial y}\frac{dy}{dx} = 0 \tag{3.9}$$

By some manipulation of Eqs. (3.3), (3.4), (3.5), (3.7), and (3.9), any possible equipotential, and therefore electrode shape, is given by the relation

$$\frac{dy}{dx} = \frac{\text{Re}\,(d\chi/dw)}{\text{Im}\,(d\chi/dw)} = \frac{\text{Re}\left(\tfrac{4}{3}w^{1/3}\right)}{\text{Im}\left(\tfrac{4}{3}w^{1/3}\right)} \tag{3.10}$$

It is the form of Eq. (3.10) which may be extended for more complicated problems.

3.3. Extension to an Arbitrary Potential and Field on a Line. We now extend the method, used for obtaining the electrodes to maintain a parallel flow, to the more general problems of solving for ϕ when both ϕ and its normal derivative are given on a line, as in Fig. 7.5, y = 0. If ϕ and its normal derivative are given at a boundary, it is clear that the tangential derivative of ϕ at this boundary is also known. We solve therefore the problem in which $\nabla\phi$ is given by an arbitrary function on the line y = 0, that is, under the conditions

$$\frac{\partial\phi}{\partial x} = \Phi_X(x) \quad \text{and} \quad \frac{\partial\phi}{\partial y} = \Phi_Y(x) \quad \text{on } y = 0 \tag{3.11}$$

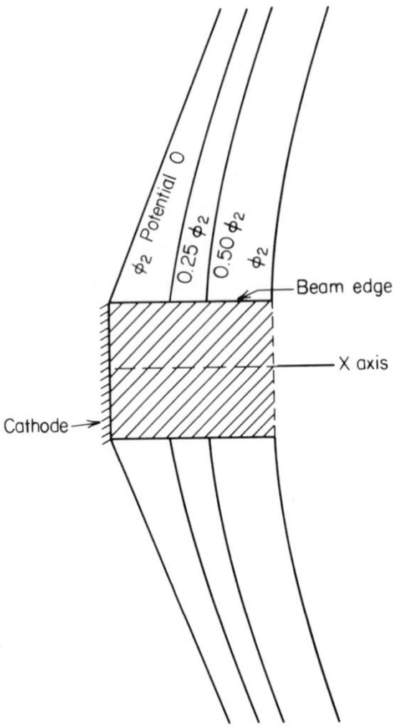

Fig. 7.6. Electrodes required to produce a parallel strip beam.

In the previous example, Φ_X was $\frac{4}{3}x^{1/3}$, Φ_y was zero. From the Cauchy-Riemann equations of Eq. (3.4) and from Eq. (3.11), the complex potential χ has the form of Eq. (3.3), where

$$\left(\frac{d\chi}{dx}\right)_{y=0} = \left(\frac{\partial\phi}{\partial x} + j\,\frac{\partial\psi}{\partial x}\right)_{y=0} = \Phi_X(x) - j\Phi_y(x) \tag{3.12}$$

From the principle of analytic continuation discussed in Appendix B, if an analytic function has the value a(x) on the line y = 0, it will have the value a(w) in the rest of the w plane. Hence, from Eq. (3.12),

$$\chi = \int^{w} [\Phi_X(w') - j\Phi_y(w')]\, dw' \tag{3.13}$$

The potential function ϕ is merely the real part of the χ of Eq. (3.13). It is clear that the χ for the parallel-beam case is obtained by putting $\Phi_X = \frac{4}{3}x^{1/3}$ and $\Phi_y = 0$ in Eq. (3.13).

We shall not go on, at this stage, to find the equipotentials of ϕ, since the problem just solved is not yet of practical interest. Usually, $\nabla\phi$ will not be given on a straight line, but on a curve. When the problem in which $\nabla\phi$ is given on a curve has been solved, the expressions for the electrode shape, and an equation analogous to Eq. (3.10), will be derived.

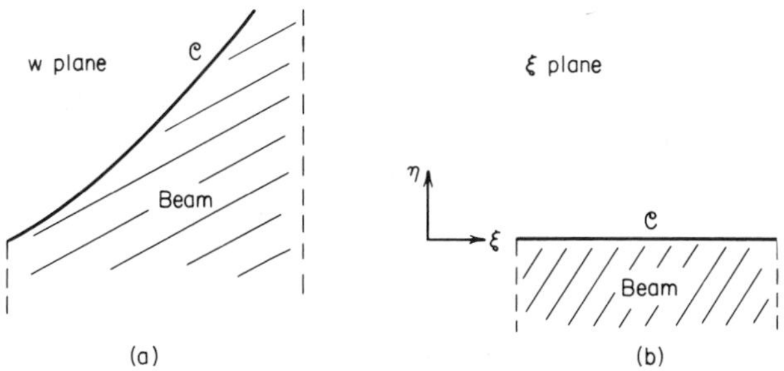

Fig. 7.7. Configuration and mapping for a curvilinear beam.

3.4. Extension to an Arbitrary Potential and Field Defined on an Arbitrary Curve. It is not necessary for the beam edge to be a straight line, which, for electrostatic beams, implies zero normal electric field. The procedure described above may be used also for curvilinear beams. If the beam edge is taken as an analytic curve $\mathcal{C}$, given parametrically by

$$x = X(\xi) \qquad \text{and} \qquad y = Y(\xi) \tag{3.14}$$

it is possible to define a conformal transformation from the x,y plane to another plane, in which $\mathcal{C}$ is a straight line analogous to $y = 0$ in Fig. 7.5.

We define w as before by Eq. (3.2), and W by the equation

$$W(\xi) = X(\xi) + jY(\xi) \tag{3.15}$$

where W has no relation, in this context, with the action function. The conformal transformation

$$w = W(\zeta) \tag{3.16}$$

where ζ is a complex variable,

$$\zeta = \xi + j\eta \qquad \xi \text{ and } \eta \text{ real} \tag{3.17}$$

and η has no relation in this context with $-q/m$, maps points of the ζ plane into the w plane. In particular, from Eq. (3.15) the line $\eta = 0$ is mapped into the contour $\mathcal{C}$ given by Eq. (3.14). The transformation is shown in Fig. 7.7.

If now ϕ and the angle θ between the gradient of the potential and the trajectory $\mathcal{C}$ are defined parametrically in terms of ξ on $\mathcal{C}$, then

$$(\nabla\phi)_{\text{tangential}} = \frac{\partial\Phi}{\partial\xi}\frac{d\xi}{ds} \qquad \text{and} \qquad (\nabla\phi)_{\text{normal}} = \frac{\partial\phi}{\partial\xi}\frac{d\xi}{ds}\tan\theta \tag{3.18}$$

where ds is the incremental element of arc length on $\mathcal{C}$. If $\Phi(\xi)$ and $\theta(\xi)$ are related to arbitrary analytic functions $\Phi_\xi(\xi)$ and $\Phi_\eta(\xi)$ by

$$\phi_\xi = \frac{d\phi}{d\xi} \qquad \text{and} \qquad \phi_\eta = \frac{d\phi}{d\xi}\tan\theta \tag{3.19}$$

the formulation of Eqs. (3.11) to (3.13) applies directly, with (ξ,η) replacing (x,y).

The potential $\phi(\xi,\eta)$ is given as the real part of the analytic function $\chi(\zeta)$, where

$$\chi(\zeta) = \int^{\zeta} [\phi_{\xi}(\zeta') - j\phi_{\eta}(\zeta')]\, d\zeta' \tag{3.20}$$

and $$w = x + jy = W(\zeta) \tag{3.21}$$

Hence, given any (ξ,η), w is obtained from Eq. (3.21), and then the potential by Eq. (3.20). Alternatively, given w, we may use Eq. (3.21) to find ζ and then, from Eq. (3.19), the potential at that value of ζ. To obtain the electrodes from Eqs. (3.20) and (3.21), Eq. (3.8) is used, with ξ and η replacing x and y. For an equipotential, η will be some function of ξ, say,

$$\eta = \overline{\eta}(\xi) \tag{3.22}$$

where $$\frac{\partial\phi}{\partial\xi} + \frac{\partial\phi}{\partial\eta}\frac{d\overline{\eta}}{d\xi} = 0 \tag{3.23}$$

From Eq. (3.4), with ξ and η replacing x and y, and Eq. (3.20), Eq. (3.23) becomes

$$\frac{d\overline{\eta}}{d\xi} = \frac{\mathrm{Re}\,[\phi_{\xi}(\zeta) - j\phi_{\eta}(\zeta)]}{\mathrm{Im}\,[\phi_{\xi}(\zeta) - j\phi_{\eta}(\zeta)]} \tag{3.24}$$

Usually, Eq. (3.24) must be solved numerically; as ξ traces out the curve $\eta = \overline{\eta}(\xi)$, the contour $w = W(\xi + j\eta)$ is traced out in the x,y plane, and this contour yields the appropriate equipotential.

3.5. Application to a Simple Problem of a Crossed-field Gun. The formalism of the earlier part of this section is applied now to the crossed-field-gun solution of Chap. II, in which the electron trajectories are parabolic. This problem, although simple, is solved in detail to illustrate the method of applying the formalism. More complicated problems are considered later in less detail, to illustrate the pitfalls which may arise in the application of the formalism.

The problem to be treated here is illustrated in Fig. 7.8. The magnetic field is perpendicular to the plane of the paper, and there is no electric field in the x direction. The beam occupies the region

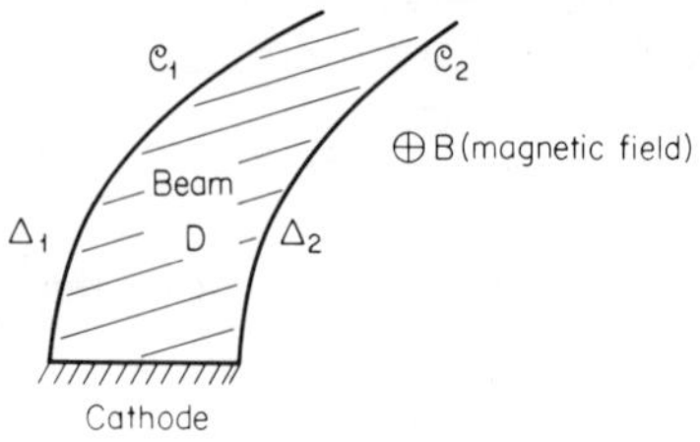

Fig. 7.8. Configuration for a beam for a crossed-field gun (simple case).

D, and the beam boundaries are $\mathcal{C}_1$ and $\mathcal{C}_2$. We wish to continue the solutions to find the equipotentials in the charge-free regions Δ_1 and Δ_2.

The formulas for the potential, the field and the curves $\mathcal{C}_1$ and $\mathcal{C}_2$, are given in normalized, parametric form in Eq. (2.27) of Chap. II. Equation (2.27) of Chap. II contains certain multiplying factors which are immaterial to the discussion and may be ignored in finding the expressions for the beam edges $\mathcal{C}_1$ and $\mathcal{C}_2$.*

$$\begin{aligned} &\text{On } \mathcal{C}_1\text{:}\quad X = \frac{1}{2}\xi^2 \qquad Y = \xi \\ &\text{On } \mathcal{C}_2\text{:}\quad X = \frac{1}{2}\xi^2 + X_0 \qquad Y = \xi \end{aligned} \tag{3.25}$$

where the cathode is taken as $y = 0$ and of width X_0, and the potential and electric field variation are given by

$$\Phi(\xi) = \frac{1}{2}\xi^2 \quad \text{and} \quad E_X = 0 \tag{3.26}$$

Since the curves $\mathcal{C}_1$ and $\mathcal{C}_2$ differ only by a translation in the x direction, it is sufficient to solve the problem defined by Eqs. (3.25) and (3.26) on both sides of $\mathcal{C}_1$. The solution for the left side of $\mathcal{C}_1$ is directly the Φ in Δ_1, and the solution on the right side of $\mathcal{C}_1$ must be displaced by the cathode width X_0 to give the solution in $\mathcal{C}_2$.

For the X and Y of Eq. (3.25), it is seen that W, as defined by Eq. (3.15), has the form

$$W(\xi) = \frac{1}{2}\xi^2 + j\xi \tag{3.27}$$

so that $W(\zeta)$ is given by

$$W(\zeta) = \frac{1}{2}\zeta^2 + j\zeta \tag{3.28}$$

It is seen, from Eq. (3.26), that the direction of $\nabla\phi$ is perpendicular to the x axis; from Eq. (3.25) the slope of the curve $\mathcal{C}_1$ is $1/\xi$. Hence the tangent of the angle between $\nabla\phi$ and $\mathcal{C}_1$, the θ of Eq. (3.18), is given by

$$\tan\theta = \xi \tag{3.29}$$

Using Eqs. (3.26) and (3.29), Eq. (3.19) becomes

$$\phi_\xi = \xi \quad \text{and} \quad \phi_\eta = \xi^2 \tag{3.30}$$

From here on, the complex potential function is obtained by substitution into the relevant formulas. Substituting Eq. (3.30) into Eq. (3.20) gives the potential function

*The expressions of Chap. II have a reversed sign for x; this denotes that the solution here is for a magnetic field −B.

$$\chi(\zeta) = \frac{1}{2}\zeta^2 - \frac{1}{3}j\zeta^3 \tag{3.31}$$

whereas the equation of the equipotentials is, from Eq. (3.24),

$$\frac{d\eta}{d\xi} = \frac{\text{Re }(\zeta - j\zeta^2)}{\text{Im }(\zeta - j\zeta^2)} = \frac{\xi + 2\xi\eta}{\eta - \xi^2 + \eta^2} \tag{3.32}$$

In this case it is not necessary to solve Eq. (3.32) itself, since it is possible to obtain the equipotentials directly, but it is instructive to do so. Equation (3.32) may be written

$$(\eta^2 + \eta)\, d\eta = \frac{1}{2}\, d(\xi^2) + d(\xi^2\eta)$$

which may be integrated to yield the relation

$$\xi^2 = \frac{{}^2\!/_3\, \eta^3 + \eta^2 + \text{constant}}{1 + 2\eta} \tag{3.33}$$

Given any potential, defined by the constant, a curve can be traced out by varying η. The appropriate x and y are then obtained from Eq. (3.31).

It is to be noted that the potentials and fields on $\mathcal{C}_1$ and $\mathcal{C}_2$ are identical, the only difference between the two curves being a shift in the x direction. For this reason, if we solve for ϕ on one side of $\mathcal{C}_1$, the resulting equipotentials will be the required ones. If we solve for ϕ on the other side of $\mathcal{C}_1$, and then shift the equipotential plots by the cathode width X_0, the equipotentials are the correct ones outside $\mathcal{C}_2$.

The resulting equipotential plots, along any of which electrodes may be placed, are shown in Fig. 7.9. A typical electrode system resulting from these plots, allowing for the shift due to cathode width, is shown in Fig. 7.10.

3.6. A More Complicated Application to Crossed-field Guns. A more complicated application from Chap. II is now discussed. In this crossed-field gun the initial electron velocity is zero, and the electron trajectories undulate about a parabolic path. Because of these undulations, the mathematical expressions obtained are much more complicated. As a result, difficulties due to branch points in

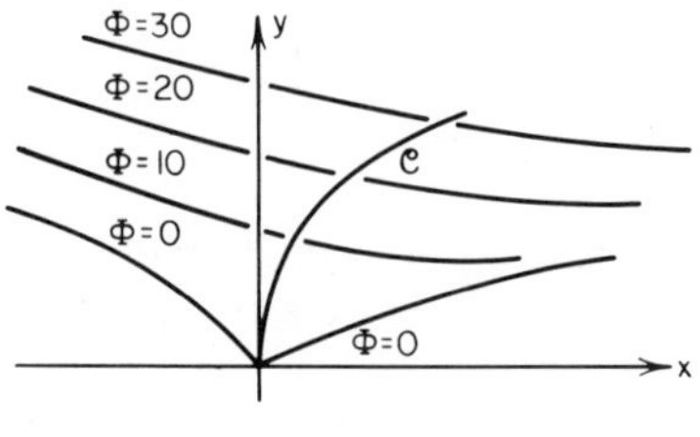

Fig. 7.9. Equipotential plots for a beam for a crossed-field gun (simple case).

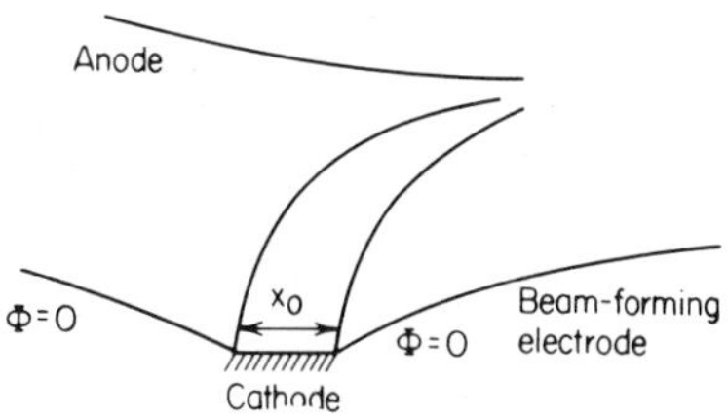

Fig. 7.10. Electrodes required to support flow for a crossed-field gun (simple case).

the solution arise. Their resolution gives some insight into the care which must be taken.

With the same general physical picture as Fig. 7.8, in this application the relevant equations for the physical quantities on the boundaries of the beam are, from Eqs. (2.22) and (2.24) of Chap. II, given on the boundaries $\mathcal{C}_1$ and $\mathcal{C}_2$ by the expressions*

$$\text{On } \mathcal{C}_1\text{: } X = \frac{1}{2}\xi^2 + \cos\xi - 1 \qquad Y = \xi - \sin\xi$$
$$\text{On } \mathcal{C}_2\text{: } X = \frac{1}{2}\xi^2 + \cos\xi - 1 + X_0 \qquad Y = \xi - \sin\xi \tag{3.34}$$

and

$$\phi = 1 - \cos\xi + \frac{1}{2}\xi^2 - \xi\sin\xi \qquad \text{and} \qquad E_X = 0 \tag{3.35}$$

These equations are very similar to Eqs. (3.25) and (3.26), but contain additional trigonometric terms. These trigonometric terms are the sources of the difficulties which arise.

If an analysis similar to that of the last section is carried out, the expressions for W, χ, and the equation of an electrode become

$$W = \frac{1}{2}\zeta^2 + j\zeta + e^{-j\zeta} - 1 \tag{3.36}$$

and

$$\chi = 1 - \frac{1}{3}j\zeta^3 + \frac{1}{2}\zeta^2 - (1 + j\zeta)e^{-j\zeta} \tag{3.37}$$

$$\frac{d\eta}{d\xi} = \frac{\text{Re}\,(\zeta - j\zeta^2 - \zeta e^{-j\zeta})}{\text{Im}\,(\zeta - j\zeta^2 - \zeta e^{-j\zeta})} \tag{3.38}$$

Details of this analysis are available in Ref. 10. The equation for the equipotentials [Eq. (3.38)] must be solved numerically.

Equations (3.36) to (3.38) formally solve the problem of designing the electrodes for the crossed-field gun; the last equation cannot be

*The sign of x is reversed in Chap. II. This denotes that the magnetic field here is −B.

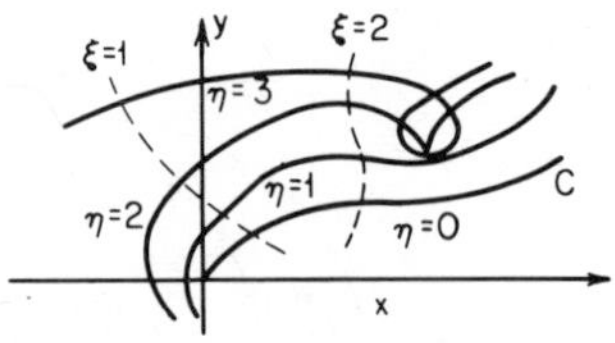

Fig. 7.11. The W-ζ mapping for beam for a crossed-field gun (complex case).

solved analytically in terms of elementary functions, but the numerical solution of the equations throws some light on the difficulties encountered in blindly applying the formalism.

Inspection of Eq. (3.36) shows that the w-ζ mapping is a multivalued one. This means that, as a curve is traced out in the ζ plane, the mapping of this curve in the w plane crosses itself. The mapping of the ζ plane into the w plane is shown in Fig. 7.11. If a curve, for example, $\eta = 3$ in Fig. 7.11, crosses itself, there are points in the w plane which arise from different values of ζ. The potentials ϕ, that is, the real part of χ, arising from the different ζ, which give the same w, are also, in general, different. The paradoxical situation arises that, at the same physical point in the w plane, there should be two values of the potential, which is physically impossible. Now the contour $\mathcal{C}$, which defined the beam edge originally, is the curve $\eta = 0$. Hence the part of the ζ plane which is interesting is in the vicinity of the line $\eta = 0$. Electrodes must be placed sufficiently close to $\mathcal{C}$ to exclude regions where the mapping becomes multivalued. The mapping of the lines ϕ = constant, obtained by integrating Eq. (3.38), is shown in Fig. 7.12. The figure shows that the maximum possible normalized potential curves, which are everywhere single-valued, are those corresponding to $\phi = 68$. For larger ϕ, it would be necessary to have additional smaller potential electrodes, to exclude the forbidden parts of the ζ plane, where multivalued potentials exist.

An electrode system which arises from the potential plot of Fig. 7.12 is shown in Fig. 7.13. A further discussion of this crossed-field gun is given in Sec. 2.3 of Chap. II

The concepts of forbidden regions, multivalued potentials, and in some cases even essential singularities, i.e., points through which

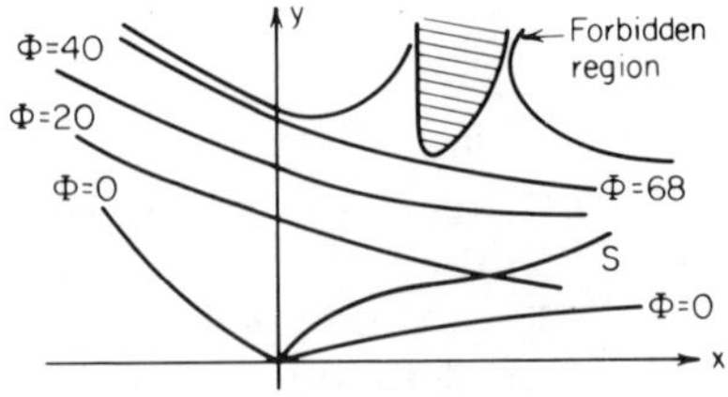

Fig. 7.12. Equipotential plots for a beam for a crossed-field gun (complex case).

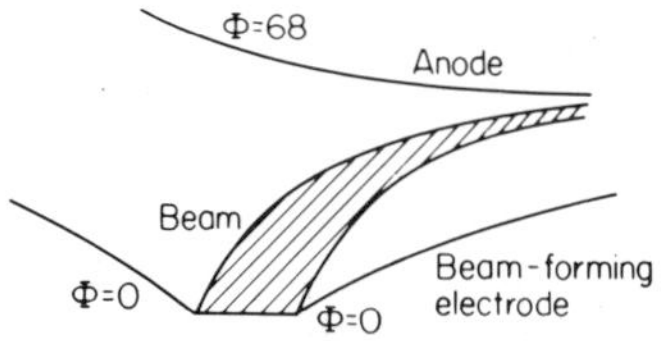

Fig. 7.13. Electrodes required to support the beam for a crossed-field gun (complex case).

all equipotentials pass, are not mere mathematical fictions. We demonstrated in Section 2 the instability of Laplace's equation, under the Cauchy conditions in which the electric field is specified at the beam edge. Rapid variation of potential at the beam edge, or even slow variations of potential in regions where the beam edge has large curvature, might inevitably require impossibly large local variation of potential. An analogy might be to attempt to describe, by a single-valued velocity function, the motion of water in a pond when excited by a long curved object. The disturbances from the surface of the object may start by spreading out smoothly. If the object is concave, however, streams of water will start crossing each other some distance from the exciting object. When this occurs, it is no longer possible to describe the motion of the water by a univalued velocity function. In the water analogy, crossing streamlines are possible. In the electrostatic field, equipotentials cannot physically cross, and the physical conditions may be impossible to realize, unless many electrodes are used very close to the beam.

3.7. The Beam-forming Electrodes near a Curvilinear Strip Beam. In Chap. VIII various analog and numerical methods will be discussed for designing electrode configuration to produce specific electron flows. Some of these configurations separate the field into two parts, one part due to space charge and one due to applied fields. Most of the methods require an initial assumption about the electrode shape; the closer the assumed shape to the correct shape, the quicker the method succeeds. In the immediate vicinity of the cathode, for space-charge-limited flow, space charge becomes infinite, and is difficult to simulate. For these reasons, it is important to design analytically the electrodes in the immediate vicinity of the beam, even if other methods of design are used for the rest of the electrode system.

In this section, therefore, the electrodes are designed analytically near the cathode. Provided that this point of interest is sufficiently near to the cathode and that the emission is space-charge-limited, all beams have substantially the same potential variation, namely,

$$\phi \propto z^{4/3}$$

where z is the distance from the cathode. Expressions are developed for the electrode shape near the cathode for strip beams with curvilinear trajectories. The relevance of the analysis to axially symmetric beams, and the distance to which the electrode shapes derived by this method are valid, are also briefly discussed.

The problem of this section serves as a further application of the methods of analytic continuation previously developed. In Eqs. (2.44) of Chap. I and (3.18) of Chap. II, it was shown that near the cathode of a space-charge-limited beam with curvature κ, the potential ϕ varies as $q_1^{4/3}$ and the normal field as $2\kappa\phi$, where q_1 is the distance from the cathode, measured along the beam. In the analyses of this chapter, it is more convenient to denote the distance along the beam by the symbol ξ. The problem to be solved in this section is that of finding the equipotentials outside the beam, provided that, at the beam edge,

$$\phi = \xi^{4/3} \qquad \text{and} \qquad \frac{\partial\phi}{\partial\eta} = 2\kappa\xi^{4/3} \tag{3.39}$$

where ξ is the distance from the cathode measured along the beam, and η is the other coordinate in a curvilinear mapping with the beam boundary as the curve $\eta = 0$. The coordinates (ξ,η) are exactly the same as those derived in Sec. 3.4.

To a first approximation, the beam boundary may be taken as having constant curvature κ. To this approximation, ξ is the distance along circles concentric with the beam edge, and η is the distance normal to the beam edge.

To find the potential ϕ in terms of the variables ξ and η, it is possible to use Eq. (3.20) directly. The potential ϕ is the real part of a function χ of the complex variable ζ, where

$$\zeta = \xi + j\eta \tag{3.17}$$

$$\chi(\zeta) = \phi + j\psi \tag{3.3}$$

and the ϕ and $\partial\phi/\partial\eta$ of Eq. (3.39) replace the $\int^{\zeta}\phi\xi(\zeta')\,d\zeta'$ and $\phi\eta$ of Eq. (3.20). Making these substitutions, Eq. (3.20) yields the expression for the complex potential χ:

$$\chi(\zeta) = \zeta^{4/3} - \frac{6}{7}\,j\kappa\zeta^{7/3} \tag{3.40}$$

For this result to be intelligible, the transformation must be found from the (ξ,η) coordinates to a more familiar kind. Defining cylindrical polar coordinates with the edge of the cathode as origin, as shown in Fig. 7.14, the following geometric relation may be deduced, assuming the beam edge has constant curvature κ:

$$\kappa\xi = \alpha \qquad \kappa r\cos\theta = (1-\kappa\eta)\sin\alpha$$
$$\text{and} \quad (1-\kappa\eta)^2 = 1 + (\kappa r)^2 - 2\kappa r\sin\theta \tag{3.41}$$

For $\kappa r \ll 1$, one may deduce

$$\kappa\eta \approx \kappa r\sin\theta - \tfrac{1}{2}(\kappa r)^2\cos^2\theta \tag{3.42}$$

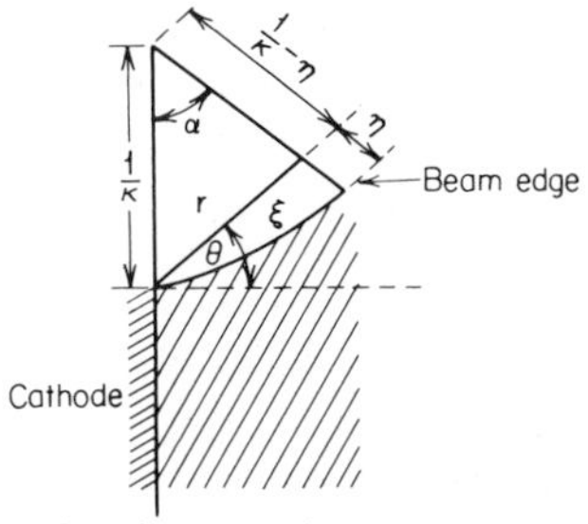

Fig. 7.14. Notation to describe the coordinate system near the edge of the cathode.

Assuming also $\sin\alpha \simeq \alpha$, it can be shown that

$$\kappa\xi = \frac{\kappa r \cos\theta}{1-\kappa\eta}$$

$$\approx \kappa r\cos\theta + (\kappa r)^2 \sin\theta\cos\theta \tag{3.43}$$

From Eqs. (3.42) and (3.43) the following relation between ζ and (r,θ) is deduced:

$$\zeta = r\exp(j\theta) + \frac{1}{4}\kappa r^2 \left[2\sin(2\theta) - j - j\cos(2\theta)\right] \tag{3.44}$$

Combining now Eq. (3.40) with Eq. (3.44), it is possible to express the complex χ in terms of (r,θ) in the form, assuming $\kappa r \ll 1$,

$$\chi = r^{4/3}\exp\left(\frac{4j\theta}{3}\right) + \kappa r^{7/3}\left\{ {}^1\!/_3 \exp\left(\frac{j\theta}{3}\right)\left[2\sin(2\theta) - j - j\cos(2\theta)\right] - \frac{6}{7}\,j\exp\frac{7}{3}\,j\theta\right\} \tag{3.45}$$

The zero-potential electrode is obtained by putting the real part of χ zero in Eq. (3.45), which yields the equation for the zero equipotential

$$\cos\left(\frac{4\theta}{3}\right) = -\kappa r\left[\frac{19}{14}\sin\left(\frac{7\theta}{3}\right) + \frac{1}{6}\sin\left(\frac{5}{3}\theta\right) + \frac{1}{3}\sin\left(\frac{\theta}{3}\right)\right] \tag{3.46}$$

It is seen that, for $r = 0$, the zero-potential beam-forming electrode has a slope of $67\frac{1}{2}°$, or ${}^3\!/_8\,\pi$, but is no longer a straight line as κr becomes larger.

Equation (3.46) is valid only for small r, but it is useful for evaluating the initial curvature of the zero-potential electrode as well as its slope. Writing

$$\theta = \frac{3}{8}\pi + \delta \tag{3.47}$$

where δ is assumed to be small, Eq. (3.46) becomes, to first-order in δ and κr,

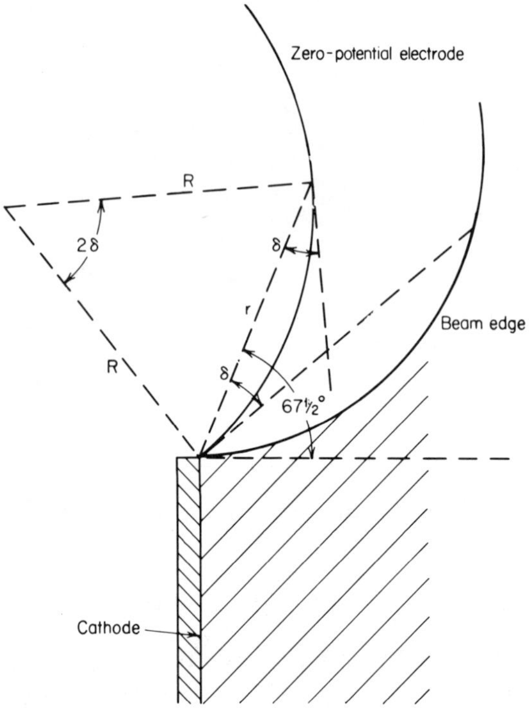

Fig. 7.15. Determining the curvature of the zero-potential electrode.

$$\frac{4}{3}\,\delta = \kappa r\left[\frac{19}{14}\sin\left(\frac{7\pi}{8}\right) + \frac{1}{6}\sin\left(\frac{5\pi}{8}\right) + \frac{1}{3}\sin\left(\frac{\pi}{8}\right)\right] \qquad (3.48)$$

or $$\delta = 0.60\,\kappa r \qquad (3.49)$$

The initial curvature of the cathode beam-forming electrodes can be determined from Eq. (3.49). If the radius of curvature of the beam-forming electrode is R, and if δ is small, then it is seen, from Fig. 7.15, that

$$2R\delta = r \qquad (3.50)$$

It follows from Eq. (3.49) that

$$R = \frac{5}{6\kappa} \qquad (3.51)$$

Therefore, if the beam edge is initially curved, the zero-potential beam-forming electrode will also be curved in the same direction with a radius of curvature somewhat smaller than that of the beam. Conversely, if the zero-potential line (or electrode) is curved in the neighborhood of the cathode, as might occur when there is a space between a negative beam-forming electrode and the cathode, there is a tendency for the edge of the beam to be curved. In this case, as is shown in Chaps. II and III, the current density near the edge of the beam is nonuniform. There is a further corollary that the configuration of the electrodes near the edge of the cathode must be mechanically accurate; otherwise the electrons near the edge of the beam will be emitted in curved paths, which may not have the curvature originally intended.

The solutions derived here are those for a strip beam infinite in one direction. These results are reasonably accurate for axially symmetric beams if the curvature of the beam edge, and hence the initial curvature of the cathode electrode, is considerably larger than the initial distance of the edge of the beam from the axis of symmetry.

3.8. Summary of the Potentialities of the Method and Its Pitfalls. The method gives possible electrode configurations to solve any problem of the form of Fig. 7.8. If the mapping of the ζ plane is multivalued, care must be taken in using the solution of the differential equation (3.24). In actual computation, it is then necessary to look into the details of the ζ-w and ζ-χ mappings.

It may require many electrodes to produce a given field pattern on $\mathcal{C}$; this is shown in the first example. It may not be possible to design the system if the proviso is added that the electrodes must be farther than a specified distance from $\mathcal{C}$. Finally, if there are singularities of w or χ at finite points of the ζ plane, a case not illustrated in this chapter, it is necessary to make a cut in the ζ plane to ensure that the path of integration never completely surrounds a singularity. With this proviso, the path of integration in the ζ plane is always arbitrary.

In the development of this section, it was stated that $X(\xi)$, $\psi(\xi)$, $\phi(\xi)$, and $\phi_n(\xi)$ were analytic functions of ξ. Although this restriction is necessary, the functions need not be defined explicitly. They may be given numerically or as solutions to ordinary differential equations. If they are given numerically, an analytic function, such as a power series, must be fitted through the points. Such a procedure is likely to be very inaccurate. If they are given as the solution of ordinary differential equations, usually in one real independent variable, the accuracy of the method is in no way affected, for the differential equation defines an analytic function. The differential equations are solved at the same time as the equipotentials of Eq. (3.24) are evaluated; now it is necessary to solve the ordinary differential equations, using a complex independent variable, and to add a defining relation between this complex variable and ζ. No extra difficulties are encountered in such a procedure.

Even if one or more of X, Y, ϕ_ξ, or ϕ_η are analytic functions, it is often convenient, for numerical computation, to replace them by their defining differential equations. For example, $X(\xi)$ might be

$P_n(\xi)$, where P_n is the Legendre[11] function of order n, and n is not integral. In this case it would be preferable to carry out the solution of the differential equation for $X(\xi)$ in the form

$$(1 - \zeta^2) \frac{d^2X}{d\zeta^2} - 2\zeta \frac{dX}{d\zeta} + n\,(n - 1)\,\zeta = 0 \tag{3.52}$$

which is the defining equation for the Legendre[11] function, at the same time as computing w and χ. An example of the solution of a problem in which the X, Y, ϕ_ξ, and ϕ_η are the solutions of differential equations is given in Ref. 9.

4. EXTERIOR-BOUNDARY-VALUE PROBLEMS FOR AXIALLY SYMMETRIC AND PLANAR SYSTEMS

4.1. Introduction. A very complete paper by Radley[2] has treated the exterior-boundary-value problem, where ϕ and $\partial\phi/\partial n$ are given on a closed or semi-infinite surface, described by two parameters. This means that the method is certainly applicable to planar and axially symmetric systems. In its original form, the method is limited to problems in which the prescribed surface is one of the level surfaces of a system in which Laplace's equation is separable. As such, it may be used to solve the problem of the last section. On a level surface of a coordinate system, one of the coordinates is kept constant; in spherical polar coordinates (r,θ,φ), for example, the sphere r = constant, the cone θ = constant, and the plane φ = constant are all level surfaces. Radley's method may be extended to problems in which the prescribed surface is not so restricted. The solution in this case is simple to express formally, but it is necessary to solve two coupled linear integral equations, which in practice may be very difficult. Lack of space forces us to pass over many of the finesses of the detailed application of the procedure. In most cases where the prescribed curve is not one of the level lines of a coordinate system in which Laplace's equation separates, it is more convenient to use the alternative method of electrode design of the next section. In those cases where the methods can be applied reasonably simply, it provides very useful approximations to the electrode shapes.

All the difficulties and pitfalls of the previous section are equally pertinent to the solutions described here. This is no fault of the methods; it is a direct result of the problem being solved. Any theoretically exact method gives the same multivalued, or sometimes infinite, solutions for the potential function. It is only approximate methods which sometimes give more usable electrode shapes. Because of the unstable nature of the exterior-boundary-value problem, these more reasonable electrode shapes may give electric field distributions on the beam edge which are indistinguishable, for all practical purposes, from the theoretically exact electrodes.

The underlying principle of the method to be used in this section is the method of superposition. If ϕ_1 and ϕ_2 each satisfy Laplace's equation, then, because the equation is linear, $\phi_1 + \phi_2$ satisfies it. Boundary-value problems are frequently solved by superposition. One or more sets of functions may be chosen, each function separately satisfying Laplace's equation, but not the required boundary conditions, and a suitable multiple of each of these functions is taken, so that their sum satisfies the boundary conditions. Attempts to take only a finite number of such functions for the solution of Cauchy-type boundary-value problems have not proved very successful. If one considers the functions $r^n \sin n\theta$, for different integers n, we showed in Sec. 2.2 that it is the high harmonics which build up most rapidly. Hence the terms neglected in such an expansion may cause serious errors in the potential away from the boundary. If one wishes to consider all functions like $r^n \sin n\theta$ at the same time, it is more convenient to express the sum by an integral. The problem of finding the appropriate amplitude of each function is then reduced to the problem of solving one or more integral equations. For the simple type of functions usually adopted, the integral transformations required are often well tabulated.

As an example of the method, we first derive in Sec. 4.2 an expression for the electrodes required to maintain a pencil beam. The particular case when the beam is infinitesimally thin can be solved analytically. It is shown that the solution derived by Radley's method gives the correct result for the infinitesimally thin pencil beam. In Sec. 4.3, the general formulation of the method is derived. In its full generality, the method is very complicated to apply; however, when the boundaries are along one of the level surfaces of coordinates in coordinate systems in which Laplace's equation separates, the analysis is greatly simplified. Radley's method is carried through in detail only for such boundaries. In Sec. 4.4, as an application of the formulation, Radley's method is shown to give the same result as the complex-variable method of Sec. 3.4.

4.2. Electrodes for Axially Symmetric Pencil Beams. For a pencil beam of radius a from a planar cathode, it was shown in Chap. II, Eq. (2.17), that the potential varies as $z^{4/3}$, where (r,z) are cylindrical polar coordinates. The boundary conditions for the electrodes are

$$\phi = z^{4/3} \quad \text{and} \quad \frac{\partial \phi}{\partial r} = 0 \quad \text{on } r = a \tag{4.1}$$

It can be shown[12] that any axially symmetric solution of Laplace's equation can be synthesized by the addition of suitable multiples of $\exp(-nz)\, J_0(nr)$ and $\exp(-nz)\, Y_0(nr)$, where J_0 and Y_0 are the Bessel and Neumann functions of zero order. These are not the only pair of functions which can be used; for instance, $\exp(nz)\, J_0(nr)$ and exp (nz) $Y_0(nr)$ are another pair. The former are adequate, however, to simulate any axially symmetric Laplacian potential by the expansion

$$\phi = \sum_{n=0}^{\infty} [A_n J_0(nr) + B_n Y_0(nr)] \exp(-nz) \tag{4.2}$$

where A_n and B_n are constants.

Although the expansion of Eq. (4.2) is possible, an alternative expansion is preferable for the solution of the problem of Eq. (4.1), namely,

$$\phi = \int_0^{\infty} [A(n)\, J_0(nr) + B(n)\, Y_0(nr)] \exp(-nz)\, dn \tag{4.3}$$

where now A(n) and B(n) are continuous functions of n. The difference between Eqs. (4.2) and (4.3) is the same as that between a Fourier series and a Fourier integral. For many purposes, the latter is more convenient.

For the solution of Eq. (4.3) to satisfy the boundary conditions of Eq. (4.1), it is necessary that

$$z^{4/3} = \int_0^{\infty} [A(n)\, J_0(na) + B(n)\, Y_0(na)] \exp(-nz)\, dn$$

and (4.4)

$$0 = \int_0^{\infty} n[A(n)\, J_0'(na) + B(n)\, Y_0'(na)] \exp(-nz)\, dn$$

when J_0', Y_0' are the derivatives of the Bessel functions with respect to their arguments. Now the right-hand sides of Eq. (4.4) are the Laplace transforms of certain functions. The left-hand sides also can be put in terms of a Laplace transform, and then the two sides may be equated to zero to determine A(n) and B(n). This is similar to making a Fourier analysis of the boundary conditions in problems where the solution is written in the form of Fourier components. The inverse Laplace transform of $z^{4/3}$ may be determined from the integral expression, given in the literature [13] and is

$$z^{4/3} = \int_0^{\infty} \frac{n^{-7/3}}{\Gamma(-\frac{4}{3})} \exp(-nz)\, dn \tag{4.5}$$

where $\Gamma(p)$ is the gamma function.[11]

Combining Eqs. (4.4) and (4.5) and putting the integrands separately to zero, we see that

$$A(n)\, J_0(na) + B(n)\, Y_0(na) = \frac{n^{-7/3}}{\Gamma(-\frac{4}{3})}$$

(4.6)

$$A(n)\, J_0'(na) + B(n)\, Y_0'(na) = 0$$

This pair of simultaneous equations for A(n) and B(n) may be solved to yield the result

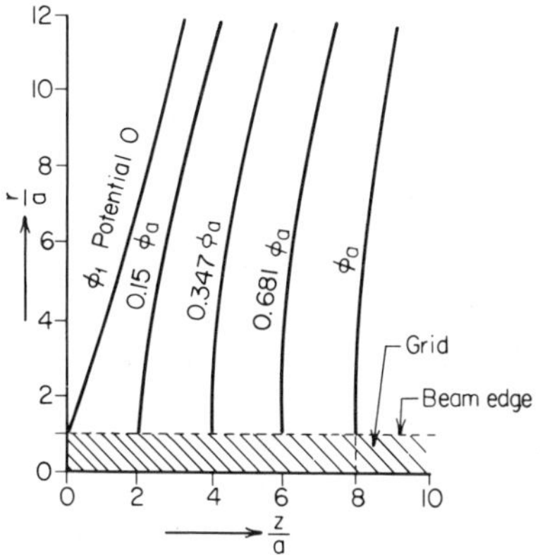

Fig. 7.16. Equipotentials for a pencil beam.

$$A(n) = \frac{n^{-7/3}}{\Gamma(-\frac{4}{3})} \frac{Y_0'(na)}{\Delta} \quad \text{and} \quad B(n) = -\frac{n^{-7/3}}{\Gamma(-\frac{4}{3})} \frac{J_0'(na)}{\Delta} \tag{4.7}$$

where $\Delta = J_0(na)\, Y_0'(na) - J_0'(na)\, Y_0(na)$ (4.8)

Using the relation[11]

$$J_0(na)\, Y_0'(na) - J_0'(na)\, Y_0(na) = \frac{2}{\pi na} \tag{4.9}$$

and substituting Eqs. (4.7) to (4.9) into Eq. (4.3), the potential distribution $\phi(r,z)$ becomes

$$\phi(r,z) = -\frac{\pi}{2} \int_0^\infty \frac{n^{-4/3}}{\Gamma(-\frac{4}{3})} e^{-nz} a \left[Y_0'(na)\, J_0(nr) - J_0'(na)\, Y_0(nr)\right] dn \tag{4.10}$$

Neither the potentials nor the equipotentials of Eq. (4.10) can be evaluated in terms of elementary functions. The equation can be integrated numerically, and the resulting equipotentials are sketched in Fig. 7.16.

The electrodes required to produce a particular pencil beam can be evaluated explicitly. We now show that the result of the exact analysis of the electrodes required to maintain a pencil beam of zero radius is the limiting case of Eq. (4.10) as $a \to 0$.

If we have an infinitely thin pencil beam, the boundary conditions of Eq. (4.1) apply on the axis. It is shown elsewhere,[11] or may be verified by substitution into Laplace's equation, that the solution of this problem is given by the potential

$$\phi = R^{4/3}\, P_{4/3}(\cos \Theta) \tag{4.11}$$

where P_m is the Legendre polynomial[11] of degree m, and to avoid confusion with cylindrical polar coordinates, R denotes the distance from the origin and Θ the usual polar angle in spherical polar coordinates. The ϕ of Eq. (4.11) satisfies Laplace's equation and, since $P_{4/3}(1) = 1$, the boundary conditions of Eq. (4.1) on the axis $\Theta = 0$.

We now consider the limiting form of Eq. (4.10) as $a \to 0$. The limit of the integral can be written, in this case, as the integral of the limit, so that Eq. (4.10) becomes

$$\phi(r,z) = \frac{\pi}{2} \int_0^\infty \frac{n^{-4/3}}{\Gamma(-\frac{4}{3})} e^{-nz} \lim_{a \to 0} \{a[Y_0'(na)\, J_0(nr) - J_0'(na)\, Y_0(nr)]\}\, dn \tag{4.12}$$

From the expansions of J_0 and Y_0 for small arguments,[11] namely

$$\lim_{a \to 0} [a\, Y_0'(na)] = \frac{2}{\pi n} \qquad \text{and} \lim_{a \to 0} [a\, J_0'(na)] = 0 \tag{4.13}$$

Eq. (4.12) may be written in the form

$$\phi(r,z) = \int_0^\infty \frac{n^{-7/3}}{\Gamma(-\frac{4}{3})} e^{-nz} J_0(nr)\, dn \tag{4.14}$$

The integral of Eq. (4.14) has been evaluated explicitly,[13] since it is the Laplace transform of a function of the form $n^\alpha J_0(nr)$, to be

$$\phi(r,z) = (z^2 + r^2)^{4/3} P_{-7/3}\left[\frac{z}{(r^2 + z^2)^{1/2}}\right] \tag{4.15}$$

Remembering that the connection between the (r,z) of cylindrical polar coordinates and R, Θ of spherical polar coordinates is

$$R^2 = r^2 + z^2 \qquad \text{and} \qquad \cos\Theta = \frac{z}{(r^2 + z^2)^{1/2}} \tag{4.16}$$

and that a property of Legendre polynomials[11] is that

$$P_m(X) = P_{-m-1}(X) \tag{4.17}$$

the solutions of Eqs. (4.11) and (4.15) are seen to be identical.

We have shown that the limiting case of the solution of an infinitely thin pencil beam may be correctly derived from the finite pencil beam of Eq. (4.10). This example demonstrates that the integrals required in the application of the method can often be found in the literature. Many integrals of Bessel, Legendre, and similar functions are tabulated, e.g., in Refs. 11 and 13.

There is one interesting feature of the solution of Eq. (4.11). The zero potential electrode, near the cathode, is the solution of the equation

$$P_{4/3}(\cos\Theta) = 0 \tag{4.18}$$

This is a cone of angle 74.16°. This angle is at variance with the 67.5° which, we proved in Sec. 3.7, was required for all beams near the cathode. The discrepancy arises from the limiting processes involved. Analysis of the finite-beam solution of Eq. (4.10) shows that the zero-potential electrode has inclination 67.5° near the cathode. The angle of the electrode steadily changes from 67.5° to a value 74.16° far from the axis. The exact angle for any particular r will depend only on the ratio r/a. In the limiting case of $a \to 0$, the transition from 67.5 to 74.16° occurs for an infinitesimally small r.

4.3. The Mathematical Formalism. Many of the basic ideas of the method are contained in the example of Sec. 4.2. The problem considered was that of finding the electrodes outside a pencil beam. This was an axially symmetric problem, in which the potential did not depend on one coordinate, the θ of cylindrical polar coordinates.

In any coordinate system, it is possible to find sets of functions which satisfy Laplace's equation. These sets may depend on one or more parameters; in cartesian coordinates, for example, $\exp[(m + n)x] \cos(my) \cos(nz)$ are a set of such functions for different m and n.

In general, superposition of these functions may be used to synthesize any Laplacian potential. When the potential depends only on two variables, as in axially symmetric or two-dimensional problems, these functions, which may be called trial functions, are each functions of only two variables. When the coordinate system is one in which Laplace's equation separates, each trial function is the product of two functions, which are called base functions, of only one variable. In Sec. 4.2, for example, the two functions $\exp(-nz) J_0(nr)$ and $\exp(-nz) Y_0(nr)$ were used as trial functions, and the four functions $\exp(nz)$, $\exp(-nz)$, $J_0(nr)$, $Y_0(nr)$ could have been used as base functions. By a suitable choice of the range of summation over n, it was possible to expand the potential considering only one function of z and two of r. In general, it is always possible to choose trial functions which depend only on one function of one variable and on two of the other. The resulting expansion of the potential may be either in the form of a series, as in Eq. (4.2), or of an integral, as in Eq. (4.3). In this section, we consider only the expansion in terms of an integral. The problem then becomes that of solving a pair of integral equations for the amplitude functions, for example, the A(n) and B(n) of Eq. (4.3). When the base functions are the commoner ones, for example, power series, Legendre, and Bessel functions, extensive tables of integrals already exist. These frequently facilitate the solution of the integral equations.

In general, the two integral equations are coupled. When the beam boundary coincides with the level surfaces of one of the coordinates, for example, the cylinder $r = a$ or the plane $z = b$ in cylindrical polar coordinates, the equations may be put into an uncoupled form. Their solution may then be carried out by straightforward integration, as in the example of Sec. 4.2. It is only this case which is treated in detail. The foregoing arguments are now put in mathematical form.

If (ξ, η, ζ) is a three-dimensional coordinate system in which Laplace's equation is separable, there always exist two sets of base functions $X_{1,n}(\xi)$, $X_{2,n}(\xi)$ and $Y_{1,n}(\eta)$. $Y_{2,n}(\eta)$ such that $X_{1 \text{ or } 2,n}$ $Y_{1 \text{ or } 2,n}$ satisfies Laplace's equation. Moreover, if the range of summation is correctly chosen, it is always possible to express any potential independent of ζ in the form

$$\phi(\xi,\eta) = \sum_{n} X_{1,n}(\xi)\left[A_n Y_{1,n}(\eta) + B_n Y_{2,n}(\eta)\right] \tag{4.19}$$

where n is integral.

In the last section, $X_{1,n}$ was exp (−nz), and $Y_{1,n}$ and $Y_{2,n}$ were $J_0(nr)$ and $Y_0(nr)$. It is also possible to express Eq. (4.19) as an integral, where now n may take all values on some, possibly complex, contour. It is clearer to indicate this by denoting $X_{1,n}(\xi)$ by $X_1(\xi,n)$, etc. Then Eq. (4.19) can be expressed in the form

$$\phi(\xi,\eta) = \int_{\mathcal{C}} X_1(\xi,n)\left[A(n)\, Y_1(\eta,n) + B(n)\, Y_2(\eta,n)\right] dn \tag{4.20}$$

where $\mathcal{C}$ is some contour related to the choice of trial functions and the convergence of the integral. For example, in the previous section, $\mathcal{C}$ was taken as the line $0 \leq n \leq \infty$, because the integral involving exp (−nz) was convergent, for $z > 0$, in this interval. The superposition in the integral form of Eq. (4.20) is related to the summation form of Eq. (4.19) in the same way that the Fourier series is related to the Fourier integral.

If now on some curve, $\eta = \eta_0(\xi)$, two linear combinations of ϕ and its derivative $\partial\phi/\partial\eta$ are given by the functions $\phi_1(\xi)$ and $\phi_2(\xi)$ on $\eta = \eta_0$, then putting $\eta = \eta_0$ in Eq. (4.20) and its derivative yields the expressions

$$\begin{aligned}\phi_1(\xi) &= \int X_1(\xi,n)\{A(n)\; Y_1\,[\eta_0(\xi),\, n] + B(n)\; Y_2[\eta_0(\xi),\, n]\}\, dn\\ \phi_2(\xi) &= \int X_1(\xi,n)\{A(n)\; Y_1'\,[\eta_0(\xi),\, n] + B(n)\; Y_2'[\eta_0(\xi),\, n]\}\, dn\end{aligned} \tag{4.21}$$

where by the prime we mean $\partial/\partial\eta$. Equation (4.21) is a pair of coupled integral equations, which is in general hard to solve.

In one very important class of cases, Eq. (4.21) may be solved comparatively simply. This occurs if it is possible to choose coordinates such that the beam boundary, and hence the original data, are given on the curve η = constant. In this case, the complicated sequence of direct and inverse transforms, which is, in general, required to solve Eq. (4.21), may be reduced to one inverse transformation. If the data are given on $\eta = c$, then Eq. (4.21) can be written

$$\begin{aligned}\phi_1(\xi) &= \int_{\mathcal{C}} X_1(\xi,n)\; F_1(n)\; dn\\ \phi_2(\xi) &= \int_{\mathcal{C}} X_1(\xi,n)\; F_2(n)\; dn\end{aligned} \tag{4.22}$$

where

$$\begin{aligned}F_1(n) &= A(n)\; Y_1(c,n) + B(n)\; Y_2(c,n)\\ F_2(n) &= A(n)\; Y_n'(c,n) + B(n)\; Y_2'(c,n)\end{aligned} \tag{4.23}$$

Now from the theory of integral equations,[11] every integral equation of the form of Eq. (4.22) has a solution. If

$$\phi_1(\xi) = \int X_1\,(\xi,n)\;\Phi_1(n)\;dn \tag{4.24}$$

there exists $x_1(\xi,n)$ such that

$$\Phi_1(n) = \int x_1(\xi,n)\;\phi_1(\xi)\;dn \tag{4.25}$$

The function ϕ_1 is called the transform of Φ_1 with respect to the kernel $X_1(\xi,n)$. Similarly, Φ_1 is the transform of ϕ_1 with respect to the kernel x_1. Moreover, Φ_1 is also called the inverse transform of ϕ_1 with respect to X_1. In the previous section, the kernels F_1 and F_2 were the functions $J_0(na)\exp(-nz)$ and $Y_0(na)\exp(-nz)$. In an equation like Eq. (4.24), it is possible to differentiate both sides with respect to ξ so that

$$\frac{\partial \phi_1}{\partial \xi} = \int \frac{\partial X_1(\xi,n)}{\partial \xi}\;\phi_1(n)\;dn\;\cdots \tag{4.26}$$

If the inverse transform with respect to $X_1(\xi,n)$ of $\Phi_i(\xi)$ is $\phi_i(n)$, a rearrangement of Eq. (4.22), using Eq. (4.23), yields

$$\begin{aligned} A(n) &= \frac{\phi_1(n)\;Y_2'(c,n) - \phi_2(n)\;Y_1'(c,n)}{\Delta} \\ B(n) &= \frac{\phi_2(n)\;Y_1(c,n) - \phi_1(n)\;Y_2(c,n)}{\Delta} \end{aligned} \tag{4.27}$$

where Δ is the Wronskian of Y_1 and Y_2, namely,

$$\Delta = Y_1(c,n)\;Y_2'(c,n) - Y_2(c,n)\;Y_1'(c,n) \tag{4.28}$$

Thus, when the beam boundaries coincide with the surface of constant value of one coordinate, in coordinate systems in which Laplace's equation separates, the solution for the potential may be expressed in terms of four integrals. These integrals are the inverse transform integrals, e.g., Eq. (4.25), and the integrals for the potential, implicit in Eq. (4.21). The integrals can be carried out to a high accuracy by choosing suitable expressions for the integration formulas when these are performed numerically. Therefore the method is much less liable to error than the direct integration of the partial differential equation, Laplace's equation, outward from the boundary. In the usual numerical techniques employed, an integral is carried out to an accuracy which depends on the fourth or fifth derivative of the function. A partial differential equation is usually solved by formulas correct only to the third derivative. To increase the accuracy to higher derivatives is far more difficult than to increase the accuracy of the integrals; hence the value of this method when it can be applied. Unfortunately, the method in the simpler form described here is valid only when the beam boundary is along one of the level surfaces in a coordinate system in which

Laplace's equation is separable. The only such three-dimensional surfaces of practical utility are axially symmetric systems; in these cases the possible beam boundaries are ellipses, parabolas, straight lines, or hyperbolas in a transverse plane. Any beam boundary is possible in two dimensions, and in Sec. 4.4 the method developed here is shown to lead to results identical with those developed in Section 3, by complex-variable techniques. If, in axially symmetric systems, a more complicated beam boundary is required, other methods, such as those of Section 5, must be employed. The complications introduced by solving the general equation (4.21) are usually greater than those in using the methods of Section 5.

5. SOLUTION OF THE AXIALLY SYMMETRIC PROBLEM BY EMBEDDING IT IN A THIRD DIMENSION

5.1. **Introduction.** In Section 4, a method was described for solving Laplace's equation outside an axially symmetric beam. The method could be used only in a limited class of problems. In this section a method is presented, due to Harker,[4] which has a wider range of validity. For those problems which can be treated by both methods, however, that of the previous section is shorter. Laplace's equation is elliptic, and was shown in Section 2 to be unsuited to step-by-step integration away from a boundary; in this method the equations and boundary conditions are transformed so that a hyperbolic differential equation is obtained. The transformation is made by introducing a third, imaginary, coordinate direction and arranging to integrate with respect to one of the original and the imaginary coordinates. The integration is carried to the point where the imaginary coordinate is again zero, which means that this point is in the original real space.

The advantage of such a procedure is not at all obvious, and a full proof will not be given here. The solution of a partial, or ordinary, differential equation is always performed numerically by replacing the differential by a difference equation. There are two sources of error. First, the difference equation is only an approximation to the differential equation; the error due to this cause is called the truncation error. Second, calculations are always made only to a certain number of figures. Any error due to loss of accuracy from this effect is called a round-off error. Although at first sight round-off errors might seem insignificant, if, as is common with computers, 10 significant figures are used, such is not the case. Because almost equal numbers are subtracted from each other in obtaining derivatives, and large numbers of operations are usually involved, the round-off errors are often dominant.[8] Truncation errors can be reduced by reducing the intervals of integration or by increasing the order of the approximation of the difference equation to the differential equation. In such cases, however, the round-off errors limit the attainable accuracy. This problem of loss of accuracy is more serious in partial than in ordinary differential equations. When the partial differential equation is elliptic, the errors may make its numerical solution by straightforward difference methods meaningless. The advantage of Harker's method is that it transforms the source of error from the region away from the beam boundary onto the boundary itself. On the boundary, the physical parameters of the beam are known either as an analytic function or as a solution of an ordinary differential equation. This can be solved to a high degree of accuracy. The hyperbolic equation which must be solved in the region away from the beam was shown, in Section 2, to have maximum error on the beam boundary. Hence the resulting solution of the partial differential equation is meaningful.

In Sec. 5.2, the simple problem of the electrodes required to produce a rectilinear sheet beam is considered. This problem has been solved previously in Section 3, and is a useful simple example of the method. The question of the errors due to slight changes in boundary conditions at the beam edge is then considered, and these errors are shown to be maximum under certain conditions at the beam edge. In this way, inasmuch as, at the beam edge, we are able to compute the boundary conditions accurately, errors are prevented from building up away from the boundary. Finally, in Sec. 5.3, the method is generalized to axially symmetric systems where the conditions at the beam edge are given parametrically. The case where the boundary conditions are given as the solution of ordinary differential equations is also discussed.

5.2. The Potentials Required to Maintain a Rectilinear Sheet Beam. As an example of the method to be developed in this section, the problem of the potentials required to maintain a rectilinear sheet beam is treated. Although this example has already been solved in Section 3, it has the merit of being soluble, by every method used, in analytic fashion; thus the methods can be illustrated without unnecessary algebraic or numerical analysis.

For this problem, as in Eqs. (3.1), it is necessary that the potential ϕ satisfy, on the beam boundary,

$$\phi = x^{4/3} \quad \text{and} \quad \frac{\partial \phi}{\partial y} = 0 \quad \text{on } y = 0 \tag{5.1}$$

and in the region outside the beam, Laplace's equation

$$\frac{\partial^2 \phi}{\partial x^2} + \frac{\partial^2 \phi}{\partial y^2} = 0 \tag{5.2}$$

We wish to determine ϕ at some arbitrary point P with coordinate (a,b). Since Eq. (5.2) is elliptical, it is not possible, as discussed in Sec. 5.1, to integrate it step by step from the boundary. Instead a

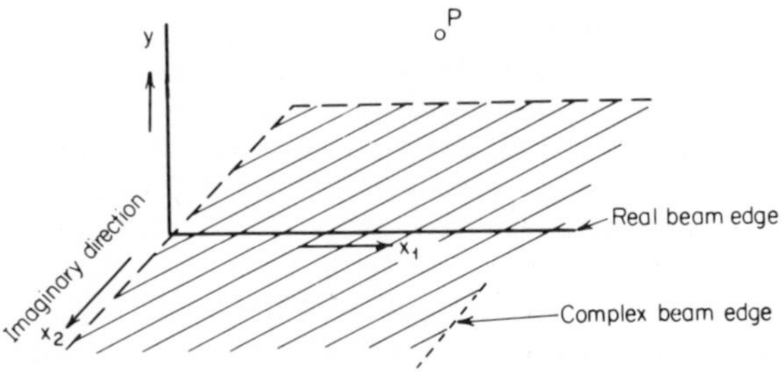

Fig. 7.17. Schematic of the complex coordinate system used in obtaining the electrodes required to maintain a parallel beam.

new imaginary direction is introduced, as illustrated in Fig. 7.17,

$$x = x_1 + jx_2 \tag{5.3}$$

so that the surface $x_2 = 0$ corresponds to the original physical system. The boundary conditions of Eq. (5.1) still hold, and, therefore, on the boundary,

$$\phi = (x_1 + jx_2)^{4/3} \quad \text{and} \quad \frac{\partial \phi}{\partial y} = 0 \quad \text{on } y = 0 \tag{5.4}$$

For simplicity, since there are now three coordinates, a point in x_1, x_2, y space is written in the form $(x_1,x_2;y)$. Any point on the original physical plane is then $(x_1,0;y)$, and in particular the point P, where the potential ϕ is to be determined, is the point $(a,0;b)$.

We now transform the problem so that, instead of having an elliptic differential equation to integrate in the (x_1,y) coordinates, as in Eq. (5.2), a hyperbolic one can be integrated in the (x_2,y) system. To make this transformation, we must first determine the conditions on ϕ on the boundary at $(a,x_2;0)$. From Eq. (5.4) these are

$$\phi = (a + jx_2)^{4/3} \quad \text{and} \quad \frac{\partial \phi}{\partial y} = 0 \quad \text{at } x_1 = a,\ y = 0 \tag{5.5}$$

Next, keeping a as a constant parameter, it is seen from Eq. (5.3) that

$$dx = j\, dx_2 \tag{5.6}$$

so that Eq. (5.2) becomes

$$-\frac{\partial^2 \phi}{\partial x_2^2} + \frac{\partial^2 \phi}{\partial y^2} = 0 \tag{5.7}$$

Equation (5.7) is hyperbolic, and could be solved by numerical step-by-step integration methods with the boundary conditions of Eq. (5.5). It is not necessary in this case to resort to numerical means, since by substitution it can be verified that

$$\phi = \frac{1}{2}\left[(a + jx_2 + jy)^{4/3} + (a + jx_2 - jy)^{4/3}\right] \tag{5.8}$$

is the solution. From Eq. (5.8), it is seen that, at the point P, (a, 0;b), the potential is

$$\phi = \frac{1}{2}\left[(a + jb)^{4/3} + (a - jb)^{4/3}\right] = \text{Re}\left[(a + jb)^{4/3}\right] \tag{5.9}$$

This result agrees with that derived previously in Eq. (3.7).

The development of this paragraph gives in essence all the method, without the numerical and algebraic routine of more complicated problems. In a more complicated example, the majority of the steps in the method would have to be made numerically. The boundary conditions of Eq. (5.1) might be given as the solution of an ordinary differential equation; in that case the derivation of the boundary conditions of Eq. (5.5) would be obtained by integrating the equation first to the point (a, 0;0) in the x_1 direction and then to the point $(a, x_2; 0)$ in the x_2 direction. In the axially symmetric case, Eq. (5.7) is rather more complicated, but still hyperbolic in form with the same characteristic part, determined by the second-order terms, of the form $\partial^2\phi/\partial y^2 - \partial^2\phi/\partial x_2^2$. This characteristic part shows, from the theory of partial differential equations,[8] that to obtain the solution at (a, 0;b), it is necessary to define the initial conditions on the line $(a, x_2; b)$ all along the line $-b \leq x_2 \leq b$.

We now consider a slightly more complicated problem to demonstrate the advantages of the method and to show how the maximum errors occur, in this method of solution, on the beam boundary. If, instead of the boundary conditions of Eq. (5.1), there is a slight difference or error in the potential on y = 0, so that the potential at the boundary is given by

$$\phi = x^{4/3} + \epsilon \sin(nx) \qquad \text{and} \qquad \frac{\partial\phi}{\partial y} = 0 \qquad \text{on } y = 0 \tag{5.10}$$

a solution similar to that of Eq. (5.9) may be obtained. The (x, y) plane may again be embedded in a three-dimensional $(x_1, x_2; y)$ space as shown in Fig. 7.17. Now the value of ϕ on the boundary is given, at the point $(a, x_2; 0)$, by the expression analogous to Eq. (5.5),

$$\phi = (a + jx_2)^{4/3} + \epsilon \sin\left[n(a + jx_2)\right] \qquad \text{and} \qquad \frac{\partial\phi}{\partial y} = 0 \tag{5.11}$$

Laplace's equation still takes the form of Eq. (5.7). In the same way as Eq. (5.8) is derived from Eq. (5.5), the potential at $(a, x_2; y)$ is given by the expression

$$\phi = \frac{1}{2}\Big\{(a + jx_2 + jy)^{4/3} + (a + jx_2 - jy)^{4/3} + \epsilon \sin\left[n(a + jx_2 + jy)\right] + \epsilon \sin\left[n(a + jx_2 - jy)\right]\Big\} \tag{5.12}$$

An examination of Eq. (5.12) now yields an interesting conclusion. If the term in ϵ denotes an error in the potential at the boundary, the error at the point $(a,x_2;y)$ is δ, where δ is given by

$$\delta(a,x_2;y) = \epsilon \sin [n (a + jx_2)] \cosh (ny) \tag{5.13}$$

The errors at (a,o;b) and (a,b;o) can be evaluated from Eq. (5.13). The following expressions are obtained:

$$\begin{aligned} |\delta(a,o;b)|^2 &= \sin^2 (na) \cosh^2 (nb) \\ |\delta(a,b;o)|^2 &= \sin^2 (na) \cosh^2 (nb) + \cos^2 (na) \sinh^2 (nb) \end{aligned} \tag{5.14}$$

Therefore $|\delta(a,b;o)| \geq |\delta(a,o;b)|$, which means that, if the potential is evaluated on the boundary up to $|x_2| = b$, the error on the boundary will not be less than that at the point (a,o;b) in the real plane.

In general, the error in the potential is less than the maximum error at the boundary, where it is defined, provided that $|y| < b$. The potential ϕ can be obtained accurately on the boundary by, at the most, integrating an ordinary differential equation in the complex plane. We conclude that this method is more accurate than a direct solution of the elliptic differential equation.

5.3. Extension of the Method to the Case of Arbitrary Potentials and Fields Prescribed, for Axially Symmetric Beams, on a Prescribed Curve. The results of Sec. 5.2 are now extended to the case where the gradient of the axially symmetric potential function is given on a boundary curve. The extension has some similarity to the development of Section 3. Again the coordinates of the beam boundary, and the gradient of potential on it, are given parametrically. Since the essence of the method is to derive a set of equations that are numerically soluble, however, it is not assumed that the boundary curve is given analytically. Again a coordinate system (ξ, η) is constructed such that the line $\eta = 0$ lies along the prescribed curve. In this section a pair of partial differential equations are solved to determine the mapping of the (z,r) into the (ξ, η) plane. This mapping is also the solution of Laplace's equation, and we use the technique of the previous section to change this elliptic equation into a hyperbolic one, by introducing a complex value for ξ. At the same time, it is possible to solve Laplace's equation for ϕ by simultaneously transforming it into a hyperbolic equation. By these means, the quantities ϕ, r, z are evaluated at a real arbitrary point (ξ, η) in the same way as in the previous sections.

First it is assumed that the boundary curve is given parametrically by (z,r) being on the boundary if

$$\frac{dr}{d\xi} = R(\xi) \qquad \frac{dz}{d\xi} = Z(\xi) \tag{5.15}$$

Any definition of the functions R, Z is admissible as long as it is meaningful for all ξ, real or complex. For example, R and Z might be given as the solutions of the differential equations which are the equations of space-charge flow for any of the solutions of Chap. II. As in Sec. 3.4, ϕ is specified on the boundary curve by

$$\frac{\partial\phi}{\partial r} = \Phi_1(\xi) \qquad \text{and} \qquad \frac{\partial\phi}{\partial z} = \Phi_2(\xi) \tag{5.16}$$

$$\text{with} \quad \phi = \phi_0 \qquad \text{on the boundary at} \qquad \xi = 0 \tag{5.17}$$

Finally, since the problem is axially symmetric, Laplace's equation becomes

$$\frac{\partial^2\phi}{\partial r^2} + \frac{1}{r}\frac{\partial\phi}{\partial r} + \frac{\partial^2\phi}{\partial z^2} = 0 \tag{5.18}$$

Equations (5.15) to (5.18) completely define the problem to be solved. First, a conformal mapping of the (z,r) into a (ξ,η) plane is determined, and then the additional solution of the potential problem is discussed. The conformal mapping can be made even if the (z,r) coordinate system is in cylindrical polar coordinates. However, in this case, the Laplacian is not invariant, and it is necessary to determine the form of Eq. (5.18) in the (ξ,η) system.

Just as in Sec. 3.4, defining

$$W(\xi) = Z(\xi) + jR(\xi) \tag{5.19}$$

the mapping of the (z,r) into the (ξ,η) plane is given by

$$z + jr = W(\xi + j\eta) \tag{5.20}$$

The mapping of Eq. (5.20) is valid only for real ξ and η, but from it the functions $U(\xi,\eta)$ and $V(\xi,\eta)$ are defined by the relation

$$W(\xi + j\eta) = U(\xi,\eta) + jV(\xi,\eta) \tag{5.21}$$

The U and V themselves satisfy the Cauchy-Riemann equations of Appendix B, Eq. (2.5),

$$\frac{\partial U}{\partial \xi} = \frac{\partial V}{\partial \eta} \qquad \text{and} \qquad \frac{\partial U}{\partial \eta} = -\frac{\partial V}{\partial \xi} \tag{5.22}$$

The z and r are then related to U and V by the expression

$$z = U(\xi,\eta) \qquad \text{and} \qquad r = V(\xi,\eta) \tag{5.23}$$

The z and r of Eq. (5.21) have a physical meaning only if ξ is real. It is permissible, however, to transform the differential equation for ϕ into one in the (ξ,η) plane with prescribed boundary conditions. This ϕ may be formally solved in a space where ξ takes on complex values, if such a solution is interesting for numerical reasons. The resulting ϕ, U, and V can be identified with physical ϕ, z, and r only when ξ and η are real. It is to be noted that the mapping of Eq. (5.22) can be derived, even if Eq. (5.19) is really an ordinary differential equation for ξ, by solving this equation for the complex independent variable indicated by Eq. (5.20).

Since the mapping of the (z,r) plane into the (ξ,η) plane has already been considered in Sec. 3.4, we demonstrate only how the equation for ϕ and the boundary conditions are transformed.

If a is any scalar function of r and z, and hence, through Eq. (5.23), of ξ and η, its partial derivatives are related by the expressions

$$\frac{\partial a}{\partial \xi} = \frac{\partial a}{\partial r}\frac{\partial r}{\partial \xi} + \frac{\partial a}{\partial z}\frac{\partial z}{\partial \xi}$$

$$\text{and} \quad \frac{\partial a}{\partial \eta} = \frac{\partial a}{\partial r}\frac{\partial r}{\partial \eta} + \frac{\partial a}{\partial z}\frac{\partial z}{\partial \eta} \tag{5.24}$$

The parameters P and Q are defined by the relations

$$P = \frac{\partial \phi}{\partial z} \quad \text{and} \quad Q = \frac{\partial \phi}{\partial r} \tag{5.25}$$

It is seen that P and Q are related by the expressions

$$\frac{\partial P}{\partial r} = \frac{\partial Q}{\partial z} \tag{5.26}$$

and from Eq. (5.18),

$$\frac{\partial Q}{\partial r} + \frac{Q}{r} + \frac{\partial P}{\partial z} = 0 \tag{5.27}$$

Equations (5.26) and (5.27) may be transformed, by use of Eqs. (5.21), (5.23), (5.24), and (5.25), into the form

$$\frac{\partial Q}{\partial \eta} = -\frac{\partial P}{\partial \xi} - \frac{1}{r}\frac{\partial U}{\partial \xi} Q$$

$$\frac{\partial P}{\partial \eta} = \frac{\partial Q}{\partial \xi} + \frac{1}{r}\frac{\partial V}{\partial \xi} Q \tag{5.28}$$

The boundary conditions on P and Q at the beam edge have been given in Eq. (5.16). Since the beam edge is $\eta = 0$, from the defining equations for P and Q of Eq. (5.25), these boundary conditions are

$$P = \Phi_1(\xi) \quad \text{and} \quad Q = \Phi_2(\xi) \quad \text{at} \quad \eta = 0 \tag{5.29}$$

So far, although the notation is slightly different from that of Section 3, the only progress has been to transform coordinates from the (r,z) into the (ξ,η) planes. The defining equations for the transformation are given in Eq. (5.22), with the boundary conditions of Eq. (5.19). The expressions for the electric field are given in Eq. (5.28), with the boundary conditions of Eq. (5.29). The transformation equation will be soluble at worst by quadrature, since at worst the R and Z of Eq. (5.15) will be solutions of ordinary differential equations. Unless these functions are very simple, however, it may be faster, in practice, to compute them from the partial differential equations.

In this case the system of Eqs. (5.15), (5.19), (5.22), and (5.29) can be written concisely as

$$\begin{pmatrix} \frac{\partial U}{\partial \eta} \\ \frac{\partial V}{\partial \eta} \\ \frac{\partial P}{\partial \eta} \\ \frac{\partial Q}{\partial \eta} \end{pmatrix} = \begin{pmatrix} 0 & -1 & 0 & 0 \\ 1 & 0 & 0 & 0 \\ 0 & \frac{Q}{r} & 0 & 1 \\ -\frac{Q}{r} & 0 & -1 & 0 \end{pmatrix} \begin{pmatrix} \frac{\partial U}{\partial \xi} \\ \frac{\partial V}{\partial \xi} \\ \frac{\partial P}{\partial \xi} \\ \frac{\partial Q}{\partial \xi} \end{pmatrix} \tag{5.30}$$

with boundary conditions

$$U = Z(\xi) \qquad V = R(\xi) \qquad P = \Phi_1(\xi) \qquad Q = \Phi_2(\xi) \qquad \text{at} \qquad \eta = 0 \tag{5.31}$$

It should be emphasized that, although Eq. (5.30) is a concise form of the partial differential equations involved, we are little nearer to their solution. The planar case of Section 3 could have been put in an identical form, with the terms in Q/r in the matrix put equal to zero. Although in the derivation of Eq. (5.30), complex variables have been used, Eq. (5.30) is a set of partial differential equations for real functions U, V, P, Q, in terms of variables ξ, η. These functions have physical meaning only for real ξ and η; however, any method of solving the equations, even using complex ξ or η, would be valid, provided there were no attempt to attach meaning to physical properties of the functions unless ξ and η are real. Just as, in Sec. 5.2, it was convenient to introduce an imaginary coordinate, so in this section we will embed the (ξ,η) coordinate systems in a three-dimensional one. No figure will be drawn at this stage to demonstrate the transformation, since it should be emphasized that the transformation is basically mathematical. The transformation to be made is the formal one of expressing ξ in the form

$$\xi = \xi_1 + j\xi_2 \tag{5.32}$$

Only when ξ_2 is zero can the functions of η, ξ_1, and ξ_2 be identified with real potentials and beams. The transformation is purely a mathematical device for changing an elliptic partial differential equation into a hyperbolic one, and has no physical significance. If the transformation of Eq. (5.31) is made and if ξ_1 is kept constant, for example,

$$\xi_1 = a \tag{5.33}$$

then, if $A(\xi,\eta)$ is any function of ξ and η,

$$\frac{\partial A}{\partial \xi} = -\frac{j\,\partial A}{\partial \xi_2} \tag{5.34}$$

Substituting Eq. (5.34) into Eq. (5.30), the set of partial derivatives for U, V, P, Q becomes

$$\begin{pmatrix} \frac{\partial U}{\partial \eta} \\ \frac{\partial V}{\partial \eta} \\ \frac{\partial P}{\partial \eta} \\ \frac{\partial Q}{\partial \eta} \end{pmatrix} = \begin{pmatrix} 0 & j & 0 & 0 \\ -j & 0 & 0 & 0 \\ 0 & \frac{-jQ}{r} & 0 & -j \\ \frac{jQ}{r} & 0 & j & 0 \end{pmatrix} \begin{pmatrix} \frac{\partial U}{\partial \xi_2} \\ \frac{\partial V}{\partial \xi_2} \\ \frac{\partial P}{\partial \xi_2} \\ \frac{\partial Q}{\partial \xi_2} \end{pmatrix} \tag{5.35}$$

It is to be noted that Eq. (5.35) is valid only for solutions of the equations for U, V, P, and Q when ξ_1 is kept constant, and the functions may be identified with physical properties only when ξ_2 is zero. However, from the first two equations, the hyperbolic differential equation

$$\frac{\partial^2 U}{\partial \eta^2} - \frac{\partial^2 U}{\partial \xi_2^2} = 0 \tag{5.36}$$

may be deduced, and from the second two, a similar hyperbolic equation results. Hence, if the boundary conditions on U, V, P, and Q are prescribed over the line $\eta = 0$, the equations may be solved by the standard numerical techniques for solving hyperbolic partial differential equations.

A point (ξ, η) in the complex space is defined by the notation $(\xi_1, \xi_2; \eta)$. In this case only the points $(\xi_1, 0; \eta)$ correspond to points in the physical space. The real beam boundary is denoted by the line $(\xi_1, 0; 0)$. However, the definition of U, V, P, and Q on the boundary $\eta = 0$, given in Eq. (5.31), applies equally well for complex ξ with $\xi_2 \neq 0$. If the values of the functions are desired at the point $\xi = a$ and $\eta = b$ of the physical plane, i.e., the point (a, 0; b), the procedure is as follows. First, the values of U, V, P, and Q are found along the complex line $(a, \xi_2; 0)$ on all points $-b \leq \xi_2 \leq b$. This range is required, because in the standard numerical technique,[9] the functions must be defined on the boundary for the same distance on either side of the desired point in the ξ_2 direction as we wish to integrate in the η direction. A schematic of the $(\xi_1, \xi_2; \eta)$ plane is shown in Fig. 7.18. Once the initial values of the functions have been prescribed on the line AB, Eqs. (5.35) is integrated by the standard methods,[4,8] to the point $\xi_2 = 0$, $\eta = b$, to obtain the functions at c (a, 0; b), which is again in the real space. Since the details of the method require the numerical solution of a hyperbolic differential equation, a further example is profitless.

It is to be noted that Eq. (5.35) is equally applicable to planar problems, although for these the methods of Section 3 are shorter.

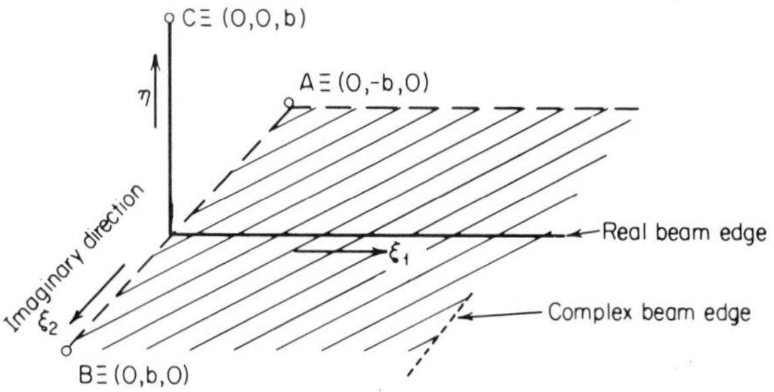

Fig. 7.18. Schematic of the complex coordinate system used in obtaining the electrodes required to maintain an axially symmetric beam.

For planar problems the Q/r coefficients in Eq. (5.35), which arose from the $(1/r)(\partial\phi/\partial r)$ term of the Laplacian, must be put zero. In the method of this section, the functions must be evaluated over an area b^2 to find their value at (a,0;b), whereas in Sections 3 and 4, it was necessary to integrate them only along a line of length b. It is for this reason that the method is more lengthy.

It is profitable to compare the details of the example of Sec. 5.2 with the general method worked out here. The U and V functions were trivial; the boundary was rectilinear, so that, using the notation of this section, x could be identified with ξ, y with η, and U and V took the simple forms

$$U = \xi \qquad \text{and} \qquad V = \eta \tag{5.37a}$$

These were of such a simple form that there was no profit in keeping them in the formalism. If one wished to keep them in, Z and R of Eq. (5.31) would be given by

$$Z = \xi \qquad \text{and} \qquad R = 0 \tag{5.37b}$$

corresponding to the values of Eq. (5.37a) on $\eta = 0$. The Φ_1 and Φ_2 of Eq. (5.30) were derivable in Sec. 5.2, from Eq. (5.1), in the form

$$\Phi_1(\xi) = 0 \qquad \text{and} \qquad \Phi_2(\xi) = \tfrac{4}{3}\,\xi^{1/3} \tag{5.38}$$

Hence, along the line AB of Fig. 7.18, these functions took the form

$$Z = a + j\xi_2 \qquad R = 0 \qquad \Phi_1 = 0 \qquad \Phi_2 = \tfrac{4}{3}\,(a + j\xi_2)^{4/3} \tag{5.39}$$

With these boundary conditions and the simple form Eq. (5.35) had for the planar case, the partial differential equation was solved exactly and the solution of Eq. (5.9) was obtained. If we had solved Eq. (5.35) exactly, instead of the partial differential equation (5.7), we should have obtained the solution, at the point $(a, \xi_2; \eta)$, for U, V, P, and Q

$$U = a + j\xi_2, \qquad V = \eta$$

$$P = \frac{2}{3}\left[(a + j\xi_2 + j\eta)^{1/3} + (a + j\xi_2 - j\eta)^{1/3}\right] \tag{5.40}$$

$$Q = \frac{-2j}{3}\left[(a + j\xi_2 + j\eta)^{1/3} - (a + j\xi_2 - j\eta)^{1/3}\right]$$

The reader can verify that the U, V, P, and Q of Eq. (5.40) satisfy the boundary condition of Eq. (5.39) and also the planar version Eq. (5.35) with the Q/r terms zero. From Eq. (5.40) the values of the functions on the real plane $\xi_2 = 0$, $\eta = b$, are given by

$$U = a, \qquad V = b, \qquad P = \frac{4}{3}\,\mathrm{Re}\left[(a + jb)^{1/3}\right], \qquad Q = \frac{4}{3}\,\mathrm{Im}\left[(a + jb)^{1/3}\right] \tag{5.41}$$

Remembering that P is the $\partial\phi/\partial x$ and Q the $\partial\phi/\partial y$ of Sec. 5.2, the solution of Eq. (5.41) is seen to be the same as that of Eq. (5.9) for ϕ.

The functions R, Z, Φ_1, and Φ_2 may not be given explicitly, but as the solutions of ordinary differential equations; such is the case when the equations of space-charge flow are solved by the method of the separation of variables of Chap. 2 or by the paraxial methods of Chap. III. In this case, the differential equation must be integrated first along the real ξ_1 direction to the point $\xi = a$, then in the imaginary ξ_2 direction to the point $\xi = a + jb$, and in the opposite ξ_2 direction to the point $\xi = a - jb$. There is no fundamental difference whether the functions are given explicitly or as the solution of ordinary differential equations. A problem in which the functions are the solutions of a set of ordinary differential equations is discussed in detail in Ref. 4. In this paper, the question of the numerical solution of a system of partial equations very similar to those of Eq. (5.35) is discussed.

It should also be remarked that Harker has developed further methods for determining electrodes, in which the potential outside the beam is obtained in the form of an integral. The interested reader should refer to the work of Harker.[14,15]

REFERENCES FOR CHAPTER VII

1. Pierce, J. R.: Rectilinear Flow in Electron Beams, *J. Appl. Phys.*, vol. 11, p. 548, 1940.
2. Radley, D. E.: The Theory of the Pierce Type Electron Gun, *J. Electronics and Control*, vol. 4, p. 125, 1958.
3. Lomax, J. R.: Exact Electrode Systems for the Formation of a Curved Space-charge Beam, *J. Electronics and Control*, vol. 3, p. 367, 1957.
4. Harker, K. J.: Determination of Electrode Shapes for Axially Symmetric Electron Guns, *J. Appl. Phys.*, vol. 31, p. 2165, 1960.
5. Richtmeyer, R. D.: "Difference Methods for Initial Value Problems," Interscience Publishers, Inc., New York, 1957.
6. Hockney, R. W.: "A Fast Direct Solution of Poisson's Equation Using

Fourier Analysis," *Stanford Electronic Lab. Rept.* 0255-1, Stanford, Calif., 1964.
7. Kellog, O. D.: "Foundations of Potential Theory," Dover Publications, Inc., New York, 1953.
8. Forsythe, G., and R. W. Wasow: "Finite Difference Methods for Partial Differential Equations," John Wiley & Sons, Inc., New York, 1960.
9. Lomax, R. J.: Exact Electrode Systems for the Formation of a Curved Space-charge Beam, II, *J. Electronics and Control*, vol. 7, p. 482, 1959.
10. Kirstein, P. T.: On the Determination of the Electrodes Required to Produce a Given Electric Field Distribution along a Prescribed Curve, *Proc. IRE*, vol. 46, p. 1716, 1958.
11. Morse, P., and H. Feshbach: "Methods of Theoretical Physics," vol. 1, McGraw-Hill Book Company, New York, 1953.
12. Smythe, W. R.: "Static and Dynamic Electricity," 2d ed., McGraw-Hill Book Company, New York, 1950.
13. Erdelyi, A., W. Magnus, F. Oberhettinger, and F. G. Triconi: "Higher Transcendental Functions," vol. 1, McGraw-Hill Book Company, New York, 1953.
14. Harker, K. J.: Solution of the Cauchy Problem for Laplace's Equation in Axially Symmetric Systems, *J. Mathematical Phys.*, vol. 4, p. 993, 1963.
15. Harker, K. J., and J. Llacer: Conditions for the Solubility of an Elliptic Difference Equation as an Initial Value Problem, *Quart. Appl. Math.*, vol. 21, p. 223, 1963.

PROBLEMS

1. Consider the beam emitted from a crossed-field gun. Show that, if the velocity of emission is zero, the initial curvature of the beam is infinite. By using the formulas for the electrode shapes given, find the values of the initial curvature of the zero-potential electrode for a gun with uniform current density at the cathode. Expand the various expressions of interest near the cathode in terms of x, the distance normal to the cathode, and y, a distance parallel to the cathode, following formulas for curvature κ:

$$\kappa = \frac{d\psi}{ds}, \quad \tan\psi = \frac{dy}{dx} = \frac{dy}{dt}\bigg/\frac{dx}{dt}, \quad \kappa = \frac{\dfrac{d^2y}{dx^2}}{\left[1 + \left(\dfrac{dy}{dx}\right)^2\right]^{3/2}}$$

2a. Repeat Prob. 1 assuming that the initial velocity of the electrons normal to the cathode is $v_{xc} = \eta i_0/\epsilon_0\omega_H^2$, where i_0 is the current density at the cathode.

2b. Find a relation between the plasma frequency and the cycltoron frequency at the cathode.

3. By applying the method of Radley and using a Taylor expansion of the potential near the beam edge, determine the initial curvature of the zero-potential electrode for a cylindrical beam of finite radius, with a potential variation $\phi = z^{4/3}$ and boundary conditions at its edge $\partial\phi/\partial r = 0$.

4. Derive Eq. (3.13), the formula for analytic continuation in a two-dimensional system, using Radley's method. To do this it is convenient to take the independent sets of Sec. 4.3 as $X_1(n) = \exp(-nx)$, $X_2(n) = \exp(nx)$, $Y_1(n) = \sin(ny)$, and $Y_2(n) = \cos(ny)$ and to use an inverse Laplace transform method to solve the resultant integral equation.

5. Determine expressions for the electrode shapes to yield the beam described in Sec. 2.3 of Chap. II. Consider only the beam in the two-dimensional system described there, not the cylindrical form of this beam.

6. Find a differential equation for the form of the electrodes to produce the circular flow described in Section 3 of Chap. II.

7. Find a differential equation for the form of the electrodes to produce a converging strip beam which is a segment of a cylinder. This type of flow, which is one of the one-dimensional solutions of Langmuir, is described in Appendix E.

VIII

Approximate Theoretical Methods of Electrode Design

1. INTRODUCTION

In the preceding chapter, the problem of the design of electrodes for electron- and ion-gun problems was treated in a one-sided manner. It was assumed that the equations of motion and of continuity and Poisson's equation had been solved inside a region containing charged particles. The solution was extended outside the beam region by solving Laplace's equation exterior to the beam boundary. In most cases of practical interest, since the electrode design is usually approximate, it is necessary to determine the form of the beam with this electrode configuration. The problem of finding a set of electrodes, given the conditions at the beam boundary, often can be solved by the methods of the preceding chapter. This problem is essentially one of working outward from the beam edge. The resulting electrodes may in practice have awkward shapes and be difficult to fabricate. For this reason, solutions to the problem of working inward from given electrodes are required. The electrodes may have been designed originally either by the theoretical methods of Chap. VII or by the analog techniques of Chap. IX. In this chapter we consider only the methods of analyzing the effects of a particular electrode configuration on the beam. The details of how specific solutions of Laplace's and Poisson's equations are found will be left until the next chapter.

The solution of Poisson's equation can be simulated by several analytic or analog methods, e.g., on resistance networks, electrolytic tanks, or on a computer by finite-difference techniques. However, the methods of using the appropriate solutions of Laplace's or Poisson's equations are independent of the manner in which the solutions are found. For example, in the analysis of a specific electron flow problem with a given electrode configuration, Poisson's equation must be solved, and the consequent electron motion evaluated by integrating the Lorentz equation of motion. The space-charge distribution must then be corrected, and the procedure repeated several times. This method of solution is quite independent of how Poisson's equation is solved or how the electron-trajectory plots are made.

Of course, in a practical problem, one is usually concerned not only with analyzing a specific electrode configuration, but also with synthesizing a specific flow. In most applications it is desirable to have uniform current density at the cathode and for the flow to be convergent and laminar. The uniform current density is required to obtain the maximum current from the cathode without reducing its life. Often the convergence is desired, because higher efficiencies and power outputs are then possible at a given frequency with an electron tube. In ion-propulsion applications this requirement will not be important, except to ensure that all particles miss the anode electrodes. Laminar flow is preferable to nonlaminar flow for two reasons: the former is simpler to analyze, and has produced more satisfactory results in most practical applications. In the case of high-efficiency klystrons, the beam need not be laminar. For practical reasons, the electrode configuration should be simple to fabricate.

The problem posed above can be solved in several steps. First, the exterior-boundary value of the preceding chapter is considered. In this way electrodes are found which will produce the required beam. Electron trajectories are traced, and thus the specific electrode system analyzed. By making slight changes in the electrode shapes, the electrode configurations which give a good approximation to the required beam can then usually be determined. Moreover, such an electrode system can be chosen, a priori, so that it is convenient to fabricate.

In Sections 4 and 5, only the problem of analyzing specific electrode systems without magnetic fields is considered explicitly. The method of solution is not changed by the introduction of a magnetic field, though the Lorentz equation of motion must be modified in the trajectory tracing.

The method of analysis where space-charge forces may be neglected is described in Section 2. This solution is important, since it is often taken as the first approximation to problems, even when space-charge forces must be considered. In Section 3, the methods to be adopted, when space-charge-simulating equipment is available, are discussed. The method of space-charge simulation will be described in Chap. IX. The space-charge simulation may require either elaborate equipment or complicated numerical computation; therefore, in Section 4, methods of resolving the potential into two parts are described. The first part of the field, the space-charge term, is that due to the electron beam and its image in the cathode. The second part is that due to the other electrodes. The first part can be evaluated once and for all for each beam configuration; in all subsequent computations only a Laplacian field need be considered.

The method of analysis of Section 4 is valid only if the image charges of the beam in the electrodes, other than the cathode, are sufficiently far away to be negligible. Such a situation does not apply for the electrodes in the cathode region near to the beam. The rectilinear Langmuir space-charge-flow solutions defined in Appendix E, which have been used frequently as the basis for the design of electron guns, have no maximum of potential in the beam. For this reason, the theoretically exact electrodes would have to pass through the beam. Such an electrode configuration would have to be synthesized in the beam region with grids. Because of the beam interception on the grid and the power restriction due to the danger of melting the grid, the use of a gridded anode is inconvenient. For this reason, most guns have a hole in the anode through which the beam passes. This hole acts as a lens. Such effects on the flow are discussed in Section 5.

The design of electrodes for paraxial beams is much simpler than the design for nonparaxial beams. The simplifications introduced are discussed in Section 6.

2. ANALYSIS OF A STEADY-ELECTRON-FLOW PROBLEM, NEGLECTING SPACE-CHARGE FORCES

2.1. Introduction. In a static-flow problem in which space-charge forces can be neglected, the equations for the electric and magnetic fields may be solved independently, and trajectories then plotted by integrating the Lorentz force law. In this section we outline the equations which must be obeyed by the field variables. The problem of determining a flow pattern when space-charge forces are neglected is considered, with emphasis on the boundary conditions at the cathode. Primarily, an electrostatic flow derived from one of the rectilinear flows of Appendix E will be envisaged. The methods may be applied to other problems, but these flows are implicitly assumed in many of the figures and arguments presented.

2.2. The Flow, Neglecting Space-charge Forces. The electrode configuration to be analyzed in this chapter is sketched in Fig. 8.1. The curve C represents an emitting surface; this might be a cathode

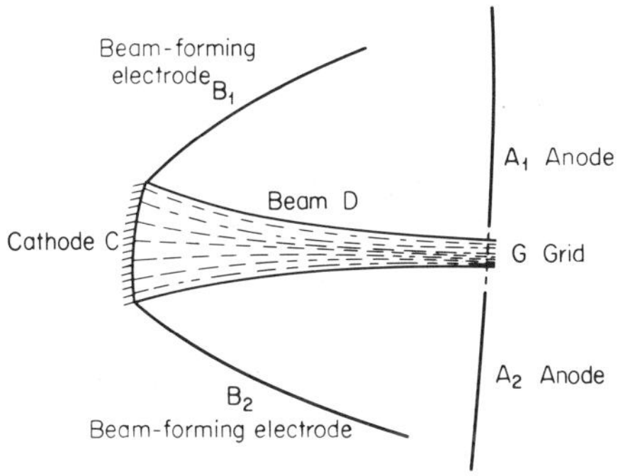

Fig. 8.1. Schematic of the electrodes for an electron gun.

coated with some emitting material and heated so that it may emit electrons. The electrodes B_1 and B_2 are beam-forming electrodes, but not necessarily at the same potentials as the cathode. A_1 and A_2 are at anode potentials, and G is the anode hole. The potential inside the gun region depends on the electric fields leaking through G. In some high-perveance guns, G may have a transverse dimension of the same magnitude as the anode-cathode spacing. In such cases the potential in the gun region depends critically on the potential distribution assumed over the anode hole G. In an electron tube this distribution may depend on the details of the propagating structure. For the purpose of this chapter, except where stated otherwise, the potential distribution across G is assumed known. The problem is therefore presented in a form where G is a grid. It should be noted that G need not be a physical grid, since the potential distribution across it need not be constant, but may follow any prescribed law.

For an electrode system to be analyzable, it must be closed. In practice, there must be a finite distance between two electrodes at different potentials. If an electrode system were not closed, it would be possible to influence the field in the beam region by putting an extra electrode at a different potential between the existing electrodes. The assumption, for example, of a uniform field between the two pairs of electrodes, B_1 and A_1, B_2 and A_2, specifies the potential in the region D. The cathode C is taken as an equipotential at zero potential. A closed-boundary-value problem has now been formulated in which the potential ϕ obeys the equation

$$\nabla^2\phi = -\frac{\rho}{\epsilon_0} \tag{2.1}$$

inside the boundary formed by $CB_1A_1GA_2B_2$ in Fig. 8.1, and the potential on the boundary has also been prescribed. The potential ϕ may be computed by a relaxation technique or by one of the analog methods of Chap. IX. For the purpose of this chapter, it is sufficient to note that the equation

$$\nabla^2\phi = 0 \qquad \phi = \Phi \qquad \text{on } \mathcal{C} \tag{2.2}$$

defines the potential ϕ uniquely inside the region bounded by $\mathcal{C}$. This fact is termed the uniqueness theorem.[1] In Fig. 8.1, $\mathcal{C}$ would be the surface defined by $CB_1A_1GA_2B_2$. The variation of the function Φ determines the value of the potential function on $\mathcal{C}$.

The electric field **E** is found by taking the gradient of the potential. In an analog it is usual, for accuracy reasons, to obtain **E** directly, rather than to find first ϕ and then its gradient.

Having determined **E**, the electron velocity **v** may be found from the Lorentz equation of motion [Eq. (2.15) of Chap. I],

$$\frac{d\mathbf{v}}{dt} = -\eta\,(\mathbf{E} + \mathbf{v} \times \mathbf{B}) \tag{2.3}$$

where by d/dt we mean the change in velocity, following the electron, and **B** refers to any magnetic field that may be present. In most cases, B will be known at each point. Just as it is possible, however, to set up an analog to determine **E**, given the electrodes at the boundary, so it is possible to set up an analog for **B**, knowing the positions and form of the magnets determining **B**.

To integrate Eq. (2.3), initial values of velocity must be specified. Once these are specified, Eq. (2.3) may be integrated, and the electron motion found. The initial condition on **v** at the cathode and the calculation of current density at the cathode will now be discussed.

2.3. Boundary Conditions at the Emitting Surface. Particles are emitted from C of Fig. 8.1 under one of two conditions; these are termed voltage-independent and space-charge-limited in Section 6 Chap. I. In the former, the velocity and current density at the emitter are given by

$$\mathbf{v} = \mathbf{v}_c \qquad \mathbf{i} = \mathbf{i}_c \tag{2.4}$$

where $\mathbf{v}_c$ and $\mathbf{i}_c$ are known a priori. With the above boundary conditions there is no need for the emitter to be an equipotential. The assumption is made, however, that the emitter can be split up into a number of regions, in each of which there is little variation of $\mathbf{i}_c$ or $\mathbf{v}_c$.

In the special case that the emitter is a space-charge-limited cathode, $\mathbf{i}_c$ is normal to the cathode and given by Eq. (6.1) of Chap. I. Usually, the velocity $\mathbf{v}_c$ will be taken to be zero at the cathode. Strictly speaking, $\mathbf{v}_c$ and $\mathbf{i}_c$ have the variation described in Eq. (2.6) of Chap. VI, and are not single-valued functions at all. Any initial values of v_c of the order of $\sqrt{kT_c/m}$,* where T_c is the cathode temperature, can be used. If there is appreciable difference caused by using different v_c in this range, the whole method is inadequate, and the more complex methods of transport theory, based on the Boltzmann equation, must be used.

If the flow is space-charge-limited, the boundary conditions are quite different. Now the electric field $\mathbf{E}_c$ and the velocity $\mathbf{v}_c$ at the cathode are taken to be zero, and the current density $\mathbf{i}_c$ depends on the variation of potential near the cathode. From Sec. 2, Chap. II, the current density $\mathbf{i}_c$ normal to the cathode is given by

$$i_c = 2.33 \times 10^{-6} \frac{\phi^{3/2}}{z^2} \tag{2.5}$$

Of course, i_c can never exceed the maximum value i_{cM} corresponding to thermal emission. The subject of the value of i_c is discussed more fully in Section 2 of Chap. VI. If $i_{c,sc}$ and i_{cM} are the emis-

*$\sqrt{kT_c/m}$ is the root-mean-square normal velocity of a particle emitted from a surface of temperature T_c [Eq. (2.8) of Chap. VI].

sion current density, under space-charge-limited conditions, as defined by Eq. (2.5), and under thermally limited conditions, the actual current density is the minimum of these two values. For later reference, this result is written symbolically:

$$i_c = \text{minimum}\ (i_{c,sc}, i_{cM}) \tag{2.6}$$

In the case of an injected beam, Eq. (2.6) is still valid, but now for i_{cM} the current density of the injected beam must be used.

It is possible for some parts of the cathode to be running under thermally limited conditions, whereas some are running space-charge-limited. For most purposes, such a situation is undesirable, and the cathode should be loaded as uniformly as possible. To run an electron emitter under thermally limited conditions is bad,* for two reasons: First, the life of the cathode is greatly reduced; second, it is more difficult to control the cathode emission. With nonuniform cathode loading some of the cathode is not producing as much current as possible, and other parts may be producing more than is compatible with long cathode lifetime.

3. THE ANALYSIS OF AN ELECTRODE SYSTEM, USING SPACE-CHARGE SIMULATION

3.1. Introduction. When space-charge effects are too large to be ignored, the space charge must be synthesized in some manner. In the next chapter, the details of the methods of simulating the electric field are discussed. In many of these methods, it is possible to simulate the space charge by making corrections to a Laplacian field at discrete points. If the whole problem is solved numerically on a digital computer, a space-charge term is added to the Laplacian at every mesh point. In an electrolytic tank or resistance network, for example, the corrections would be made by injecting charge at a number of discrete points. The rate of charge injection is related to the total charge in the vicinity of that point. In this section, we discuss how a given electrode system may be analyzed, assuming that the appropriate simulation of space-charge fields can be made.

A complete discussion of the use of an electrolytic tank with current probes for simulating the effects of space charge for the design of guns is given in papers by Brewer and Van Duzer.[2,3] A similar discussion, when the whole problem is solved on a digital

*But in some cases, particularly in the crossed-field guns discussed in Sec. 2.4 of Chap. II, for research purposes the cathode is run thermally limited. The resulting beam is found to be much less noisy. In ion propulsion applications, where an ion beam is emitted from a porous tungsten ionizer, it is best to design the gun for the equivalent of a thermally limited beam. In this case the efflux of neutrals from the emitter is minimized.

computer, is presented in Refs. 4 and 5. In this section some of the more important features of the design method are described.

A gun study has two aspects, that of analysis and that of synthesis. We discuss the former here. An iteration procedure is set up to modify repetitively the space-charge-field-simulation terms, until a sufficiently accurate self-consistent solution is obtained.

In the physical beam, there are so many electrons that the space-charge distribution can be assumed continuous. Hence, the space-charge fields in a system are simulated only approximately by a fairly small number of finite charges or regions of charge injection. In this section one such method of simulation is presented, and its convergence and accuracy are evaluated in one specific example.

Several special devices may be used to speed up convergence of the iteration procedure. Several criteria for convergence may be adopted. Both these subjects are discussed in detail.

Because of inaccuracies in the representation of electric fields near the boundaries in both analog and digital approaches, the behavior of the beam is difficult to determine near the cathode. This is particularly serious when the flow is space-charge-limited, because there is an infinite space charge there. Of course, there is no infinite space charge in the physical system. Very near the cathode the potential does not vary exactly with the four-thirds-power law (Section 2 of Chap. VI). The methods of this chapter, however, cannot distinguish the fine detail very near the potential minimum, and the four-thirds-power law is assumed to hold right to the cathode. For this reason, in the iteration methods, a Langmuir distribution of potential is assumed up to a small but appreciable distance from the cathode. This assumption introduces two difficulties: First, the asymptotic solution of the iteration procedure is no longer unique. Second, even when an additional condition is required which ensures uniqueness, the assumption leads to an error near the cathode. This error is estimated for the planar diode, and methods of reducing it are described.

3.2. The Iteration Procedure. The usual method of analysis consists of assuming a space-charge distribution, solving Poisson's equation, tracing trajectories, and then modifying the space-charge distribution as a result of the trajectory plots. This procedure can then be repeated until the trajectories and electron velocities obtained are consistent with the space-charge distribution.

The usual procedure is first to plot the equipotentials with a zero or assumed space charge field. The current density of the emitter is computed from Eq. (2.5), using for ϕ the potential derived from the solution of the previous Poisson's or Laplace's equation. The cathode is divided into several equal segments, and trajectories are plotted. The approximation is made that all the electron paths from one section of the cathode are similar. Following the notation of Fig. 8.2, I_k is the cathode current in the kth section. It is as-

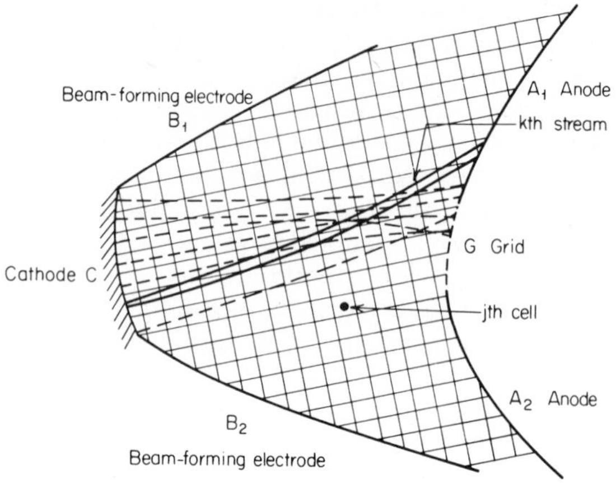

Fig. 8.2. Schematic of the electrode system for an electron gun with angular mesh superposed. The solid lines designate the different cells into which the interelectrode space is divided, and the dotted lines show particle trajectories.

sumed that all the current may be concentrated in the center of each stream, so that only this center need be considered; the kth stream is therefore referred to as the kth ray. The error introduced by this assumption can be tested by increasing the number of rays considered.

The region within the electrodes is divided into cells. In the middle of the jth cell is a space charge field simulating element representing a charge, Q_j. The part of Q_j arising from the kth ray, Q_{kj}, is calculated from

$$Q_{kj} = -I_k t_{kj} \tag{3.1}$$

where t_{kj} is the length of time that the kth ray is in the jth cell.* The time t_{kj} is given by

$$t_{kj} = \ell_{kj}(2\eta\phi_j)^{-1/2} \tag{3.2}$$

where ℓ_{kj} and ϕ_j are the length of the kth trajectory and the potential in the jth cell. Equation (3.2) assumes that the cathode is at zero potential and that all electrons left the cathode with zero velocity. If these assumptions are not fulfilled, Eq. (3.2) must be slightly modified.

From Eqs. (3.1) and (3.2) the following expression for Q_j can be derived:

$$Q_j = -\sum_k I_k \ell_{kj}(2\eta\phi_j)^{-1/2} \tag{3.3}$$

Equation (3.3) leads to an iterative method of solution. If $Q_j^{(n)}$ is de-

*The usual convention of this book is used that $\mathbf{i} = -\rho\mathbf{v}$.

fined as the charge in the jth cell, at the nth iteration, and $\phi_j^{(n)}$, $\ell_{kj}^{(n)}$, $I_k^{(n)}$ are similarly defined, then

$$Q_j^{(n+1)} = -\sum_k I_k^{(n+1)} \ell_{kj}^{(n+1)} (2\eta\phi_j^{(n)})^{-1/2} \tag{3.4}$$

It is now possible to obtain $I_k^{(n+1)}$ by using the boundary conditions of Section 2. Using the notation of Eq. (2.7), let $i_{cM,k}$ be the current density of the injected or thermally limited beam at the emitter position referring to the kth stream, and let $i_{c,sc,k}^{(n+1)}$ be the space-charge-limited current density at the emitter at the (n + 1)st iteration in the region of the kth stream. Then $i_{c,sc,k}^{(n+1)}$ is given, by analogy with Eq. (2.5), by

$$i_{c,sc,k}^{(n+1)} = K \frac{(\phi_k^{(n)})^{3/2}}{z_k^2} \tag{3.5}$$

where $\phi_k^{(n)}$, z_k correspond to the potential and distance from the center of a specified point near the emitter on the kth ray. The current density at the emitter $i_{c,k}^{(n+1)}$ is now given by Eq. (2.6), where for i_{cM} the maximum injected current $i_{cM,k}$ is used, and for $i_{c,sc}$ the current density of Eq. (3.5) is used. The total current in the kth stream is now $I_k^{(n)}$, where $I_k^{(n)}$ is given by the expression

$$I_k^{(n+1)} = S_k i_{c,k}^{(n+1)} \tag{3.6}$$

where $i_{c,k}^{(n+1)}$ is the current density defined above, and S_k is the emitter area corresponding to the kth stream. Generally, guns are designed to have space-charge-limited emission, and Eq. (3.5) is applicable for $i_{c,k}^{(n+1)}$.

We are now in a position to set up an iterative procedure. First, assuming there is a charge $Q_j^{(n)}$ in the jth cell after the nth iteration, this charge may be converted into a space-charge-density distribution by the formula

$$\rho_j^{(n)} = \frac{Q_j^{(n)}}{\tau_j} \tag{3.7}$$

where τ_j is the volume of the jth cell. Using analog or digital techniques, $\phi^{(n)}$ may be found by solving Poisson's equation in the form

$$\nabla^2\phi^{(n)} = -\frac{\rho^{(n)}}{\epsilon_0} \tag{3.8}$$

with the specified ϕ on the boundary.

In practice, the correction to $\nabla^2\phi$, due to the charge density of the right-hand side of Eq. (3.8), is made only at the center of each cell. Therefore the total charge $Q_j^{(n)}$ is used rather than the charge density $\rho^{(n)}$.

With the $\phi^{(n)}$ determined, the Lorentz equation of motion in the form

$$\frac{d\mathbf{v}^{(n)}}{dt} = \eta(-\nabla\phi^{(n)} + \mathbf{v}^{(n)} \times \mathbf{B}^{(n)}), \qquad \frac{d\mathbf{x}^{(n)}}{dt} = \mathbf{v}^{(n)} \tag{3.9}$$

is integrated for each ray, by the methods of Section 9 of Chap. IX. The initial conditions are that the ray starts at the cathode at the appropriate point, with zero velocity.

From these trajectory plots, a new current in the kth ray may be evaluated from Eq. (3.5), and a new charge distribution $Q_j^{(n+1)}$ from Eq. (3.4). This completes the iteration loop.

We summarize the complete procedure for clarity:

1. Without space charge, or with an assumed space-charge distribution $\rho^{(n)}$, find the potentials at the center of the jth cell by solving Poisson's equation. On subsequent iterations, the result of the previous iteration for the space charge should be used.

2. From these potentials and Eqs. (3.5) and (3.6), compute $I_k^{(n+1)}$ from the values of $\phi^{(n)}$ obtained in step 1.

3. Trace trajectories, and then, from Eq. (3.4), determine $Q_j^{(n+1)}$ from $\phi_j^{(n)}$, $I^{(n+1)}$, and the trajectories plotted.

4. Repeat steps 1 to 3 for n = 1, 2, 3 until successive iterations differ by less than the desired accuracy of the potential distribution and flow pattern.

The procedure is shown in block-diagram form in Fig. 8.3. In passing, it should be noted that the above procedures allow the analysis of a gun or focusing structure by purely numerical means without resorting to analog techniques. At no stage in the analysis is it material whether the numerical or analog methods are used to trace the trajectories, solve Poisson's equation, or synthesize space charge.

3.3. Convergence and Rate of Convergence. Many different criteria may be adopted for testing convergence of the iteration procedure. The most obvious ones are the variation of trajectory, charge or cathode current density, and potential. The accuracy of criteria related to trajectory shape alone depends on the problem being solved. For example, in the planar-diode problem, all trajectories are rectilinear, and the trajectory shape cannot be used as criterion. Partly because $\rho = \infty$ at the cathode, the variation of charge density is a test which is too sensitive to relate to other performance criteria. The usual test is whether the fractional change in the current in each ray $I_k^{(n)}$ or the potential $\phi^{(n)}$ is less than a certain value between iterations. Symbolically, the former criterion can be written

$$\max_k \left| 1 - \frac{I_k^{(n)}}{I_k^{(n-1)}} \right| < \epsilon \tag{3.10}$$

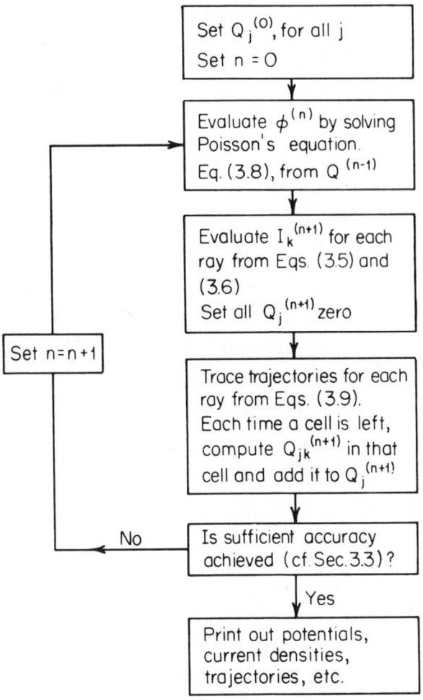

Fig. 8.3. Block-diagram schematic of the iteration procedure.

where ϵ is a preset parameter, e.g., 0.001.

If Poisson's equation is solved by the finite-difference methods of Section 3 of Chap. IX, a very convenient criterion is that the relaxation procedure should converge in one minor iteration. By a minor-iteration cycle, in this context, is meant one application of Eq. (3.4) of Chap. IX at each mesh point.

Whatever the convergence criterion chosen, it is desirable to achieve that criterion in as few iterations as possible. It has been shown empirically that one method of speeding up convergence is undercorrection of the cathode current. Undercorrection consists of using not the $I_k^{(n+1)}$ of Eq. (3.6) to determine $Q_j^{(n+1)}$, but instead $\bar{I}_k^{(n+1)}$, where

$$\bar{I}_k^{(n+1)} = \bar{I}_k^{(n)} + \gamma(I_k^{(n+1)} - \bar{I}_k^{(n)}) \tag{3.11}$$

In Eq. (3.11), $I_k^{(n+1)}$ is defined in Eq. (3.6), and γ is a constant which may be specified. It is easily verified that choosing $\gamma = 1$ is equivalent to using Eq. (3.6) as it stands. Of course, the procedure must be initiated, and hence γ is always chosen as unity on the first iteration (so that the terms in $\bar{I}_k^{(0)}$ cancel). Usually, values of about 0.7 have been found empirically to lead to the quickest convergence.

The effect of different γ is shown in the specific example of the crossed-field gun of Sec. 2.3 of Chap. II. The theoretical electrodes

Table 8.1 Variation of the Number of Iterations Required to Achieve a Given Accuracy as a Function of γ for One Example

γ	0.5	0.6	0.667	0.75	1.0
No of iterations. . .	8	7	5	8	10

of Fig. 7.13 were used. The number of iterations required to achieve a given convergence criterion for different γ is given in Table 8.1.

It is seen from Table 8.1 that the quickest convergence is for $\gamma = 0.667$. Although it would be very difficult to prove that this would be always the case, one can give a plausibility argument by considering the planar diode. The use of the equations of Sec. 3.2 leads to other effects which complicate the argument; therefore we shall consider a simplified set of equations.

Instead of Eqs. (3.8) and (3.9), Poisson's equation is written in iterative form [Eq. (2.15) of Chap. II],

$$\frac{d^2\phi^{(n)}}{dz^2} = \frac{I^{(n)}}{\epsilon_0(2\eta\phi^{(n-1)})^{1/2}} \tag{3.12}$$

where $(2\eta\phi^{(n-1)})^{1/2}$ is substituted for the velocity from the conservation-of-energy relation; Eq. (3.12) already contains the information which might be derived from the Lorentz equation of motion. As boundary conditions, it is assumed that

$$\begin{aligned} \phi &= 0 \quad \text{at} \quad z = 0 \\ \phi &= 1 \quad \text{at} \quad z = 1 \end{aligned} \tag{3.13}$$

and that $I^{(n)}$ is determined so that Eq. (3.13) is always satisfied [this is not the same condition as Eq. (3.5), but greatly simplifies the algebra]. We assume, further, that $\phi^{(n-1)}$ is known and has the form

$$\phi^{(n-1)}(z) = z^{4/3+\delta_{(n-1)}} \tag{3.14}$$

where $\delta_{(n-1)}$ is small. This means that Eq. (3.12) can be integrated twice to give

$$\phi^{(n)}(z) = \frac{I^{(n)}(2\epsilon_0^2\eta)^{-1/2} z^{\frac{4}{3}-\frac{1}{2}\delta_{(n-1)}}}{\left(\frac{4}{3} - \frac{1}{2}\delta_{(n-1)}\right)\left(\frac{1}{3} - \frac{1}{2}\delta_{(n-1)}\right)} + az + b \tag{3.15}$$

From Eq. (3.15) it is seen that $\phi^{(n)}$ satisfies the boundary conditions of Eq. (3.13) and has the form of Eq. (3.14) if

$$a = b = 0, \qquad \delta_n = -\frac{\delta_{(n-1)}}{2}, \qquad \frac{I^{(n)}}{\epsilon_0(2\eta)^{1/2}} = \frac{4}{9} - \frac{5}{6}\delta_{(n-1)} + \frac{1}{4}\delta^2_{(n-1)} \tag{3.16}$$

Therefore the correct value of $I^{(n)}$ is, using Eq. (3.16),

$$\frac{9}{4}\frac{I^{(n)}}{\epsilon_0(2\eta)^{1/2}} - 1 = \frac{9}{4}\delta_n\left(\delta_n + \frac{5}{3}\right) \tag{3.17}$$

If now it is assumed that $I^{(n-1)}$ and $I^{(n)}$ satisfy Eq. (3.17), it will be shown that a more accurate expression for the current at the nth iteration would be obtained by using $\bar{I}^{(n)}$, where

$$\bar{I}^{(n)} = I^{(n-1)} + \gamma \,|\, I^{(n)} - I^{(n-1)} \,| \tag{3.18}$$

for suitable choice of γ. The use of Eqs. (3.16) and (3.17) yields

$$\frac{9}{4}\frac{\bar{I}^{(n)}}{\epsilon_0(2\eta)^{1/2}} - 1 = \frac{9}{4}\left[\delta_{(n-1)}\left(\frac{5}{3} - \frac{5\gamma}{2}\right) + \delta^2_{(n-1)}\left(1 - \frac{3\gamma}{4}\right)\right] \tag{3.19}$$

Although, to make this error disappear completely, it is necessary that γ be related to $\delta_{(n-1)}$, the term linear in $\delta_{(n-1)}$ disappears if

$$\gamma = 2/3 \tag{3.20}$$

This argument contains several unrealistic assumptions and, in any case, applies to the one-dimensional problem only. However, the result gives some analytical justification for the use of $2/3$ as an optimum undercorrection factor in Eq. (3.11) and its numerical corroboration in Table 8.1.

3.4. Uniqueness of the Iterative Solutions. There are many proofs of uniqueness of the simple boundary-value problem;[1] in all these proofs, the potential satisfies Poisson's equation with a known space-charge distribution and has known values on the boundary. Although no proof is known to the authors that the self-consistent field problem of this chapter has a unique solution, it seems likely that the solution is indeed unique. However, the iterative procedure of Sec. 3.2 can definitely be shown not to have a unique solution. This is principally due to the fact that the current in each ray is calculated by Eq. (3.5), assuming a Langmuir variation at a distance z_k from the cathode. If z_k could be made indefinitely small, the solution would probably be unique; however, practical considerations always impose minimum dimensions on z_k. In resistance networks or difference meshes on computers, there is a natural minimum to z_k of the order of the mesh size. In electrolytic tanks or similar analogs, the potential cannot be measured or synthesized too near the surface of the cathode, for practical reasons.

In this section, the planar diode is considered. It is shown that, with the equations outlined in Sec. 3.2, the solution is not unique, but can have errors of order h/d in cathode current; here h is the minimum distance at which the potential can be measured, and d is the anode-cathode spacing.

From Eq. (2.15) of Chap. II, we may deduce the one-dimensional form of Poisson's equation,

$$\frac{d^2\phi}{dz^2} = \frac{4i}{9K}\,\phi^{-1/2} \tag{3.21}$$

where $$K = \frac{4}{9}\epsilon_0\sqrt{2\eta} \tag{3.22}$$

and the boundary conditions at the cathode and anode are

$$\begin{aligned} \phi &= 0 \quad \text{at the cathode } z = 0 \\ \phi &= \phi_0 \quad \text{at the anode } z = z_0 \end{aligned} \tag{3.23}$$

and the correct condition for space-charge-limited emission is

$$\frac{d\phi}{dz} = 0 \quad \text{at } z = 0 \tag{3.24}$$

It has been shown in Sec. 2.2 of Chap. II, after simplifying some of the constants, that the ϕ, i satisfying

$$\phi = \phi_0 \left(\frac{z}{z_0}\right)^{4/3}, \qquad i = K\left(\frac{\phi_0^{3/2}}{z_0^2}\right) \tag{3.25}$$

are the solutions of this system. In the iteration procedure of Sec. 3.2, the boundary condition of Eq. (3.24) is replaced by Eq. (3.5), which, in a slightly different form, may be written

$$i = K\left(\frac{\phi_0^{3/2}}{z_0^2}\right)\left[\frac{\phi(H)^{3/2}}{H^2}\right] \tag{3.26}$$

where it is assumed that the Langmuir relation is applied at a particular distance H from the cathode.

The replacement of the boundary condition of Eq. (3.24) by Eq. (3.26) may alter slightly the possible solutions of Eq. (3.21), though Eq. (3.25) is still one solution. We assume that the solution of Eq. (3.21) is

$$\begin{aligned} \phi &= \phi_0\left[\left(\frac{z}{z_0}\right)^{4/3} + \delta(z)\right] \\ i &= K\frac{\phi_0^{3/2}}{z_0^2}(1 + \xi) \end{aligned} \tag{3.27}$$

where δ and ξ are small, and ξ is a constant. On substituting this solution and neglecting terms in $\delta\xi$ and δ^2, Eq. (3.21) becomes

$$\frac{d^2\delta}{dz^2} + \frac{2}{9}\frac{\delta}{z^2} = \frac{4}{9}\frac{\xi}{z^{2/3} z_0^{4/3}} \tag{3.28}$$

which has the solution

$$\delta(z) = \alpha_1 z^{1/3} + \alpha_2 z^{2/3} + \frac{2}{3}\xi\left(\frac{z}{z_0}\right)^{4/3} \tag{3.29}$$

The boundary conditions of Eqs. (3.23) and (3.24) can be written

$$\delta = 0 \quad \text{at } z = 0,\ z = z_0 \tag{3.30}$$

and

$$\frac{d\delta}{dz} = 0 \quad \text{at } z = 0 \tag{3.31}$$

Using Eqs. (3.30) and (3.31) in Eq. (3.29), it is seen that

$$\alpha_1 = \alpha_2 = \xi = 0 \tag{3.32}$$

showing that the only solution to the system is

$$\delta(z) = \xi = 0 \tag{3.33}$$

If, instead of the space-charge-limited conditions of Eq. (3.24), we apply those of the iteration procedure [Eq. (3.26)], the condition

$$\xi = \frac{3}{2}\,\delta(H)\left(\frac{z_0}{H}\right)^{4/3} \tag{3.34}$$

must be satisfied in place of Eq. (3.31). Equation (3.34) is obtained by substituting Eq. (3.27) into Eq. (3.24) and neglecting terms in δ^2. The solution of Eq. (3.29) satisfies the boundary conditions of Eqs. (3.30) and (3.34) if

$$\alpha_1 = -\alpha_2 H^{1/3} = \delta(H)\,\frac{z_0}{H}\,(z_0^{1/3} - H^{1/3})^{-1} \tag{3.35}$$

Thus a solution which satisfies the boundary conditions is

$$\delta(z) = \delta(H)\left[\frac{(z/z_0)^{1/3} - (z^2/z_0H)^{1/3}}{(H/z_0) - (H/z_0)^{4/3}} + \left(\frac{z}{H}\right)^{4/3}\right] \tag{3.36}$$

Note that this solution satisfies all the boundary conditions imposed in the iteration procedure of Sec. 3.2. Of course, the assumption has been made that $\delta(z) \ll (z/z_0)^{4/3}$; this cannot be true very near the cathode, because $\delta(z)$ is proportional to $z^{1/3}$ and tends to zero much slower than $z^{4/3}$. However, if there is some minimum distance from the cathode, say, h, at which the potential can be observed, this analysis is valid provided

$$\delta(H) \ll \frac{hH}{z_0^2} \tag{3.37}$$

Equation (3.37) is obtained by using the relation

$$\delta(z) \ll \left(\frac{z}{z_0}\right)^{4/3}$$

It is important to note that the ϕ of Eq. (3.27), with $\delta(z)$ and ξ given by Eqs. (3.34) and (3.36), is a solution of the differential equations satisfying all the boundary conditions for any $\delta(H)$ satisfying Eq. (3.37).

This means that, by suitable choice of initial $\phi^{(0)}$ and iteration procedure, any solution satisfying these relations can be obtained. For minimum variation in ϕ it is clear, from Eq. (3.37), that h and H should be as small as possible. Writing Eq. (3.37) in the form

$$\delta_M(H) = k\,\frac{hH}{z_0^2} \tag{3.38}$$

where k is some constant (often about 0.1 to 0.2) and $\delta_M(H)$ is

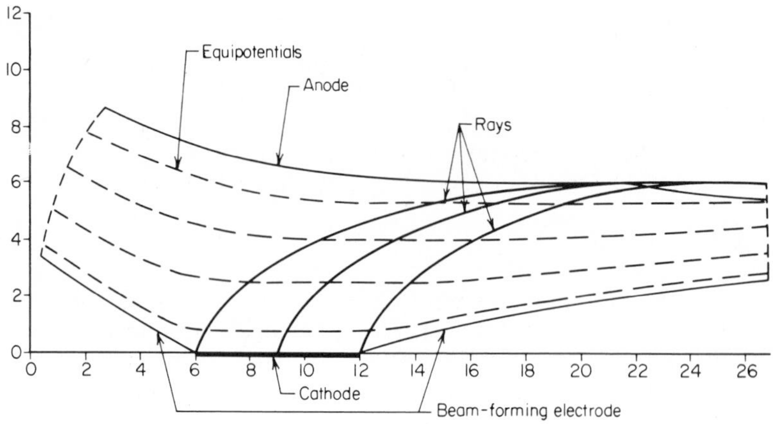

Fig. 8.4. Diagram of the electrode system for a sheet-beam crossed-field gun. (Reproduced from Ref. 6, courtesy of the Institute of Electrical and Electronic Engineers.)

the maximum permissible $\delta(H)$, then, from Eqs. (3.34) and (3.38), it is seen that

$$\xi_M = \frac{3}{2}\, k\, \frac{h}{z_0}\left(\frac{z_0}{H}\right)^{1/3} \tag{3.39}$$

To reduce the errors in current, h should be small, but H, where the current is evaluated from the Langmuir condition, large. However, since the z_0/H term comes in only as the cube root, its exact value is not very significant.

To give an idea of the magnitude of the effect, let us evaluate ξ_M, assuming a k of 0.2 and an $h = H = 0.06\, z_0$. In this case substitution in Eq. (3.39) gives $\xi_M \simeq 4.5$ per cent.

Although this analysis is valid only for the one-dimensional planar diode, it is qualitatively correct for other electrode configurations. This effect has been evaluated, as an example, for the crossed-field gun of Sec. 3.7 of Chap. VII. The electrode system used is shown in Fig. 8.4; the errors due to using different undercorrection factors γ and different initial guesses of cathode current density are shown in Fig. 8.5. From the figure it is seen that different iteration procedures, i.e. different γ, produce different final total currents. The curve marked a, which started with a different assumed current than the curve b with the same γ, also results in a different final value of current.

If for z_0 of the planar diode the length of a trajectory is taken, h/z_0 is about 0.06 for this case. It is seen that the final current is in error by about 12 ± 5 per cent. The 12 per cent error is introduced by solving Poisson's equation on a difference mesh and by evaluating the current at a finite distance from the cathode. The ± 5 per cent variation in the current attained after a large number of

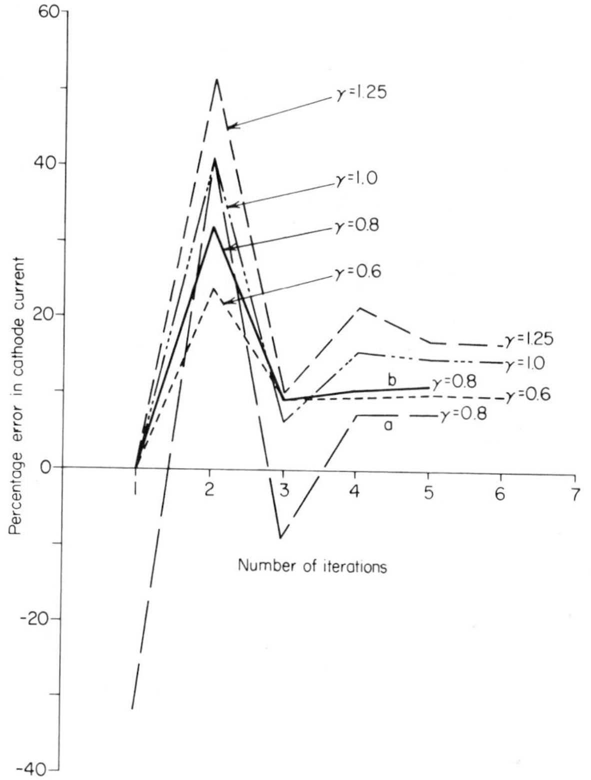

Fig. 8.5. The percentage error in total current of the beam of the electrode system of Fig. 8.4 plotted versus the number of iterations. The different curves refer to different values of the underrelaxation coefficient γ of Eq. (3.14). The two curves for $\gamma = 0.8$ refer to different initial guesses for the cathode current. (Reproduced from Ref. 6, courtesy of the Institute of Electrical and Electronic Engineers.)

iterations is due to the effects described in this section. The beam trajectories in this case were very little affected by the different γ of the initial conditions. The beam current is a much more sensitive test than the beam shape or potential distribution. The lack of uniqueness in the solutions is discussed in such detail because it is important to note the limitations of all the methods which rely on computing the current at a finite distance from the cathode. It is necessary to realize that the solutions are not unique and to have an estimate, as given in Eqs. (3.36) and (3.37), of how much the solutions can vary.

3.5. Accuracy of the Method. One source of error, that due to the lack of uniqueness of the solution, was treated in Sec. 3.4. The errors due to the representation of the potential or boundary in the analog or finite-difference model are discussed in Chap. IX. The errors due to the numerical integration of the trajectories are mentioned in Section 9 of Chap. IX. Some errors are inherent to the whole iteration procedure; these are discussed in Secs. 3.6 and 3.7. Most of the discussion is independent of the model used to represent the potential and to solve Poisson's equation; some is applicable only to cases where numerical-difference procedures or resistance networks are used to solve Poisson's equation. In the first category are the errors due to the concentration of space charge at the center of each ray, the effects of the number of rays, and the computation of current density from a Langmuir potential at a finite distance from the cathode. In the second category is the effect of mesh size. A specific example is given in some detail which illustrates the ef-

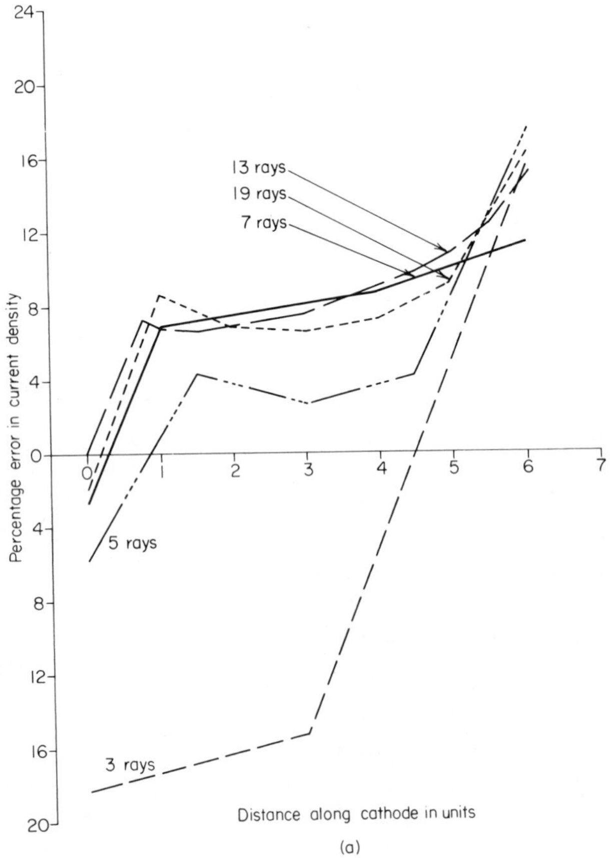

Fig. 8.6. The error in cathode-current density and particle trajectories for a beam from the electrode system of Fig. 8.4. The different curves in each figure refer to different numbers of rays along the cathode. (a) The percentage error in cathode-current density versus distance along the cathode;

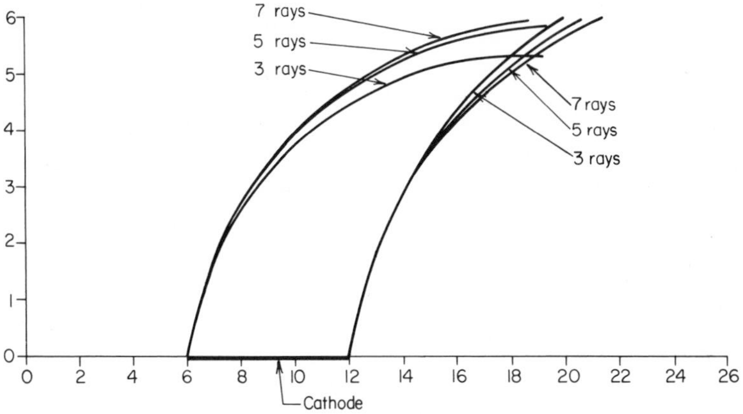

(b)

(b) the edges of the beam. (Reproduced from Ref. 6, courtesy of the Institution of Electrical and Electronic Engineers.)

fects of the various errors described. More curves illustrating the errors in another example are given in Ref. 6.

3.6. Errors Due to the Discrete Nature of the Space-charge Simulation. Because of the simulation of the beam by a number of rays, a certain error is introduced. This error is not serious if sufficient rays are taken, and the number required is often surprisingly small. In Fig. 8.6a and b, the percentage errors in current density and in particle trajectory are shown for the beams from the electrode system of Fig. 8.4. The different curves in each figure refer to taking different numbers of rays at the cathode. This calculation was done entirely numerically, and seven rays correspond to one per mesh at the cathode. It is seen that taking fewer rays causes some error in both cathode current and trajectory, but taking more rays does not improve the accuracy.

Van Duzer and Brewer[3] and Erikson and Sutherland[5] have presented an alternative method of synthesizing space charge. In this the cathode is still divided into a number of segments; the boundaries of the beams from each segment are traced, and the space charge assumed constant across each beam. This method is probably more accurate than that of Fig. 8.2, but is far more laborious to evaluate. It is no longer so simple to add up the space-charge contributions in each cell. Since increasing the number of trajectories, using the equations of Sec. 2.2, does not appreciably change the results, it seems clear that these equations are adequate. In certain cases, when the charge density over the whole beam cross section is known to be uniform, the alternative method will allow the use of fewer rays and will be faster. The interested reader should consult Ref. 5.

3.7. Errors Due to Mesh Size in the Difference Analog for the Potential. To some extent, all analogs suffer from problems due to

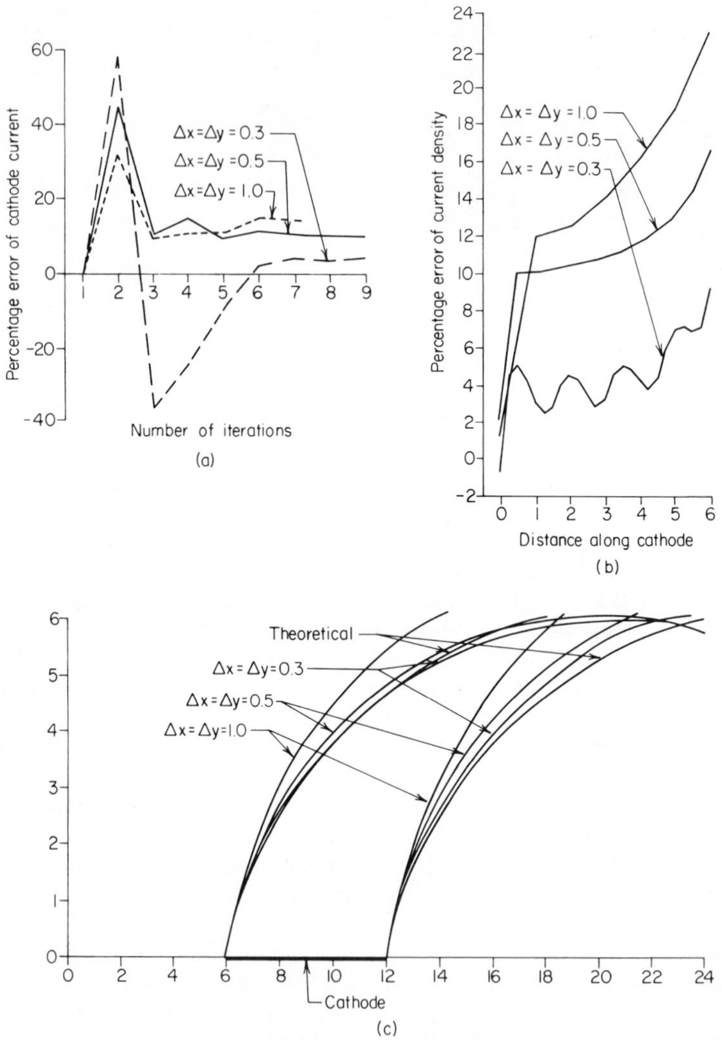

Fig. 8.7. The error in various beam parameters for the beam for the electrode system of Fig. 8.4. The different curves in each figure refer to different mesh sizes. (a) The percentage error in total cathode current of the beam; (b) the error in cathode current density distribution; (c) the particle trajectories. (Reproduced from Ref. 6, courtesy of the Institution of Electrical and Electronic Engineers.)

this effect. Even if a difference analog is not used for the potential, it is always used for the synthesizing of space charge. The errors produced in perveance, cathode-current variation, and trajectories, for the electrode system of Fig. 8.4, due to mesh size, are illustrated in Fig. 8.7a to c. Again the whole computation was performed digitally, and the mesh size was that of the difference mesh. In Fig.

8.7a, it is seen that the smaller the mesh size, the more iterations it takes to converge but the better the final accuracy in perveance. However, the error does not decrease as $O(h)^2$, which is the error due to the analog itself (Sec. 3.4 of Chap. IX). Figure 8.7b and c shows that the errors in cathode current density distribution, and in trajectories, also depend almost linearly on mesh size h.

The main reason for the unexpectedly high error as a function of h is the behavior near the cathode. Here there is a singularity in the space charge, so that considerable errors can be introduced. Hamza and Kino[7] have made a very careful analysis of the two-dimensional planar diode. They first consider the parallel-plane diode of Eq. (3.21),

$$\frac{d^2\phi}{dz^2} = K_1\phi^{-1/2} \tag{3.40}$$

and take only second-order terms for the difference-equation expansion of the left-hand side. By using Eq. (2.15) of Chap. IX, they obtain the equation

$$\phi_{i+1} + \phi_{i-1} - 2\phi_i = K_1h^2\phi_i^{-1/2} \tag{3.41}$$

where ϕ_i is the potential at the nth point from the cathode, at the point x = nh. When this difference equation is solved, with the appropriate initial conditions, there is a 3 per cent error with h = 0.01d. When a fourth-order expansion is used for the left side of Eq. (3.40), it becomes, from Eq. (2.15) of Chap. IX,

$$\phi_{i+1} + \phi_{i-1} - 2\phi_i = K_1h^2\phi_i^{-1/2} - \left(\frac{h^4}{12}\right)\left(\frac{d^4\phi_i}{dz^4}\right) \tag{3.42}$$

Using Eq. (3.40) to express $d^4\phi_i/dz^4$ in terms of $d^2(K_1\phi_i^{-1/2})/dz^2$, and expressing this in terms of a difference equation, Eq. (3.42) becomes

$$\phi_{i+1} + \phi_{i-1} - 2\phi_i = \frac{K_1h^2}{12}(\phi_{i+1}^{-1/2} + \phi_{i-1}^{-1/2} + 10\phi_i^{-1/2}) \tag{3.43}$$

There is still one problem, in that, at the first mesh point from the cathode, $\phi_0^{-1/2}$ gives a singularity. For this reason, at the first mesh point, the right-hand side must be rewritten so that

$$\phi_0 + \phi_2 - 2\phi_1 = \frac{K_1h^2}{12}\left[(10 + \alpha)\phi_1^{-1/2} + \phi_2^{-1/2}\right] \tag{3.44}$$

where α is an arbitrary constant. By plotting the error in current density versus α, it can be shown theoretically that α = 3.41 gives the best results; a computer solution[7] of the iterative problem for different α has shown that the best results are obtained for α in the range 3.75 to 3.4. In the two-dimensional case, for a finite-strip beam, it has been shown empirically[7] that α = 10.3 gives the best results.

It has been shown in this section that the errors in ϕ and i_c are of order h. This fact is now used to get a better estimate for ϕ and i_c, assuming the problem has already been solved for two different mesh sizes h_a, h_b.

The potential distributions and cathode-current distributions using mesh sizes h_a and h_b are defined to be ϕ_a, i_{ca} and ϕ_b, i_{cb}. If the correct values are ϕ and i_c, then to order h,

$$\phi_a = \phi + h_a\epsilon \qquad \phi_b = \phi + h_b\epsilon \tag{3.45}$$

$$i_{ca} = i_c + h_a\bar{\epsilon} \qquad i_{cb} = i_c + h_b\bar{\epsilon} \tag{3.46}$$

where $\epsilon, \bar{\epsilon}$ are error terms independent of h to a first approximation. From Eqs. (3.45) and (3.46), the terms in $\epsilon, \bar{\epsilon}$ may be eliminated to give better estimates.

$$\phi = \frac{h_b\phi_a - h_a\phi_b}{h_b - h_a} \tag{3.47}$$

$$i_c = \frac{h_b i_{ca} - h_a i_{cb}}{h_b - h_a} \tag{3.48}$$

The particular case when $h_b = 2h_a$ is particularly useful. In this case

$$\phi = 2\phi_a - \phi_b \qquad i_c = 2i_{ca} - i_{cb} \tag{3.49}$$

In a numerical analysis of the parallel-plane diode Hamza and Kino[7] show that the final error in i_c as a function of h is that given in Table 8.2. By using Eq. (3.49) with $h_b = 0.025$ and $h_a = 0.5$, the error in i_c is reduced to 0.054 per cent; choosing $h_b = 0.05$ and $h_a = 0.10$, the error in i_c becomes 0.094 per cent.

A similar situation has been computed for the error in the potential variation in a parallel-plane diode (see Table 8.3).

Thus the use of Eq. (3.49) dramatically improves the accuracy of the potential, particularly near the cathode.

If the electrode problem is solved by numerical techniques, the number of iterations required increases as h^{-1}. The number of points at which a difference equation (Section 3 of Chap. IX) has to be solved increases as h^{-2}; hence the length of time required to solve the problem increases as h^{-3}. For this reason, a considerable gain in speed results if the problem is solved for two mesh sizes 2h and h, and then the final ϕ, i_c are obtained by using Eq. (3.49).

In this way, the time required to solve a given problem on a digital computer may often be reduced by at least an order of magnitude.

Table 8.2 Percentage Error in Cathode-current Density in a Planar Diode*

h	0.025	0.05	0.10
Percentage error in i_c.	0.638	1.330	2.756

*From Ref. 7.

Table 8.3 Percentage Error in Potential in a Planar Diode and Its Correction by Eq. (3.49)*

z	Per cent error in ϕ for h = 0.05	Per cent error in ϕ for h = 0.10	Per cent error in ϕ from Eq. (3.49)
0.1	3.18	6.13	0.25
0.2	0.88	1.83	−0.07
0.3	0.30	0.67	−0.07
0.4	0.094	0.23	−0.042
0.5	0.009	0.046	−0.028
0.6	−0.023	−0.029	−0.017
0.7	−0.031	−0.051	−0.011
0.8	−0.026	−0.046	−0.006
0.9	−0.015	−0.027	−0.003
1.0	0	0	0

*Based on figures given in Ref. 7.

Using a resistance network, the change in mesh size is a little more difficult to arrange. However, the improvement in resulting accuracy is equally impressive.

Although these analyses have been proved for only the one-dimensional case, their use in the more complex problems still improves accuracy. For example, the current in the ith ray could be computed from Eq. (3.5) at a distance H from the cathode (where H = 3h or 4h); then, for the first three or four mesh points, Eqs. (3.43) and (3.44) could be used. It is not difficult to make these modifications if the cathode is straight and aligned parallel to one of the coordinate axes. It is more difficult if the cathode is straight, but not parallel to, one of the coordinate axes, and rather hard for curvilinear cathodes.

4. ANALYSIS AND SYNTHESIS OF ELECTRODE SYSTEMS BY THE SUPERPOSITION PRINCIPLE

4.1. Introduction. It is possible, by the methods described in the last section, to analyze any electrode system, taking space-charge fields into account. However, the analog or digital equipment required is complex, and costly, and may be unavailable. Moreover, the effort required for the analysis rapidly increases with the number of space-charge-simulating cells. For these reasons, methods of analysis which dispense with space-charge-simulating cells are developed in this section.

In most of the problems treated in this book, the required beam behavior is specified in advance. The problem is not to analyze the properties of an arbitrary system of electrodes and emitting surfaces, but rather to devise a particular electrode system which will produce a given flow pattern. In the majority of these problems, the total potential ϕ in the beam region and the space-charge configuration are known a priori. In the anode-hole problem, which is treated further in the next section, the potential distribution for a similar space-charge configuration is known. The methods of this and the next section express ϕ as the sum of two potential distributions. One of these potential distributions includes all the space-charge contribution ϕ_{sc} to the potential. The other ϕ_L is Laplacian, and may be analyzed or synthesized by the methods of Section 2 in a digital or analog manner. It is important to note that, since the space-charge density is only a correction to the second derivative of the potential, errors in ϕ_{sc} only slightly affect ϕ. For this reason the space-charge distribution from a slightly different problem may often be used to determine ϕ_{sc}.

The determination of ϕ_{sc} may be a lengthy problem. The method to be described for synthesis problems is useful, because the ϕ_{sc} calculated for one electrode system can serve in different electrode configurations. Now any charge distribution produces image charges in the surrounding conductors. Since image charges depend on the shape of the conductors and their proximity to the space-charge distribution, ϕ_{sc} cannot be completely independent of the electrodes. However, in the electrode configurations that are considered in this chapter, those similar to Fig. 8.1, the beam is near the electrodes at the cathode, in the vicinity of the beam-forming electrodes at the beam edge and near the anode. In the anode-hole problem the electrode system is still similar to Fig. 8.1; G in that figure no longer represents a grid, but a hole in the anode electrodes. The electric field beyond G is usually taken to be zero in this problem. Again, it is only in the vicinity of the cathode, and perhaps the anode, that the beam is near the electrodes. Potentials due to charge distributions drop rapidly with distance from the source. Therefore image-charge effects are important only when the beam is near an electrode. In the anode vicinity, the energy of the particles is usually fairly high and the potentials due to image charges in the anode are comparatively unimportant. Near the cathode, the energy of the particles is low and the image-charge effects are important. The potential ϕ_{sc} is therefore taken as the potential due to the free charges in the beam and their images in either the cathode or in some logical extension of the cathode. If the cathode is a rectangular strip, for example, the logical extension which eases the computation of image-charge effects will be an infinite plane.

The resulting ϕ_{sc}, and even ϕ_L, may be seriously in error if the image charges in the beam-forming electrodes near the cathode are not taken into account. These electrodes in the beam vicinity are usually designed independently by the methods of Section 3 of Chap. VII.

There are many methods for determining ϕ_{sc}, the space-charge contribution to the potential. Some methods can be rigorously justified; others can be explained only qualitatively, and are defended best by their empirical success. It should be emphasized that methods are developed in this section only for splitting up the potential into a space-charge distribution ϕ_{SC} and a Laplacian part ϕ_L. It is assumed that ϕ_L can be synthesized or analyzed in an analog or digital manner, although the representation of a potential satisfying Poisson's equation might be beyond the available facilities.

In the synthesis problem, one wishes to determine the correct ϕ_L at the beam edge and at the cathode with an easily fabricated electrode structure. If the assumptions made in the division of the potential into ϕ_{SC} and ϕ_L are justified, the use of the uniqueness theorem, discussed in Section of Chap. VII, establishes that this electrode system will give the correct electric fields in the beam region in the presence of space charge. In Sec. 4.2 a simple method of synthesizing ϕ_{SC} is discussed. An electrode system known to give the correct fields in the presence of space charge, but difficult to fabricate, is synthesized. From this simulation, the required ϕ_L at the beam edge and at the cathode is determined. Another electrode system, easier to fabricate, may now be found which will produce the same ϕ_L at the beam edge and at the cathode. Under certain assumptions this electrode system will also produce the required beam.

The methods of Sec. 4.2 assume that one electrode system is known a priori. When this is not the case, an alternative method of determining ϕ_{SC} analytically for certain specific cathode shapes is discussed. The method is due to Picquendar and Cahen.[9] In this method, the potential due to the space charge and its images in the cathode are integrated numerically. For some cathode shapes, simple image charges represent the image effects in the cathode; in others, Green's-function techniques must be employed. A numerical example of the method for the parallel-plane diode is presented. For a detailed exposition of the method, with the curves and tables relevant to the rectilinear flows of Appendix E, the reader should consult Ref. 9. The method has also been applied to a more complicated problem, the production of a hollow beam from a cylindrical cathode.

The superposition principle can also be applied to a completely different problem. The effect of changing the electrode configuration from a gridded to a nongridded gun can be estimated by use of this technique. This problem is considered in Section 5.

The emphasis, in this section and the next, on electrode systems, synthesizing the rectilinear flows of Appendix E, should not be taken to imply that the methods are restricted to these applications. A large percentage of the published work has dealt with these flows, which provide good illustrations of the methods.

4.2. The Determination of One Electrode System from Another to Produce the Same Beam. In some problems an electrode system to produce a certain beam is known; this electrode system may not be suitable for a practical electron gun. By using the exact methods of

Chap. VII, for example, an electrode system to produce a specified flow may be derived by integrating out from the beam edge. The electrode system which results from such an integration may be very awkward to realize practically. The electric field need be correct only in the beam region; if the electric field had to be exactly correct in the beam region, very little variation of the electrodes would be possible. If, however, the fields are to be only approximately correct in the beam region, then from the reverse of the blow-up phenomena discussed in Sec. 2 of Chap. VII, the electrode system may be varied considerably. One method of obtaining a more convenient electrode system without using a space-charge-simulating devices is now derived.

Let ϕ be the total potential distribution to be realized in the region of the beam. This potential may be split up into a space-charge contribution ϕ_{sc} and a Laplacian ϕ_L, satisfying the relation

$$\phi = \phi_{sc} + \phi_L \tag{4.1}$$

In Eq. (4.1), ϕ_{sc} represents the contribution to the potential from the space charge in the beam and its image charges in the electrodes. The Laplacian term is defined from Eq. (4.1), and is the potential distribution when the electrodes are held at their correct potentials and there is no space charge.

If a correct closed electrode system, as sketched in Fig. 8.1, is known, ϕ_L may be determined experimentally. The known electrode system can be synthesized without space charge, and the resulting potential distribution determined in the beam region. Throughout this chapter, we use the terms synthesizing and determining potential distributions without specifying whether these are accomplished numerically or in an analog manner. The means employed are immaterial to the argument of this chapter. The potential is defined uniquely in the beam region if it is specified at the beam edges, at the cathode, and over the anode plane in the beam. In Fig. 8.8 are sketched both a low- and a high-perveance gun; in both cases the cathode is at zero potential. In the former it is sufficient to determine ϕ_L over the edges of the beam and the anode plane; in the high-perveance case, however, where the length of the beam is comparable to its width, even small errors of ϕ_L at the beam edge can lead to large errors in the electric field at the cathode. These field errors would lead to appreciable errors in cathode emission. For this reason, in high-perveance guns with microperveance greater than about 1 for solid beams, it is necessary to determine ϕ_L along the beam edge and the anode plane, and the electric field E_{Lc} at the cathode.

We may now determine new, and more convenient, electrodes outside the beam, which produce the same ϕ_L at the beam edge and the same E_{Lc} at the cathode, whereas the cathode is kept at zero potential. If the ϕ_{sc} for the two electrode systems are the same, the

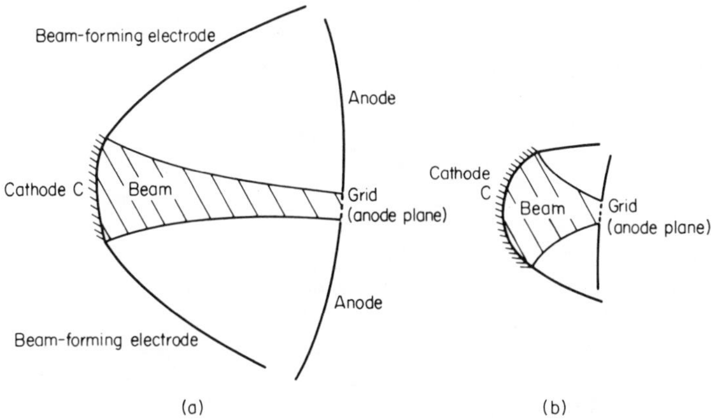

Fig. 8.8. Schematic of the electrode systems for high- and low-perveance gridded guns. (a) Low-perveance guns; (b) high-perveance guns.

beam which will result from the new electrode system will be identical with the originally required beam. Provided that the cathode and the electrodes near the beam edge have not been altered, the change in ϕ_{SC} will not be significant. Of the image charges in the electrodes which could alter ϕ_{SC} and render this method inaccurate, only those in the cathode and beam-forming electrodes are usually significant. In high-perveance guns (Fig. 8.8b), the beam is rather close to the anode electrode; this fact may introduce some errors if the parts of the anode close to the beam are altered too drastically. If space charge field simulating equipment is not available, and if the complications of evaluating exactly image-charge effects in complex electrodes systems are to be avoided, this method is the most reliable one. An illustration of the direct use of this technique is given in Ref. 9.

4.3. The Analytic Determination of the Space-charge Potential. If no electrode system is known to produce the desired flow a priori, an alternative method must be used to determine ϕ_{SC}. A Laplacian potential ϕ_L is then found from the difference between the required total potential ϕ in the beam and ϕ_{SC}. The method then proceeds as in the foregoing section.

The image charges which have strong effects are those in the cathode, so that ϕ_{SC} is again defined as the potential due to the space charge and its image in the cathode. As previously discussed, this ϕ_{SC} is not very different from the potential due to the space charge and its image in all the electrodes.

One method of obtaining the space-charge contribution ϕ_{SC} is to integrate the potential due to the individual charge and their image charges in the cathode. A schematic of the electrode and beam configuration is shown in Fig. 8.9 for a planar cathode. In Fig. 8.9, D is the beam region, C the cathode z = 0, B_1 and B_2 are the beam-form-

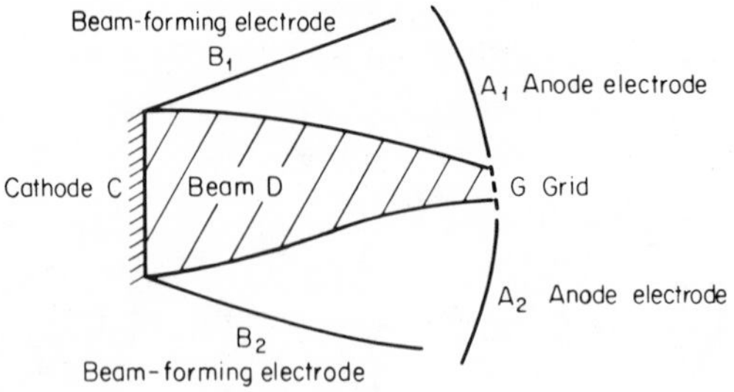

Fig. 8.9. Diagram of the electrode system for a gridded gun.

ing electrodes, as yet unknown, and A_1 and A_2 are the anodes, also unknown, corresponding to the required perveance. B_1 and B_2 are usually at the same voltage, as are A_1 and A_2. Again a gridded gun with a grid G is considered.

We discuss, first, the determination of ϕ_{SC} for a beam from a planar cathode. This problem has been solved for certain beam configurations by Picquendar and Cahen.[9] The results for a rectilinear pencil beam are presented, and then more complex geometries are discussed.

It is more convenient in deriving ϕ_{SC} to consider the image charges resulting, not from the finite planar cathode C, but from the finite plane K, which is the logical extension of C. This extension and the coordinate system are sketched in Fig. 8.10. The potential at the point P, with coordinates (x,y,z), due to a point charge $4\pi Q(x',y',z')$, at the point P′, with coordinates (x′,y′,y′), is ϕ_{SC}, where ϕ_{SC} is given by the expression

$$\phi_{SC}(x,y,z) = \frac{Q}{\epsilon_0}\left[(x-x')^2 + (y-y')^2 + (z-z')^2\right]^{-1/2} \tag{4.2}$$

The image charge of P′ in the plane K is, for the cathode shape being considered, a point charge $-4\pi Q$ at a point $(x',y',-z')$; when the effect

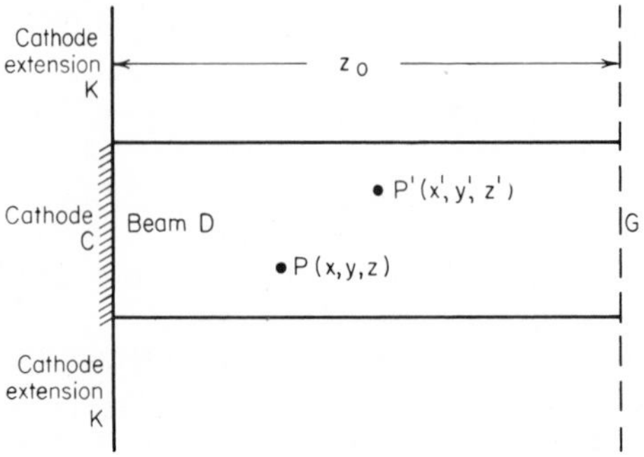

Fig. 8.10. Diagram of the notation for the determination of the space-charge potentials in a pencil beam.

of the image charge is included, ϕ_{SC} takes the form

$$\phi_{SC}(x,y,z) = \frac{Q}{\epsilon_0}(x',y',z')\{[(x-x')^2+(y-y')^2+(z-z')^2]^{-1/2} - [(x-x')^2+(y-y')^2+(z+z')^2]^{-1/2}\} \tag{4.3}$$

From Eq. (4.3) ϕ_{SC} can be deduced for an arbitrary space-charge distribution in the beam; the potential may be expressed in the form

$$\phi_{SC}(x,y,z) = \int_0^{z_0} dz' \iint_S dx'\, dy' \left[\frac{\rho(x',y',z')}{4\pi\epsilon_0}\right]$$
$$\{[(x-x')^2+(y-y')^2+(z-z')^2]^{-1/2} - [(x-x')^2+(y-y')^2+(z+z')]^{-1/2}\} \tag{4.4}$$

where S = cross section of the beam
$\rho(x',y',z')$ = space-charge density
z_0 = grid-cathode spacing.

The curves for ϕ_{SC} which arise from considering a circular beam of radius a from a planar cathode, where the total potential in the beam has the variation

$$\phi(x,y,z) = \phi_0\left(\frac{z}{z_0}\right)^{4/3} \tag{4.5}$$

are shown in Fig. 8.11. This is the pencil-beam problem discussed in Sec. 4.2 of Chap. VII. It is clear that the space-charge potentials in this case are important only in the cathode region up to a distance of about 2a, where a is the beam radius. In Fig. 8.11, the ratio $(1 - \phi_{SC}/\phi)^{-3/2}$ is plotted for a particular cathode-grid spacing. The ratio plotted is less than unity, because ϕ_{SC} is negative. Be-

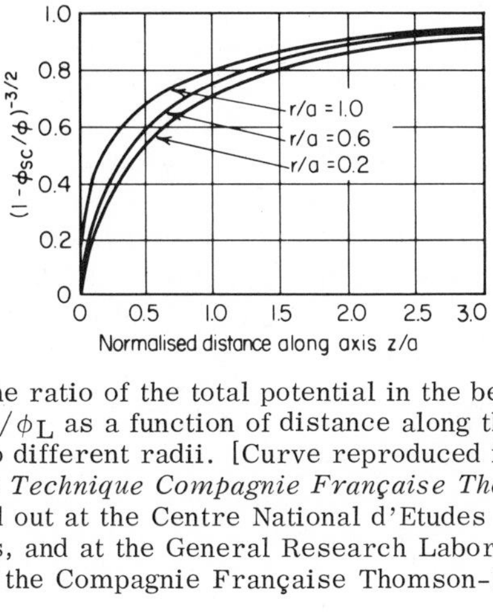

Fig. 8.11. Graph of the ratio of the total potential in the beam to the Laplacian potential ϕ/ϕ_L as a function of distance along the beam. The different curves refer to different radii. [Curve reproduced from Ref. 9, courtesy of the *Revue Technique Compagnie Française Thomson-Houston*. The work was carried out at the Centre National d'Etudes des Telecommunications (SNET), Paris, and at the General Research Laboratory of the Electron Tube Division of the Compagnie Française Thomson-Houston (CFTH).]

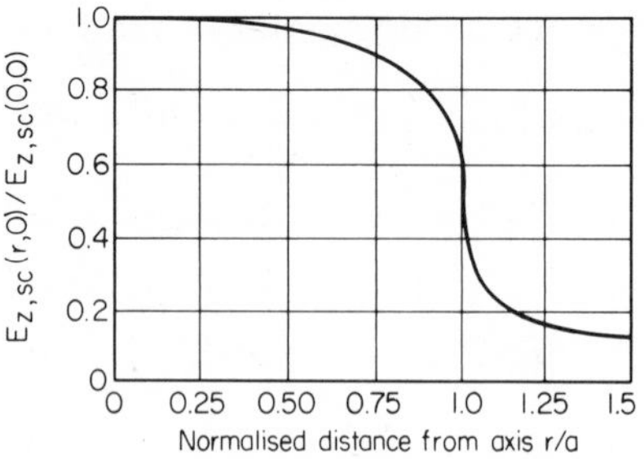

Fig. 8.12. Graph of the distribution of space-charge fields $E_{2,sc}(r,0)/E_{2,sc}(0,0)$ at the cathode. [Curve reproduced from Ref. 9, courtesy of the *Revue Technique Compagnie Francaise Thomson Houston*. The work was done at the Centre National d'Etudes des Telecommunications (SNET), Paris, and at the General Research Laboratory of the Electron Tube Division of the Compagnie Francaise Thomson-Houston (CFTH).]

cause there is axial symmetry, r and z are taken as coordinates, and both ϕ_{sc} and $\mathbf{E}_{sc}$ can be written $\phi_{sc}(r,z)$ and $\mathbf{E}_{sc}(r,z)$.

For high-perveance guns, it is also necessary to compute the normal component of the space-charge field $E_{z,sc}$ at the cathode. In the case of the beam from the planar cathode, $E_{z,sc}$ may be computed in the same way as the potential from the expression

$$E_{z,sc}(x,y,o) = \frac{1}{2\pi\epsilon_0} \int_0^{z_0} z'\,dz' \int_S dy'\,dx' \frac{\rho(x',y',z')}{[(x-x')^2+(y-y')^2+z'^2]^{3/2}} \tag{4.6}$$

The evaluation of Eq. (4.6) is shown, for the same $z^{4/3}$ variation of potential as before, in Fig. 8.12.

Once the formulas for ϕ_{sc} and $E_{z,sc}$ at the cathode have been evaluated, it is a straightforward problem to evaluate boundary conditions on the Laplacian potential ϕ_L; these boundary conditions are that $\phi_L = \phi - \phi_{sc}$ at the beam edges and that the gradient of ϕ_L is in the z direction of magnitude $E_{z,sc}$, at the cathode. Then it is sufficient to use the methods of Section 2 to find electrodes which give rise to a ϕ_L satisfying the boundary conditions. The second boundary conditions arise since, for space-charge-limited emission, **E**, is zero at the cathode. The procedure at this stage is identical with that considered in the preceding section.

It has been necessary to go through a much more tedious analysis to determine ϕ_L and $-E_{Lc}$ because no electrode system was known a priori. The question of the uniqueness of the electrodes, and the possibility of choosing convenient ones, was discussed in the preceding section. In this application, since image charges in the electrodes near the beam have not been taken into account, errors result unless the electrodes near the edge of the beam at the cathode are designed by the methods of Sec. 3.7 of Chap. VII. In the preceding section this problem did not arise, since the electrodes at the beam edge near the cathode were known a priori. With this exception, it is again possible to solve a Laplacian problem. The electrodes may be found numerically, in an electrolytic tank, or on a resistance network without current probes, by the methods of Chap. IX.

Similar calculations have been made by Picquendar and Cahen[9] for sheet beams from a planar cathode and cylindrical beams from a spherical one. In the former example Eqs. (4.4) and (4.6) still apply. The area S over which the integration is carried out is somewhat different. In the latter case the image-charge concepts can still be used, although Eqs. (4.4) and (4.6) must be modified slightly. Detailed curves for the variables encountered in these problems may be found in Ref. 9.

For different cathode shapes, the image-charge concept becomes less useful and a Green's-function formulation must be employed. For a further discussion of Green's functions, the reader should consult a mathematical text such as Ref. 1.

The processes involved in the use of this method are complicated. It is therefore desirable to trace trajectories in the new electrode system, using the ϕ_L synthesized during the design of the electrodes with the space-charge correction ϕ_{SC}. In the same way as in the space-charge-simulation method of Sec. 3, it is now possible to correct the space-charge distribution as a result of these trajectory plots. It is usually possible to obtain several different electrode systems which will produce substantially the same potentials at the beam edge and at the cathode. From the trajectory plots, the electrode system which gives most closely the desired beam can be determined.

5. THE ANODE-HOLE PROBLEM

5.1. Introduction. In the analytic electrode designs of Chap. VII and in the methods previously described in this chapter, one very serious problem arises. The theoretical design requires a certain potential distribution to be maintained, not only in the region outside the beam, but also in the beam region. This requirement may be satisfied by putting a grid in the anode region of the gun. Unfortunately, since to be effective such a grid intercepts a substantial percentage of the beam and, particularly in high-power guns, tends to evaporate, it is usually impractical.

It is to be noted that this anode-hole problem arises only because the original beam solution envisaged is unsuitable for gridless guns. A solution for the beam could be chosen in which there is a maximum potential in the beam. In such models, for example, the one discussed in the circular flow described in Sec. 3 of Chap. II, analyzed theoretically by Lomax,[10] the theoretical electrodes would not pass through the beam; this type of solution would be an excellent basis for the design of a gridless gun. The anode-hole effects discussed in this section modify the original solution to enable electrodes to be found which do not pass through the beam.

There are two effects of the anode hole: First, even at low perveance, the hole acts as a lens, producing a change in direction of the emerging beam. By the methods described, the amount of divergence can be calculated. The beam may then be respecified, so that when the effect of the anode hole is added, a more satisfactory beam emerges from the hole, usually as measured by beam divergence and transmission. The second effect is that, in high-perveance guns, the hole perturbs the field near the cathode, and so changes the uniformity of cathode current emission. These anode-hole effects, and the means developed to produce a more satisfactory beam, are discussed in Sec. 8 of Chap. III and in Sec. 5.6 of this chapter. First, methods of estimating the effects of the anode hole must be developed.

The discussion of the effect of the anode hole falls naturally into two categories. In the first, the anode hole affects the behavior of the beam in the anode region without greatly affecting the current emission or space charge near the anode; this occurs when the perveance is less than about 1 microperv for solid beams, and equivalent ratios of anode-cathode spacing to beam width for hollow and sheet beams. This division into high-, medium-, and low-perveance beams is somewhat arbitrary. It is similar to that discussed previously in Section 1 of Chap. VII and illustrated in Figs. 7.1 to 7.3. A solid parallel-flow pencil beam of microperveance 1 has, from Eq. (6.4) of Chap. I, a ratio of anode-cathode spacing to beam diameter of 1.35. For hollow or strip beams, the significant ratio is that of anode-cathode spacing to the beam thickness. If this ratio is less than about 1.35, the gun is termed a high-perveance gun; if the ratio is between 1.35 and 4, it is termed a medium-perveance gun; and with the ratio less than 4, it is termed a low-perveance gun. The value of 4 for this ratio corresponds to a microperveance of about 0.1 for solid pencil beams. In high-perveance guns, the presence of the anode hole may also drastically alter the current emitted by the cathode. This type of problem can be treated only by considering the design of the gun as a whole. In this range of perveance, the anode hole no longer requires merely a correction to the electrode configuration. It is necessary to employ methods which use space-charge simulators, or to subtract the effect of the space charge by some other means, such as those described in the previous sections. Most of this section is concerned with the consideration of the effect of the anode hole in guns with a medium perveance, 0.1 to 1 microperv for solid beams and similar ratios of cathode diameter to cathode-anode spacing for hollow beams.

The problem of designing a gun considering the anode hole is rather different from the problems previously discussed. If a potential distribution ϕ_b in the beam satisfying Poisson's equation is specified, it is not usually possible to design an electrode system to produce ϕ_b without electrodes passing through the beam. However, it is possible to design an electrode system to produce ϕ_b, neglecting, or only crudely considering, the hole. Methods will be given in this section for estimating the effect of the actual hole. If the resulting beam has undesirable characteristics, the gun may be redesigned, making allowance for the previously found effects of the anode hole, and a new electrode design will be obtained.

It is not the purpose of this chapter to give the details of specific gun designs, but to describe the methods which may be used and to present illustrative examples. An elaborate discussion of the anode-hole problem, as applied to medium-perveance guns, is given in a paper by Danielson et al.[11] It is to a large extent his methods that are developed in this section. In medium-perveance guns, the cathode is sufficiently far from the anode so that the space-charge distribution near the cathode is altered very little by the introduction of the anode hole. Therefore, it is again possible to use the method of superposition described, for a different application, in Section 4.

The anode-hole problem has two aspects, which must be solved consecutively. The first is to determine how it is possible, given an electrode system, to estimate the effect of the hole in the anode. The second is to redesign the electrode system to compensate for any undesirable effect due to the hole.

5.2. The Determination of the Effect of the Anode Hole with Space-charge-simulation Equipment. If an electrolytic tank with space-charge-simulating probes or similar equipment is available, the design of a gun with an anode hole is no more difficult than that of a gridded gun. On the side of the anode, away from the cathode, there is usually a field-free region, with or without magnetic fields. Since space-charge effects are usually not important in this region, it is possible to simulate an approximate space-charge distribution there, and then trace particle trajectories through the hole. Corrections may be made to the space-charge distribution in the light of the trajectory plots. A discussion of the subject of plotting trajectories is given in Section 9 of Chap. IX. This method is applicable, however high the perveance may be, i.e., however large the anode hole relative to the anode-cathode spacing.

5.3. The Effect of the Anode Hole in Very Low Perveance Guns. In low-perveance guns, the anode-cathode spacing is much larger than the diameter of the anode hole. As is shown in Sec. 8 of Chap. III, the effect of the hole may be represented by a thin lens having focal length f, and

$$f = \frac{4\Phi}{E_e} \tag{5.1}$$

where Φ = mean voltage in the hole

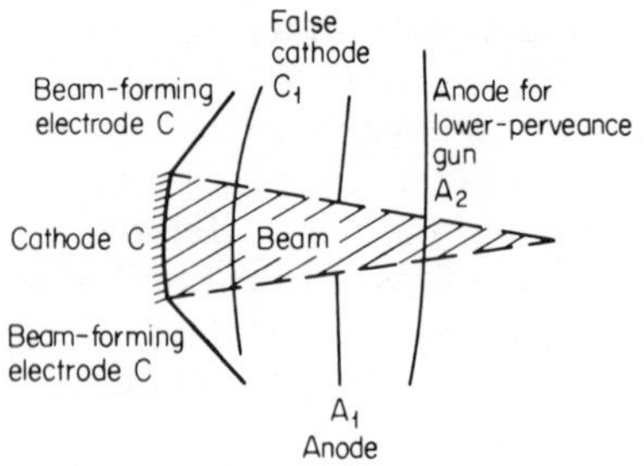

Fig. 8.13. Schematic of the real or virtual electrodes used for determining the equivalent space-charge fields in the anode-hole region.

E_e = axial field which would exist in the hole if it were gridded

This well-known formula due to Davisson and Calbick[12] was deduced from the paraxial-flow equations in Eq. (8.12) of Chap. III, and has been modified by Danielson et al.[11] The formula assumes that the effect of the hole is localized in the immediate vicinity of the gap. The derivation is valid only to the approximation that E_z changes abruptly at the hole. Space charge would affect only the derivative of E_z; hence this formula ignores the effects of space charge. Two methods are given below to extend the calculation to medium-perveance guns where the effects of space charge are included. Both may be used to correct Eq. (5.1).

5.4. The Use of a Dummy Cathode to Determine Effects in Medium-perveance Guns. The space-charge effects are important, in medium-perveance guns, only in the cathode region. A method has been developed to use this property in the estimation of the effects of the anode hole. First an equipotential for a gridded gun is determined at a distance about halfway to the cathode. This equipotential is determined outside the beam by the methods of Secs. 4.2 to 4.4. The equipotential is the same as that for a gridded gun, and passes through the beam region. In the analog or digital computation of this problem, a conductor at the correct potential is simulated along the equipotential, and Laplace's equation is solved in the anode region by the method of Section 2. An illustration of the electrode system is shown in Fig. 8.13. Here C is the cathode and beam-forming electrode, and C_1 is the equipotential in the gridded gun, halfway between the cathode and the anode. The equipotential which would correspond to the required perveance beam would consist of the anode A_1, outside the beam, and a grid passing through the beam. A_2 is the equipotential corresponding to a lower-perveance gridded gun. In the physical problem, C and A_1 would exist, and there would be a field-free region beyond A_1. The potentials of C, C_1, A_1, A_2, for an appropriate gridded gun, are denoted by 0, Φ_C, Φ_1, Φ_2. The gridded-gun situation would be correctly simulated with C at 0 and A_1 at Φ_1. An alternative simulation of the gridded gun between A_1 and A_2 is to put A_1 at Φ_1 and A_2 at Φ_2. We now assume that the introduction of the anode hole has little effect on the space-charge potential in the region between C_1 and A_1 (a reasonable assumption for medium-perveance guns) and that ϕ_{SC} is significant only between C and C_1. Here ϕ_{SC} is defined in the same way as in Section 4. Moreover, the field-free region beyond A_1 may be synthesized by putting both A_1 and A_2 at the same potential Φ_1. The electrode configuration of C_1 at Φ_C and both A_1 and A_2 at Φ_1 can now be synthesized, and the resulting Laplacian potential distribution in the anode region may be used either to trace trajectories directly or to correct the Davisson equation [Eq. (5.1)].

The assumption that ϕ_{SC} is not significant in the anode region has been demonstrated by Brown and Susskind.[13] They consider the rectilinear flow from a spherical cathode, discussed in Appendix E, in which the equipotentials C, C_1, and A_1 may be synthesized as in Fig. 8.13, except that a gridded gun with A_1 passing through the beam is considered. The correct Langmuir potentials on the axis, obtained from Appendix E, are shown in the curve c of Fig. 8.14. The correct Langmuir potentials for this flow would result, as before, from holding C at 0, C_1 at Φ_C, and A_1 at Φ_1 and synthesizing the space-charge potential ϕ_{SC}. The result of holding C at 0 and A_1 at Φ_1 and ignoring space-charge effects, so that ϕ is Laplacian, is shown in curve a of

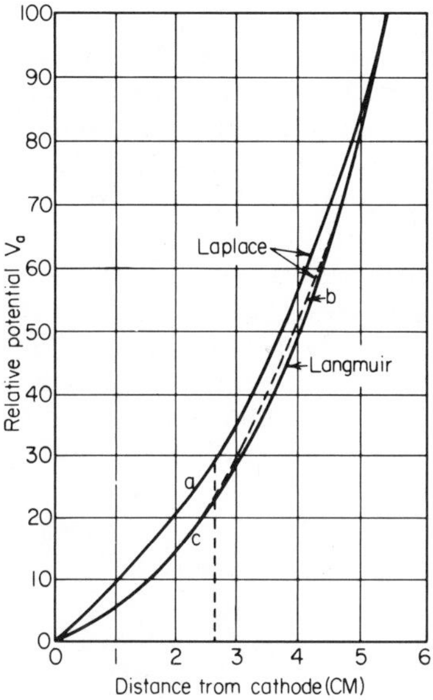

Fig. 8.14. Comparison of a Laplacian potential in an electron gun with that obtained from a Langmuir solution out to one-third of the anode-cathode spacing, followed by a Laplacian superposition. The dotted curve represents the result of the superposition. (Curve reproduced from Ref. 13, courtesy of the American Institute of Electrical and Electronic Engineers.)

Fig. 8.14. There is considerable discrepancy between the two curves, showing that ϕ_{SC} is not negligible. When C_1 is held at Φ_C and A_1 at Φ_1, the resulting potential variation on the axis is given by curve c of Fig. 8.14. This curve differs little from the correct curve b, showing that ϕ_{SC} is adequately synthesized by the introduction of the false cathode C_1. This demonstrates that the assumptions made in the method are satisfactory in a particular case.

5.5. The Use of the Superposition Method in Medium-perveance Guns. In Section 4, one application of the superposition principle was discussed. In that application, the potential was divided into two parts, a Laplacian contribution ϕ_L and a space-charge term ϕ_{SC}. In Sec. 4.2 a method of determining ϕ_L was described for the case where one set of electrodes was known and a different set was desired in order to produce the same beam. In this section an electrode configuration is again prescribed for a gridded anode passing through the beam. We wish to use the same electrode configurations, removing only the part of the anode passing through the beam. Beyond the anode there is usually a field-free region. The effects of the hole in the anode and of the field-free region are required. For this problem, it is not possible to use the method of Sec. 4.2 directly. The method may be slightly modified, however, and the superposition principle used. Again, it is possible to analyze the electrode system, including space-charge effects, without explicitly synthesizing the space charge.

The electrode system to be analyzed is shown in Fig. 8.15. Here C is the zero-potential cathode and beam-forming electrode. The anodes which have been computed to give the desired beam are A_1 and A_2, though in both cases the theoretical anode would have to pass through the beam. The theoretical potentials at which A_1, assumed gridded, and A_2 must be held to produce the desired beam are Φ_1 and Φ_2. We wish to estimate the behavior of the beam when there is a hole in the anode A_1, when A_1 is held at Φ_1, and when there is zero electric field beyond A_1. It is assumed that a device is available for simulating Laplacian potential distributions, but not for ones satisfying Poisson's equation. The condition of zero electric field between A_1 and A_2 will be assumed adequately simulated if A_1 and A_2 are at

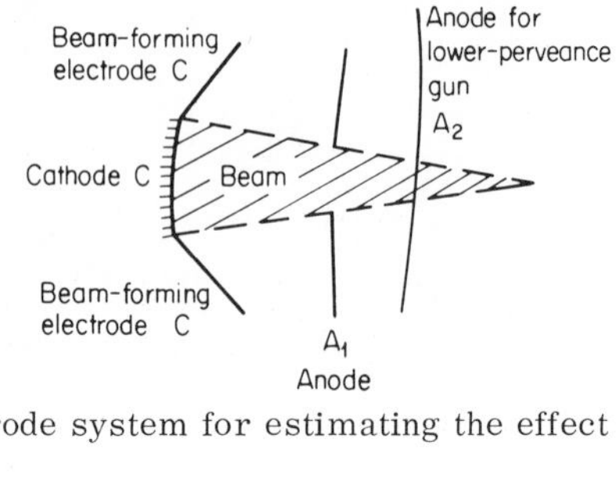

Fig. 8.15. An electrode system for estimating the effect of the anode hole.

the same potential. The potential distribution ϕ_T in the desired beam (with the gridded A_1 at Φ_1 and A_2 at Φ_2) is known a priori. We wish to analyze the potential distribution in the electrode system of Fig. 8.13 with C at zero potential, A_1 at Φ_1, and A_2 at Φ_1. This system may be analyzed by the application of the superposition method.

We consider three possible potential distributions, Φ_a, Φ_b, and Φ_{sc}. The potential distribution ϕ_a arises when no space charge is present, A_1 is at the potential Φ_1, and C and A_2 are both at zero potential. The distribution ϕ_b arises from no space charge, C and A_1 at zero potential, and A_2 at its correct potential Φ_2 for a lower-perveance gun. Finally, ϕ_{sc} is the potential due to space charge when C, A_1, and A_2 are all at zero potential. By superposition of these three potentials, it is possible to determine the required potential, namely, that occurring when space charge is present and when A_1 and A_2 are at the potential Φ_1. This potential ϕ is given by the expression

$$\phi = \phi_a + \frac{\Phi_1}{\Phi_2}\phi_b + \phi_{sc} \tag{5.2}$$

The potential in the beam with space charge present is the known potential distribution ϕ_T to be simulated. Superposition then yields the expression

$$\phi_T = \phi_b + \phi_a + \phi_{sc} \tag{5.3}$$

where the assumption is made that the space-charge contribution is most important in the cathode region, and is altered little, whatever the potential on A_2. The space-charge contribution from A_1 at Φ_1 and A_2 at Φ_1 is the same as that from A_1 at Φ_1 and A_2 at Φ_2. This assumption is implicit in writing the same ϕ_{sc} in Eqs. (5.2) and (5.3).

From Eqs. (5.2) and (5.3) we can eliminate the space-charge term and write

$$\phi = \phi_T - \left(1 - \frac{\Phi_1}{\Phi_2}\right)\phi_b \tag{5.4}$$

Any of the space-charge-free analogs may be used to obtain ϕ_b, and then, by using Eq. (5.4), the required distribution ϕ. The potential distribution ϕ of Eq. (5.4) may be used to trace trajectories, and thus determine the effect of the anode hole, or alternatively, to modify the electron-lens formula [Eq. (5.1)]. For the details of the modification of the Davisson formula, the reader should consult Ref. 11.

5.6. The Compensation for the Deteriorating Effect of the Anode Hole. In this section we have considered the calculation of the effect of the anode hole. Such a calculation is really useful only in low- and medium-perveance guns, to respecify the beam properties in the absence of the hole, in order to compensate for any perturbing effect of the hole. For high-perveance guns, this respecification cannot be made properly, and semiempirical measures are necessary to obtain a satisfactory beam. It is possible to choose different analytic forms of the potential in the beam along one line, and then to derive expressions for the resulting beam characteristics. For a suitable choice of potential distribution, it is possible to produce electrodes which do not pass through the beam. Usually, however, empirical designs based on experimental guns, or analogs with space-charge simulation, have been used to design high-perveance guns.

As already stated, the anode hole has at any perveance a lens effect. This effect can be calculated and allowed for in the electrode design. The second effect of the anode hole is to perturb the field near the cathode, and so change the uniformity of the cathode emission.

Unfortunately, the first empirical attempts to improve the variation of current density introduced nonlaminarities in the flow.[2,14] Nonlaminarities are very difficult to treat analytically when space-charge effects are included. It is not the purpose of this book to give actual gun designs, but rather to present the methods. Hence we describe only the effects of the anode hole and sketch some of the approaches which have been used to compensate them.

With the spherical Pierce gun taken as an illustration, the measured equipotential distribution of a gun designed without considering the anode hole is shown in Fig. 8.16a. The Langmuir solution is superimposed on the figure. It is clear that the effect of the anode hole is to reduce the field, and consequently the current density, in the middle of the cathode. It is possible to reduce this effect by putting a third electrode at a higher potential before the anode, as shown in Fig. 8.16b. This approach, however, introduces an electrode at a second potential, and is usually avoided.

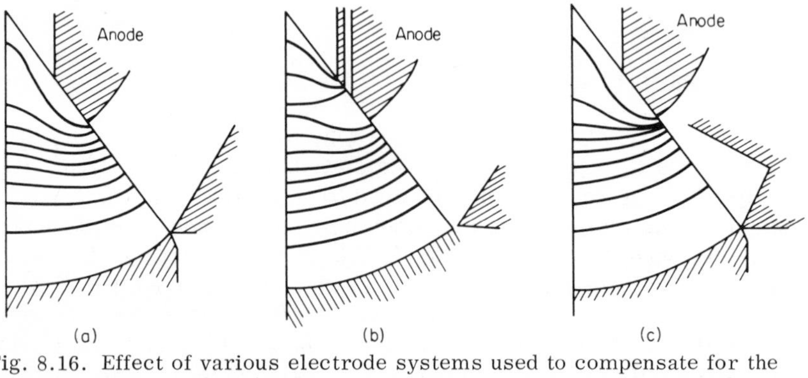

Fig. 8.16. Effect of various electrode systems used to compensate for the anode-hole effect. The solid lines in the beam represent equipotentials. (a) Unmodified electrodes; (b) electrodes modified with an extra anode; (c) the electrode system with modified beam-forming electrode. (Reproduced from Ref. 2, courtesy of the American Institute of Physics.)

Another approach is to alter the shape of the beam-forming electrode, in order to improve the potential distribution in the cathode region, even at the expense of deteriorating it in the anode region; the method is illustrated in Fig. 8.16c. This approach has two advantages: First, the deterioration of the potential distribution is in the anode region, where it may be expected to have less effect. Second, it is now possible to use some of the methods described earlier in this section to redesign the anode shape without seriously disturbing the cathode region. Picquendar and Cahen[9] and Brewer[2] have achieved satisfactory solid-beam convergent guns with microperveances of 1 to 4 by these methods. A third approach to this problem is to determine the equipotentials set up by the anode, considered as an isolated charged electrode. The cathode is then shaped to follow one of the equipotential surfaces. Heil and Ebers[14] have used this method to design a gun with a perveance of 4.5 and area compression (area of cathode to focused beam) of 230. Two gun designs by Van Duzer and Brewer[3] and Heil and Ebers,[14] using the last two methods, are shown in Figs. 8.17 and 8.18.

6. ELECTRODE ANALYSIS FOR PARAXIAL BEAMS

6.1. General Simplifications in the Methods Due to the Paraxial Assumptions. In the class of beams for which the paraxial equations of Chap. III are a sufficiently good approximation, the problem of

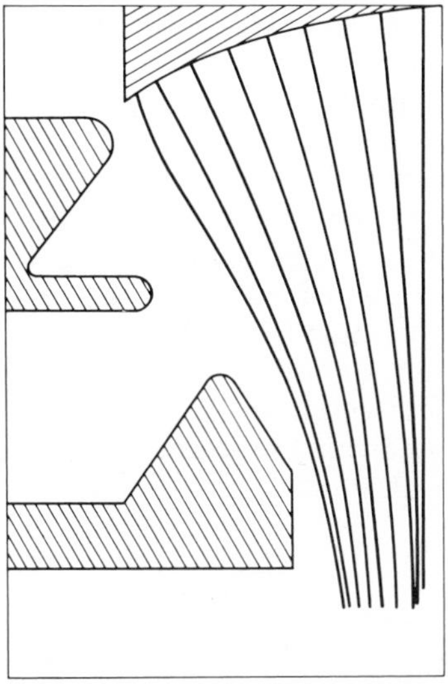

Fig. 8.17. The electrode system for a high-perveance gun; the solid lines represent particle trajectories. (Reproduced from Ref. 3, courtesy of the American Institute of Physics.)

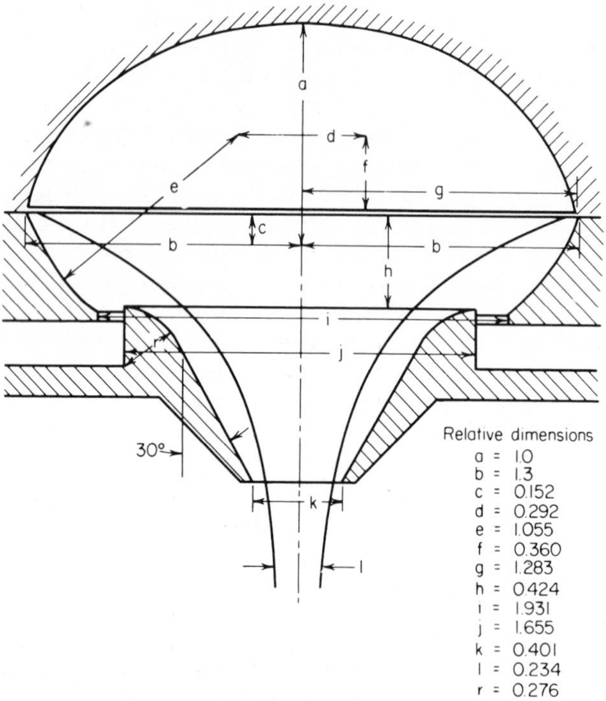

Fig. 8.18. The electrode system for a Heil gun. (Reproduced courtesy of the Institute of Electrical and Electronic Engineers and of the Academic Press Inc. The figure first appeared in Ref. 14, but was reproduced from the article by C. Süsskind in *Advances in Electronics*, vol. 8, p. 389, 1956.)

electrode analysis is simplified. An example of a paraxial beam in an electrode system is sketched in Fig. 8.19.

If the electrode system is being analyzed by iterative techniques, the fact that all trajectories are assumed similar means that only the two edge rays ($\mathcal{C}_1$ and $\mathcal{C}_2$ in Fig. 8.19) need be traced. The other rays, which are required for computing the space-charge corrections, can be calculated by interpolation between $\mathcal{C}_1$ and $\mathcal{C}_2$.

To the paraxial approximation, the effect of transverse variations of space charge on the electric field are ignored; several simplifications are possible in analyzing electrode systems for paraxial beams

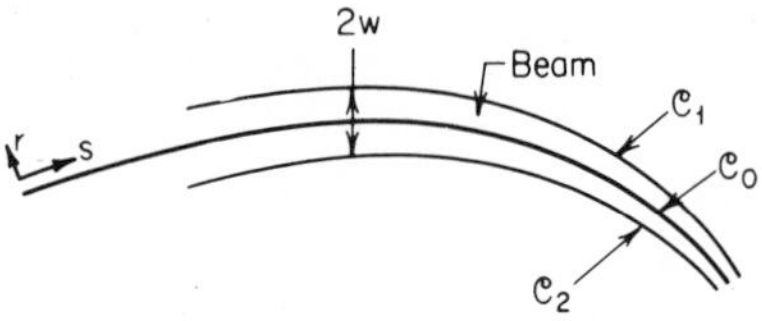

Fig. 8.19. Schematic for the electrode system and beam edge for a paraxial beam.

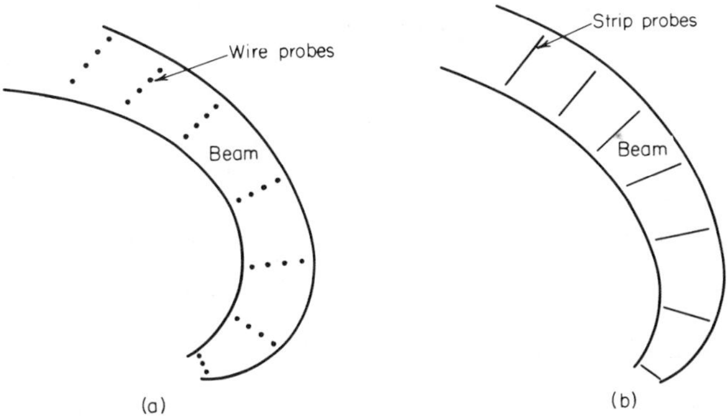

Fig. 8.20. Schematic of probes required to simulate space-charge effects in a paraxial beam. (a) Simulation by discrete wire probes; (b) simulation by strip electrodes.

due to this effect. A first simplification is that the current, carried by the rays between $\mathcal{C}_1$ and $\mathcal{C}_2$, can be calculated from the cathode current density at $\mathcal{C}_0$ on the ray axis.

If the relaxation or the resistance network methods of Sections 3 and 4 of Chap. IX are used to solve Poisson's equation, no simplification in the synthesis of the space-charge fields results. If charge injection, as described in Section 6 of Chap. IX, is used to simulate space-charge fields in an electrolytic tank, the simulation problem is simplified. Instead of injecting charge in wire probes, as in Fig. 8.20a, to simulate the space-charge fields of Fig. 8.19, metal strips can be used, as in Fig. 8.20b. As a result, a much smaller number of charge-injection elements is required.

6.2. Simplifications Due to the Form of the Potential. The approximate form of the potential near the ray axis permits other simplifications. It is possible to modify the expression for the potential and normal fields on $\mathcal{C}_0$ of Fig. 8.19 so that the effects of the beam can be concentrated onto the ray axis. This means that if ϕ_{SC} must be calculated as in Section 4, this ϕ_{SC} is required only on one curve. If one of the exact methods of Chap. VII is used, modified potentials and normal fields on $\mathcal{C}_0$ may be used directly as boundary conditions to obtain the electrodes.

If s is measured along the central trajectory $\mathcal{C}_0$ of the paraxial beam and r is measured normal to it, as shown in Fig. 8.19, the potential in the beam has been shown in Chap. III to be ϕ, where ϕ has the form

$$\phi = \Phi(s) + r\Phi_1(s) + \frac{r^2}{2}\left[\Psi(s) - k\frac{\rho_0}{\epsilon}\right] + \cdots \qquad (6.1)$$

where r is the distance normal to the central trajectory $\mathcal{C}_0$, and $\Phi(s)$, $\Phi_1(s)$, $\Psi(s)$, and $\rho_0(s)$ are functions of position specified on the central trajectory $\mathcal{C}_0$ of Fig. 8.19.

In Eq. (6.1), the function Φ is the potential on the ray axis. For rectilinear symmetric beams, Φ_1 is zero, $k = \frac{1}{2}$, and $\Psi = -\Phi''/2$ [Eq. (2.10) of Chap. III]. For sheet beams, Φ_1 and Ψ are given by Eqs. (6.16) and (6.10) of Chap. III, and $k = 1$.

In curvilinear axially symmetric beams, k is still $\frac{1}{2}$ and the corresponding expressions for Φ and Ψ can be evaluated from the equations of Ref. 15.

Using the conservation of charge and energy equations, Eq. (6.1) may be transformed into the form

$$\phi = \Phi(s) + r\Phi_1(s) + \frac{r^2}{2}\left[\frac{I}{\epsilon_0[2\eta\Phi(s)]^{1/2}} F + \Psi(s)\right] \tag{6.2}$$

where I is the total current in the beam, and F is a form factor which depends on the geometrical form of the beam being considered.

For sheet beams of width ℓ and thickness 2w, the form factor of F is given by the expression

$$F = \frac{1}{2\ell w} \tag{6.3a}$$

For hollow beams, distance R from the axis and thickness 2w, F has the value

$$F = \frac{1}{8\pi R w} \tag{6.3b}$$

and for solid beams, of radius w, F is given by

$$F = \frac{1}{2\pi w^2} \tag{6.3c}$$

From Eqs. (6.2), (6.3a), and (6.3b), it is seen that, for sheet and hollow beams, the normal electric field at the beam edge is independent of w to the paraxial approximation and depends only on the total current I. For solid beams, however, it is ϕ which is independent of w. These results allow the simulation of paraxial beams in an analog device without space charge field simulating devices. Since the potential ϕ of Eq. (6.2) satisfies Poisson's equation, it is possible to define a new set of Laplacian potentials by the relation

$$\phi_L = \phi - \phi_{sc} \tag{6.4}$$

which may be synthesized in a space-charge-free analog device. It is then sufficient to find electrode systems which will produce the correct ϕ_{L0} and E_{nL0} along the central trajectory $\mathcal{C}_0$, where E_{nL} is the transverse component of the electric field, and $_0$ refers to the values of $\mathcal{C}_0$.

From Eq. (6.2), for hollow and sheet beams, ϕ_{L0} and E_{n0} are given by the expressions

$$\phi_{L0} = \Phi \qquad \text{and} \qquad E_{nL0} = E_{n0} + \frac{I}{\epsilon_0}[2\eta\Phi(s)]^{-1/2} F_W \tag{6.5}$$

where Φ and E_{n0} correspond to the values of ϕ and E_n on the central trajectory $\mathcal{C}_0$, and F is given by whichever of Eqs. (6.3a) and (6.3b) is appropriate. Note that F_w does not depend on w.

For solid beams, E_{nL0} is always zero. The value of ϕ_L on the axis will be different from Φ, and from Eq. (6.2) will take the form

$$\phi_{L0} = \Phi - \frac{I}{4\pi\epsilon_0}(2\eta\Phi)^{-1/2} \tag{6.6}$$

This possibility of evaluating ϕ_{L0} and E_{nL0} from Φ, E_{n0}, and I greatly simplifies the problem of designing electrodes. It is valid only when the correction terms of Eqs. (6.5) and (6.6) are small compared with the main terms. In other cases, higher-order terms must be taken into account. The discussion of the variation of ϕ with current assumed that the longitudinal variation of ϕ on $\mathcal{C}_0$ was perturbed only slightly. This is not the case near the cathode, where Φ is small; inspection of Eqs. (6.5) and (6.6) shows that the correction terms, in this case, become large. In these regions it is necessary again to use the methods of Section 3 or 4 to evaluate the effects of the space charge, with the simplifications described in Sec. 6.1.

7. AN EVALUATION OF THE METHODS OF ANALYZING ELECTRODE CONFIGURATIONS

It is impossible to make generalizations that one of the methods of electrode analysis of this chapter is always best. The method which is most suitable for a particular application depends on the equipment available and the frequency with which the problem is encountered.

If a large high-speed computer is available, the iteration procedures of Section 3 are usually the most convenient. The whole electrode system, including the structure just beyond the anode hole, can be represented on the computer. Even corrections due to relativistic and thermal-velocity effects can be included without too much difficulty. If electrode-analysis problems are encountered often, the gun designer may find it convenient to develop his own computer program; if not, one of the existing programs can be obtained and modified. It is far easier—and cheaper—to obtain a computer program of this type than to construct a sophisticated analog device. If variations of the same problem are encountered often, it is convenient to keep the results of previous computations in backing store. The use of previous results as initial guesses for new problems reduces computation time considerably.

There is one class of problem which is not yet treated very satisfactorily on the computer. If there is a considerable amount of important detail, such as a fine grid near the cathode, it is sometimes difficult to obtain a satisfactory mesh size without an impractically large number of mesh points. In most cases this difficulty can be resolved by choosing variable mesh sizes in different regions. In some cases, if there are awkward-shaped grids or sharp corners in electrodes near the beam at a large number of places, it could prove difficult to adjust the mesh. In these cases, the electrolytic tank may be preferable because there the analog is continuous.

If only analog devices are available, the method used depends on the problem. In low-perveance guns, it is adequate to adjust electrodes until the correct potentials and normal fields are attained at the beam boundary; the boundary can be simulated by the resistance-paper analog of Section 5 of Chap. IX. In medium- or high-perveance guns such a method is too inaccurate, and leads to impermissibly large errors in the electric field at the cathode. In these cases some method of simulating space-charge fields is required.

If a sophisticated analog, such as a resistance network or electrolytic tank with space charge field simulating equipment, is available, the iteration methods of Section 3 can still be used profitably, though probably with more labor. It is preferable to trace trajectories on a digital computer, but now only a much smaller and slower computer is required.

If the electrode-analysis problem is encountered very seldom, if the computer program (or computer) or sophisticated analog required in Section 3 is not available, and if a simple analog is at hand, the superposition methods of Section 4 are convenient.

If similar problems are encountered frequently, e.g., different designs of convergent flows from a spherical cathode, the superposition methods are also fairly convenient. The same space-charge potentials can be used each time; this obviates the need for repeated iterations as in Section 3. However, these methods are exactly equivalent to one iteration of Section 3; if one iteration is adequate, the methods of Section 4 are not faster than those of Section 3, but do require less sophisticated apparatus.

Which of the superposition methods is used depends on whether an identical problem has been solved previously. If it has, and only more convenient electrodes are required, it is easier to use the method of Sec. 4.2. If no correct electrode system is known, the ϕ_{sc} must be computed analytically by the method of Sec. 4.3.

If the methods of Section 3 have not been used to analyze the electrode system, it is necessary to use one of the superposition methods of Section 5 to estimate the effect of the anode hole. For low-perveance guns, the Davisson formula of Sec. 5.3 is adequate. For medium-perveance guns, the method discussed in Sec. 5.5 has given excellent results in practice.

The simplifications discussed in Section 6 are applicable, whatever the method used to analyze the electrode system, if the beam is thin (in the sense that it can be treated paraxially by the methods of Chap. III).

We wish to end this chapter on a note of caution. Care must be taken, whatever method of electrode analysis is used, that the appropriate assumptions are not violated. For example, if the iteration method of Section 3 is used, is the current density being computed so near the cathode that the four-thirds-power law is no longer valid (Section 2 of Chap. VI)? If a superposition method of Section 4 is used, are image-charge effects in the anode negligible? If the validity of the underlying assumptions are checked carefully, good agreement will be found between theory and experiment; properly applied, the methods of this chapter can dramatically reduce the engineering time required to develop a new electron gun.

REFERENCES FOR CHAPTER VIII

1. Morse, P. M., and H. Feshbach: "Methods of Theoretical Physics," vol. 1, McGraw-Hill Book Company, New York, 1953.
2. Brewer, G. R.: Formation of High-density Beams, *J. Appl. Phys.*, vol. 28, p. 7, 1957.
3. Van Duzer, T., and G. R. Brewer: Space Charge Simulation in an Electrolytic Tank, *J. Appl. Phys.*, vol. 30, p. 291, 1959.
4. Kirstein, P. T., and J. S. Hornsby: The Numerical Analysis of Curvilinear Electrode Systems with an Emitting Surface, *Proc. 4th Intern. Conf. on Microwave Tubes*, Scheveningen, The Netherlands, p. 566, 1962.
5. Erikson, E. E., and A. D. Sutherland: Analysis of Nonlaminar Space Charge Flow, *Proc. 4th Intern. Conf. on Microwave Tubes*, Scheveningen, The Netherlands, p. 533, 1962.
6. Kirstein, P. T., and J. S. Hornsby: An Investigation into the Use of Iterative Methods for the Analysis of Axially Symmetric and Sheet Beam Electrode Shapes with an Emitting Surface, *Trans. IEEE*, ED-11, p. 196, 1964.
7. Hamza, V. and G. S. Kino: The Accuracy of Numerical Solutions for Electron Gun Design, *Microwave Lab. Rept.* 1423, Stanford University, Stanford, Calif. (March, 1966). Submitted to *Journal of Applied Physics*.
8. Kino, G. S., and N. Taylor: The Design and Performance of a Magnetron Injection Gun, *IRE Trans. on Electron Devices*, vol. ED-9, 1, 1962.
9. Picquendar, J. E., and O. Cahen: Methods of Theoretical Investigation of "O" Type Focusing, *Rev. Tech. Comp. Franç. Thomson-Houston*, vol. 32, p. 7, 1960.
10. Lomax, R. J.: Exact Electrode Systems for the Formation of a Curved Space Charge Beam, *J. Electronics and Control*, vol. 3, p. 367, 1957.
11. Danielson, W. E., J. L. Rosenfeld, and J. A. Saloom: A Detailed Analysis of Beam Formation with Electron Guns of the Pierce Type, *Bell System Tech. J.*, vol. 35, p. 375, 1956.
12. Davisson, J. C., and J. C. Calbick: Electron Lenses, *Phys. Rev.*, vol. 42, 580, 1932.
13. Brown, K. L., and C. Susskind: The Effects of the Anode Aperture in a Pierce Electron Gun, *Proc. IRE*, vol. 42, p. 598, 1954.
14. Heil, O., and J. J. Ebers: A New Wide Range, High Frequency Oscillator, *Proc. IRE*, vol. 38, p. 645, 1950.
15. Kirstein, P. T.: A Paraxial Formulation of the Equations for Space Charge Flow in a Magnetic Field, *J. Electronics and Control*, vol. 8, p. 207, 1960.

PROBLEMS

1. An electron beam is injected in crossed fields into a region between two parallel plates a distance d apart, with the uniform magnetic field B in the x direction. The charge density in the beam is uniform and of value ρ_0 with $\omega_p = \omega_H$. This solution is discussed in Section 7.3 of Chap. IV. Now suppose the beam is of thickness 2δ and the center located a distance s from the lower plate. Let the potential of the upper plate be Φ_0 and the lower be zero. Find the field and potential at the upper and lower edges of the beam. Determine ϕ_{sc}, the potential due to space charge, and E_{sc}, the field due to

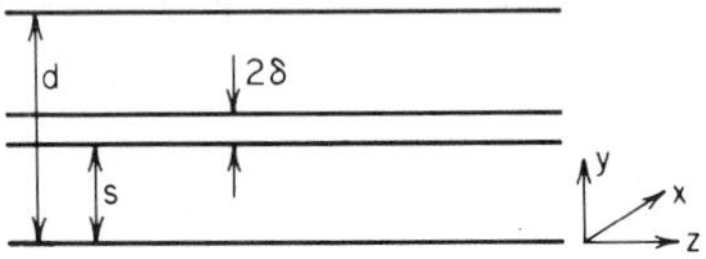

space charge, when the upper and lower plates are at zero potential. What is ϕ_L in this case? Give a condition for $|\phi_{sc}| \ll |\phi_L|$ in the beam. Determine ϕ_{sc} and E_{sc} at the center of the beam in terms of the total beam current per unit width I_0.

2. By using the difference-equation form of Poisson's equation given by Eq. (3.41), find the difference-equation solution for a plane diode three mesh points long. Assume that $\phi_1 = 0$ and ϕ_3 is the specified anode potential. Take the current to be given by Child's law, specified at point 2; i.e., the current density is $i = K_1 \epsilon_0 \sqrt{2\eta}$ and $i = (4/9)\, \epsilon_0 \sqrt{2\eta}\, \phi_2^{-3/2}$. Determine the error in i from the correct solution.

3. Assuming that the beam is paraxial, use the methods of Section 6 to find the potential outside a cylindrical beam in which the potential varies as $Az^{4/3}$.

4. A beam is emitted from a spherical cathode. The current density at the emitter is uniform. Determine the relevant space-charge-flow equations for this rectilinear flow. By expanding in series, show that the potential near the cathode varies as $\phi = \alpha s^{4/3}(1 + \beta s + \cdots)$, where $s = r_0 - r$, and r_0 is the radius of the cathode. Find the values of α and β in terms of the current density at the cathode and r_0. Assume $|r - r_0| \ll r_0$. Suppose now, as shown in the diagram, the area of a spherical cathode is known, as is the potential

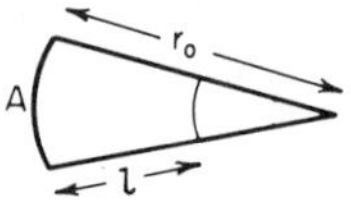

Φ, at a distance $\ell \ll r_0$ from it. Find the total current emitted from a cathode area $A = r_0^2 \Lambda$ (Λ is the solid angle subtended at the center of the sphere by A) in terms of Φ and ℓ. Compare your result with that which you would obtain for a plane diode of area A, spacing ℓ. This is the correction required when applying Child's law in front of a curved cathode surface.

IX

Analogs Used for Electrode Design

1. INTRODUCTION

1.1. Background. One of the greatest advances in physics in the seventeenth and eighteenth centuries was the realization that apparently widely differing physical phenomena were subject to the same laws. The equations governing the flow of heat, the deformation of elastic bodies, and the flow of electrons in conducting media are very similar. It is possible in principle, but difficult in practice, to construct an electron gun and adjust its electrodes until a beam is formed which has the desired properties. However, the equations governing the flow of current in a tank of water, or the motion of pellets on a rubber sheet, are under certain conditions very similar to the corresponding equations for electron motion; a study of these analog systems allows us to predict the motion of electrons in vacuum. A full analysis of all analog devices which can be and have been studied to solve the problem of electrode design would be beyond the scope of this book. This chapter is restricted to the consideration of a small number of analogs which are appropriate to the design of electrodes to produce prescribed flow patterns, namely, rubber membranes, electrolytic tanks, resistance networks, and resistance paper.

In the rubber-membrane, resistance-paper, or electrolytic-tank analogs, the differential equations for the analog are similar to the differential equations for the potential in a particle beam in vacuum. In the resistance network, a difference equation is simulated, which is similar to the difference-equation approximation to the equations for space-charge flow. It is possible to consider a further analog, the digital computer, for approximating the differential equations. The reasons why the use of the computer is the most satisfactory method for solving Poisson's equation are discussed fully later in this chapter.

The solution of electrode design problems has been discussed in the preceding chapter. In this chapter, we present methods of simulating and solving Poisson's equation inside a specified boundary. The relation between such a solution and the design of electrodes is only touched upon here.

1.2. The Plan of the Chapter. It is necessary to establish the equations for the electron flow which are to be simulated. For this reason, in Section 2, the equations for the electron flow are presented, and their analogs derived. In this section, the emphasis is on the relations between the equations for the beam in vacuum and those satisfied by the analogs. There is no discussion of the analogs themselves.

In Section 3, the use of a digital computer to simulate electron-beam equations is discussed. In Section 4, the exact analog of the computer, namely, the resistance network, is described. For some purposes a continuous analog is preferable to the discrete analogs of Sections 3 and 4. The simplest analog is a sheet of resistance paper, and this analog is presented in Section 5. Resistance paper has only a limited accuracy; hence its three-dimensional equivalent, the electrolytic tank, is an important analog device which has been extensively studied. The electrolytic tank is described in Section 6.

A nonelectrical analog for the electron flow equations can be found in the motion of pellets over a contoured rubber sheet. This analog is one of the few which give the electron trajectories directly. It is rather imprecise, and cannot be used for accurate electrode designs. It has some intrinsic interest, however, and is described in Section 7.

No presentation of a number of methods of attacking a problem is complete without an evaluation of the different methods of solution. The advantages and drawbacks of the different analog devices are discussed in Section 8.

One initial step assumed in the solutions of the electrode design problems of previous chapters was that electron trajectories could be traced. In Section 9 various methods of tracing trajectories are presented.

2. EQUATIONS OBEYED BY THE POTENTIAL FOR STEADY FLOW IN VACUUM AND ITS ANALOGS

2.1. Introduction. In this section, we present the equation obeyed by the potential function in an electron beam with planar or axial symmetry. The boundary conditions at the electrodes and the beam boundary are described. The equations obeyed by an electric current in an electrolyte are discussed and shown to be similar to those governing a beam <u>in vacuo</u>.

Any differential equation can be approximated by a difference equation. The difference-equation approximation for the electron flow is presented, and its ramifications are discussed. The formal connection between the electron beam and its analogs is pursued; the detailed discussion of each analog, however, is delayed until later sections.

2.2. The Equations for Steady Planar or Axially Symmetric Flow. The most frequent practical problems are concerned with two-dimensional strip beams or axially symmetric beams. In the former, the electrostatic potential $\phi(x,y)$ obeys the equation

$$\frac{\partial^2 \phi}{\partial x^2} + \frac{\partial^2 \phi}{\partial y^2} = -\frac{\rho}{\epsilon_0} \tag{2.1}$$

and for the axial symmetric case $\phi(z,r)$ obeys

$$\frac{1}{r}\frac{\partial}{\partial r}\left(r\frac{\partial \phi}{\partial r}\right) + \frac{\partial^2 \phi}{\partial z^2} = -\frac{\rho}{\epsilon_0} \tag{2.2}$$

where ρ = space-charge density
ϵ_0 = dielectric constant of free space
(x,y) = cartesian coordinates in Eq. (2.1)
(z,r) = cylindrical polar coordinates in Eq. (2.2).

The potential ϕ is related to the field **E** by the equation

$$\mathbf{E} = -\nabla\phi \tag{2.3}$$

On a conductor there is no tangential electric field; hence the potential obeys the relation

$$\phi = \text{constant on a conductor} \tag{2.4}$$

In addition, since charge must be conserved, it follows that

$$\nabla \cdot (\rho\, \mathbf{v}) = 0 \tag{2.5}$$

Equation (2.5) may be integrated over any volume τ to yield the result

$$0 = \int_\tau \nabla \cdot (\rho\, \mathbf{v})\, d\tau = -\oint_S \mathbf{i} \cdot d\mathbf{S} \tag{2.6}$$

where S is the surface enclosing τ, and **i** is $-\rho\mathbf{v}$, the current density.* Equation (2.6) states that the total current flowing into any closed surface is zero.

In addition to the above relations, the particle motion obeys the Lorentz equation of motion of Eq. (2.15) of Chap. I.

$$\frac{d\mathbf{v}}{dt} = -\eta(\mathbf{E} + \mathbf{v} \times \mathbf{B}) \tag{2.7}$$

It is to be noted that, in a sense, Eq. (2.7) is explicit. Given any **E** and **B**, the **v** can be computed from Eq. (2.7). Hence, if an analog system is found to synthesize the **E** and ρ of Eqs. (2.1) or (2.2), (2.5), and (2.7), an analog for **v** is not required.

*In Eq. (2.6) single-valued velocity is implied. If there are a number of discrete streams, an equation analogous to Eq. (2.6) is valid for each stream. Velocity distributions, due to thermal effects, for example, are excluded here. Also, as usual, the convention $\mathbf{i} = -\rho\mathbf{v}$ is used, so that a flow of electrons in the positive direction corresponds to a positive current.

2.3. The Equations for Steady Current Flow in an Electrolyte. Provided that the conductivity is high enough to dominate over dielectric effects, the current density **i** in an isotropic conducting sheet --whether water, resistance paper, or solid material—satisfies Ohm's law,

$$\mathbf{i} = -\tau_0 \mathbf{E} \tag{2.8}$$

where **i** is used for the current density in the electrolyte, **E** for the electric field within it, and τ_0 is the scalar-volume conductivity of the sheet. If the sheet is so thin that there is no current flow in the z direction, the conservation-of-current law [Eq. (2.5)] may be integrated over the z direction to yield the result

$$\frac{\partial j_x}{\partial x} + \frac{\partial j_y}{\partial y} = J \tag{2.9}$$

where J is the charge density per unit area injected at (x,y), and j_x, j_y are the components of the surface current density there. Using Eq. (2.8) integrated in the z direction, Eq. (2.9) becomes

$$\frac{\partial}{\partial x}(\sigma E_x) + \frac{\partial}{\partial y}(\sigma E_y) = -J \tag{2.10}$$

where now σ is the surface conductivity. Equation (2.10) may be transformed into

$$\frac{\partial}{\partial x}\left(\sigma \frac{\partial \phi}{\partial x}\right) + \frac{\partial}{\partial y}\left(\sigma \frac{\partial \phi}{\partial y}\right) = J \tag{2.11}$$

If σ is constant, Eq. (2.11) is formally identical with Eq. (2.1), with J/σ replacing $-\rho/\epsilon_0$. If σ is proportional to r, writing

$$\sigma = \sigma_0 r \tag{2.12}$$

dividing by σ, and replacing (x,y) by (z,r), Eq. (2.11) becomes

$$\frac{1}{r}\frac{\partial}{\partial r}\left(r\frac{\partial \phi}{\partial r}\right) + \frac{\partial^2 \phi}{\partial z^2} = \frac{J}{r\sigma_0} \tag{2.13}$$

Equation (2.13) is formally identical with Eq. (2.2), if $J/\sigma_0 r$ is replaced by ρ/ϵ_0. Note that the thickness of the sheet does not appear explicitly. If the electrolyte had uniform volume conductivity and a thickness that varied linearly—but was too thin to allow currents normal to the sheet to flow in it—Eq. (2.12) would still hold for the surface conductivity, and Eq. (2.13) would still be satisfied. The formal identity of the equations obeyed by the potential function in a two-dimensional or axially symmetric beam and that of current flow in a conducting sheet has thus been established. The question of how the identity may be used will be discussed later.

2.4. The Difference-equation Approximation. If $\phi(x,y)$ is a continuous function, the following is the Taylor expansion about a point (x,y):

$$\phi(x_0 + h, y_0) = \sum_{n=0}^{\infty} \frac{h^n}{n!} \frac{\partial^n \phi_0}{\partial x_0^n}$$

$$\phi(x, y + h) = \sum_{n=0}^{\infty} \frac{h^n}{n!} \frac{\partial^n \phi_0}{\partial y_0^n} \tag{2.14}$$

where $\partial^n \phi_0/\partial x_0^n$ and $\partial^n \phi_0/\partial y_0^n$ are the values of the nth partial derivatives of ϕ with respect to x and y evaluated at (x_0, y_0). If now the mesh of Fig. 9.1 is considered, where the point A_i has potential Φ_i, the Φ_i are given by the expressions

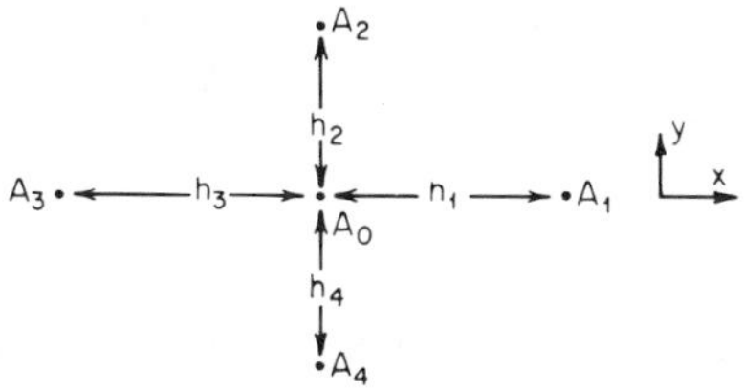

Fig. 9.1. Mesh diagram for the difference equations.

$$\Phi_0 = \phi(x_0, y_0) \qquad \Phi_1 = \phi(x_0 + h_1, y_0) \qquad \cdots$$

and the following expressions may be deduced for the partial derivatives of ϕ at (x_0, y_0):

$$\frac{\partial^2 \phi_0}{\partial x_0^2} = 2\left[\frac{h_3 \Phi_1 + h_1 \Phi_3 - (h_1 + h_3)\Phi_0}{h_1 h_3 (h_1 + h_3)}\right] + \epsilon_{xx}$$

$$\frac{\partial^2 \phi_0}{\partial y_0^2} = 2\left[\frac{h_4 \Phi_2 + h_2 \Phi_4 - (h_2 + h_4)\Phi_0}{h_2 h_4 (h_2 + h_4)}\right] + \epsilon_{yy}$$

$$\frac{\partial \phi_0}{\partial x_0} = \left[\frac{h_3^2 \Phi_1 - h_1^2 \Phi_3 - (h_3^2 - h_1^2)\Phi_0}{h_1 h_3 (h_1 + h_3)}\right] + \epsilon_x \tag{2.15}$$

$$\frac{\partial \phi_0}{\partial y_0} = \left[\frac{h_4^2 \Phi_2 - h_2^2 \Phi_4 - (h_4^2 - h_2^2)\Phi_0}{h_2 h_4 (h_2 + h_4)}\right] + \epsilon_y$$

where ϵ_{xx}, etc., represent error terms. If the h_i are all considered to be small and of order h, the error terms are

$$\epsilon_x = -\frac{h_1 h_3}{6} \frac{\partial^3 \phi_0}{\partial x_0^3} + 0(h^3)$$

$$\epsilon_y = -\frac{h_2 h_4}{6} \frac{\partial^3 \phi_0}{\partial y_0^3} + 0(h^3)$$

$$\epsilon_{xx} = -\frac{h_1^2 - h_3^2}{3(h_1 + h_3)} \frac{\partial^3 \phi_0}{\partial x_0^3} + 0(h^2)$$

$$\epsilon_{yy} = -\frac{h_2^2 - h_4^2}{3(h_2 + h_4)} \frac{\partial^3 \phi_0}{\partial y_0^3} + 0(h^2)$$

Thus ϵ_x and ϵ_y are of order h^2, and in general ϵ_{xx} and ϵ_{yy} are or order h. If, however, h_1 and h_3 are equal, the term of order h vanishes in the expression for ϵ_{xx}, and ϵ_{xx} is of order h^2. Similarly, if h_2 and h_4 are equal, ϵ_{yy} is of order h^2.

The difference form of Poisson's equation may now be deduced. Substituting Eq. (2.15) into Eq. (2.1), Poisson's equation becomes

$$\mathcal{R} = 0 \tag{2.16}$$

where $\mathcal{R}$ is given by the expression

$$\mathcal{R} = 2\left(\frac{\Phi_1/h_1 + \Phi_3/h_3}{h_1 + h_3} + \frac{\Phi_2/h_2 + \Phi_4/h_4}{h_2 + h_4}\right) - 2\Phi_0\left(\frac{1}{h_1h_3} + \frac{1}{h_2h_4}\right) + \frac{\rho_0}{\epsilon_0} \tag{2.17}$$

Because of the order of the error terms ϵ_{xx} and ϵ_{yy}, the error in Eq. (2.17) is usually of order h; if $h_1 = h_3$ and $h_2 = h_4$, the error is of order h^2.

The boundary condition usually given in this type of problem is the specification of ϕ on the boundary. In this case, near the boundary, one or more of the Φ_i in Eq. (2.17) may be known. At an interior point, a square mesh with

$$h_1 = h_2 = h_3 = h_4 = h \tag{2.18}$$

is usually chosen. In this case Eq. (2.17) takes the simple form

$$\mathcal{R} = \frac{\Phi_1 + \Phi_2 + \Phi_3 + \Phi_4 - 4\Phi_0}{h^2} + \frac{\rho_0}{\epsilon_0} \tag{2.19}$$

A numerical iterative method of solution of Eq. (2.19), called the relaxation method, is commonly used; this technique and its ramifications are discussed in Section 3. An analog method of solution of Eq. (2.16) is discussed in Section 4.

If we consider an axially symmetric system, and replace (x_0, y_0) by (z_0, r_0), etc., substitution of Eq. (2.15) into Eq. (2.2) yields the difference equation of Eq. (2.16), where $\mathcal{R}$ is now given by the expression

$$\mathcal{R} = \frac{2}{h_1 + h_3}\left(\frac{\Phi_1}{h_1} + \frac{\Phi_3}{h_3}\right) + \frac{2}{h_2 + h_4}\left[\left(1 + \frac{h_4}{2r_0}\right)\frac{\Phi_2}{h_2} + \left(1 - \frac{h_2}{2r_0}\right)\frac{\Phi_4}{h_4}\right] - \left(\frac{2}{h_1h_3} + \frac{2}{h_2h_4} + \frac{1}{h_2 r_0} - \frac{1}{h_4 r_0}\right)\Phi_0 + \frac{\rho_0}{\epsilon_0} \tag{2.20}$$

As in the two-dimensional case, Eq. (2.20) must be used near a boundary. At interior points, h_i is chosen to satisfy Eq. (2.18), and Eq. (2.20) takes the form

$$\mathcal{R} = \frac{1}{h^2}\left[\Phi_1 + \Phi_2\left(1 + \frac{h}{2r_0}\right) + \Phi_3 + \Phi_4\left(1 - \frac{h}{2r_0}\right) - 4\Phi_0\right] + \frac{\rho_0}{\epsilon_0} \tag{2.21}$$

On the axis, the grid cannot take the form of Fig. 9.1, but must take the form of Fig. 9.2. Since the electric field $-\partial\phi/\partial r$ must be single-

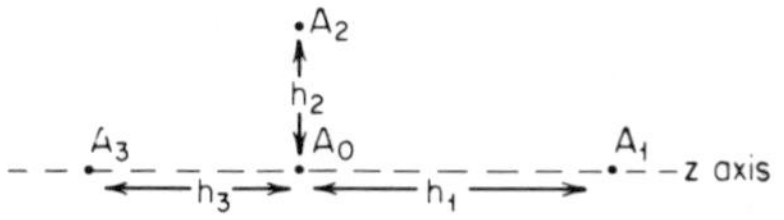

Fig. 9.2. Mesh diagram for the difference equation on the axis of an axially symmetric system.

valued, for axially symmetric systems, $\partial\phi/\partial r$ must be zero on the z axis. On the z axis, $(1/r)(\partial\phi/\partial r)$ is therefore replaced by its limiting value $\partial^2\phi/\partial r^2$, and the differential equation for ϕ becomes

$$2\frac{\partial^2\phi}{\partial r^2} + \frac{\partial^2\phi}{\partial z^2} + \frac{\rho}{\epsilon_0} = 0 \tag{2.22}$$

The residue derived from Eq. (2.22) may be shown, from Eq. (2.14), to be

$$\mathcal{R} = \frac{1}{h^2}(4\Phi_2 + \Phi_1 + \Phi_3 - 6\Phi_0) + \frac{\rho_0}{\epsilon_0} \tag{2.23}$$

The $\mathcal{R}$ of Eq. (2.23) is again in error only to order h^2.

Any method of solution developed for the two-dimensional case is equally valid for the axially symmetric case, with the $\mathcal{R}$ of Eqs. (2.20), (2.21), and (2.23) replacing those of Eqs. (2.17) and (2.19).

An alternative method of treating axially symmetric systems is to make the substitution

$$\Psi = r^{1/2}\phi \tag{2.24}$$

Poisson's equation then becomes

$$\frac{\partial^2\Psi}{\partial r^2} + \frac{\partial^2\Psi}{\partial z^2} + \frac{1}{4}\frac{\Psi}{r^2} + \frac{\rho r^{1/2}}{\epsilon_0} = 0 \tag{2.25}$$

with the additional boundary condition $\Psi = 0$ on $r = 0$. It is now possible to use exactly the same difference equations as in the two-dimensional case, with $\rho_0 r_0^{1/2}/\epsilon_0 + \Psi_0/4r_0^2$ replacing ρ_0/ϵ_0 in Eqs. (2.17) and (2.19).

In order to obtain $\phi(r,z)$ on the axis from $\Psi(r,z)$, the fact that $\partial\phi/\partial r$ is zero on $r = 0$ is used to deduce, from Eq. (2.14), that

$$\phi(0,z) = \frac{1}{3}[4\phi(h,z) - \phi(2h,z)] + 0(h^3) \tag{2.26}$$

for $r \neq 0$, $\phi(r,z)$ is obtained from $\Psi(r,z)$ by Eq. (2.24). With the residue written in terms of Ψ, fewer operations and less memory space are required for the iterative calculations. On the other hand, it is necessary to calculate $r^{1/2}$ once for each set of r. Usually, the formulation in terms of Ψ is somewhat faster in practice than that based on Eqs. (2.20) and (2.21).

It should be noted that if the mesh lengths h_i are equal (or even $h_1 = h_3$ and $h_2 = h_4$), the equations for $\mathcal{R}$ are in error only to order

h^2. In the case of unequal h_i, the error is of order h. Hence the use of unequal meshes should be avoided where possible; of course, near a curved boundary the use of unequal h_i is unavoidable. In Sec. 3.4 other examples are given where the mesh lengths are unequal in different regions but errors of order h are avoided.

2.5. Scaling. In Section 7 of Chap. I, a set of scaling laws was derived which showed how all the parameters of a flow could be scaled without changing the configuration of the flow. In an analog representation, it is often convenient to scale potentials, currents, lengths, etc., by using Table 1.1 of Chap. I. It is assumed in the rest of this chapter that the problem has been scaled previously, so that the potential and linear dimensions in the beam correspond directly with those in the analog. For example, the interelectrode potentials are usually scaled to a few tens of volts, and the linear dimensions to a few decimeters.

3. RELAXATION TECHNIQUES

3.1. Introduction. In the last section the differential equation for the potential was put in a difference-equation form. It is shown in this section how the difference equation may be solved by numerical techniques. A square grid is superposed on the region in which the difference equation is to be solved. At each point of this grid, the difference equation must be satisfied. The technique of solution consists in assuming a potential distribution, and then adjusting the potential at each mesh point in turn to make it satisfy the difference equation. Because it has been shown elsewhere[1,2] that the procedure is convergent for Poisson's equation, we shall not concern ourselves with this problem here.

The method is very laborious to do by hand calculation, since a large number of mesh points are usually required. The method is suitable for use on digital computers, however, and is most useful when a computer is available. The procedure must be applied at several hundred or thousand mesh points, in a typical problem. The fast memory of the computer should have a storage capacity of several times the number of mesh points considered in the relaxation procedure.

The relaxation technique is most useful when the boundaries are rectilinear; it is convergent only when they are in the Dirichlet, Neumann, or mixed form discussed in Section 2 of Chap. VII. The boundary conditions must be carefully considered, particularly if, as usually occurs, the bounding surface does not pass through a normal mesh point. Formulas for these cases are given.

The literature on the relaxation methods is copious.[1-5] In this section we attempt to present only the salient points. The method is discussed in some detail for two reasons: First, in its own right, it is interesting, useful, and often the best method of approach. It is the only purely theoretical method which may be used to analyze complicated electrode systems. Second, a thorough understanding of the relaxation technique is very valuable for the understanding of resistance networks, which are discussed in the next section. For a more thorough discussion of relaxation techniques, the reader should consult Refs. 1 and 2.

3.2. The Relaxation Method for Two-dimensional Systems. In Section 2, the difference equations for two-dimensional and axially symmetric potential problems were derived. If a mesh as shown in Fig. 9.1 is used, with all the h_i equal to h, the difference equation at mesh points inside the boundary for a two-dimensional problem was shown to be

$$\mathcal{R} = 0 \tag{2.16}$$

where $\mathcal{R}$ is termed the residue, and is given, for points distant more than h from the boundary, by the expression

$$\mathcal{R} = \frac{1}{h^2}(\Phi_1 + \Phi_2 + \Phi_3 + \Phi_4 - 4\phi_0) + \frac{\rho_0}{\epsilon_0} \tag{2.19}$$

Near the boundary, some of the mesh distance will be less than h. This is illustrated in Fig. 9.3. There are four categories of points:

1. Interior points distant more than h from the boundary (often termed regular interior points)

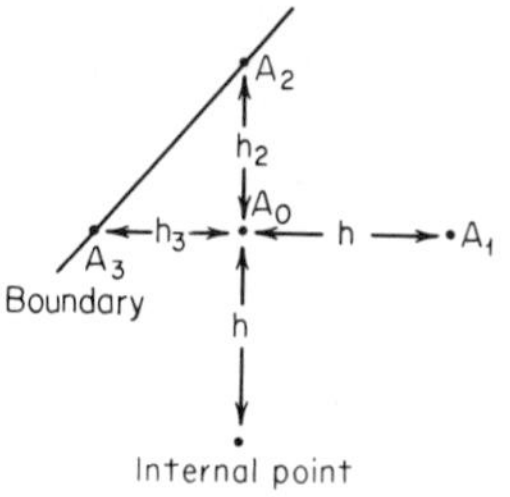

Fig. 9.3. Mesh diagram near a boundary.

2. Interior points distant less than h from the boundary (often termed irregular interior points)
3. Points on the boundary
4. Points outside the boundary

A complete mesh diagram, with the number indicating the category of the mesh point, is shown in Fig. 9.4a. For regular interior points, an $\mathcal{R}$ based on Eq. (2.19) must be used; for irregular interior points, the $\mathcal{R}$ of Eq. (2.17) is appropriate. Points on the boundary are used only to correct the residue of irregular interior points; their potential is never changed in the computation. Exterior points, being outside the region of interest, are not used at all. The problem can be posed with curved boundaries, since the only points of

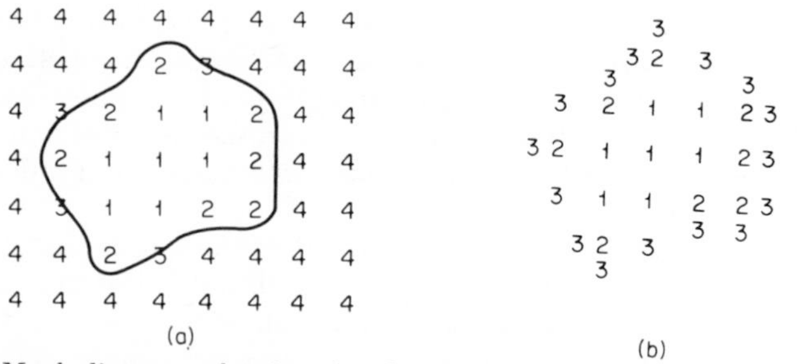

Fig. 9.4. Mesh diagram showing the classification of mesh points relative to a boundary. The numbers denote the category of the mesh point. (a) The complete mesh diagram; (b) the mesh points used.

interest are those where the boundaries, or electrodes, cut the grid lines. These intersections and the potentials on them are then evaluated, and the mesh shown, for example, in Fig. 9.4b is used.

For each unknown potential at an interior mesh point, there is one equation, Eq. (2.16). If there are n interior mesh points, there are n linear algebraic equations for the n unknown potentials. There are exact methods for solving such linear algebraic equations; however, with a large number of unknowns these methods become useless. The time required for solution becomes intolerably long, and there is great danger that round-off errors will make the resulting solution meaningless. Instead, an iteration procedure is set up by which the residue $\mathcal{R}$ at each mesh point is progressively reduced in an orderly fashion.

The simplest such procedure is called the relaxation process. The system of equations which must be satisfied has, from Eq. (2.16), zero residue at each point. In the relaxation process, the point with the largest residue is treated at each step and is reduced to zero by subtracting $\mathcal{R}/4$ from each of its neighbors. It can be shown[2] that this process is convergent, in the sense that eventually all residues will become arbitrarily small.

This method is not ideally suited for automatic computation, since it demands that one choose, at each step, the point with the largest residue; this is a very time-consuming process on a computer. A refinement is to relax in an orderly fashion. Starting at the bottom left, in Fig. 9.4b, working from left to right along each row, and then moving up to the next row, one may iterate according to the relation

$$\Phi_0^{(k+1)} = \Phi_0^{(k)} + \frac{1}{4h^2}\left[\Phi_1^{(k)} + \Phi_2^{(k)} + \Phi_3^{(k+1)} + \Phi_4^{(k+1)} - 4\Phi_0^{(k)} + \frac{h^2\rho_0}{\epsilon_0}\right] \qquad (3.1)$$

where $\Phi_i^{(k)}$ is the value of Φ_i after it has been corrected k times. It is clear from the method used that points at the positions A_1 and A_2 of Fig. 9.1 will have been corrected only k times, and those at positions A_3 and A_4 will have been corrected k + 1 times. It may be verified that if $\Phi_0^{(k)}$ satisfies Eq. (2.18) at each point, the application of Eq. (3.1) will produce a $\Phi_0^{(k+1)}$ equal to $\Phi_0^{(k)}$. It must be remembered, of course, that for points near the boundary, an iteration equation must be derived from Eq. (2.17) rather than Eq. (2.19). The iteration equation is derived in the same way according to the formula

$$\Phi_0^{(k+1)} = \Phi_0^{(k)} + \frac{\mathcal{R}^{(k)}}{4} \tag{3.2}$$

where $\mathcal{R}^{(k)}$ is obtained from Eq. (2.17), and for Φ_1, Φ_2 one writes $\Phi_1^{(k)}$, $\Phi_2^{(k)}$, and for Φ_3, Φ_4 one writes $\Phi_3^{(k+1)}$, $\Phi_4^{(k+1)}$. When the top right interior point has been corrected, the (k + 1)st iteration is complete. A search is then made to determine whether the new set of potentials is sufficiently accurate; if not, the process is repeated with the (k + 2)nd iteration. A suitable criterion to test the accuracy of the (k + 1)st iteration is to evaluate at each point the fractional change of potential δ, where σ is given by

$$\delta = \left| \frac{\Phi_0^{(k)}}{\Phi_0^{(k+1)}} - 1 \right| \tag{3.3}$$

If the maximum value of δ for all the mesh points is less than some preset figure, sufficient accuracy has been attained. A typical figure might be that the potential has 0.1 per cent accuracy, and this figure is chosen for the maximum permissible value of δ. A more sophisticated error criterion which gives an estimate of the actual error in ϕ is described in Refs. 4 and 5.

3.3. Overrelaxation. A further refinement which considerably speeds up the convergence is the method of overrelaxation.[1-5] In this, the residue is deliberately overcompensated, and instead of Eq. (3.2), the expression

$$\Phi_0^{(k+1)} = \Phi^{(k)} + \frac{\beta\,\mathcal{R}^{(k)}}{4} \tag{3.4}$$

is used, where $\mathcal{R}^{(k)}$ is defined as in Eq. (3.2). The quantity β is the overrelaxation factor, and the rate of convergence depends critically on β. Usually, β will lie between 1 and 2; the best value for β depends on the configuration. Methods of determining an optimum β have been developed.[2-4] If the user has had no previous experience with the particular problem, a β of about 1.4 is often a good guess. As a further refinement, the β can be changed from iteration to iteration. The reader wishing to know more about these aspects of the procedure should consult the references cited.

3.4. The Effect of Mesh Size. The difference equation of Eq. (2.19) is in error by the order of $h^2\phi^{(IV)}$, where h is the mesh size, and $\phi^{(IV)}$ is a combination of the fourth partial derivatives of ϕ. Hence the error is reduced as the number of mesh points is increased, and h is reduced. It is possible to formulate more elaborate difference equations, accurate to $h^4\phi^{(IV)}$, for example, which will allow a smaller number of mesh points to be used. The formula of Eq. (2.19) is the most often used, however, since the added complication of the higher-order equations usually offsets the reduced number of points required.

Since the error of the difference equation from the differential equation is $h^2\phi^{(IV)}$, a crude argument is now given for a better approximation. Let ϕ_a be the result of applying the relaxation procedure to each point in turn with a grid of size h_a, and ϕ_b that of using a grid mesh of size h_b. Finally, ϕ is the solution of the differential equation. Since the error* in ϕ is of the order h^2, ϕ is related to ϕ_a, ϕ_b by

$$\phi_a \simeq \phi + h_a^2\phi^{(IV)} \quad \text{and} \quad \phi_b \simeq \phi + h_b^2\phi^{(IV)} \tag{3.5}$$

where $\phi^{(IV)}$ is related to the fourth derivative of ϕ and does not depend on h to a first approximation. Subtracting a multiple of the second equation from the first, one obtains the relation

$$\phi = \frac{h_b^2\phi_a - h_a^2\phi_b}{h_b^2 - h_a^2} \tag{3.6}$$

The most frequently used form of Eq. (3.6) is where $h_b = h_a/2$. Then Eq. (3.6) becomes

$$\phi = \frac{1}{3}(4\phi_b - \phi_a) \tag{3.7}$$

Equation (3.6) or (3.7) is a better approximation to ϕ than ϕ_a or ϕ_b. The results of this section should be compared with those of Sec. 3.7 of Chap. VIII. In that case the cathode-current density was in error to order h, leading to somewhat different results.

It is not necessary to use a constant mesh size. Where greater detail is required, or the potential varies more rapidly, greater accuracy is achieved by using a smaller mesh size. The places where this is important are near a cathode, a grid, or a sharp boundary. One method of locally increasing the mesh size is shown in Fig. 9.5a. Since the new points are diagonally placed inside the old ones, the difference mesh which must be used is rotated through 45°. To improve the residue at the point B_0, the points A_1, A_2, A_3, A_4 must be used. Since this means that it is difficult to improve the residues by the method of Eq. (3.1), it is more usual to apply the procedure leading to Fig. 9.5a again. The mesh of Fig. 9.5b, with a mesh size of h/2, then results. Now at the join of the two meshes, that is, B_1, B_2, etc., the diagonal mesh must still be used. For example, the $\phi_1 - \phi_4$ used in Eq. (3.1) to improve B_2 are A_2, A_3, A_7, A_6 in Fig.

*Actually, it is $\nabla^2\phi$ which is in error by h^2, but this causes errors in ϕ of $0(h^2)$. In some cases (Sec. 3.7 of Chap. VIII), the error in ϕ near the cathode may even be $0(h)$.

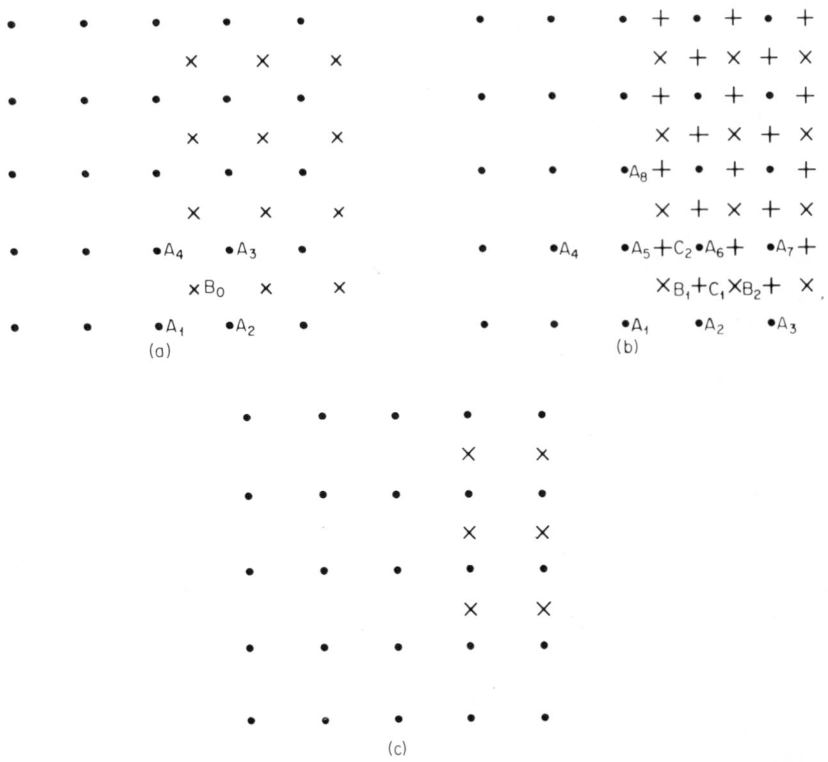

Fig. 9.5. Mesh diagram used for subdividing the mesh. The dots denote the crude mesh of size h; the crosses, a finer one of mesh $h/\sqrt{2}$; and the plus, h/2. (a) Subdivision to $h/\sqrt{2}$ in both directions; (b) subdivision to h/2 in both directions; (c) subdivision to h/2 in one direction.

9.5b. However, to improve the C's, for example, C_1 in the figure, a normal array, A_2, B_2, A_6, B_1, can be used again.

It is desirable that the mesh be changed along boundaries which are parallel to the x or y axes. Otherwise, if the problem is being solved on a computer, it is awkward to program the changes at the boundary between the meshes. It should be noted that, since the error from using unequal mesh sizes is one order of magnitude worse than using a rectangular mesh, it is better to use A_1, A_6, A_8, A_4 in Fig. 9.5b to improve A_5 than to use A_1, C_2, A_8, A_4. It is not necessary that the mesh size be halved in both directions. For example, the mesh of Fig. 9.5c is satisfactory for a reduction of mesh size in only one direction. If it is desired to reduce the mesh size by more than a factor 2, the technique illustrated in Fig. 9.5b or c may be applied several times; it is usual to have a small transition region, not less than two mesh diameters, between reductions of mesh size. The question of the reduction of mesh size is discussed further in Refs. 1 and 2.

It is often advantageous to reduce the mesh size between iteration cycles. If there are n points in each direction in the mesh, the number of times the iteration procedure must be applied, to achieve a given accuracy, is proportional to n. Therefore it is often useful to start with a coarse grid, and then halve the grid size every two or three iteration cycles.

3.5. The Relaxation Technique in Axially Symmetric Systems. In axially symmetric systems, most of the results of the previous section hold without change. It is necessary to use (z,r) in place of (x,y) and to replace the $\mathcal{R}^{(k)}$ of Eq. (3.2) by those derived from Eq. (2.20) or (2.22). The procedure for deriving $\mathcal{R}^{(k)}$ from the appropriate $\mathcal{R}$ is exactly that discussed after Eq. (3.2). It is necessary to remember that, in the two-dimensional case, the boundary was determined only by the electrode system; in the axially symmetric system the z axis is also a boundary. Near the electrodes the $\mathcal{R}$ is derived from Eq. (2.20); near the z axis, it is obtained from Eq. (2.22). It should be noted that in this context "near" implies less than the mesh size h.

4. THE RESISTANCE-NETWORK ANALOG

4.1. Introduction. In the preceding section, the use of relaxation techniques to solve Poisson's equation inside a closed boundary was described. The difference-equation approximation to Poisson's equation was discussed, both in two-dimensional and axially symmetric systems; formulas were given for the effects of mesh size and the simulation of curved boundaries. The difference equation can be represented in analog form by the potentials at the node points of a rectangular mesh of resistors. In this case the currents in the resistor network adjust themselves until the difference equation is satisfied exactly. Near curved boundaries, and in axially symmetric systems, the resistance network only approximates, and does not exactly represent, the difference equation of the last section. However, it is not difficult to analyze the equations being solved on the network and to estimate the error between the analog and the difference-equation solution.

The space-charge term in Poisson's equation is represented, in the resistance network, by current injected at the node points. There is a direct analogy between the space-charge term and these injected currents. Electrodes are represented by short circuits or by shunting certain resistances in the mesh.

There are two principal advantages of a resistance network over other analog representations of Poisson's equation. First, by appropriate feedback of the voltages at the node points, a wide range of difference equations may be solved. Liebman[6,7] has discussed the solution of the wave equation, the biharmonic equation, problems of helical symmetry, eigenvalue problems, heat-conduction problems, and neutron-diffusion problems on the resistance network. Hence, if a wide variety of equations are to be solved, the resistance network is an excellent tool. Moreover, since there is a statistical cancellation of errors due to incorrect resistor values, the accuracy of a resistance network is potentially higher than that of any other analog representation of Poisson's equation. Of course, purely numerical difference-equation techniques can be used to attain any desired accuracy. Although these methods are described in Section 3, they are not included in the above category.

4.2. The Equation for the Resistance Network. By analogy with Fig. 9.1, Fig. 9.6a shows a network of four equal resistors R. If the potential at A_1 is Φ_1, etc., and if a current I_0 is injected at the mesh point A_0, application of Kirchhoff's law to A_0 gives the relation

$$\frac{1}{R}(\Phi_1 + \Phi_2 + \Phi_3 + \Phi_4 - 4\Phi_0) - I_0 = 0 \tag{4.1}$$

Equation (4.1) is identical with Eqs. (2.16) and (2.19) if

$$R\,I_0 = -h^2\,\frac{\rho_0}{\epsilon_0} \tag{4.2}$$

The analogy between the two-dimensional difference equation and the potential in the network is thus demonstrated.

Figure 9.6b shows a mesh in which resistances are unequal. Application of Kirchhoff's law to this mesh yields the expression

$$\frac{\Phi_1}{R_1} + \frac{\Phi_2}{R_2} + \frac{\Phi_3}{R_3} + \frac{\Phi_4}{R_4} - \Phi_0\left(\frac{1}{R_1} + \frac{1}{R_2} + \frac{1}{R_3} + \frac{1}{R_4}\right) - I_0 = 0 \tag{4.3}$$

From Eq. (4.3) all important results, such as the analog of axially symmetric systems, the representation of potentials near the axis, and the effects of curved boundaries, may be obtained.

4.3. The Analog of the Axially Symmetric Poisson's Equation. We shall consider the resistance network shown schematically in Fig.

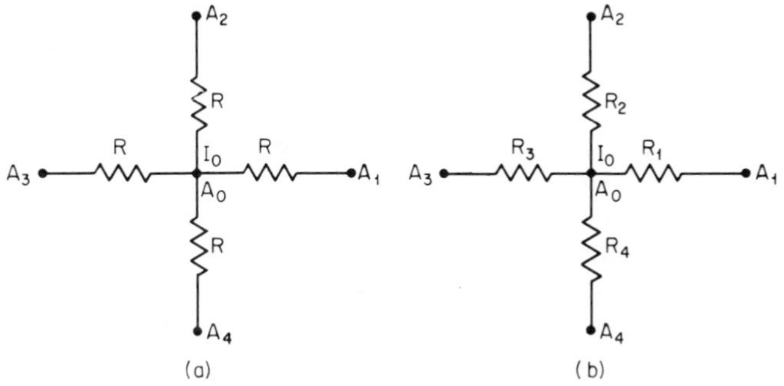

Fig. 9.6. Resistors around a typical node point. (a) Equal resistors; (b) unequal resistors.

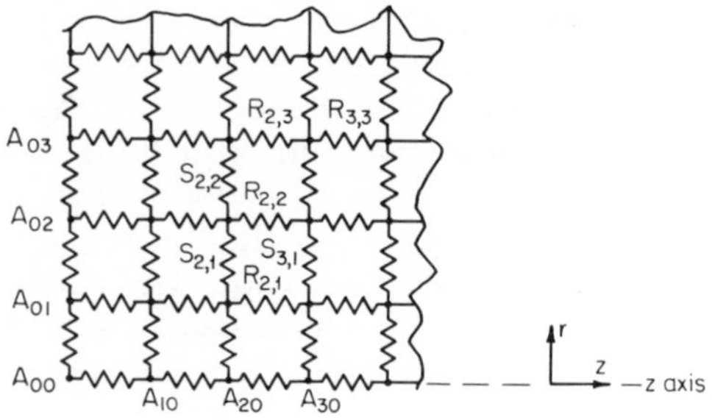

Fig. 9.7. Schematic of an axially symmetric resistance network.

9.7. Here $A_{a,b}$ represents a point with coordinates (z,r) of (ah, bh). The resistance between $A_{a,b}$ and $A_{(a+1),b}$ is $R_{a,b}$, and that between $A_{a,b}$ and $A_{a,(b+1)}$ is $S_{a,b}$. The values of $R_{a,b}$ and $S_{a,b}$ are chosen to vary according to the relations

$$R_{a,b} = \frac{R_0}{b} \qquad S_{a,b} = \frac{R_0}{b + \frac{1}{2}} \tag{4.4}$$

For the difference equation at the point $A_{a,b}$, the $R_{a,b}$, $S_{a,b}$ may be identified with the R_i of Fig. 9.6 and Eq. (4.3) by the relations

$$R_1 = R_3 = \frac{R_0}{b} \qquad R_2 = \frac{R_0}{b + \frac{1}{2}} \qquad R_4 = \frac{R_0}{b - \frac{1}{2}} \tag{4.5}$$

Substitution of Eq. (4.5) into Eq. (4.3) yields the expression

$$\Phi_1 + \Phi_2\left(1 + \frac{1}{2b}\right) + \Phi_3 + \Phi_4\left(1 - \frac{1}{2b}\right) - 4\Phi_0 - \frac{4I_0R_0}{b} = 0 \tag{4.6}$$

Comparison of Eqs. (2.21) and (4.6) shows that the equations are identical, provided that a current I_0, given by the relation

$$I_0 = -\frac{bh^2\rho_0}{R_0\epsilon_0} \tag{4.7}$$

is injected at $A_{a,b}$.

On the axis, the difference equation to be simulated is given by Eq. (2.23). The mesh is illustrated in Fig. 9.8; one resistance of the star centered on A_0 no longer exists. Alternatively, Eq. (4.3) could still be utilized with R_4 infinite. The R_2 of Fig. 9.8 must still have the value $2R_0$, indicated by Eq. (4.5) with $b = 0$; this is required so that the difference equation for A_{ij} may be correct. Comparison of Eq. (4.3) with the relevant expression on the axis, Eq. (2.23), shows that these are identical provided that R_1 and R_3 are given by

$$R_1 = R_3 = 8R_0 \tag{4.8}$$

and the space charge on the axis is represented by an injected current I_0 given by

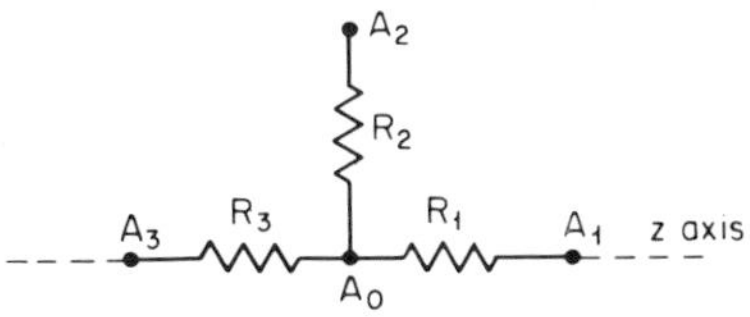

Fig. 9.8. The resistances around a typical node point on the axis.

$$I_0 = -\frac{h^2 \rho_0}{8\epsilon_0 R_0} \tag{4.9}$$

The value of R_1, R_3 of Eq. (4.8), when compared with the R_1, R_3 of Eq. (4.5), gives rise to the concept that the axis is equivalent to a cylinder of radius h/8. However, the value of R_2 is not consistent with this statement. It is not easy to identify the b = 0 line with anything physical.

4.4. The Simulation of Boundary Conditions. If the boundary consists of a set of electrodes at different potentials, and if each electrode passes exactly through the mesh points of a square grid, the boundary may be simulated easily. All the node points through which such an electrode would pass are strapped together by wires and maintained at the required potential. A diagram of such an electrode is shown in Fig. 9.9. In Fig. 9.9a, the position of the electrode is indicated, and in Fig. 9.9b, the simulation of the electrodes in a network by short circuits is illustrated. No resistance values need be altered to simulate the boundary.

If the electrode does not pass through the node points of a square mesh, the boundary may still be simulated. In Section 3, the difference equation used near a boundary had to be altered from that used elsewhere. In a resistance network, however, the values of most of the resistors must remain unaltered; if the difference equation in the rest of the network should remain unaltered, only the value of the resistance between the last mesh point and the hypothetical boundary may be changed.

Let us consider the representation of an electrode which does not pass through mesh points as indicated in Fig. 9.10a. The difference

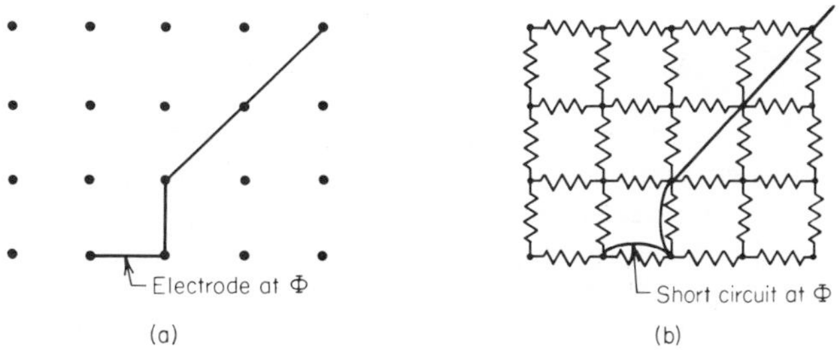

Fig. 9.9. Schematic of a boundary passing through node points. (a) Schematic of boundary; (b) representation in the network.

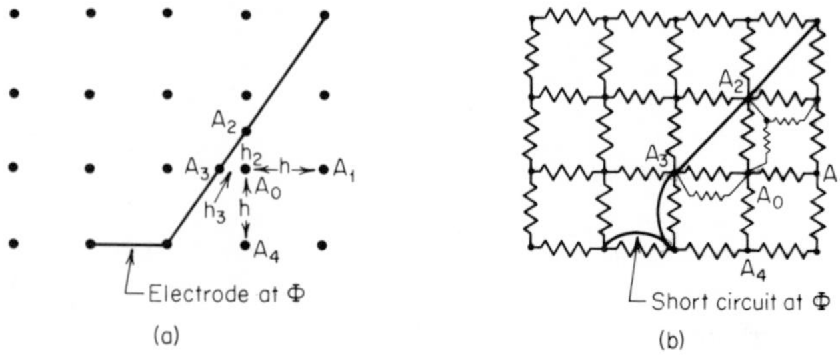

Fig. 9.10. Schematic of a boundary not passing through node points. (a) Schematic of the boundary; (b) representation in the network.

equation at the point A_0 was given by Eqs. (2.16) and (2.17). To simulate exactly such an equation with resistors, it would be necessary, from Eqs. (4.3) and (4.6), to alter all four resistances from their nominal values. This would alter the difference equations in the rest of the network, which cannot be tolerated. The difference equation of Eq. (2.17) was shown to differ from the differential equation of Eq. (2.1) only in terms of order h. Other difference equations which may be derived from Eq. (2.14), and which ensure that the first derivatives ϕ_x, ϕ_y in that equation are continuous, are the equations

$$\frac{\Phi_1 - \Phi_0}{h_1} + \frac{\Phi_3 - \Phi_0}{h_3} = \frac{\Phi_2 - \Phi_0}{h_2} + \frac{\Phi_4 - \Phi_0}{h_4} = 0 \tag{4.10}$$

Equation (4.10), though one order of magnitude less accurate than Eq. (2.17), can be simulated without changing R_1 and R_4. Since these equations match the electric field only at the boundary, they are applicable both for two-dimensional and axially symmetric systems.

Comparison of Eqs. (4.3) and (4.10) shows that the boundary is adequately simulated by shunt resistances placed between A_0 and A_2 and between A_0 and A_3 of Fig. 9.10b, so that the total resistances R_2, R_3 between these nodes are given by

$$R_2 = \frac{h_2}{h} R_0 \qquad R_3 = \frac{h_3}{h} R_0 \tag{4.11}$$

for two-dimensional systems and, using Eq. (4.4),

$$R_2 = \frac{h_2}{h} \frac{R_0}{b + 1/2} \qquad R_3 = \frac{h_3}{h} \frac{R_0}{b} \tag{4.12}$$

for axially symmetric systems, where bh is the r coordinate of A_0. It is to be noted that the new resistances are always less than the original ones, so that the boundary can be simulated by shunting the original resistances. Since Eqs. (4.11) and (4.12) serve only to match the electric field at the boundary, neither space-charge effects nor the curvature of electrodes would affect the values of the shunt resistances. Both these would give only higher-order corrections. If, for another mesh point, A_0A_1 or A_0A_4 is less than h, the

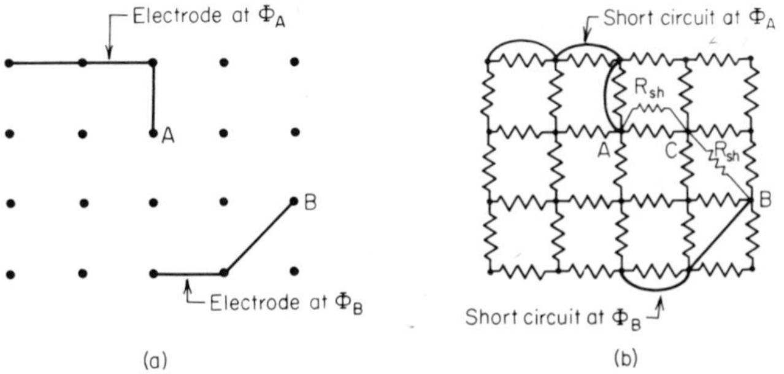

Fig. 9.11. Schematic of the representation of the potential between the electrodes by shunting resistors. (a) Schematic of electrodes; (b) representation in the network.

appropriate shunts are calculated in the obvious manner by analogy with Eqs. (4.11) and (4.12); for example, if any A_0A_i has length h_i in a two-dimensional problem, the relevant R_i should be $(h_i/h)\,R_0$.

4.5. Termination of the Network. In Section 3, it was assumed that ϕ was specified on a closed boundary. At the position of electrodes, the mesh points appropriate to an electrode were held at the same potentials, and between electrodes a linear variation of potential was assumed. It is possible to carry out the same procedure to simulate the electrodes on a resistance network by strapping together and shunting the appropriate mesh points as in Sec. 4.4. The linear variation of potential between electrodes may be achieved by putting low-resistance shunts across the mesh points which represent the straight line between the electrodes. Since the assumption is made that the gap between the electrodes is so far from the beam that the exact potential law between them is unimportant, the shunts need only follow the mesh points nearest a straight line joining the appropriate points. In Fig. 9.11a, a typical electrode configuration is indicated. The electrodes end at mesh points A and B. In the network, resistances R_{sh} should be placed as shown. Although there are arguments for having different R_{sh} depending on whether the shunt is as AC in Fig. 9.11b or as BC, such a difference is probably unimportant. If choosing different R_{sh} makes a substantial difference to the fields near the beam, the simulation of the electrodes should be carried farther away from the beam region.

There are alternative methods of terminating the network. The simplest is to adjust the resistances along one line so that the effective mesh size h is altered. In Fig. 9.12a an abrupt change in mesh spacing from h to H is shown along a line x = constant of a planar system. Using the arguments which led to Eq. (4.11), it is seen that this change in mesh size is represented in the network by changing the horizontal resistors to RH/h, where R is the resistance corresponding to a mesh size h. A similar mesh-size change may be made in the other direction. By this means, the resistance network

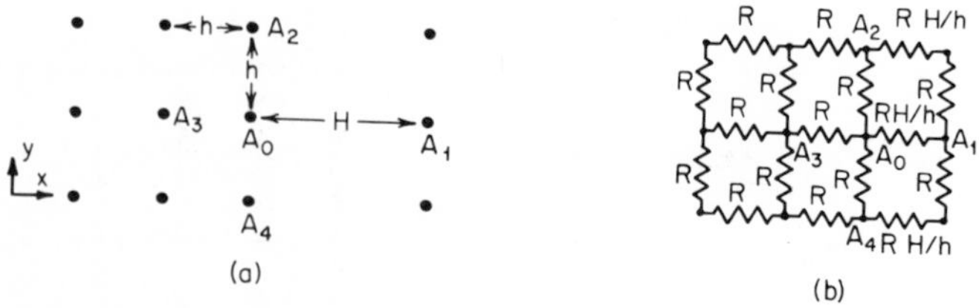

Fig. 9.12. Schematic of the change in mesh size from one region to another. (a) Schematic of the nodes points; (b) representation in the network.

may generally enlarge the region in which Poisson's equation is being simulated. The termination employed at the edge of the network would have the same effect, in the beam region of the network, as a grounded metal plate would have if placed at the appropriate distance from the beam in the physical electrode system. A useful check on the quality of the termination is to shunt the resistors at the edge of the network. If the shunts drastically change the potential in the beam region, the network is too small.

The same method may be used to decrease the mesh size in certain regions where the potential changes are so large that a smaller mesh size is desirable.[8]

A simpler method may be used to terminate the network. If there were a second electrode system identical with a reflection of the first, placed as shown in Fig. 9.13, the center line between these two systems would have zero E_X. Hence the network may be extended artificially by a factor of 2, by synthesizing the boundary conditions $\partial\phi/\partial x = 0$ at the edge of the network. This synthesis may be made by simple shunts. If $\partial\phi/\partial x$ is zero at a point such as A_0 in Fig. 9.14a, it may be verified from Eq. (2.14) that Eqs. (2.16) and (2.19) may be replaced, to order h, by the expression

$$2\,\Phi_3 + \Phi_2 + \Phi_4 - 4\,\Phi_0 = 0 \qquad (4.13)$$

The right-hand side of Eq. (4.13) is put equal to zero because we are assuming that the network is terminated far from the beam,

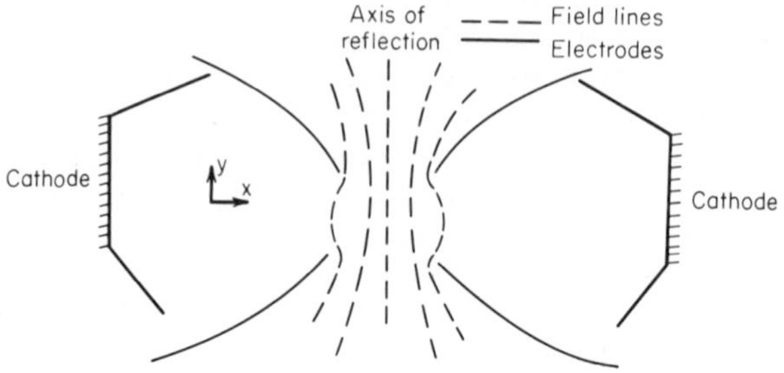

Fig. 9.13. Diagram showing the equipotential plots between two identical electrode systems.

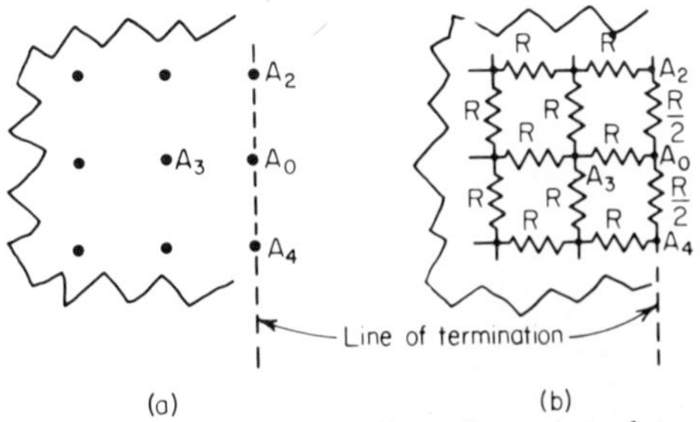

Fig. 9.14. Schematic of the representation of a point where $\partial\phi/\partial x$ is zero but Laplace's equation is satisfied. (a) Schematic of the mesh points; (b) representation in the network.

where there is no space charge. A resistance-network analog of Eq. (4.13) is the mesh of Fig. 9.14b. Thus the simplest, and a fairly effective, form of termination is simply to halve the resistances of the edge being terminated.

In axially symmetric networks, the justification for this procedure is not quite as clear since the radial resistances, the $S_{a,b}$ of Fig. 9.7 are themselves varying. The reflection is not perfect for the termination at r = constant. From Eq. (4.4), however, the $S_{a,b}$ are slowly varying for the large b, which will apply at the edge of the network, and therefore the same termination procedure is valid.

4.6. Description of the Network. A typical resistance network, developed by Hechtel and Seeger,[9] is described in this section. The network of resistances, which in this case are for the axially symmetric problem, has a characteristic impedance, the R_0 of Eq. (4.5), of 25 kilohms. The network is made of 50 meshes in the z direction and 25 in the r direction, requiring therefore 2575 resistors, with resistances having a variation in accord with Eq. (4.5). The resistors along the perimeter of the network have half the value given by Eq. (4.5); this ensures a reflection of the boundary in accordance with Eq. (4.13). The analog incorporates 100 current feeding points, fed by up to 40 volts through resistances of 0.1 to 5 megohms; these currents may be set individually and fed in at the appropriate node points. There are several outputs for setting the voltages on the electrodes. Although a precision potentiometer bridge could be used for measuring voltage at any mesh point, a better method of voltage measurement would be to use a digital-reading voltmeter. The potential at each point may be measured directly, or alternatively, the fields may be measured directly by means of a four-point-probe system, which can be plugged into the network and the voltage-measuring device. For further description of this and another network, Refs. 7 to 13 should be consulted.

In order to obtain the potential at each point of the grid, a multi-position selector switch may be used. Hechtel[10] has used such a switch, together with a digital voltmeter and a card punch, to print

Fig. 9.15. A resistance network. (Photograph courtesy of Dr. J. R. Hechtel and Litton Industries.)

on cards the value of the potential at each point of the mesh. Trajectory plots may be made by one of the methods of Section 9. If the values of the potentials on the nodes are already on punched cards, the data may be processed directly on a digital computer. An actual network is shown in Fig. 9.15.

The practical circuits for the selector switch, the bridge, and the four-position probe are described in detail by Archard.[11] His report gives a thorough description of all facets of one resistance network.

4.7. Accuracy of the Resistance Network. There are three principal sources of error in the resistance network: First, there is a systematic error due to the finite mesh size of the analog model. Second, there is a measuring error, due to the practical limitation on measuring techniques. Third, there is the error due to the statistical variation in the values of the resistances used. The measuring error can be reduced, through the use of a bridge or digital voltmeter, to a few parts in 10^5. The error due to variations in the resistance values has been shown by Liebman and Bailey[12] to be considerably less than the individual errors of the resistors due to a statistical averaging process. The root-mean-square error due to this effect is σ, where

$$\sigma = 0.6\bar{\sigma}\left(\frac{1}{m^2} + \frac{1}{n^2}\right)^{1/2} \tag{4.14}$$

The network has m × n meshes, and $\bar{\sigma}$ is the root-mean-square deviation of individual resistors. A 30 × 30 network having a value of $\bar{\sigma}$ of 0.2 per çent would, from Eq. (4.14), give an accuracy of a little better than 0.01 per cent; these numbers characterize the network used by Liebman.[12,13] On the other hand, Hechtel,[10] using a 25 × 50 network with standard 0.5 per cent resistors, would also obtain 0.01 per cent, or one-fortieth of a mesh division.

The error due to the difference between the exact problem and its analog representation depends on the problem being solved. Hechtel and Seeger[9] have analyzed several simple electrode shapes on a network of 25 × 50 units. The maximum error for the different configurations is given in Ref. 9; in this reference the subject of errors in resistance network is treated fully.

5. RESISTANCE-PAPER ANALOG

5.1. Introduction. A resistance-paper analog can be used to simulate the potential variation in a planar system. Space-charge simulation is possible, in principle, by injecting current at points of the paper; such a simulation is more cumbersome for resistance-paper analogs than in electrolytic tanks or resistance networks and is not used in practice. It has been shown, in Section 2, that for axially symmetric systems a linear variation of resistivity would be required in one direction. Paper with such a variation is not at present available, so that it is possible to use resistance paper only for planar problems. For such problems, the resistance-paper analog is the simplest to set up. Its accuracy is limited to a few per cent, by the variation of resistivity of commercially available resistance papers.

6. CHARACTERISTICS OF ELECTROLYTIC TANKS

6.1. Introduction. The earlier analysis of Section 2, giving the variation of potential in a thin conductor, clearly applies when the conductor is a conducting fluid. In the fluid model it is much easier than with resistance paper to maintain a uniform resistivity. A series of studies by Sander and Yates[14-16] present a comprehensive discussion of the different problems arising in the design of a typical electrolytic tank. In this section we give merely a brief description of an electrolytic tank and of the principal difficulties which arise in using the tank. References are given to the literature for a fuller discussion of the subjects mentioned.

The theory of the analogy between potentials in conducting fluids and in electron beams has already been described in Section 2. In this section the practical aspects of electrolytic tanks are discussed, particularly the problem of the simulation of space charge.

Almost all the discussion is limited to liquid electrolytes, although a model with a solid electrolyte is described also.

6.2. Physical Description. An electrolytic tank is a tank filled with an electrolyte; the surface conductivity of the electrolyte is proportional to the product of the depth of electrolyte and its volume conductivity. Hence for a planar problem the tank should be level; for an axially symmetric problem it should be tilted. An electrolytic-tank system is shown in Fig. 9.16. If, for an axially symmetric problem, the tank were tilted too much, an excessively deep tank would be required. In addition, the electrodes, which are merely conductors placed in the electrolyte, would have to be doubly curved rather than flat strips. With too small a tilt of the tank, inaccuracies would be introduced near the axis of the system, which is the line where the depth of the electrolyte becomes zero. In liquid electrolytes, these errors are due to surface-tension effects at the edge of the liquid; in solid electrolytes, the errors are due to inhomogeneities in the electrolyte itself. A common compromise is to use a 5° slope in the tank. Liquid electrolytes are far more common than solid ones in practice. First the characteristics of tanks with liquid electrolytes are described, and later the differences introduced by solid electrolytes are discussed.

The choice of liquid-electrolyte solution and electrode material has been investigated extensively. As in many such problems, each experimenter has his favored solution, and many appear to give sat-

Fig. 9.16. The double electrolytic tank with analog computer attached used at Hughes Aircraft Company. (Photograph courtesy of Dr. G. Brewer and the Hughes Aircraft Company.)

isfactory results. Stainless-steel-sheet electrodes in an electrolytic solution of resistivity 2×10^4 ohm-cm have been found to give consistently good results. If the local tap water has this resistivity, it is satisfactory. Often, deionized water is used with sufficient sulfuric acid added to bring its resistivity to this level. A detergent, in the ratio of about one teaspoonful to one gallon of electrolyte, is recommended to reduce surface-tension and meniscus effects. Satisfactory results may be obtained with almost any low-sudsing household detergent. Nickel- or chromium-plated brass electrodes are often used also.

In addition to the errors mentioned previously, due to capillary action, there are others due to deposits which form on the electrode surfaces. For this reason it is important to keep electrodes clean and use materials with low surface resistivity. These considerations are particularly important for the traveling probe. Here the amount of material involved is slight, and platinum probes are recommended by many writers; expense would usually prohibit the use of platinum for the electrode material. An ordinary sewing needle is a satisfactory probe; it is often made of stainless steel and has a very sharp point, but should be degreased before use.

For field measuring probes, it is important that both members of the pair should be equally deep in the water. One possible probe system due to Hartill[17] is shown in Fig. 9.17; the probes are embedded in lucite, and coated, all but the lower 2 mm, in a silicone varnish, thus minimizing the meniscus and depolarization effects.

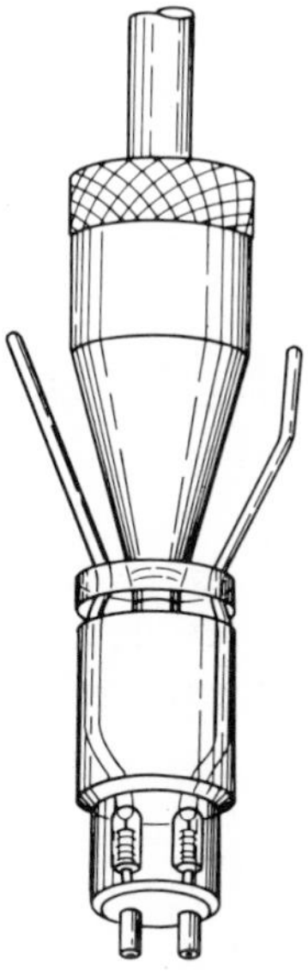

Fig. 9.17. Diagram of a probe system used for field measurements. (Reproduced from Ref. 17, courtesy of *Electronic Engineering*.)

An alternative scheme is to enclose the whole tank in glass with the probes at the bottom;[15] in this scheme the whole tank is moved and the field measuring probe remains stationary.

In a liquid electrolyte at d-c or low frequencies, polarization effects in the liquid may cause serious errors. At high frequencies, capacitive effects both between the electrodes and in the leads may cause errors. For this reason a working frequency of 400 cps is commonly used as a compromise. Because in conventional tanks measurements are made by bridge techniques, it is important to keep all leads short and screened to avoid stray pick-up. Alternatively, a square wave of 2-kc frequency may be used rather than a sine-wave input. In this scheme, stray capacities first cause a spike in the waveform, but then, for nearly 0.2 msec, the voltage is almost constant. For most purposes this voltage would be constant enough. Even in 0.2 msec, however, polarization effects will produce a slight droop in the pulse shape. In order to achieve an overall accuracy of the order of 0.1 per cent, the measured voltage waveform must be sampled at the same time in the cycle.

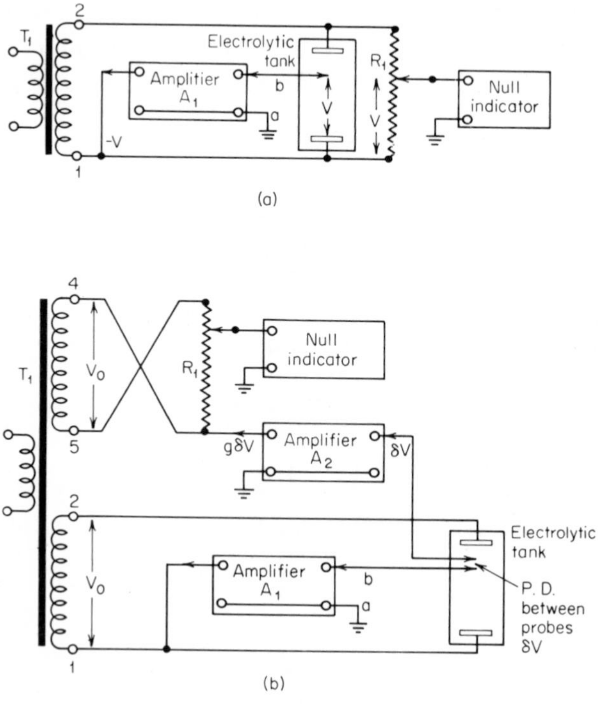

Fig. 9.18. Basic circuits used for the measurement of potential and potential gradient. (a) Basic circuit for potential measurements; (b) basic for potential gradients measurements. (Reproduced from Ref. 18, courtesy of the Institution of Electrical Engineers.)

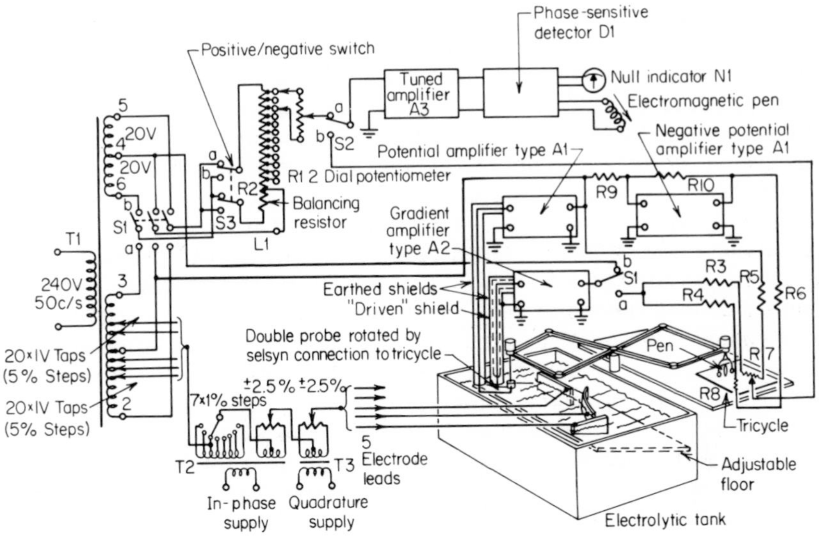

Fig. 9.19. Layout of the electrolytic-tank equipment, showing electrode supply transformers and amplifiers for the electrolytic tank of Ref. 18. The layout also shows the pantograph and tricycle used for ray tracing. (Courtesy of the Institution of Electrical Engineers.) For different functions the circuits are switched as follows: For potential measurements, S1 and S2 are set in position a; for gradient measurement, S1 is set to b, S2 is set to a; for electron trajectory tracing, S1 is set to a, S2 is set to b.

Reference 18 gives circuit diagrams of the elements of Fig. 9-19 in sufficient detail to permit fabrication of the electronics of a tank installation. The variable probe should be maintained at zero potential; a circuit to accomplish this operation is called a Wagner earth.[18] Electric field is measured normally by determining the voltage between two probes close together. Usually, two pairs of perpendicular probes are desirable for field measurements; by taking an appropriate correction factor from one pair to the other, errors in alignment may be compensated. When equipotential curves are to be plotted, it is useful to have a relay circuit which may be set to any desired voltage. By having a pantograph attached to the probe, equipotential lines can be traced. The probe is within a few millivolts of the prescribed voltage, a relay will close, causing the pen to make a point.

The size of the tank depends again on the available equipment. In a tank which is too deep, it is difficult to position the traveling probe accurately. If the tank is too small in its lateral dimensions, accurate positioning of the probes and electrodes is difficult, and proximity effects due to the edge of the tank may become important. If the tank is not well supported, the sags in the supports and in the floor of the tank will cause errors. A convenient size is 30 by 30 by

6 in. Several institutions have bought xy plotters, of a smaller size, 20 by 20 in., to avoid the design and construction of the tank and the circuitry and supports relevant to the positioning of the probes. Such a plotter is equipped with a rigid base and is intended as a plotting table. Since, in addition, a carriage with a movement in two directions is already present, such an xy plotter is a useful base for a tank. Otherwise, a bottom plate of $\frac{1}{2}$-in. plate glass or $\frac{3}{4}$-in. lucite is frequently used; these are smooth, stiff, easy to clean, and resistant to the commonly used electrolytes. Bakelite, $\frac{1}{2}$ in. thick, may be used for the side walls. If electrodes are simulated in the usual way with pieces of bent metal, a large-scale drawing of the electrodes on a piece of regular coordinate paper may be placed beneath the glass for convenience. As an alternative way of simulating electrodes, several pieces of window screens, held at the potential of the electrodes, may be placed over the tank (above the electrolyte). The electrodes are then simulated by dropping pins through the holes in the screens until the desired shape is found. Since it is easy to put pins in the screens and move them about, this is a very quick way of changing electrode shapes. If the screen is accurate (as most screens are), the final position of the electrode is accurately recorded, in xy coordinates, on the screen. It is possible to start by using pins fairly widely spaced; an electrode a few inches long can be simulated with five or ten pins. A dust cover for the tank is recommended. By the use of the precautions suggested in this section, overall inaccuracies due to the electrolytic tank and relevant measuring gear can be kept down to 1 per cent. Using extremely elaborate arrangements, Sander has kept the errors in the Cambridge tank to less than 0.1 per cent.

6.3. **Tanks with Solid Electrolytes.** Some of the principal disadvantages of electrolytic tanks with liquid electrolytes have been mentioned. Meniscus effects cause errors; variation of conductivity with time, due to deposits forming on the electrodes, to contamination of the electrolyte and to polarization effects, is troublesome and necessitates the use of alternating current; the use of a-c instrumentation then introduces errors due to capacity effects. For these reasons Rowe and Martin[19] have developed a solid electrolyte molded into a block which they call a Poisson cell. The electrolyte is made by using a 300-mesh graphite powder, in the amount of 40 per cent by weight, as the conducting filler in an insulated matrix of Hydrostone (gypsum cement). They keep the variation of resistance in a block $\frac{3}{8}$ by 20 by 20-in down to 1 per cent by ball-milling the mixture for a long time, often several days. The powder is mixed with a small amount of water, and poured into a mold. For a planar problem, the mold will be brick-shaped; for an axially symmetric problem, wedge-shaped. A variation of resistivity of several orders of magnitude can be obtained, but the best results have been achieved at a slightly higher resistivity than is used in liquid electrolytes, about 10^5 ohm-cm. Such a high resistivity would be undesirable in a liquid electrolyte, because interelectrode-capacity effects could cause considerable errors at 400 cps. With the Poisson cell it is possible to work with direct current. All meniscus, capacitive, polarization, and time variation of resistivity effects are thus avoided in the Poisson cell.

Although the Poisson cell overcomes most of the difficulties presented by the liquid electrolyte, it brings new problems of its own. For best electrical contact, the electrodes for the system to be investigated must be embedded into the mold. This has two effects which may or may not be serious: First, there is not a very uniform contact between the electrode and the electrolyte, causing some errors in potential near the electrodes. Second, every new electrode configuration requires a new cell. On the other hand, one has a permanent record of each configuration.

For some problems, these two effects are not serious drawbacks. When one wishes to analyze a specific gun by varying the voltages on different electrodes, it is usually necessary to make some assumptions on the behavior near the cathode; in this case, the exact fields near the electrodes, particularly near the cathode, may not be required. There may be no interest in varying the electrode shapes; in these cases, the solid electrolyte is very satisfactory, provided one does not need to measure fields in the vicinity of an electrode. Rowe has shown that it is possible to place metal electrodes on top of the electrolyte and still obtain fairly good contact. In other problems, particularly in most of those posed in this book, it is necessary to adjust the electrode until a particular voltage configuration is achieved. This kind of problem is not as tractable with a solid electrolyte as in a liquid tank.

It is possible to avoid the problems of making contact with the solid electrolyte by embedding a large number of pins vertically in the mold. This form of electrolyte is then a cross between a discrete analog, such as the resistance network, and a continuous analog. A screen with pins could be used to simulate the electrodes in the mold in the same way as in the electrolytic tank. In this case, it is not necessary to make a new mold for each electrode system. The wires which are not used for the simulation of electrodes can be used to simulate space charge, as in Sec. 6.4.

For planar problems a very thin Poisson cell has been developed, usually applied to plexiglass or plate glass; this form of cell is functionally the same as resistance paper. Fairly good contact can be made by clamping electrodes to the sheet. This technique is not applicable to axially symmetric problems; because of the wedge shape of the electrolyte, considerable errors may be caused by the electrodes not passing through the cell.

6.4. The Simulation of Space Charge by Current Sources. The usual method of representation of space charge by an analog in an electrolytic tank is by the use of current probes. From a comparison of Eqs. (2.2) and (2.13), for axially symmetric problems, we see that the space-charge term in the former will be adequately synthesized by continuous distribution of current sources of magnitude $\rho r \sigma_1/\epsilon_0$. It is almost impossible to synthesize a continuous, controlled, variable current distribution, and in practice the simulation is done by sticking discrete wires into the electrolyte, carrying specified currents.

Many problems arise in this representation of a continuous distribution by discrete sources. The problems are well described by, among others, Hollway[20] and Van Duzer and Brewer,[21] and it is on their findings that we have drawn heavily. For the theoretical and experimental evidence for their results, it is necessary to refer to their original papers.

Unlike the problem without space charge, absolute quantities now become important, because an actual current must be introduced into the electrolyte; this current depends on the voltage and the conductivity of the electrolyte; the latter is a quantity which could be ignored before. Following Van Duzer and Brewer,[21] the parameters of the gun to be synthesized are assumed to have been scaled up to be equal in physical size to that of the tank model; the electrical parameters in the gun have subscript g, and those in the tank have subscript t.

The differential equations which are analogous in Section 2 can be rewritten. In the gun, the potential ϕ_g obeys Poisson's equation,

$$\nabla^2 \phi_g = -\frac{\rho_g}{\epsilon_0} \tag{6.1}$$

If there is a factor of k between tank and gun voltages,

$$\phi_t = k\phi_g \tag{6.2}$$

then, since physical dimensions are conserved, the same ratio will apply to electric fields. In the tank the current density $\mathbf{i}_t$ is related to the field by

$$\mathbf{i}_t = -\sigma \mathbf{E}_t \tag{6.3}$$

Hence, from Eqs. (6.1) to (6.3),

$$\nabla \cdot \mathbf{i}_t = -\frac{\sigma k \rho_g}{\epsilon_0} \tag{6.4}$$

Before Eq. (6.4) can be used to determine how much current each discrete wire in the tank must carry to simulate the real space-charge distribution, it is necessary to know the effect of one such wire.

It is usual to introduce the current by wires protruding through the bottom of the tank. A drawing of one typical probe is shown in

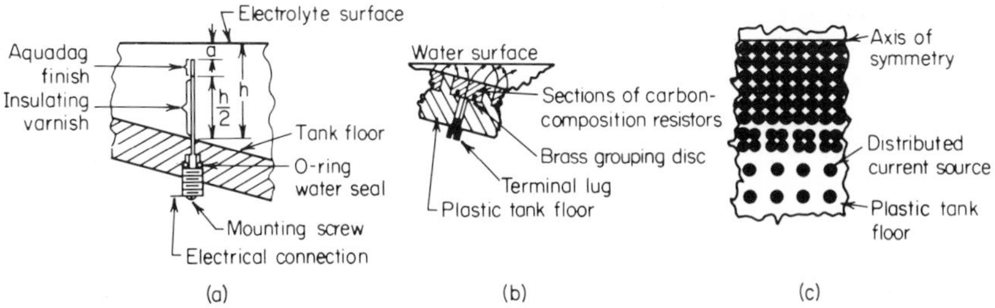

Fig. 9.20. Space-charge-simulation probes used in an electrolytic-tank installation at Hughes Aircraft Company. (a) Wire probe; (b) distributed button probe, (c) distribution of distributed probes in the tank. (Reproduced from Ref. 21, courtesy of The American Institute of Physics.)

Fig. 9.20a; a is the distance of the probe end below the water level, and I_p the current carried by the probe. Hollway[20] has shown that a thin wire of this type has the same potential at the water surface as an infinite uniformly charged cylinder of radius a carrying current I_p. This result allows Eq. (6.4) to be used to obtain the expression for I_p:

$$I_p = \int_S \mathbf{i}_t \cdot d\mathbf{S} = \int_\tau \nabla \cdot \mathbf{i}_t \, d\tau = -\int \frac{\sigma k}{\epsilon_0 \tau} \rho_g \, d\tau = -\frac{\sigma k Q_g}{\epsilon_0} \tag{6.5}$$

where S is the area surface bounding the volume τ which is being simulated, and Q_g is the total charge being simulated in the relevant section of the gun. The volume being simulated is, in the two-dimensional problem, a cylinder of unit length with cross section S; in the axially-symmetric case it is a torus of minor cross section tion s and major radius r.

We know, therefore, that a wire carrying current I_p and at a depth a below the surface is an analog of a cylinder of radius a and carries total charge per unit length $I_p \epsilon_0/\sigma k$ in the two-dimensional case. The only remaining question is how to use this result to simulate a variable charge density ρ_g. In an axially symmetric system the wire is the analog of a torus of minor radius a.

Several methods of simulation are possible. The surface of the electrolyte may be subdivided into a number of square cells. A good approximation to the correct current distribution is obtained by injecting into the middle of each square a current equivalent to the charge in the corresponding torus in the gun. In order to simulate a cylinder of radius a, the probe should be placed a radius a below the surface of the electrolyte and the cylinder of radius a should have the same cross-sectional area as the cell. From these considerations we see that, if A is the area of the cell in which the space charge is to be simulated, the probe should be $\sqrt{A/\pi}$ below the surface.

Near the axis of an axially symmetric system, it is not possible to have the tip of the wire protruding below the surface a sufficiently large amount, since $\sqrt{A/\pi}$ may be less than the depth of water. It is then necessary to replace the wire by a button probe instead of a sharp point, a little smaller in diameter than the cell simulated.

Since it is usually necessary to preset, and sometimes vary, the current in each probe, it is desirable to have each probe connected to a high-impedance source. It is best to have each probe connected to a constant-current source such as a pentode, but with many probes this becomes an exceedingly elaborate and expensive procedure.

Since it is necessary to change the depth of each probe, depending on which area it is supposed to simulate, the wire-probe depths must be adjustable. Drawings of wire probes and button probes used in one tank[21] are shown in Figs. 9.20a and b. When button probes are required, they must not shunt the electrolyte, and so must have resistivities at least two orders of magnitude higher than the electrolyte. Since a resistivity 2×10^4 to 10^5 ohms-cm was recommended in Sec. 6.2, depending on the nature of the electrolyte, the distributed sources must have resistivities of 10^6 to 10^7 ohm-cm. A suitably homogeneous material has proved to be sections of commercial carbon-composition resistors.

Since building and setting the current probes is a time-consuming task, it is desirable to reduce the number of probes to as few as possible. Space-charge effects are less important in the anode than in the cathode region, and it is usually possible to tolerate larger errors in space-charge simulation in the former. However, where electron trajectories cross over or otherwise deviate sharply, errors in space charge become important, and more probes are required. In the cathode region, it is necessary to treat the cathodes as a series of diodes, and so avoid the complications arising from the infinite-space-charge density there; a surface is chosen a little in front of the emitter, and the boundary conditions of Section 3 of Chap. VIII are used.

Unlike the case for zero space charge, the height of the water is very important, since it affects the depth of the probes. This means that evaporation can cause errors; these errors have been avoided by Sander and Yates,[15] who have completely enclosed their tank. The conductivity must also be carefully measured, since it affects the conversion ratio of injected current to space charge. Care must be taken not to let the measuring probes vary in depth, because this would again cause errors in measurement.

Certain other methods of space-charge simulation are possible. One, in which the bottom of the tank is shaped,[22] has now only historical interest. A second has been described by Gregory and Sander.[23]

7. THE RUBBER-MEMBRANE ANALOG

7.1. Description of the Analog. It can be shown that a small displacement from equilibrium of a thin stretched rubber membrane obeys Laplace's equation,

$$\frac{\partial^2 h}{\partial x^2} + \frac{\partial^2 h}{\partial y^2} = 0 \tag{7.1}$$

where h is the displacement of a point on the membrane. This fact has been used to derive an analog method of obtaining particle trajectories in two-dimensional systems.

If a body slides without friction on a plane of slope α, its acceleration along the plane is given by

$$m \frac{d^2 s}{dt^2} = g \sin \alpha = g \frac{dh}{ds} \tag{7.2}$$

where g is the acceleration due to gravity. If the slope is always small, so that ds/dt may be approximated by dx/dt, Eq. (7.2) can be generalized to give the relations

$$m\ddot{x} = \frac{\partial h}{\partial x} \qquad m\ddot{y} = \frac{\partial h}{\partial y} \tag{7.3}$$

Thus the sliding of the body on a contoured sheet obeys the same equations as the motion of particles in a two-dimensional electrostatic field.

The electrodes are simulated by holding specific curves of the rubber membrane at constant heights; this is analogous to maintaining specific curves in the electrolytic tank at specified potentials with metal electrodes.

The metal balls are released onto the membrane at the required initial velocities—usually zero. Their trajectories will then be analogous to those of charged particles in the original electrode system. These trajectories may be photographed by illuminating the particles with a bright light. In order to obtain information on the velocity of the particles, it is usual to illuminate the balls with intermittent light. From comparison of the visible portions of the photographed trajectories and the known times at which the balls are illuminated, it is possible to evaluate the velocities of the balls along their trajectories.

With sufficient care, trajectories can be obtained by this method, which qualitatively give the motion of charged particles in two-dimensional, electrostatic, Laplacian fields. However, because of friction, rotational energy of the ball, and nonuniformities of the rubber membrane and its finite thickness, the error in the trajectories tends to be large, the accuracy usually being considerably less than 5 per cent. Consequently, the method is not widely used for obtaining quantitative results.

References 24 to 26 may be consulted for a fuller description of the use of the rubber membrane, the synthesis of space-charge effects, and sources of error.

8. AN EVALUATION OF THE METHODS OF SOLVING POISSON'S EQUATION

An evaluation of the different methods of solving Poisson's equation is difficult to make. The advantages of various analogs depend so much on the problems to be solved that a definitive case cannot be made for any single analog.

Although the rubber-sheet analog is capable of quick results for the electron trajectories, it is too imprecise for accurate work. Space-charge simulation is possible, but difficult; therefore this analog has mainly historical interest.

The resistance-paper analog is satisfactory for Laplacian problems in two dimensions with a limited accuracy of 2 to 5 per cent. It is not worth the trouble to add current probes to this analog for most purposes. The inhomogeneity of resistivity is still too great for accurate work; the unavailability of paper with a linear variation of resistivity in one direction precludes the use of the paper for axially symmetric systems. The attempts to stick layers of paper together to give a stepwise, rather than linear, variation of resistance have not been very successful.

The logical extension of the resistance-paper analog is the solid electrolyte. This has been fairly successful for a certain class of problems. In conjunction with an analog computer to trace trajectories, the analog has been very successful, according to the inventor, in analyzing specific electrode systems, but it has not achieved wide acceptance. It is more unsatisfactory for electrode design because of the difficulties of varying the electrode configuration. The accuracy is limited to about 1 per cent by the inhomogeneities in its electrolyte; the idea of embedding pins to make a general-purpose structure, as suggested in Sec. 6.3, has not been tested in practice.

The electrolytic tank without current probes has proved very powerful for low-perveance applications. The prior removal of the potential due to space charge by analytic methods, as described in Section 4 of Chap. VIII, has extended the use of this analog to medium- and high-perveance applications. However, the difficulty of obtaining the space-charge potentials ϕ_{sc} of Section 4 of Chap. VIII makes this method cumbersome, except where a large number of similar guns are to be designed. In this case the ϕ_{sc} can be calculated once and for all.

The electrolytic tank with current probes has been very successfully used for the space-charge problems described here. With great care, accuracies of 0.1 per cent in the potential have been obtained. With reasonable care 1 per cent can be attained.

The resistance network is the most versatile of the experimental analogs. With great care accuracies of 0.1 per cent have been obtained for the potentials. A much more varied class of problems can be treated than on the electrolytic tank. The time and expense in setting up a simple network are greater, however, than for a similar tank facility. Making allowances for its limitations, the network is faster to use.

Because of the continuous nature of the analog, it is easier to build an analog or digital computer for trajectory tracing and magnetic field simulation on to an electrolytic tank than on to a resistance network. The desirability of such a step depends on how much the facility is used. It can be very expensive and wasteful to tie up a computer exclusively to such a special-purpose device. A digital output for the potential at discrete points in the plane, together with off-line processing of the data in a large and fast computer, has been successfully used.

The method of analysis which requires the least special-purpose hardware is the use of relaxation and iteration techniques on a high-speed digital computer. This method is potentially the fastest, most accurate, and most flexible. Although the design of the required computer program may take several months, it may well be possible to obtain copies of programs already developed at other institutions. For most problems of interest, however, a computer with microsecond floating-point arithmetic and at least 32,000 words of fast memory is required. As large computers become more readily available, this method of solution is displacing the use of experimental analogs.

In summary, for those establishments with a very high utilization of an electrolytic tank, the building of such an installation may be desirable, even with a small computer attached. For establishments with a broad class of analog problems, such as thermal- or neutron-diffusion problems, a resistance network complete with computer may be justifiable. If a large high-speed digital computer is available, it is most economical to solve the whole problem on the computer.

9. FIELD AND TRAJECTORY PLOTTING

9.1. Introduction. Plotting equipotentials and trajectories has been mentioned frequently in the preceding sections. Clearly, no discussion of gun design is complete without consideration of so important a topic. In this section both elementary methods of plotting with ruler and pencil and complex ones with analogs and computers are discussed.

First, the general procedure for plotting equipotentials, either manually or more or less automatically, is given without proof. The expressions for interpolating between potentials given only at discrete mesh points are derived.

Second, methods of trajectory plotting, both graphically and numerically, are derived. The formulas appropriate to integrating the differential equations are quoted without proof.

Unless a complete automatic facility, a computer combined with an analog device, is available, the most convenient method of ray tracing is the numerical one of Sec. 9.5. Accurate equipotentials can be evaluated at the same time by the numerical methods of Sec. 9.2. For lack of space, many curves useful in gun design are omitted. There is copious literature on the design of the spherical diode,[27-29] and much work has been done which would make design of such guns easier. This book is more concerned with design procedure than specific designs, so that most of such information has been omitted. A full account of the methods of ray tracing in use up to 1950 is given in a review paper by Liebman.[30]

9.2. Field Plots in an Electrolytic Tank or Resistance Network. The simplest method of field plotting in an electrolytic tank is to add a special relay circuit to the probe which measures the potential difference between probe and cathode and compares it with a preset voltage, as described in Sec. 6.2. The equipotential is mapped by tracing it on a sheet of graph paper with a pen attached by a pantograph to the probe. Equipotential plots may be obtained by presetting the reference voltage to the required potential, moving the probe in the x direction by discrete steps, and at each step moving the probe in the y direction until the pen relay plots a point. By this method, each equipotential line can be plotted in a minute or two.

In a resistance network, the problem of the automatic plotting of equipotentials is not quite so simple. It is usual for the exact equpotential to miss the mesh points of the resistors and for the grid size to be greater than the required accuracy of equipotentials. To determine the exact equipotential, an interpolation has to be made from the voltages on the end points of the resistor in question. It is possible to use a less sensitive difference circuit which will plot a rough equipotential as given by the corners of the mesh points, and then to obtain the more accurate plot by interpolation.

Although the methods just described give good equipotential plots, their use for particle trajectory plots is somewhat limited. In such a plot, it is the electric field which is required; the field probe configurations, described in Section 6, are more useful for plotting trajectories with an electrolytic tank. The evaluation of fields from potential differences is more satisfactory in the network analog.

Since these accurate field plots may be very time-consuming to obtain for trajectory plotting, it is often more useful to evaluate the field only at the points where it is required in the plot; when the approximate trajectories are known in advance, time can be saved. Because of the inaccuracy in plotting and rereading, it is usually better to have the potential in numerical rather than graphical form. Depending on the nature of the problem being considered, for obtaining meaningful trajectory plots an accuracy of between 0.1 and 2 per cent[13] is required in the field determination. Still higher accuracy is necessary to investigate third-order phenomena, like the variation of current density and the aberration of a lens.

In order to obtain the electric fields to the high accuracies required, numerical methods are the most satisfactory. In standard texts, such as Ref. 31, the numerical-analysis formulas are developed in great generality. For the purpose of this book only, special formulas are required, and these are presented here. In particular, care is taken to avoid using inconsistently high-accuracy formulas in one part of the computation. From the development of Section 2, it is seen that the potential ϕ is usually obtained to $0(h^2)$, where h is the mesh size. Near the boundary, ϕ is accurate only to 0(h). In some cases, particularly near the cathode, it was shown in Section 3 of Chap. VIII that ϕ is accurate only to 0(h), even at interior points. For these reasons formulas are presented below which give the potential to $0(h^2)$. The appropriate electric fields are accurate to 0(h).

It is assumed that the potential is known over the two-dimensional array of points $A_{i,j}$ in Fig. 9.21a. The mesh lengths are h and k in the two directions, and the potential at $A_{i,j}$ is $\Phi_{i,j}$. We wish to evaluate the potential and the electric field at the point P with coordinate x_p and y_p. The argument is identical in an axially symmetric system if z_p and r_p replace x_p and y_p. It is assumed that (x_p, y_p) is at least h and k away from the boundary. The modifications if (x,y) is nearer the boundary are discussed later. By redefining the origin of coordinates, it is clearly possible to express (x,y) in the form $[(m + a)h, (n + b)k]$, where m and n are integers and

$$0 < a, \quad b < 1 \tag{9.1}$$

It is assumed that x and y are expressed in this form, and the grid is renumbered as in Fig. 9.21b.

In interpolating a function of two variables, it is best to interpolate in the two variables separately. Using the Taylor's expansion of Eq. (2.14), it can be shown, by the same arguments that led to Eq. (2.15), that if f(u) has the values f_i at u = i,

$$f(u) = (1 - u)f_0 + uf_1 + 0(u^2) \tag{9.2}$$

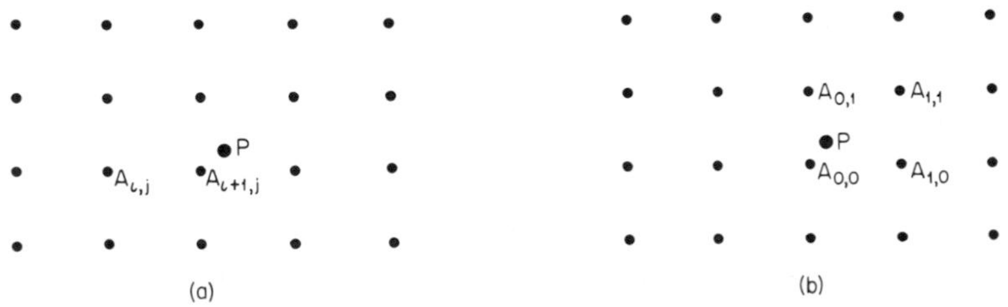

Fig. 9.21. Schematic of the mesh-point diagram used for interpolating for the potential. (a) Mesh-point diagram with P as an arbitrary point; (b) Mesh diagram renumbered.

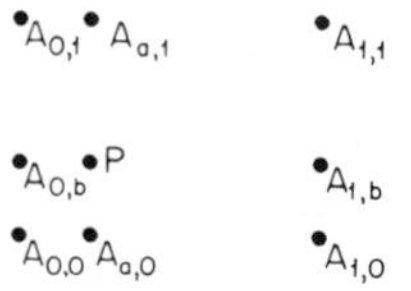

Fig. 9.22. Schematic showing how new points $A_{\alpha,\beta}$ are defined between the mesh points of Fig. 9.28.

Repeated use will be made of Eq. (9.2) in the following argument.

The simplest grid that can be used to evaluate the potential ϕ and the electric field at P is shown in Fig. 9.22. It is assumed that the potentials $\Phi_{i,j}$ at the mesh points $A_{i,j}$ are known for integral i and j. It is convenient to define the intermediate points $A_{\alpha,\beta}$ as the points where $x = \alpha$ and $y = \beta$. Using Eq. (9.2) and writing $\Phi_n(u)$ for f(u), where n is a parameter, it is seen that

$$\Phi_0(a) = (1 - a)\,\Phi_{0,0} + a\Phi_{1,0} + 0[(ha)^2] \tag{9.3a}$$

$$\Phi_1(a) = (1 - a)\,\Phi_{0,1} + a\Phi_{1,1} + 0[(ha)^2] \tag{9.3b}$$

Writing now $\Phi(a,u)$ for f(u), where a is a parameter, Eq. (9.2) gives

$$\Phi(a,b) = (1 - b)\Phi_0(a) + b\Phi_1(a) + 0[(ha)^2] + 0[(kb)^2] \tag{9.4}$$

If P is nearer the boundary than h, Eqs. (9.3) and (9.4) must be slightly modified. The details are left as an exercise for the reader.

If h and k are of the same order, the error in $\Phi(a,b)$ of Eq. (9.4), with the defining equations (9.3), is $0(h^2)$. It is possible to treat $\Phi(a,b)$ as a continuous function of a and b. From the definitions of a and b, it is seen that

$$\frac{\partial\phi}{\partial x} = \frac{1}{h}\frac{\partial\Phi(a,b)}{\partial a} \qquad \frac{\partial\phi}{\partial y} = \frac{1}{k}\frac{\partial\Phi(a,b)}{\partial y} \tag{9.5}$$

Differentiating Eq. (9.4) with respect to b, the following expression for the y component of the electric field is obtained:

$$E_y = -\frac{\partial\phi}{\partial y} = -\frac{1}{k}\frac{\partial\Phi(a,b)}{\partial b} = \frac{\Phi_0(a) - \Phi_1(a)}{k} + 0(h) \tag{9.6a}$$

By an exactly similar procedure, it is seen that

$$E_x = -\frac{\partial\phi}{\partial x} = -\frac{1}{h}\frac{\partial\Phi(a,b)}{\partial a} = \frac{\psi_0(b) - \psi_1(b)}{h} + 0(h) \tag{9.6b}$$

where $\psi_0(b) = (1 - b)\,\Phi_{0,0} + b\Phi_{0,1}$ (9.7a)

$$\psi_1(b) = (1 - b)\,\Phi_{1,0} + b\Phi_{1,1} \tag{9.7b}$$

Expressions (9.7) give the potential and the electric field to at least as good an accuracy as the original $\Phi_{i,j}$. Equipotentials can be computed from the interpolation formulas of Eq. (9.4) in a straightforward manner. Assuming **B** is also known at the mesh point, it is possible to evaluate B_x, B_y, B_z by very similar expressions. The derivation of the appropriate expressions for B is left as an exercise for the reader.

9.3. The Basic Equations for Ray Tracing. In this section the special form of the Lorentz equation of motion [Eq. (2.15) of Chap. I],

$$\frac{d\mathbf{v}}{dt} = -\eta(\mathbf{E} + \mathbf{v} \times \mathbf{B}) \tag{9.8}$$

and its defining equation,

$$\frac{d\mathbf{x}}{dt} = \mathbf{v} \tag{9.9}$$

are discussed for two-dimensional and axially symmetric electrode systems.

It is possible to integrate Eqs. (9.8) and (9.9) either with respect to time or distance. The former requires one more differential equation than the latter. If distance is chosen as the independent variable, however, great care must be taken in two regions. Near the cathode and a position where the particle turns back, there is a singularity in one component of the gradient of velocity. For example, if a particle trajectory has the form of Fig. 9.23, it is unsatisfactory to use x as the independent variable in the region B. In the region A, very short increments of position must be taken.

Choosing x as the independent variable and using the relation

$$v_x \frac{da}{dx} = \frac{da}{dt} \tag{9.10}$$

where a is any function of x, Eqs. (9.8) and (9.9) become

$$\frac{dv_x}{dx} = \frac{\eta}{v_x}\left(\frac{\partial \phi}{\partial x} - v_y B_z + \dot{z} B_y\right) \tag{9.11a}$$

$$\frac{dv_y}{dx} = \frac{\eta}{v_x}\left(\frac{\partial \phi}{\partial y} + v_x B_z - \dot{z} B_x\right) \tag{9.11b}$$

$$\frac{dy}{dx} = \frac{v_y}{v_x} \tag{9.11c}$$

The z component of the motion can be computed directly from the conservation-of-energy equation [Eq. (2.27) of Chap. I] in the form

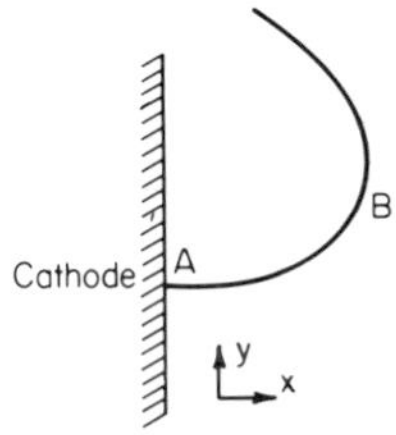

Fig. 9.23. Schematic of a particle trajectory leaving the cathode normally.

$$\dot{z} = \pm[2\eta(\phi - \phi_0) + v_0^2 - v_x^2 - v_y^2]^{1/2} \tag{9.12}$$

where the particle has initial speed v_0 and potential ϕ_0 at the initial point (e.g., the cathode). The sign of $\dot{z}$ is the same as its initial value $\dot{z}_0$ unless $\dot{z}$ becomes zero during the integration. In that case, from the behavior of the third component of Eq. (9.8), namely,

$$\frac{dv_z}{dx} = \frac{\eta}{v_x}\left(v_y B_x - v_x B_y\right) \tag{9.13}$$

the new sign of $\dot{z}$ can be computed.

If at any place $|v_x| < |v_y|$, it is more accurate to use y as the independent variable. At a cathode x = 0, the right side of Eq. (9.11a) has a singularity; hence short steps of Δx must be taken near the cathode. To avoid the complications caused by two sets of equations and the singularity, it is preferable to use time as the independent variable. In this case Eqs. (9.8) and (9.9) can be written

$$\frac{dv_i}{dt} = f_i(x_1,x_2,v_1,v_2) \qquad \text{and} \qquad \frac{dx_i}{dt} = v_i \tag{9.14}$$

where i can take the values 1 and 2, and x_1,x_2,v_1,v_2 have been written for x,y,v_x,v_y. The f_i do not depend on t explicitly, and are given by

$$\begin{aligned} f_1 &= \eta\left(\frac{\partial\phi}{\partial x} - v_y B_z + \dot{z}B_y\right) \\ f_2 &= \eta\left(\frac{\partial\phi}{\partial y} + v_x B_z - \dot{z}B_x\right) \end{aligned} \tag{9.15}$$

and $\dot{z}$ is still defined by Eq. (9.12). Equations (9.14) and (9.15) are the only equations required in two-dimensional systems, where the z motion is immaterial.

In axially symmetric systems, where ϕ and **B** are independent of θ, it is more convenient to use cylindrical polar coordinates (r,θ,z). In all the problems we have considered in this book, $B_\theta = 0$. It can be shown by considering the Lagrangian of Eq. (2.1) of Chap. III that the form of Eq. (9.8) in cylindrical polar coordinates, with $B_\theta = 0$, is

$$\frac{dv_r}{dt} = \eta\left(\frac{\partial\phi}{\partial r} - r\dot{\theta}B_z\right) + r\dot{\theta}^2 \tag{9.16a}$$

$$\frac{dv_z}{dt} = \eta\left(\frac{\partial\phi}{\partial z} + r\dot{\theta}B_r\right) \tag{9.16b}$$

A similar equation can be deduced for the θ motion, but this equation has already been integrated in Eq. (3.12) of Chap. I and has the form

$$r^2\dot{\theta} = r_0^2\dot{\theta}_0^2 + \eta(rA - r_0A_0) \tag{9.17}$$

In Eq. (9.17), r_0, $\dot{\theta}_0$, A_0 are the initial values of $r,\dot{\theta},A$ at t = 0, and A is the θ component of the vector potential. If $B_\theta = 0$, it was shown in Sec. 3.1 of Chap. I that any **B** could be derived from a function A(r,z)

$$B_r = -\frac{\partial A}{\partial z} \qquad B_z = \frac{\partial A}{\partial r} \tag{9.18}$$

If the magnetic field has a very simple form, A can be evaluated from B_r and B_z by integration; if not, it is usually A(r,z) which is the known function, and the B_r and B_z of Eqs. (9.16) are evaluated from A by Eq. (9.18).

From Eqs. (9.16) to (9.18), it is seen that in axially symmetric systems, the trajectory equations again take the form of Eq. (9.14), with x_1, x_2, v_1, v_2 written for z, r, v_z, v_r, and where f_i take the form

$$\begin{aligned} f_1 &= \eta\left(\frac{\partial \phi}{\partial z} + r\dot{\theta}B_r\right) \\ f_2 &= \eta\left(\frac{\partial \phi}{\partial r} - r\dot{\theta}B_z\right) + r\dot{\theta}^2 \end{aligned} \tag{9.19}$$

and $\dot{\theta}, B_r$, and B_z are defined by Eqs. (9.17) and (9.18). Again z or r can be used as independent variables instead of t. The appropriate form of the equations is left as an exercise for the reader.

In focusing systems in which no particles reverse their z motion, it is very convenient always to integrate with z as the independent variable.

9.4. Ray Tracing by Graphical Means. Although graphical methods of ray tracing are usually of low accuracy, they are fast to use if no computing facilities are available. The simplest such method is the use of Snell's law for electrostatic systems. In this method, the analogy between optics and the electron optics is used. The method is not practical in the presence of magnetic fields. The region in which a purely magnetic field acts is split up into a number of regions bound by equipotentials, Φ_1, Φ_2, Φ_i, ... This is illustrated in Fig. 9.24. The equipotentials are sketched as Φ_1, Φ_2, . . . , and the electric field is directed along PP′ at the ith equipotential. The trajectory of a particle crossing the ith equipotential is AB, and BD is the direction of the trajectories at the (i + 1) st equipotential. Let α_i be the angle between PP′ and AB, and α_{i+1} that between PP′ and BD. The trajectory AB extended cuts Φ_{i+1} at C. At B the velocity is v_s along AB; at C it is $v_s + \delta v_s$ along BC, and δv_n perpendicular to BC. From Newton's force law, Liebman[30] has deduced the relation between the trajectories at ith and (i + 1) st equipotentials in the form

$$\frac{\sin \alpha_{i+1}}{\sin \alpha_i} \simeq \left(\frac{\Phi_i}{\Phi_{i+1}}\right)^{1/2} \tag{9.20}$$

The construction indicated by Eq. (9.20) is done graphically in Fig. 9.25. The trajectory AB is continued to some point C. The

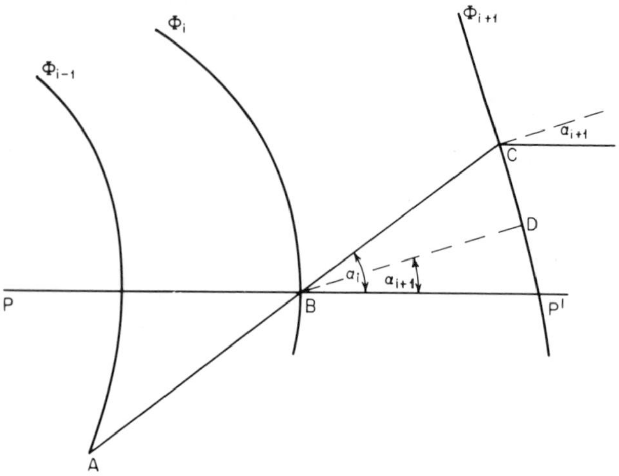

Fig. 9.24. Schematic of equipotentials and trajectories to illustrate the construction required for Snell's law.

perpendicular CC′ is drawn to PP′. Finally, DD′, of length CC′× $(\Phi_i/\Phi_{i+1})^{1/2}$, is drawn from PP′ to the circle center B radius BC. BD is drawn from PP′ to the circle center B radius BC. BD is then the required direction. This construction may be verified by simple geometry. To obtain greater accuracy, it is better to use the average value of ϕ between the (i − 1) st and the ith trajectory instead of Φ_i, and the same for Φ_{i+1}. Equation (9.20) then takes the form

$$\frac{\sin \alpha_{i+1}}{\sin \alpha_i} = \left(\frac{\Phi_i + \Phi_{i-1}}{\Phi_{i+1} + \Phi_i}\right)^{1/2} \qquad (9.21)$$

The use of the right-hand side of Eq. (9.21) for the ratio of the lengths CC′ and DD′ is more accurate than that of Eq. (9.20).

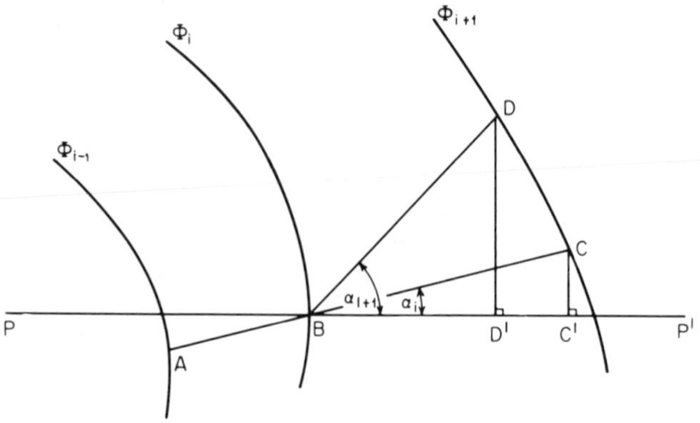

Fig. 9.25. Diagram of the construction required to integrate trajectories by Snell's law.

If the equipotentials have been measured in the presence of space charge, Eq. (9.21) gives the change in direction for an electrostatic field with moderate accuracy. If magnetic fields are present, it is more convenient to use numerical techniques.

A second graphical method is more accurate, and can be made the basis of the automatic trajectory tracer. In essence, this method is similar to that just given, but a higher order of approximation is used. The formula

$$\kappa = -\frac{E_n}{2\phi} \tag{9.22}$$

for the local curvative is used directly. E_n is either measured directly in the tank or is computed by the methods of Sec. 9.2. Then, with a compass, an arc of a curve may be drawn tangential to the trajectory direction with the radius given from Eq. (9.22). Of course, the deviation may be computed, rather than measured, by fitting the trajectory to a series of parabolas. It is possible by this method to include magnetic field effects by using the correct Lorentz equation in a magnetic field,

$$\kappa = \frac{-E_n + B_n v}{2\phi} = \frac{-E_n}{2\phi} + \frac{B_n}{(2\phi/\eta)^{1/2}} \tag{9.23}$$

where B_n is the magnetic field normal to the path, and v the speed. For planar motion $\mathbf{E}_n$ and $\mathbf{B} \times \mathbf{v}$ are in the same direction.

9.5. Plotting Trajectories by Integrating the Lorentz Force Law. The straightforward method of plotting trajectories is to integrate directly the Lorentz force law in the form of Eq. (9.14):

$$\frac{dv_i}{dt} = f_i \qquad \frac{dx_i}{dt} = v_i \tag{9.24}$$

The f_i are given in Eqs. (9.15) and (9.19) for two-dimensional and axially symmetric systems, and $i = 1$ or 2. If the integration is done automatically by computer, this procedure is the most accurate. For hand plotting, one of the previous methods is more convenient. All methods are derived, of course, from the fundamental equation, Eq. (9.24). In this section, two sets of formulas, which may be used to integrate Eq. (9.24), are stated without proof.

On an analog computer, attached to a continuous analog such as an electrolytic tank, Eq. (9.24) can be set up and solved directly.

If the problem is being solved on an on-line digital computer attached to a continuous analog, the **E**, **v**, and **B** required for the f_i can be measured only at the location of the probe. Therefore the simplest integration formulas

$$x_i(t + \Delta t) = x_i(t) + \Delta t\, v(t) \qquad v_i(t + \Delta t) = v_i(t) + \Delta t\, f_i(t) \tag{9.25}$$

will be used, where $f_i(t)$ is the acceleration of Eqs. (9.15) and (9.19), and **E**, **v**, **B** are determined by the instantaneous position of the particle. It is possible to store past values of **x**, **v**, **E**, **B** and to use the methods described below; usually an on-line computer for this purpose is very simple, and such storing would be beyond its capability.* It has been preferred[16] to use the simple formulas of Eq. (9.25) with a Δt sufficiently small so that accuracy is not lost.

On a digital computer working off line, with stored fields, different methods are preferable. Instead of using very small Δt and formulas of low accuracy, such as Eqs. (9.25), more accurate formulas are used with larger Δt.

In this section, one set of equations is stated. For a more complete survey of the subject of the integration of systems of differential equations, the reader should consult a book on numerical analysis, e.g., Ref. 31.

One common method of integrating differential equations of the form of Eq. (9.24) is the Runge-Kutta method.[31] The theory of the Runge-Kutta procedure can be found in Ref. 31, but the results are quoted here. To integrate one step Δt, there are several possible Runge-Kutta formulas. Some have error $0[(\Delta t)^4]$, and some only $0[(\Delta t)^5]$. The f_i of Eq. (9.24) are themselves accurate only to $0(h)$, where h is the mesh size. It is usual to choose the step size smaller than the mesh size; in that case there is no need to use a much more accurate formula. However, it is usually faster, to use a more accurate method, with a larger integration step. For these reasons the third-order Runge-Kutta procedure accurate to $0[(\Delta t)^4]$ is quoted. Note that, because the errors in integrating the equation accumulate, it is desirable to use an integrating procedure more accurate than the desired result.

For the third-order procedure, the six pairs of functions D_j^i, D_j^{ii}, D_j^{iii}, Δ_j^i, Δ_j^{ii}, Δ_j^{iii} are constructed. The D_j and Δ_j are defined by

$$D_j^i = f_j[\mathbf{x}(t), \mathbf{v}(t)]\,\Delta t \qquad \Delta_j^i = v_j(t)\,\Delta t \tag{9.26a}$$

$$D_j^{ii} = f_j[\mathbf{x}(t) + \tfrac{2}{3} D_j^i, \quad \mathbf{v}(t) + \tfrac{2}{3}\Delta_j^i]\,\Delta t, \quad \Delta_j^{ii} = [v_j(t) + \tfrac{2}{3}\Delta_j^i]\,\Delta t \tag{9.26b}$$

$$\begin{aligned} D_j^{iii} &= f_j[\mathbf{x}(t) + \tfrac{1}{3}(D_j^i + D_j^{ii}), \quad \mathbf{v}(t) + \tfrac{1}{3}(\Delta_j^i + \Delta_j^{ii})]\,\Delta t \\ \Delta_j^{iii} &= [v_j(t) + \tfrac{1}{3}(\Delta_j^i + \Delta_j^{ii})]\,\Delta t \end{aligned} \tag{9.26c}$$

If, first, Eq. (9.26a) is evaluated for $j = 1$ and 2, all the terms in Eq. (9.26b) are known. Evaluating now Eqs. (9.26b), it is possible to proceed to Eq. (9.26c), etc. With the definitions of D_j^i, etc., of Eqs. (9.26), it is shown in Ref. 31 that good approximations for $\mathbf{x}(t + \Delta t)$ and $\mathbf{v}(t + \Delta t)$ are

*With the use of a large multiaccess computer in a time-shared mode this restriction does not apply.

$$x_j(t + \Delta t) = x_j(t) + \tfrac{1}{4}(D_j^{i} + 3\, D_j^{iii} \tag{9.27a}$$

$$v_j(t + \Delta t) = v_j(t) + \tfrac{1}{4}(\Delta_j^{i} + 3\, \Delta_j^{iii}) \tag{9.27b}$$

The approximations of Eqs. (9.27) are in error to order $(\Delta t)^4$. More accurate formulas, with error of order $(\Delta t)^5$, are derived in Ref. 31. Since f_j must itself be computed by the interpolation formulas of Section 2, and the error in the formulas used is 0(h), where h is the mesh size, it is pointless to use higher-order formulas.

Using the results of Eqs. (9.27), the values of $x_j(t + 2\Delta t)$, etc., can be evaluated from $x_j(t + \Delta t)$ and $v_j(t + \Delta t)$. It is advisable to use a larger time interval near the cathode, where the velocity is low, than near the anode. A convenient time interval which guarantees that the step size is of the order of the mesh diagonal is

$$\Delta t = \left(\frac{h^2 + k^2}{2\eta\phi}\right)^{1/2} \tag{9.28}$$

where h and k are the mesh sizes in the two directions. If a larger step size than a mesh diagonal is desired, a multiple of the Δt of Eq. (9.28) should be used.

To start the solution at t = 0, it is necessary to have nonzero f_i or v_i. If the particle starts at the cathode, usually $\mathbf{E} = f_j = \mathbf{v} = 0$. In order to get the particle away from the cathode, it is possible to use a series expansion in t for **x** and **v** as in Eqs. (2.10) and (2.12) of Chap. II. Alternatively, the particle can be started with a small velocity of the order of the thermal velocity, that is, $v \simeq 10^5$ m/sec for electrons. If a very small initial velocity is used, a correspondingly large time interval Δt, as indicated by Eq. (9.28), must be used. The ϕ in Eq. (9.28) should be the ϕ at the nearest interior mesh point to the starting position of the particle.

9.6. Automatic Trajectory Tracing with a Computer. The details of the computation of fully automatic trajectory plotters with electrolytic tanks are beyond the scope of this book. In such a computation, it is usual to integrate the two equations of motion twice by either a digital or analog computer. The two components of the electric field are measured in the usual way in the tank, and the resulting voltages are rectified and fed into the computer.[16,21]

In the only digital facility known to the authors,[16] only the simplest equations, Eq. (9.25), were used in the integration. The more sophisticated equations, those developed later in Sec. 9.5, required too much expensive memory and computational complexity to be justified in this special-purpose equipment.

The results of the computer are converted into electrical signals, which are transformed by selsyn motors into displacements of the probe. Magnetic field effects may be treated in several ways. Simple ones, especially those due to a constant magnetic field or to a field which is a simple function of position, may be obtained by modifying the equation of motion to include the magnetic field term. Since velocity is automatically generated in the computer, this factor causes no essential problem; in an analog computer, it requires a function multiplier. Alternatively, Van Duzer and Brewer[21] have built a second tank exactly similar to the first, with probes rigidly connected from one tank to the other. In the one tank the electric fields are generated; in the other, the magnetic. Naturally, only one tank requires current probes, the magnetic field being Laplacian. One such installation, that at Hughes Aircraft Company, is shown in Fig. 9.16. Such combinations are expensive, take a long time to build, and need considerable maintenance.

REFERENCES FOR CHAPTER IX

1. Allen, D. N. de G.: "Relaxation Methods," McGraw Hill Book Company, New York, 1954.
2. Forsythe, G. E., and W. R. Wasow: "Finite Difference Methods for Partial Difference Equations," John Wiley & Sons, Inc., New York, 1960.
3. Martin, D. W., and G. J. Tee: Iterative Methods for Linear Equations with Positive Definite Matrix, *Computer J.*, vol. 4, p. 242, 1961.
4. Carré, B. A.: The Determination of the Optimum Accelerating Factor for Successive Over-relaxation, *Computer J.*, vol. 4, p. 73, 1961.
5. Hornsby, J. S.: A Computer Programme for the Solution of Elliptical Partial Differential Equations (Potential Problems), *CERN Rept.* 63-7, Geneva, 1963.
6. Liebman, G.: The Precise Solution of Partial Differential Equations by Resistance Networks, *Nature*, vol. 164, p. 149, 1949.
7. Liebman, G.: The Solution of Plane Stress Problems by an Electrical Analog Method, *Brit. J. Appl. Phys.*, vol. 6, p. 145, 1955.
8. Liebman, G.: Resistance Network Analogues with Unequal or Subdivided Meshes, *Brit. J. Appl. Phys.*, vol. 5, p. 362, 1954.
9. Hechtel, J. R., and J. A. Seeger: Accuracy and Limitation of the Resistance Network for Solving Poisson's and Laplace's Equations, *Proc. IRE*, vol. 49, p. 933, 1961.
10. Hechtel, J. R.: Electron Ray Tracing by Means of Resistor Network and Digital Computer, *Trans. IRE*, vol. ED-9, p. 62, 1962.
11. Archard, G. D.: Resistance Networks in Aldermaston, *Assoc. Elec. Ind. Res. Lab.*, *AEI Rept. A*, p. 568, Aldermaston, Berkshire, England, 1957.
12. Liebman, G., and R. Bailey: An Improved Experimental Iteration Network for Use with Resistance Network Analysers, *Brit. J. Appl. Phys.*, vol. 5, p. 32, 1954.
13. Liebman, G.: Solution of Partial Differential Equations with a Resistance Network Analogue, *Brit. J. Appl. Phys.*, vol. 1, p. 92, 1950.
14. Sander, K. F., and J. G. Yates: The Accurate Mapping of Electrical Fields in an Electrolytic Tank, *Proc. IEEE*, vol. 100 (pt. 2), p. 167, 1953.
15. Sander, K. F., and J. G. Yates: A New Form of Electrolytic Tank, *Proc. IEEE*, vol. 104C, p. 81, 1957.
16. Pizer, H. I., J. G. Yates, and K. F. Sander: An Automatic Trajectory Tracer, *J. Electronics and Control*, vol. 2, p. 65, 1956.
17. Hartill, E. R.: The Use of a Deep Electrolytic Tank for the Solution of

Field Problems in Engineering, part 1, *Elect. Energy*, vol. 2, p. 118, 1958.
18. Hollway, D. L.: An Electrolytic Tank Equipment for the Determination of Electron Trajectories, Potential and Gradient, *Proc. IEEE*, vol. 103B, p. 155, 1956.
19. Rowe, J. E., and R. J. Martin: An Electron Trajectory Calculator and Its Component Poisson Cell, *Proc. IEEE*, vol. 105B, suppl. 12, p. 1024, 1958.
20. Hollway, D. L.: The Determination of Electron Trajectories in the Presence of Space Charge, *Australian J. Phys.*, vol. 8, p. 75, 1955.
21. Van Duzer, T., and G. R. Brewer: Space Charge Simulation in Electrolytic Tanks, *J. Appl. Phys.*, vol. 30, p. 291, 1959.
22. Musson-Genon, R.: Représentation à la curve electronique de l'effet de charge d'espace dans les tubes à vide, *Onde Elec.*, vol. 28, p. 236, 1948.
23. Gregory, B. C., and K. F. Sander: New Method of Simulating Space Charge in the Electrolytic tank, *Proc. IEEE*, vol. 3, p. 1766, 1964.
24. Alma, G. A., G. Diemer, and H. Greendijk: A Rubber Membrane Model for Tracing Electron Paths in Space Charge Fields, *Philips Tech. Rev.*, vol. 14, p. 336, 1953.
25. Harries, J. H. O.: Rubber Membrane and Resistance Paper Analogies, *Proc. IRE*, vol. 44, p. 236, 1956.
26. White, D. A., and D. L. Perry: Notes on the Use of a Rubber Membrane Model, *Rev. Sci. Instr.*, vol. 32, p. 730, 1961.
27. Danielson, W. E., J. L. Rosenfeld, and J. A. Saloom: A Detailed Analysis of Beam Formation with Electron Guns of the Pierce Type, *Bell System Tech. J.*, vol. 35, p. 375, 1956.
28. Picquendar, J. E., and O. Cahen: Method for Theoretical Investigation of Type-O-focusing, *Rev. Tech. Comp. Franç. Thomson-Houston*, vol. 32, p. 7, 1960.
29. Brewer, G. R.: Formation of High Density Electron Beams, *J. Appl. Phys.*, vol. 28, p. 7, 1957.
30. Liebman, G.: Field Plotting and Ray Tracing in Electron Optics: A Review of Numerical Methods, *Advances in Electronics*, vol. 2, Academic Press Inc., New York, 1950.
31. Kunz, K. S.: "Numerical Analysis," McGraw-Hill Book Company, New York, 1957.

PROBLEMS

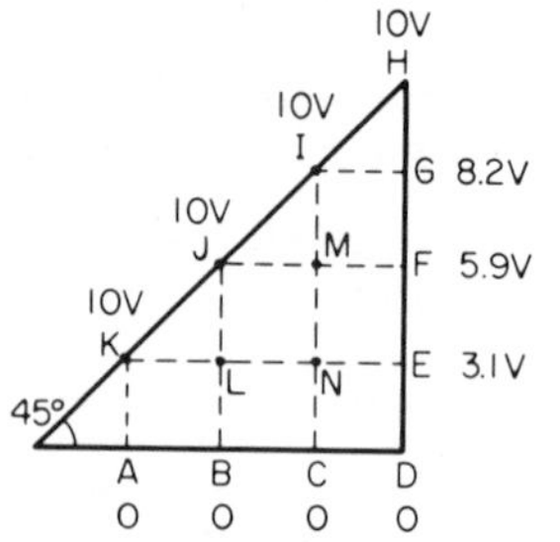

1. The correct solution for the potential in the region between two plates placed at an angle, one at zero potential, the other at a potential Φ_0, is $\Phi_0\theta/\theta_0$, where θ_0 is the angle between the two plates. Consider the system shown in the figure. The upper plate is at a potential 10 volts, the lower at zero potential, and the potentials at EFG are chosen in conformity with the correct solution. Use a relaxation technique to find the potentials at the points LMN. With an overrelaxation factor of $\beta = 1$, how many tries are needed to come within 5 per cent of the correct answer? Compare this result with using overrelaxation factors of $\beta = 1.4$ and $\beta = 2$.

2. Solve Prob. 1 by determining the solution of the difference equations involved by regarding them as a set of simultaneous equations for the potentials at L, M, and N. What is the error in the solution at the points L, M, and N?

APPENDIX A

The Vector Operators in Orthogonal Curvilinear Coordinates

1. INTRODUCTION

In many sections of this book, reference is made to the operators gradient, divergence, curl, and Laplacian. Although the rigorous proofs of the formulas for these operators have been derived in many textbooks (e.g., Morse and Feshbach), it is useful to recall, for reference, the relevant formulas in this appendix. In Section 2 we derive the formulas for the vector operators in general orthogonal curvilinear coordinates; in Section 3, these formulas are evaluated in some particular coordinate systems.

2. THE EXPRESSIONS FOR THE VECTOR OPERATORS IN A GENERAL ORTHOGONAL COORDINATE SYSTEM

If (q_1,q_2,q_3) is an arbitrary point in an orthogonal coordinate system, the differential element of length $d\ell$ can be defined, in terms of the differential increments of the coordinates, by the expression

$$d\ell^2 = h_1^2\, dq_1^2 + h_2^2\, dq_2^2 + h_3^2\, dq_3^2 \tag{2.1}$$

From Eq. (2.1), it is seen that an infinitesimal element of volume, with vertices $(q_1 \pm \tfrac{1}{2}\, dq_1,\ q_2 \pm \tfrac{1}{2}\, dq_2,\ q_3 \pm \tfrac{1}{2}\, dq_3)$, would take the form of a curvilinear cube of sides $h_1\, dq_1$, $h_2\, dq_2$, $h_3\, dq_3$. This volume element is sketched in Fig. A.1, where the coordinates of the vertices are given by

$$A_1 = \left(q_1 - \frac{1}{2}\, dq_1,\ q_2 - \frac{1}{2}\, dq_2,\ q_3 - \frac{1}{2}\, dq_3\right)$$

$$A_2 = \left(q_1 + \frac{1}{2}\, dq_1,\ q_2 - \frac{1}{2}\, dq_2,\ q_3 - \frac{1}{2}\, dq_3\right)$$

$$A_3 = \left(q_1 + \frac{1}{2}\, dq_1,\ q_2 + \frac{1}{2}\, dq_2,\ q_3 - \frac{1}{2}\, dq_3\right)$$

$$A_4 = \left(q_1 - \frac{1}{2}\, dq_1,\ q_2 + \frac{1}{2}\, dq_2,\ q_3 - \frac{1}{2}\, dq_3\right)$$

$$A_5 = \left(q_1 - \frac{1}{2}\,dq_1,\ q_2 - \frac{1}{2}\,dq_2,\ q_3 + \frac{1}{2}\,dq_3\right)$$

$$A_6 = \left(q_1 + \frac{1}{2}\,dq_1,\ q_2 - \frac{1}{2}\,dq_2,\ q_3 + \frac{1}{2}\,dq_3\right)$$

$$A_7 = \left(q_1 + \frac{1}{2}\,dq_1,\ q_2 + \frac{1}{2}\,dq_2,\ q_3 + \frac{1}{2}\,dq_3\right)$$

$$A_8 = \left(q_1 - \frac{1}{2}\,dq_1,\ q_2 + \frac{1}{2}\,dq_2,\ q_3 + \frac{1}{2}\,dq_3\right) \tag{2.2}$$

If $\mathbf{q}$ is the point (q_1,q_2,q_3), and $d\ell$ a line element in any particular direction, the component of the gradient of a scalar function $a(q_1,q_2,q_3)$ in the direction $d\ell$ is

$$(\nabla a)_{\text{along } d\ell} = \lim_{d\ell\to 0}\left[\frac{a(\mathbf{q} + d\ell) - a(\mathbf{q})}{d\ell}\right] \tag{2.3}$$

By letting $d\ell$ be directed along each coordinate axis in turn, it is seen, taking Eq. (2.3) to the limit and using Eq. (2.1), that

$$(\nabla a) = \left[\frac{1}{h_1}\frac{\partial a}{\partial q_1},\ \frac{1}{h_2}\frac{\partial a}{\partial q_2},\ \frac{1}{h_3}\frac{\partial a}{\partial q_3}\right] \tag{2.4}$$

The divergence of a vector $\boldsymbol{\alpha}(q_1,q_2,q_3)$, with components $(\alpha_1,\alpha_2,\alpha_3)$, is defined by the expression*

$$\nabla\cdot\boldsymbol{\alpha} = \lim_{\tau\to 0}\frac{\int_S \boldsymbol{\alpha}\cdot\mathbf{n}\,dS}{\tau} \tag{2.5}$$

where τ is any volume, S is a surface bounding it, and $\mathbf{n}$ is the unit normal to S. Let τ be taken as the curvilinear cube of Fig. A.1. Integrating $\int_S \boldsymbol{\alpha}\cdot\mathbf{n}\,dS$ over the face $A_1A_2A_3A_4$ gives a contribution

$$(-h_1h_2\alpha_3)_{q_1,q_2,q_3 - \frac{1}{2}dq_3}\,dq_1\,dq_2$$

where, by the notation $(p)_{q_1,q_2,q_3}$, we mean the value of p at the point (q_1,q_2,q_3). It has been assumed that the sides of the rectangle are sufficiently small so that α may be replaced by its value at the center of the face. In the same way, $\int_S \boldsymbol{\alpha}\cdot\mathbf{n}\,dS$ over the face $A_5A_6A_7A_8$ gives a contribution

$$(h_1h_2\alpha_3)_{q_1,q_2,q_3 + \frac{1}{2}dq_3}\,dq\,dq_2$$

*Sometimes the divergence of a vector is defined by Eq. (2.6), and then the definition of Eq. (2.5) is called Gauss' theorem.

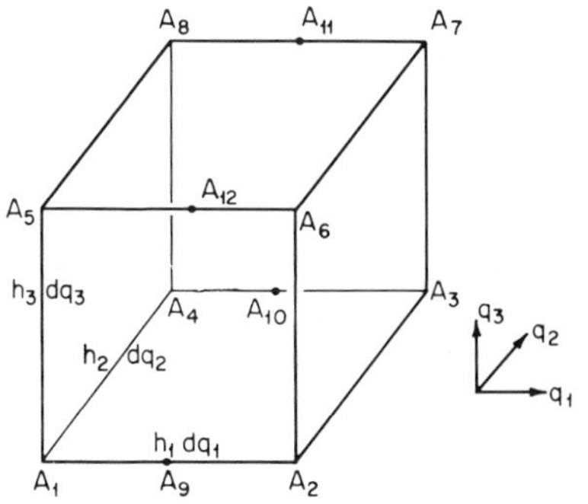

Fig. A.1. Diagram of a cube in a (q_1, q_2, q_3) orthogonal curvilinear coordinate.

Therefore, the sum of these two terms gives a contribution to $\nabla \cdot \alpha$, from Eq. (2.5) of

$$\frac{1}{h_1\, h_2\, h_3} \frac{\partial(h_1\, h_2\, \alpha_3)}{\partial q_1}$$

The integrals over the other faces give similar terms, so that the full expression for $\nabla \cdot \alpha$ becomes

$$\nabla \cdot \alpha = \frac{1}{h_1 h_2 h_3}\left[\frac{\partial(h_2 h_3 \alpha_1)}{\partial q_1} + \frac{\partial(h_3 h_1 \alpha_2)}{\partial q_2} + \frac{\partial(h_1 h_2 \alpha_3)}{\partial q_3}\right] \tag{2.6}$$

When $\nabla \cdot \alpha = 0$, α is called a solenoidal vector.

The definition of the curl of a vector in a direction n is*

$$(\nabla \times \alpha)_{\text{in direction } \mathbf{n}} = \lim_{S \to O} \frac{\int_{\mathcal{C}} \alpha \cdot d\ell}{S} \tag{2.7}$$

where S is any planar surface with normal n bounded by the contour $\mathcal{C}$. In Fig. A.1, let A_9 be the mid-point of $A_1 A_2$; A_{10}, of $A_3 A_4$; A_{11}, of $A_7 A_8$; and A_{12}, of $A_5 A_6$. Then

$$A_9 = \left(q_1,\ q_2 - \frac{1}{2}\,dq_2,\ q_3 - \frac{1}{2}\,dq_3\right)$$

$$A_{10} = \left(q_1,\ q_2 + \frac{1}{2}\,dq_2,\ q_3 - \frac{1}{2}\,dq_3\right)$$

$$A_{11} = \left(q_1,\ q_2 + \frac{1}{2}\,dq_2,\ q_3 + \frac{1}{2}\,dq_3\right)$$

$$A_{12} = \left(q_1,\ q_2 - \frac{1}{2}\,dq_2,\ q_3 + \frac{1}{2}\,dq_3\right) \tag{2.8}$$

*Sometimes the curl of a vector is defined by its coordinate form, Eq. (2.9), and then the definition of Eq. (2.7) is called Stokes' theorem.

If we take S as the plane q_1 = constant bounded by the contour $A_9A_{10}A_{12}A_{11}$, the contribution $\int_{\mathcal{C}} \boldsymbol{\alpha} \cdot d\boldsymbol{\ell}$ of the segment A_9A_{10} is

$$(h_2\alpha_2)_{q_1,q_2,q_3 - \frac{1}{2} dq_3}\, dq_2$$

where it has been assumed dq_2 is sufficiently small so that it is permissible to take the value for $\boldsymbol{\alpha}$ at the middle of the line A_9A_{10}. In the same way, the contribution to the integral from the segment $A_{11}A_{12}$ is

$$(-h_2\alpha_2)_{q_1,q_2,q_3 + \frac{1}{2} dq_3}\, dq_2$$

The integrals over the sections $A_{10}A_{11}$ and $A_{12}A_9$ may be evaluated in a similar way. The normal **n** is in the q_1 direction, so that the substitution into Eq. (2.7) yields the expression for the q_1 component of $\nabla \times \boldsymbol{\alpha}$:

$$(\nabla \times \boldsymbol{\alpha})_1 = \frac{1}{h_2\, h_3}\left[\frac{\partial(\alpha_3\, h_3)}{\partial q_2} - \frac{\partial(\alpha_2\, h_2)}{\partial q_3}\right]$$

The other components of $\nabla \times \boldsymbol{\alpha}$ may be deduced similarly to give the expression

$$(\nabla \times \boldsymbol{\alpha})_i = \frac{1}{h_j\, h_k}\left[\frac{\partial(h_k\, \alpha_k)}{\partial q_j} - \frac{\partial(h_j\, \alpha_j)}{\partial q_k}\right] \tag{2.9}$$

where i,j,k are any cyclic combination of 1,2,3; that is, $i = 1$, $j = 2$, $k = 3$, or $i = 2$, $j = 3$, $k = 1$, or $i = 3$, $j = 1$, $k = 2$. When $\nabla \times \boldsymbol{\alpha} = 0$, $\boldsymbol{\alpha}$ is called an irrotational vector.

The Laplacian of a scalar is defined as

$$\nabla^2 a = \nabla \cdot (\nabla a) \tag{2.10}$$

Substitution of Eqs. (2.4) and (2.6) into Eq. (2.10) yields

$$\nabla^2 a = \frac{1}{h_1h_2h_3}\left[\frac{\partial}{\partial q_1}\left(\frac{h_2h_3}{h_1}\frac{\partial a}{\partial q_1}\right) + \frac{\partial}{\partial q_2}\left(\frac{h_3h_1}{h_2}\frac{\partial a}{\partial q_2}\right) + \frac{\partial}{\partial q_3}\left(\frac{h_1h_2}{h_3}\frac{\partial a}{\partial q_3}\right)\right] \tag{2.11}$$

When $\nabla^2 a = 0$, a is called a Laplacian scalar.

The final vector operator which is often required in space-charge-flow equations is $(\boldsymbol{\beta} \cdot \nabla)\, \boldsymbol{\alpha}$. The general expression for this operator is rather lengthy to derive, because of the variation in a general orthogonal coordinate system of the unit vectors with position. The expression for this operator is given without proof. An excellent derivation of the expression is given in Morse and Feshbach.[1] The operator $(\boldsymbol{\beta} \cdot \nabla)\, \boldsymbol{\alpha}$ has the form, in the (q_1, q_2, q_3) coordinate system,

$$[(\boldsymbol{\beta} \cdot \nabla)\, \boldsymbol{\alpha}]_i = \sum_{\ell} \frac{\beta_\ell}{h_\ell}\frac{\partial \alpha_i}{\partial q_\ell} + \frac{\alpha_j}{h_ih_j}\left(\beta_i \frac{\partial h_i}{\partial q_j} - \beta_j \frac{\partial h_j}{\partial q_i}\right) + \frac{\alpha_k}{h_ih_k}\left(\beta_i \frac{\partial h_i}{\partial q_k} - \beta_k \frac{\partial h_k}{\partial q_i}\right) \tag{2.12}$$

where $\sum_{\ell}$ denotes the sum over $\ell = 1, 2$, and 3, and i, j, k are a cyclic permutation of 1, 2, 3.

There is an important corollary of Eqs. (2.6) and (2.9) when β is solenoidal and one component of β is zero. If, for example,

$$\beta = (\beta_1, 0, \beta_3) \tag{2.13}$$

and $$\nabla \cdot \beta = 0 \tag{2.14}$$

then, from Eq. (2.6),

$$\frac{\partial}{\partial q_1}(h_2 h_3 \beta_1) + \frac{\partial}{\partial q_3}(h_1 h_2 \beta_3) = 0 \tag{2.15}$$

Hence we can define a scalar a with the property

$$h_2 h_3 \beta_1 = -\frac{\partial a}{\partial q_3} \quad \text{and} \quad h_1 h_2 \beta_3 = \frac{\partial a}{\partial q_1} \tag{2.16}$$

Comparing Eqs. (2.9) and (2.16), it is seen that Eq. (2.16) is the condition

$$\beta = (\beta_1, 0, \beta_3) = \nabla \times \left(0, \frac{a}{h_2}, 0\right) \tag{2.17}$$

This can be written slightly more generally. If β has the form

$$\beta = \nabla \times \alpha \quad \text{and} \quad \beta_i = 0 \tag{2.18}$$

then α can be written so that it has only an i component and

$$\beta_j = \frac{1}{h_i h_k}\frac{\partial}{\partial q_k}(\alpha_i h_i) \quad \text{and} \quad \beta_k = -\frac{1}{h_i h_j}\frac{\partial}{\partial q_j}(\alpha_i h_i) \tag{2.19}$$

3. THE VECTOR OPERATORS IN SOME SPECIAL COORDINATE SYSTEMS

In this section, the expressions for the vector operators are given for certain frequently used coordinate systems. The formulas are given for easy reference and without comment or proof. In every case, the formulas have been derived by substituting into Eqs. (2.4), (2.6), (2.9), and (2.11) the relevant h_i of the coordinate system being considered.

The coordinate systems treated are cartesian coordinates, cylindrical polar coordinates, spherical polar coordinates, and conformal transformations. The first three require no explanation; the last is fully described in Appendix B.

Cartesian coordinates are defined by

$$d\ell^2 = dx^2 + dy^2 + dz^2 \tag{3.1}$$

so that if a is a scalar and α and β are vectors with components $(\alpha_1, \alpha_2, \alpha_3)$ and $(\beta_1, \beta_2, \beta_3)$, the vector operators have the form

$$\nabla a = \left(\frac{\partial a}{\partial x}, \frac{\partial a}{\partial y}, \frac{\partial a}{\partial z}\right) \qquad \nabla \cdot \boldsymbol{\alpha} = \frac{\partial \alpha_1}{\partial x} + \frac{\partial \alpha_2}{\partial y} + \frac{\partial \alpha_3}{\partial z}$$

$$\nabla \times \boldsymbol{\alpha} = \left(\frac{\partial \alpha_3}{\partial y} - \frac{\partial \alpha_2}{\partial z}, \frac{\partial \alpha_1}{\partial z} - \frac{\partial \alpha_3}{\partial x}, \frac{\partial \alpha_2}{\partial x} - \frac{\partial \alpha_1}{\partial y}\right)$$

$$\nabla^2 a = \frac{\partial^2 a}{\partial x^2} + \frac{\partial^2 a}{\partial y^2} + \frac{\partial^2 a}{\partial z^2}$$

$$(\boldsymbol{\beta} \cdot \nabla) \boldsymbol{\alpha} = \left(\beta_1 \frac{\partial \alpha_1}{\partial x} + \beta_2 \frac{\partial \alpha_1}{\partial y} + \beta_3 \frac{\partial \alpha_1}{\partial z}, \beta_1 \frac{\partial \alpha_2}{\partial x} + \beta_2 \frac{\partial \alpha_2}{\partial y} + \beta_3 \frac{\partial \alpha_2}{\partial z}, \beta_1 \frac{\partial \alpha_3}{\partial x} + \beta_2 \frac{\partial \alpha_3}{\partial y} + \beta_3 \frac{\partial \alpha_3}{\partial z}\right) \tag{3.2}$$

Cylindrical polar coordinates are defined by

$$d\ell^2 = dr^2 + r^2\, d\theta^2 + dz^2 \tag{3.3}$$

so that the vector operators have the form

$$\nabla a = \left(\frac{\partial a}{\partial r}, \frac{1}{r} \frac{\partial a}{\partial \theta}, \frac{\partial a}{\partial z}\right)$$

$$\nabla \cdot \boldsymbol{\alpha} = \frac{1}{r}\left[\frac{\partial}{\partial r}(r\alpha_1) + \frac{\partial \alpha_2}{\partial \theta}\right] + \frac{\partial \alpha_3}{\partial z}$$

$$\nabla \times \boldsymbol{\alpha} = \left[\frac{1}{r} \frac{\partial \alpha_3}{\partial \theta} - \frac{\partial \alpha_2}{\partial z}, \frac{\partial \alpha_1}{\partial z} - \frac{\partial \alpha_3}{\partial r}, \frac{1}{r} \frac{\partial}{\partial r}(r\alpha_2) - \frac{1}{r} \frac{\partial \alpha_1}{\partial \theta}\right]$$

$$\nabla^2 a = \frac{\partial^2 a}{\partial r^2} + \frac{1}{r} \frac{\partial a}{\partial r} + \frac{1}{r^2} \frac{\partial^2 a}{\partial \theta^2} + \frac{\partial^2 a}{\partial z^2}$$

$$(\boldsymbol{\beta} \cdot \nabla) \boldsymbol{\alpha} = \left(\beta_1 \frac{\partial \alpha_1}{\partial r} + \frac{\beta_2}{r} \frac{\partial \alpha_1}{\partial \theta} + \beta_3 \frac{\partial \alpha_1}{\partial z} - \beta_2 \frac{\alpha_2}{r}, \beta_1 \frac{\partial \alpha_2}{\partial r} + \frac{\beta_2}{r} \frac{\partial \alpha_2}{\partial \theta} + \beta_3 \frac{\partial \alpha_2}{\partial z} + \beta_2 \frac{\alpha_1}{r}, \beta_1 \frac{\partial \alpha_3}{\partial r} + \frac{\beta_2}{r} \frac{\partial \alpha_3}{\partial \theta} + \beta_3 \frac{\partial \alpha_3}{\partial z}\right) \tag{3.4}$$

Spherical polar coordinates are defined by

$$d\ell^2 = dr^2 + r^2\, d\theta^2 + r^2 \sin^2\theta\ d\varphi^2 \tag{3.5}$$

so that the vector operators have the form

$$\nabla a = \left(\frac{\partial a}{\partial r}, \frac{1}{r} \frac{\partial a}{\partial \theta}, \frac{1}{r \sin\theta} \frac{\partial a}{\partial \theta}\right)$$

$$\nabla \cdot \boldsymbol{\alpha} = \frac{1}{r^2} \frac{\partial}{\partial r}(r^2\alpha_1) + \frac{1}{r \sin\theta} \frac{\partial}{\partial \theta}(\alpha_2 \sin\theta) + \frac{1}{r \sin\theta} \frac{\partial \alpha_3}{\partial \varphi}$$

$$\nabla \times \boldsymbol{\alpha} = \left[\frac{1}{r \sin\theta}\frac{\partial}{\partial\theta}(a_3 \sin\theta) - \frac{1}{r\sin\theta}\frac{\partial \alpha_2}{\partial\varphi}, \frac{1}{r\sin\theta}\frac{\partial a_1}{\partial\varphi} - \frac{1}{r}\frac{\partial}{\partial r}(a_3 r), \frac{1}{r}\frac{\partial}{\partial r}(ra_2) - \frac{1}{r}\frac{\partial a_1}{\partial\theta}\right]$$

$$\nabla^2 a = \frac{1}{r^2}\frac{\partial}{\partial r}\left(r^2 \frac{\partial a}{\partial r}\right) + \frac{1}{r^2 \sin\theta}\frac{\partial}{\partial\theta}\left(\sin\theta\frac{\partial a}{\partial\theta}\right) + \frac{1}{r^2\sin^2\theta}\frac{\partial^2 a}{\partial\varphi} \tag{3.6}$$

$$(\boldsymbol{\beta}\cdot\nabla)\boldsymbol{\alpha} = \left[\beta_1\frac{\partial\alpha_1}{\partial r} + \frac{\beta_2}{r}\frac{\partial\alpha_1}{\partial\theta} + \frac{\beta_3}{r\sin\theta}\frac{\partial\alpha_1}{\partial\varphi} - \frac{\alpha_2\beta_2}{r} - \frac{\alpha_3\beta_3}{r},\right.$$
$$\beta_1\frac{\partial\alpha_2}{\partial r} + \frac{\beta_2}{r}\frac{\partial\alpha_2}{\partial\theta} + \frac{\beta_3}{r\sin\theta}\frac{\partial\alpha_2}{\partial\varphi} - \frac{\alpha_3\beta_3\cos\theta}{r\sin\theta} + \frac{\alpha_1\beta_2}{r}$$
$$\left.\beta_1\frac{\partial\alpha_3}{\partial r} + \frac{\beta_2}{r}\frac{\partial\alpha_3}{\partial\theta} + \frac{\beta_3}{r\sin\theta}\frac{\partial\alpha_3}{\partial\varphi} + \frac{\alpha_1\beta_3}{r} + \frac{\alpha_2\beta_3\cos\theta}{r\sin\theta}\right]$$

A planar conformal transformation has the property, from Appendix B, that

$$d\ell^2 = h^2(d\xi^2 + d\eta^2) + dz^2 \tag{3.7}$$

where h is independent of z. Hence

$$\nabla a = \left(\frac{1}{h}\frac{\partial a}{\partial\xi}, \frac{1}{h}\frac{\partial a}{\partial\eta}, \frac{\partial a}{\partial z}\right)$$

$$\nabla\circ\boldsymbol{\alpha} = \frac{1}{h^2}\left[\frac{\partial}{\partial\xi}(h\alpha_1) + \frac{\partial}{\partial\eta}(h\alpha_2)\right] + \frac{\partial\alpha_3}{\partial z} \tag{3.8}$$

$$\nabla\times\boldsymbol{\alpha} = \left[\frac{1}{h}\frac{\partial\alpha_3}{\partial\eta} - \frac{\partial\alpha_2}{\partial z}, \frac{\partial\alpha_1}{\partial z} - \frac{1}{h}\frac{\partial\alpha_3}{\partial\xi}, \frac{1}{h^2}\frac{\partial}{\partial\xi}(h\alpha_2) - \frac{1}{h^2}\frac{\partial}{\partial\eta}(h\alpha_1)\right]$$

$$\nabla^2 a = \frac{1}{h^2}\left(\frac{\partial^2 a}{\partial\xi^2} + \frac{\partial^2 a}{\partial\eta^2}\right) + \frac{\partial^2 a}{\partial z^2}$$

REFERENCE FOR APPENDIX A

Morse, P., and H. Feshbach: "Methods of Theoretical Physics," vol. I, McGraw-Hill Book Company, New York, 1953.

APPENDIX B

Conformal Transformations and the Principle of Analytic Continuation

1. INTRODUCTION

The techniques of complex variable theory are often useful in the solution of two-dimensional problems. In those problems in which the initial conditions are given on a curve, it is often convenient to transform coordinates so that this curve becomes the real axis and the xy plane becomes the complex plane. It is always easier to work with orthogonal transformations, and of these one, the conformal transformation, is particularly useful. The transformation is treated most simply using complex variables. Those properties of the transformation required in this book are presented in Section 2.

One reason why the conformal transformation is so useful in two-dimensional problems is the invariance of Laplace's equation under this transformation. A consequence of this invariance is that it is possible to determine simply the value of a function satisfying Laplace's equation from its behavior on a curve. The method of determining the potential is called the principle of analytic continuation, and is described in Section 3.

2. THE PROPERTIES OF CONFORMAL TRANSFORMATIONS

It is usual in textbooks on complex variable theory to define conformal transformations in terms of their physical attributes, and then deduce the formulas for the transformation. In this appendix, we wish only to sketch briefly the properties of the transformation, and therefore reverse the normal procedure. The transformation of coordinates, which transforms points in the xy plane into points of a $\xi\eta$ plane, is a conformal transformation if, and only if, there exists a function $W(\zeta)$ such that

$$w = W(\zeta) \tag{2.1}$$

where

$$w = x + jy \qquad \text{and} \qquad \zeta = \xi + j\eta \tag{2.2}$$

In this context, $W(\zeta)$ should not be confused with the action function.

All the properties of conformal transformations can be deduced from Eq. (2.1). We assume that the function W is well-behaved, having no singularities in the region of interest. Many of the transformations given in Chap. VII do not have this property; however, a full discussion of the theory of singular and multivalues mappings is beyond the scope of this appendix.

Differentiating Eq. (2.1), one obtains, using Eq. (2.2),

$$\begin{aligned} \frac{\partial x}{\partial \xi} + j\frac{\partial y}{\partial \xi} &= \frac{\partial W}{\partial \xi} = \frac{dW}{d\zeta}\frac{\partial \zeta}{\partial \xi} = \frac{dW}{d\zeta} \\ \frac{\partial x}{\partial \eta} + j\frac{\partial y}{\partial \eta} &= \frac{\partial W}{\partial \eta} = \frac{dW}{d\zeta}\frac{\partial \zeta}{\partial \eta} = j\frac{dW}{d\zeta} \end{aligned} \tag{2.3}$$

From Eq. (2.3),

$$\frac{\partial x}{\partial \xi} - \frac{\partial y}{\partial \eta} + j\left(\frac{\partial x}{\partial \eta} + \frac{\partial y}{\partial \xi}\right) = 0 \tag{2.4}$$

Since x, y, ξ, and η are real, the real and imaginary parts of Eq. (2.4) must be separately zero, so that

$$\frac{\partial x}{\partial \xi} = \frac{\partial y}{\partial \eta} \qquad \text{and} \qquad \frac{\partial x}{\partial \eta} = -\frac{\partial y}{\partial \xi} \tag{2.5}$$

Equations (2.5) are called the Cauchy-Riemann equations. From Eqs. (2.5), one can deduce

$$\frac{\partial^2 x}{\partial \xi^2} + \frac{\partial^2 x}{\partial \eta^2} = \frac{\partial^2 y}{\partial \xi^2} + \frac{\partial^2 y}{\partial \eta^2} = 0 \tag{2.6}$$

Every step leading to Eq. (2.6) is reversible, with (ξ,η) taking the place of (x,y), and vice versa.

In all formulas for the vector operators, the infinitesimal line elements are important. For this conformal transformation, using Eqs. (2.1) and (2.2),

$$\begin{aligned} d\ell^2 &= dx^2 + dy^2 = dw\,dw^* \\ &= \frac{dW(\zeta)}{d\zeta}\frac{dW^*(\zeta^*)}{d\zeta^*}\,d\zeta\,d\zeta^* \\ &= h^2(d\xi^2 + d\eta^2) \end{aligned} \tag{2.7}$$

where

$$w^* = x - jy \qquad \zeta^* = \xi - j\eta \qquad \cdots$$

and $$h^2 = \frac{dW(\zeta)}{d\zeta}\frac{dW^*(\zeta^*)}{d\zeta^*} \tag{2.8}$$

In general, by the asterisk (*) we mean the complex conjugate. All the formulas for the vector operators are usually given for three-dimensional transformations. The three-dimensional form of Eq. (2.1) is

$$w = W(\xi) \qquad \text{and} \qquad z = z \tag{2.9}$$

so that the infinitesimal line element $d\ell$ becomes

$$d\ell^2 = h^2(d\xi^2 + d\eta^2) + dz^2 \tag{2.10}$$

3. THE PRINCIPLE OF ANALYTIC CONTINUATION

The principal reason why the conformal transformations are so useful is that they allow the principle of analytic continuation. The principle concerns any pair of functions which satisfy the Cauchy-Riemann equations. From the value of the functions on the y axis, it is possible to write down immediately their value in the interior of the xy plane. Moreover, the method can be extended to yield the values of the function if the initial conditions are given on any curve. It is then necessary to make a conformal transformation so that the given curve becomes the y axis. The formulas for the principle of analytic continuation will now be developed.

Let the function χ be defined by

$$\chi = \phi + j\psi \tag{3.1}$$

Writing (ϕ,ψ), χ for (x,y), w and (x,y), w for $(\xi,\eta),\zeta$, Eqs. (2.1) and (2.6) become

$$\chi = \chi(w) \tag{3.2}$$

where $\chi(w)$ is equivalent to the $W(\zeta)$ of Eq. (2.1), and

$$\frac{\partial^2\phi}{\partial x^2} + \frac{\partial^2\phi}{\partial y^2} = 0 \qquad \text{and} \qquad \frac{\partial^2\psi}{\partial x^2} + \frac{\partial^2\psi}{\partial y^2} = 0 \tag{3.3}$$

Moreover, on the real axis,

$$\phi = \phi_0(x) \qquad \text{and} \qquad \psi = \psi_0(x) \tag{3.4}$$

where $\phi_0(x)$ and $\psi_0(x)$ are the values of ϕ and ψ for $y = 0$.

Since, in potential problems, one is usually concerned only with the potential function ϕ, Eq. (3.4) may be written, using the Cauchy-Riemann equation [Eq. (2.5)],

$$\phi = \phi_0(x) \qquad \text{and} \qquad \frac{\partial\phi}{\partial y} = -\frac{d\psi_0(x)}{dx} \qquad \text{on } y = 0 \tag{3.5}$$

In other words, if the function ϕ is harmonic, i.e., satisfies Laplace's equation [Eq. (3.3)], and if ϕ and its normal derivative are given on the real axis by

$$\phi = \phi_0(x) \qquad \text{and} \qquad \frac{\partial\phi}{\partial y} = -\frac{d\psi_0}{dx} \qquad \text{on } y = 0 \tag{3.6}$$

then its value at any point in the xy plane is given by

$$\phi(x,y) = \text{Re}\,[\phi_0(x + jy) + j\psi_0(x + jy)] \tag{3.7}$$

Equations (3.6) and (3.7) embody the principle of analytic continuation.

Now, from Eq. (3.8) of Appendix A, the Laplacian or any scalar independent of z in the (ξ,η,z) system is given by

$$\nabla^2 a = \frac{1}{h^2}\left(\frac{\partial^2 a}{\partial \xi^2} + \frac{\partial^2 a}{\partial \eta^2}\right) \tag{3.8}$$

where (ξ,η) are a conformal transformation of (x,y) satisfying Eq. (2.1), and h is defined by Eq. (2.8).

Hence, if a function ϕ satisfies Laplace's equation, it also satisfies

$$\frac{\partial^2 \phi}{\partial \xi^2} + \frac{\partial^2 \phi}{\partial \eta^2} = 0 \tag{3.9}$$

The principle of analytic continuation is valid, therefore, not only when ϕ and its normal derivative are given on the y axis, but also when they are prescribed on any η axis, where (ξ,η) are a conformal transformation of (x,y).

REFERENCE FOR APPENDIX B

Morse, P., and H. Feshbach: "Methods of Theoretical Physics," vol. 1, McGraw-Hill Book Company, New York, 1953.

APPENDIX C

Matrix Theory for Periodic Systems

It is the purpose of this appendix to derive certain general formulas relating the stability properties of a periodic system to the expressions which give the exit position and slope of an electron from one period of the system in terms of its entrance position and slope. We consider the situation where there is a linear relation between these two sets of parameters. In this case the following matrix form relates the input and output parameters:

$$\begin{bmatrix} r_2 \\ r_2' \end{bmatrix} = \begin{bmatrix} A & B \\ C & D \end{bmatrix} \begin{bmatrix} r_1 \\ r_1' \end{bmatrix} = \mathfrak{M} \begin{pmatrix} r_1 \\ r_1' \end{pmatrix} \tag{1}$$

For the systems of the kind considered in this book, the Wronskian of the matrix $\mathfrak{M}$ is always given by

$$AD - BC = 1 \tag{2}$$

In this case the matrix $\mathfrak{M}$ can be expressed in the form

$$\begin{bmatrix} A & B \\ C & D \end{bmatrix} = \mathcal{I} \cos \theta + \mathcal{K} \sin \theta \tag{3}$$

where θ is defined by the relation

$$2 \cos \theta = A + D \tag{4}$$

and the square matrices $\mathcal{I}$ and $\mathcal{K}$ are given by

$$\mathcal{I} = \begin{bmatrix} 1 & 0 \\ 0 & 1 \end{bmatrix} \tag{5}$$

and

$$\mathcal{K} = \operatorname{cosec} \theta \begin{bmatrix} \tfrac{1}{2}(A - D) & B \\ C & -\tfrac{1}{2}(A - D) \end{bmatrix} \tag{6}$$

It may be shown by using Eq. (2) that

$$\mathcal{K}^2 = -\mathcal{I} \tag{7}$$

Consequently, it follows that

$$\mathfrak{M}^2 = \begin{pmatrix} A & B \\ C & D \end{pmatrix} \cdot \begin{pmatrix} A & B \\ C & D \end{pmatrix}$$

$$= \mathcal{I}^2 \cos^2\theta + 2\,\mathcal{I}\mathcal{K} \sin\theta \cos\theta + \mathcal{K}^2 \sin^2\theta$$

$$= \mathcal{I}\cos(2\theta) + \mathcal{K}\sin(2\theta) \tag{8}$$

Continuing the process n times, it is seen that

$$\mathfrak{M}^n = \begin{bmatrix} A & B \\ C & D \end{bmatrix}^n = \mathcal{I}\cos(n\theta) + \mathcal{K}\sin(n\theta) \tag{9}$$

The angle θ, when real, is often referred to as the characteristic phase of the system. In a periodic transmission system, if this same method of attack were used to determine the voltage and current at any point of the system, this angle would be the phase delay per period of the system. A periodic focusing system will be stable provided θ is real. In this case, all the terms of the matrix $\mathfrak{M}^n$ are bounded in value. On the other hand, if θ becomes imaginary, the matrix $\mathfrak{M}^n$ is no longer bounded in value but can increase indefinitely with n, and the periodic focusing system is then unstable. Therefore the criterion of stability is seen, from Eq. (4), to be

$$|A + D| < 2 \tag{10}$$

where $|\mathbf{a}|$ is the modulus of **a**. When this condition is satisfied, the system is stable. Conversely, when

$$|A + D| > 2 \tag{11}$$

the system is always unstable.

The special condition

$$|A + D| = 2 \tag{12}$$

must be considered separately. When Eq. (12) is satisfied, then $\cos\theta = \pm 1$, so that $\cos n\theta = \pm 1$ and $\theta = 0$ or π. It follows that

$$\frac{\sin(n\theta)}{\sin\theta} = \pm n \tag{13}$$

when Eq. (12) is satisfied. Thus we may write, from Eq. (9),

$$\mathfrak{M}^n = \begin{bmatrix} A & B \\ C & D \end{bmatrix}^n = \pm\mathcal{I} \pm n \begin{bmatrix} \tfrac{1}{2}(A - D) & B \\ C & -\tfrac{1}{2}(A - D) \end{bmatrix} \tag{14}$$

The matrix $\mathfrak{M}^n$ remains bounded with increasing n only if all the terms of the second matrix in Eq. (14) are zero. Thus, when the condition of Eq. (12) is satisfied, the system is stable only if

$$A = D = \pm 1 \qquad \text{and} \qquad B = C = 0 \tag{15}$$

The Wronskian Eq. (2) implies that, if $A = D = \pm 1$, either B or C is zero. For stability, all the conditions of Eq. (15) must be satisfied. If Eq. (15) is not satisfied, the solution of the periodic system is unstable when $|A + D| = 2$.

APPENDIX **D**

Hill's and Mathieu's Equations

The theory of the stability of a beam in a periodic focusing system can in most cases be expressed in terms of the solutions of Hill's equation. Hill's equation is a linear second-order differential equation having the canonical form

$$y'' + [a - 2q\,\psi(\omega z)]\,y = 0 \qquad (1)$$

where $\psi(z)$ is a periodic, twice-differentiable function of z, such that $|\psi|_M = 1$, and a, q and ω are adjustable parameters*, a prime (′) denotes differentiation with respect to z. Usually, $\psi(\omega z)$ is even in z. Extensive studies of Hill's equation have been made; the major results are summarized in McLachlan's text.

An important special case of Hill's equation is that for which $\psi(\omega z) = \cos 2z$. The resulting equation, known as Mathieu's equation, has the standard canonical form

$$y'' + [a - 2q\cos(2z)]\,y = 0 \qquad (2)$$

Mathieu's equation is far simpler to study than is the more general Hill equation. It is not, except in certain special cases, possible to solve the former equation in closed form, in terms of elementary functions. However, its solutions have been tabulated and their behavior is known. The theory of solutions of Hill's equations, although far more difficult in detail, is similar in nature. Here we discuss certain particularly important properties of the solutions of Mathieu's equation without proof, referring the interested reader to McLachlan's text or to other available literature.

The general solution of Eq. (2) has the form

$$y = C_1 e^{\mu z}\,P(z) + C_2 e^{-\mu z}\,P(-z) \qquad (3)$$

where P(z) is a periodic function of z, having period π; C_1 and C_2 are arbitrary constants; and μ is, in general, a complex constant whose real and imaginary components are both functions of a and q.

---

*The transformation $S' = \omega S$ would eliminate ω as an explicit parameter; the canonical form represented by Eq. (2.1) has been chosen to conform with that used by McLachlan.[1]

The character of the general solution, Eq. (3), is determined entirely by the nature of μ. If μ is wholly imaginary, y is either periodic or almost periodic,* as μ either is or is not commensurate with $j\pi$. For example, if $\mu = j\pi/7$, y contains terms having the form $\cos(\pi z/7)\cos(nz)$, $\sin(\pi z/7)\cos(nz)$, etc., where n is an integer. It is clear that such functions are bounded, and further, they are oscillatory and undamped.

On the other hand, if the real part of μ does not vanish, either $e^{\pi z}P(z)$ or $e^{-\pi z}P(-z)$ possesses an exponentially increasing envelope, whereas the other solution exponentially decays. The exponentially increasing solution is said to be unstable. In a focusing system characterized by an unstable solution of Mathieu's (or Hill's) equation, paraxial electrons oscillate back and forth across the ray axis, but on each successive oscillation, the amplitude of the excursion increases. In a periodic focusing system having many periods, such behavior is disastrous.

There are regions in the aq plane in which solutions of Mathieu's equation are stable, and other regions in the aq plane where they are unstable (Fig. D.1). The region in the half-plane $a > 0$, immediately adjacent to the origin, is a region of stability, implying that if a and q are sufficiently small, the system is stable. The boundary curve separating stable and unstable regions is given by the series relation

$$a = 1 - q - \frac{q^2}{8} + \frac{q^3}{64} - \frac{q^4}{1536} - \cdots \tag{4}$$

When a lies between zero and the value given by Eq. (4), the parameter μ is a purely imaginary number. Thus, when $a \ll 1$, this condition is satisfied if $q < 0.91$. In this case the corresponding solutions of Mathieu's equation are stable.

For values of a slightly exceeding the value calculated from Eq. (4) for a given value of q, the parameter μ becomes complex, and one of the linearly independent solutions of Mathieu's equation possesses an exponentially increasing envelope. The upper bounding curve for the unstable region in the aq plane is given by the series relation

$$a = 1 + q - \frac{q^2}{8} - \frac{q^3}{64} - \frac{q^4}{1536} + \cdots \tag{5}$$

It is possible to divide the entire aq plane into still further regions of stability and instability. By substituting $z' = z + \pi$, it is seen that the character of the solutions of Mathieu's equation is unaltered by reversing the sign of q. Thus, without loss of generality, the sign of q may always be taken as positive.

*An almost periodic function is the product of two periodic functions having noncommensurate periods.

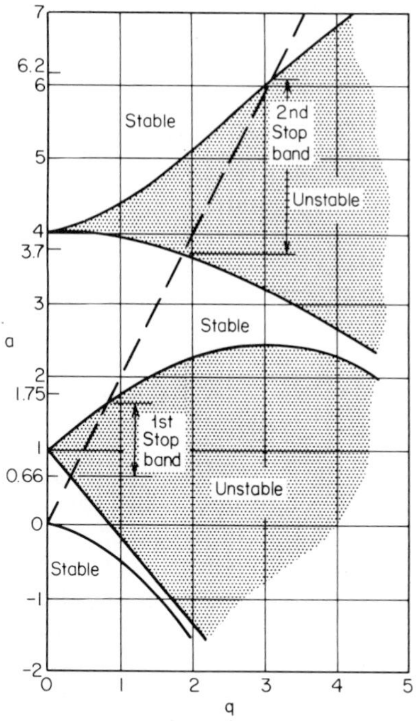

Fig. D.1. A stability plot of Mathieu's equation. The dotted line is for the condition a = 2q, which applies to several types of periodic focusing structure. (Reproduced courtesy of the Institute of Electrical and Electronic Engineers from Proc. IRE, vol. 42, p. 808, 1954.)

It is possible to obtain useful approximate solutions to Mathieu's equation [Eq. (2)], valid when $q << 1$, and other convenient forms of solution, valid when both $a \ll 1$ and $q \ll 1$. The general solution of Mathieu's equation may be written

$$y = e^{j\mu z} \sum_n A_n e^{2jnz} \tag{6}$$

Substituting this form in Eq. (2), we find the following recurrence relation:

$$[a - (2n + \mu)^2] A_n = q(A_{n+1} + A_{n-1}) \tag{7}$$

When $q = 0$, Eq. (2) reduces to the equation of simple harmonic motion, with the solution corresponding to $\mu = a^{1/2}$ and $A_n = 0$, $n \neq 0$. When q is finite and the other terms small, it follows from Eq. (7) that $A_1 = 0(qA_0)$, $A_2 = 0(q^2A_0)$, etc. Thus, in the recurrence relation, we shall neglect all terms for $n \geq 2$. This yields the result

$$(a - \mu^2) A_0 = q(A_1 + A_{-1}) \tag{8}$$

$$[a - (\mu + 2)^2] A_1 = qA_0 \tag{9}$$

$$[a - (\mu - 2)^2] A_{-1} = qA_0 \tag{10}$$

Substitution of Eqs. (9) and (10) in Eq. (8) gives the following relation for μ:

$$a - \mu^2 = q^2 \left[\frac{1}{a - (\mu + 2)^2} + \frac{1}{a - (\mu - 2)^2} \right] \tag{11}$$

Assuming $q \ll 1$, this has solutions $\mu = \pm a^{1/2} + \delta$, with $\delta \ll a$. Thus, to first order in δ,

$$\mu = \pm \left[a^{1/2} + \frac{q^2}{4a^{1/2}(1 - a)} \right] \tag{12}$$

with $$A_{-1} = \frac{q}{4(\pm a^{1/2} - 1)} A_0 \tag{13}$$

$$A_1 = \frac{q}{4(\mp a^{1/2} - 1)} A_0 \tag{14}$$

Thus, as predicted, the amplitude of the second-harmonic term is much less than the amplitude of the fundamental. Note, however, that if $|a| \simeq 1$, it is not sufficient to keep only first-order terms in δ; instead it is necessary to keep terms up to second order in δ in Eq. (11). In this case, if $1 - q < a < 1 + q$, it is found that μ becomes imaginary. Thus the solution is unstable. This is an approximation to the condition for instability that is obtained from the full solution of Mathieu's equation. It arises because of the parametric pumping action of the trigonometric term in Matheiu's equation. This may be seen by considering the situation when $a = 1$ and $q = 0$ and no trigonometric term is present in Mathieu's equation; there would be a solution which varies as $y = \exp(\pm jz)$. Therefore, when q is finite, the product $\cos(2z) \exp(-jz)$ gives rise to a term which varies as $\exp jz$, and hence there is coupling between the two independent solutions of the equation for $q = 0$. These coupled solutions are driven by the trigonometric term and become growing terms. Hence they become unstable solutions of the equation. A closer study of this equation also yields the result that there should be unstable solutions in the neighborhood of $a = n^2$.

Consider now the situation when both a and q are small. We should expect a solution with $\mu \ll 1$. Using this condition in Eq. (11), we find that

$$\mu^2 \simeq a + \frac{q^2}{2} \tag{15}$$

and $$A_1 = A_{-1} = -\frac{q}{4} A_0 \tag{16}$$

where it has been assumed that $q \ll 1$ and $a^{1/2} \ll 1$. The appropriate solution to Mathieu's equation when $a^{1/2} \ll 1$, $q \ll 1$ is therefore

$$y = [C_1 \cos(\mu z) + C_2 \sin(\mu z)] \left[1 - \frac{q}{2} \cos(2z) \right] \tag{17}$$

μ being given by Eq. (15).

REFERENCE FOR APPENDIX D

McLachlan, N. W.: "Theory and Application of Mathieu Functions," Oxford University Press, Fairlawn, N. J., 1947.

APPENDIX E

The Spherical and Cylindrical Diodes

An important space-charge-flow solution which has formed the basis of many gun designs is that for rectilinear flow between two spheres. The method of solution, first given by Langmuir and Compton[1] for this flow, is described, and some of the more important parameters are tabulated.

Another type of solution is derived, which it is possible to represent parametrically in terms of Bessel functions. This solution is often useful as a basis of perturbation solutions, because all the parameters are expressed in terms of well-known functions. Finally, another problem, the rectilinear flow between coaxial cylinders, is mentioned, and its solutions are tabulated.

When there is rectilinear flow between two spheres, the potential varies only in the radial direction. Thus Poisson's equation becomes

$$\frac{1}{r^2}\frac{d}{dr}\left(r^2\frac{d\phi}{dr}\right) = -\frac{\rho}{\epsilon_0} \tag{1}$$

Because current is conserved, it follows that the current density at at any point is

$$i = \frac{I_c}{4\pi r^2} \tag{2}$$

where I_c is the total current leaving the cathode. The relationship between charge density and current density is then used in combination with the equation of conservation of energy to yield the result

$$i = -(2\eta\phi)^{1/2}\rho \tag{3}$$

where it is assumed that, at the cathode,

$$r = r_c \qquad \text{and} \qquad \phi = \mathbf{E} = -\frac{d\phi}{dr} = 0 \tag{4}$$

so that $v^2 = 2\eta\phi$ (5)

The substitution of Eqs. (2) and (3) in Eq. (1) then yields the defining equation for the potential:

$$\frac{d}{dr}\left(r^2\frac{d\phi}{dr}\right) = \frac{I_c}{4\pi(2\eta\phi)^{1/2}\epsilon_0} \tag{6}$$

The current density in the plane diode is, from Eq. (2.17b) of Chap. II,

$$i_c = \tfrac{4}{9}\,(2\eta)^{1/2}\,\epsilon_0\,\frac{\phi^{3/2}}{x^2} \tag{7}$$

Thus, for a spherical diode with very close spacing between the anode and cathode, the total current delivered should be

$$I_c = \frac{16\pi}{9}\,(2\eta)^{1/2}\,\epsilon_0\,\phi^{3/2}\left(\frac{r_c}{r - r_c}\right)^2 \tag{8}$$

In general, we take the solution to be

$$I_c = \frac{16\pi}{9}\,(2\eta)^{1/2}\,\epsilon_0\,\frac{\phi^{3/2}}{\alpha^2} = \frac{29.34 \times 10^{-6}\,\phi^{3/2}}{\alpha^2}\ \text{(MKS units)} \tag{9}$$

where $\alpha(r/r_c)$ is a dimensionless parameter.

It can be shown that the parameter α obeys a nonlinear differential equation with the series solution

$$\alpha = \mu - 0.3\mu^2 + 0.075\mu^3 - 0.00143\mu^4 + 0.0021\mu^5 - \cdots \tag{10a}$$

where $$\mu = \ell n\,\frac{r}{r_c} \tag{10b}$$

and the series is valid for both $r/r_c < 1$ and $r/r_c > 1$. The function $-\alpha(r/r_c)$ and other quantities of interest are tabulated in Table E.1 for values of $r/r_c < 1$.

It should be noted that, for a conical beam of half-angle θ, the total current I_θ in the beam is related to I_c as follows:

$$I_c = I_\theta\left(\frac{\pi}{\theta}\right)^2 \tag{11}$$

and the radius a of the cathode is, from Fig. E.1,

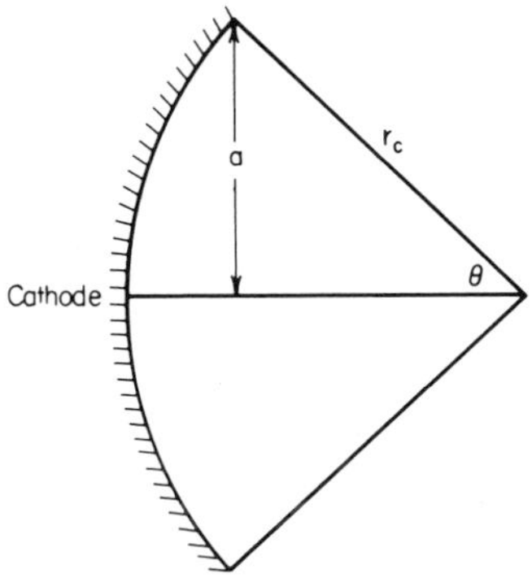

Fig. E.1. Schematic of the beam from a portion of a spherical cathode.

$$a = r_c \sin\theta \tag{12}$$

A very similar solution for the rectilinear flow between two cylinders has also been found.[2] For this type of flow the current emitted by a length ℓ of the cathode is given by the relations

$$I_c = \frac{8\pi}{9}(2\eta)^{1/2}\,\epsilon_0\,\frac{\phi^{3/2}\ell}{\beta^2 r} \tag{13a}$$

$$I_c = 14.66 \times 10^{-6}\,\frac{\phi^{3/2}\ell}{\beta^2 r} \quad \text{(MKS units)} \tag{13b}$$

where the function $\beta(r/r_c)$ is given by the series

$$\beta = \mu - \frac{2\mu^2}{5} + \frac{11\mu^3}{120} - \frac{47\mu^4}{3300} + \cdots \tag{14a}$$

$$\text{with} \quad \mu = \ln\frac{r}{r_c} \tag{14b}$$

Values of β^2 as a function of r/r_c or r_c/r are given in Table E.2.

We consider now an alternative method of solution for the spherical diode. It is convenient to use the function $\xi(r)$, defined by

$$r\,\frac{d\xi}{dr} = \frac{d}{dr}\left(r^2\,\frac{d\phi}{dr}\right) \tag{15a}$$

which can be written

$$\frac{d\xi}{dr} = 2\,\frac{d\phi}{dr} + r\,\frac{d^2\phi}{dr^2} \tag{15b}$$

After integration by parts, it is found that

$$r\,\frac{d\phi}{dr} = \xi - \phi \tag{16}$$

Now Eq. (6) can be written in the form

$$r\,\frac{d\xi}{dr} = \frac{C}{2\phi^{1/2}} \tag{17}$$

$$\text{where} \quad C = \frac{I_c}{2\pi(2\eta)^{1/2}\,\epsilon_0} \tag{18}$$

On division of Eq. (16) by Eq. (17), the variable r can be eliminated, with the result

$$\frac{d\phi}{d\xi} = 2\left(\frac{\xi - \phi}{C}\right)\phi^{1/2} \tag{19}$$

By writing $\phi = U^2$, this becomes the Riccatti equation

$$-\frac{dU}{d\xi} = \frac{U^2 - \xi}{C} \tag{20}$$

The standard method of solution of this equation is to put

$$U = \frac{C}{S}\frac{dS}{d\xi} \tag{21}$$

in Eq. (19) to obtain the differential equation for S,

$$\frac{d^2S}{d\xi^2} = \frac{\xi S}{C^2} \tag{22}$$

Equation (22) is a standard form for a Bessel function of imaginary argument and of order ($\frac{1}{3}$). It has the solution[3]

$$S = \xi^{1/2}\left[C_1 I_{1/3}\left(\frac{2\xi^{3/2}}{3C}\right) + C_2 I_{-1/3}\left(\frac{2\xi^{3/2}}{3C}\right)\right] \tag{23}$$

Thus we have represented the potential in terms of a parametric variable ξ. To find a representation of distance in terms of the same parametric variable, we write Eq. (17) in the form

$$\frac{1}{r}\frac{dr}{d\xi} = \frac{d}{d\xi}(\ell n\ r) = \frac{2U}{C} = \frac{2}{S}\frac{dS}{d\xi} \tag{24}$$

which is integrated to give the result

$$r = r_C S^2 \tag{25}$$

where r_C is the radius of the cathode, and S has been chosen to be unity at $r = r_C$.

At the cathode, $\phi = 0$ and $\partial\phi/\partial r = 0$, under space-charge-limited conditions. Consequently, it follows from Eq. (16) that $\xi = 0$ at the cathode.

The constant C_1 in Eq. (23) must be zero because ϕ, and hence U and $(1/S)(dS/d\xi)$, are zero at $\xi = 0$. The correct form for S is

$$S = C_2\xi^{1/2} I_{-1/3}\left(\frac{2\xi^{3/2}}{3C}\right) \tag{26}$$

The constant C_2 must be chosen so that $S = 1$ on $r = r_C$ when $\xi = 0$. It follows that

$$C_2 = (3C)^{-1/3}\ \Gamma(\tfrac{2}{3}) = 0.94C^{-1/3} \tag{27}$$

It is convenient to change the parametric variable ξ and replace it by a new one, σ, defined as follows:

$$\xi = C^{2/3}\sigma \tag{28}$$

In this case, Eq. (26) can be written in the form

$$\left(\frac{r}{r_C}\right)^{1/2} = S = 0.94 I_{-1/3}\left(\frac{2}{3}\sigma^{3/2}\right) \tag{29}$$

where $$U = C^{1/3}\frac{1}{S}\frac{dS}{d\sigma} \tag{30}$$

and $$\phi = C^{2/3}\left(\frac{1}{S}\frac{dS}{d\sigma}\right)^2 \tag{31}$$

It follows, therefore, from Eqs. (9), (18), and (31), that

$$\alpha(S) = \alpha\left(\frac{r}{r_c}\right) = \left(\frac{8}{9}\right)^{1/2}\left[\frac{d}{d\sigma}(\ell n\ S)\right]^{3/2} = 0.33\left(\frac{d\mu}{d\sigma}\right)^{3/2} \tag{32}$$

where

$$\mu = \ell n\left(\frac{r}{r_c}\right) = 2\ell n\left[0.94 I_{-1/3}\left(\frac{2\sigma}{3}\right)\right] \tag{33}$$

We have thus obtained a solution for the potential and distance along the flow from a spherical cathode as functions of a parametric variable σ. No solution of this type is available for the flow from a cylindrical cathode.

A solution which has the spherical and cylindrical diodes as limiting cases has been derived by Hartnagel.[4] This solution is only approximate, unlike the solutions discussed in this appendix, but gives the flow from a toroidal cathode. The derivation of the solution and both graphical and tabular values for ϕ and its derivatives are presented in Ref. 4.

REFERENCES FOR APPENDIX E

1. Langmuir, I., and K. Compton: Electrical Discharges in Gas, Part II, *Rev. Modern Phys.* vol. 13, p. 191, 1931.
2. Langmuir, I., and K. B. Blodgett: Currents Limited by Space Charge between Coaxial Cylinders, *Phys. Rev.*, ser. 2, vol. 22, p. 347, 1923.
3. Erdelyi, A., W. Magnus, F. Oberhattinger, and F. G. Triconi: "Higher Transcendental Functions," vol. 2, McGraw-Hill Book Company, New York, 1953.
4. Hartnagel, H.: The Potential of a Concentric Toroidal Space Charge Diode, *J. Electronics and Control*, vol. 17, p. 425, 1964.

Table E.1. Table of Functions of $-\alpha$ for the Spherical Diode

A	B	C	D	E	F	DE	F/C
r_c/r	$-\alpha^2$	$-\alpha^{4/3}$	$-\alpha^{2/3}$	r_c/r $-\alpha^{-2/3}\, d\frac{r_c}{r}$	$\frac{d\left(-\alpha^{4/3}\right)}{d(r_c/r)}$		
1.0	0.0000	0.0000	0.0000	0.0000		0.0000	0.0000
1.025	0.0006	0.0074					
1.05	0.0024	0.0179	0.134				
1.075	0.0052	0.0306	0.173				
1.10	0.0096	0.0452	0.212	1.392	0.590	0.295	13.053
1.15	0.0213	0.0768	0.277				
1.20	0.0372	0.1114	0.334	1.767	0.716	0.590	6.4272
1.25	0.0571	0.1483	0.385				
1.30	0.0809	0.1870	0.432	2.031	0.790	0.877	4.2245
1.35	0.1084	0.2273	0.476				
1.40	0.1396	0.2691	0.519	2.243	0.874	1.164	3.2478
1.45	0.1740	0.3317	0.558				
1.50	0.2118	0.3553	0.596	2.423	0.886	1.444	22.4936
1.60	0.2968	0.4450	0.667	2.583	0.915	1.722	2.0561
1.70	0.394	0.5374	0.733	2.725	0.939	1.997	1.7473
1.80	0.502	0.6316	0.795	2.855	0.954	2.2697	1.5104
1.90	0.621	0.7279	0.853	2.975	0.970	2.537	1.3326
2.00	0.750	0.8255	0.908	3.087	0.982	2.803	1.1895
2.10	0.888	0.9239	0.961	3.192	0.993	3.068	1.0747
2.20	1.036	1.024	1.012	3.292	1.003	3.332	0.9794
2.30	1.193	1.125	1.061	3.388	1.012	3.595	0.8995
2.40	1.358	1.226	1.107	3.481	1.020	3.853	0.8319
2.50	1.531	1.328	1.152	3.570	1.028	4.113	0.7740
2.60	1.712	1.431	1.196	3.655	1.034	4.371	0.7225
2.70	1.901	1.535	1.239	3.738	1.039	4.631	0.6768
2.80	2.098	1.639	1.280	3.817	1.044	4.886	0.6369
2.90	2.302	1.743	1.320	3.894	1.048	5.140	0.6012
3.00	2.512	1.848	1.359	3.968	1.052	5.393	0.5692
3.1	2.729	1.953	1.397	4.040	1.056	5.644	0.5407
3.2	2.954	2.059	1.435	4.111	1.059	5.899	0.5143
3.3	3.185	2.164	1.471	4.180	1.062	6.149	0.4907
3.4	3.421	2.270	1.507	4.247	1.064	6.400	0.4687
3.5	3.664	2.376	1.541	4.315	1.066	6.649	0.4486
3.6	3.913	2.483	1.576	4.377	1.068	6.898	0.4301
3.7	4.168	2.590	1.609	4.441	1.070	7.146	0.4264
3.8	4.429	2.697	1.642	4.501	1.072	7.391	0.3974
3.9	4.696	2.804	1.674	4.563	1.074	7.638	0.3830
4.0	4.968	2.912	1.706	4.621	1.076	7.883	0.3708

Table E.2 Values of β^2 as a Function of r/r_c for the Cylindrical Diode

β^2 applies where $r > r_c$; $-\beta^2$ applies where $r < r_c$.

$\frac{r}{r_c}$ or $\frac{r_c}{r}$	β^2	$-\beta^2$	$\frac{r}{r_c}$ or $\frac{r_c}{r}$	β^2	$-\beta^2$
1.00	0.0000	0.0000	3.8	0.6420	5.3795
1.01	0.00010	0.00010	4.0	0.6671	6.0601
1.02	0.00039	0.00040	4.2	0.6902	6.7705
1.04	0.00149	0.00159	4.4	0.7115	7.5096
1.06	0.00324	0.00356	4.6	0.7313	8.2763
1.08	0.00557	0.00630	4.8	0.7496	9.0696
1.10	0.00842	0.00980	5.0	0.7666	9.887
1.15	0.01747	0.02186	5.2	0.7825	10.733
1.20	0.02815	0.03849	5.4	0.7973	11.601
1.30	0.05589	0.08504	5.6	0.8111	12.493
1.40	0.08672	0.14856	5.8	0.8241	13.407
1.50	0.11934	0.2282	6.0	0.8362	14.343
1.60	0.1525	0.3233	6.5	0.8635	16.777
1.70	0.1854	0.4332	7.0	0.8870	19.337
1.80	0.2177	0.5572	7.5	0.9074	22.015
1.90	0.2491	0.6947	8.0	0.9253	24.805
2.0	0.2793	0.8454	8.5	0.9410	27.701
2.1	0.3083	1.0086	9.0	0.9548	30.698
2.2	0.3361	1.1840	9.5	0.9672	33.791
2.3	0.3626	1.3712	10.0	0.9782	36.976
2.4	0.3879	1.5697	12.0	1.0133	50.559
2.5	0.4121	1.7792	16.0	1.0513	81.203
2.6	0.4351	1.9995	20.0	1.0715	115.64
2.7	0.4571	2.2301	40.0	1.0946	327.01
2.8	0.4780	2.4708	80.0	1.0845	867.11
2.9	0.4980	2.7214	100.0	1.0782	1174.9
3.0	0.5170	2.9814	200.0	1.0562	2946.1
3.2	0.5526	3.5293	500.0	1.0307	9502.2
3.4	0.5851	4.1126	∞	1.000	∞
3.6	0.6148	4.7298			

INDEX

Index

D

E